Preface

THE REPUBLIC OF LETTERS

FROM every land in the world an ambitious people has been drawn to America by the dream of democracy—of a nation where each and all might share the culture which our mingled races are developing from their blended heritage. There is another great republic in which citizenship is free to all men of every color and every nation, and in which the treasures of the whole world's culture are open to every eager aspirant. This is the international republic of literature. The only test for citizenship in this Republic of Letters is the ability to read. For he who reads can share the thoughts, ideals, and wisdom of the best thinkers from every race and clime.

The intellectual democracy of the Republic of Letters is divided into sovereign states, each with its own laws and customs. These states are the different literary types—such as the story, the drama, the essay, and the various kinds of poetry. From the beginning of history, wherever men have risen above the animal level of eating, drinking, playing, and sleeping merely to eat and drink and play and sleep again; wherever they have hoped and feared and dreamed; wherever they have really thought about this beautiful, tantalizing, puzzling life of ours, and tried to tell their thoughts to others and preserve from generation to generation the wisdom won from their own struggle and success—these thoughts have universally been expressed in certain literary forms, which closely resemble each other whether the author wrote in ancient China, in medieval England, in Renaissance Italy, in revolutionary France, or in modern America. Every nation in the world which has produced a literature has produced short stories, ballads, metrical tales, novels, epics, fables, essays, letters, lyrics, diaries, biographies, histories, state papers, oratory and debate. These literary types represent the universal types of human thought; and to read and study these types is to study the universal processes of the human mind and trace, as it were on a map, the intellectual continents men have conquered from the dark jungles, burning deserts, and frozen arctic circles of thought and feeling. If we are to read and enjoy the literature of any race and period, we must be able to read each of these literary types with understanding, ease, and pleasure. Therefore, the selections in this book have been grouped by literary types, so that you can practice each kind of reading and watch the mind of every great nation working in the same ways upon the problems of life. Thus we shall see that all men are alike in spirit. And perhaps we shall recognize this so strongly that we shall believe at last in the possibility of international understanding, brotherhood and peace.

Acknowledgment

For permission to use selections we are indebted to the following:

D. Appleton-Century Company for *Advice to a Young Frenchman Starting for England* from A PRIVATE UNIVERSE by André Maurois, and for *Harrow* on the *Hill* from BYRON by André Maurois.

Brandt and Brandt for *To the Not Impossible Him* from A FEW FIGS FROM THISTLES, published by Harper and Brothers, copyright 1922 by Edna St. Vincent Millay, and for *The Pioneer* from THE BUCK IN THE SNOW, published by Harper and Brothers, copyright 1928 by Edna St. Vincent Millay.

Everett Rhodes Castle for a selection from *Clean Up* which appeared in the *Saturday Evening Post*.

Feodor Chaliapin for a selection from PAGES OF MY LIFE.

Octavus Roy Cohen for a selection from *The First Shall Be Last*.

W. Collins Sons and Company, Ltd., for *The Colour of Japan* from FUJI FROM HAMPSTEAD HEATH by Gonnoské Komai.

Columbia University Press for *Enshrined Within This Heart of Mine* by Antonin Sova, translated by Libuse Breuer Scholten, from AN ANTHOLOGY OF CZECHOSLOVAK POETRY by Manning.

Dodd, Mead and Company, Inc., for *The Birthday of the Infanta* from A HOUSE OF POMEGRANATES by Oscar Wilde, for *With the Photographer* from BEHIND THE BEYOND by Stephen Leacock, and for *Our Friend the Dog* by Maurice Maeterlinck.

Doubleday, Doran and Company, Inc., for a selection from *The Third Ingredient* from OPTIONS by O. Henry, copyright 1908, 1936 by Doubleday, Doran and Company, Inc.; for a selection from LORD JIM by Joseph Conrad, copyright 1920 by Doubleday, Doran and Company, Inc.; for a selection from THE STORY OF GÖSTA BERLING by Selma Lagerlöf, copyright 1898, 1926 by Doubleday, Doran and Company, Inc., and for *The Silver Mine* from THE GIRL FROM THE MARSH CROFT by Selma Lagerlöf, copyright 1910 by Doubleday, Doran and Company, Inc.

Doubleday, Doran and Company, Inc., and A. P. Watt and Son for *Gunga Din* from DEPARTMENTAL DITTIES AND BARRACK ROOM BALLADS, and for *Chant Pagan* from THE FIVE NATIONS by Rudyard Kipling.

Duke University Press for *Angelina* by Paul Laurence Dunbar from AN ANTHOLOGY OF VERSE BY AMERICAN NEGROES by Newman I. White and Walter C. Jackson.

E. P. Dutton and Company, Inc., for *Sicilian Limes,* translated by Elizabeth Abbott, taken from THE ONE ACT PLAYS OF LUIGI PIRANDELLO, edited by

Arthur Livingston, published and copyrighted by E. P. Dutton and Company, Inc., New York, and for *Spring Song* taken from POETS OF THE GREEK ANTHOLOGY, translated by F. A. Wright, published by E. P. Dutton and Company, Inc., New York.

Farrar and Rinehart, Inc., for *Tears* from THE SELECTED POEMS OF LIZETTE WOODWORTH REESE, copyright 1926, and reprinted by permission of Farrar and Rinehart, Inc., publishers.

Follett Publishing Company for a selection from BY DOG SLED FOR BYRD by John S. O'Brien.

Samuel French for *The Marriage Proposal* by Anton Chekhov, copyright 1914 by Barrett H. Clark; for *The Doctor in Spite of Himself* by Molière, copyright 1914 by Samuel French,

    CAUTION: Amateurs may produce these plays without payment of royalty. All other rights are reserved and application must be made to Samuel French, 25 West 45th Street, New York, N. Y. These plays are also published in separate form by Samuel French.

and for *Two Crooks and a Lady* by Eugene Pillot, copyright 1917 by Eugene Pillot, copyright 1918, by Brentano's in volume PLAYS OF THE 47 WORKSHOP I.

    CAUTION: Professionals and amateurs are hereby warned that TWO CROOKS AND A LADY, being fully protected under the copyright laws of the United States of America, the British Empire, including the Dominion of Canada, and all other countries of the Copyright Union, is subject to a royalty. All rights, including professional, amateur, motion pictures, recitation, public reading, radio broadcasting, and the rights of translation into foreign languages are strictly reserved. Amateurs may produce this play upon payment of a royalty of Ten Dollars for each performance, payable one week before the play is to be given, to Samuel French, at 25 West 45th Street, New York, N. Y., or 811 West Seventh Street, Los Angeles, Cal., or if in Canada, to Samuel French (Canada), Ltd., at 480 University Ave., Toronto, Ontario.

Harcourt, Brace and Company for *Florence Nightingale* from EMINENT VICTORIANS by Lytton Strachey; for *Spanish Dancer* by Rainer Maria Rilke, translated by Babette Deutsch and Avrahm Yarmolinsky from CONTEMPORARY GERMAN POETRY; for a selection from ARROWSMITH by Sinclair Lewis, and for a selection from GARGANTUA AND PANTAGRUEL by Rabelais.

Harper and Brothers for a selection from TESS OF THE D'URBERVILLES by Thomas Hardy, for *Tony Kytes* from LIFE'S LITTLE IRONIES by Thomas Hardy, and for a selection from PERSONAL RECOLLECTIONS OF JOAN OF ARC by Mark Twain.

Henry Holt and Company for *Silver* from COLLECTED POEMS by Walter de la Mare, for *The Road Not Taken* from COLLECTED POEMS by Robert Frost, and for *Chicago* from CHICAGO POEMS by Carl Sandburg.

Houghton Mifflin Company for *Patterns* from MEN, WOMEN AND GHOSTS by Amy Lowell, for *Love's Minor Frictions* from LIFE'S MINOR COLLISIONS by Frances and Gertrude Warner, for *The Searchings of Jonathan* from MORE JONATHAN PAPERS by Elizabeth Woodbridge, and for *Come Not Near My Songs* by Mary Austin.

Edith Thomas Medairy Howe for *Frost Tonight* by Edith M. Thomas.

Alfred A. Knopf for *The Infant Prodigy* from STORIES OF THREE DECADES by Thomas Mann, for *The Noblest Instrument* from LIFE WITH FATHER by Clarence Day, and for *Velvet Shoes* from COLLECTED POEMS OF ELINOR WYLIE.

International Publishers Company for *In the White Land* by Konstantin Balmont, and for *The Coach of Life* by Alexander Pushkin from RUSSIAN POETRY.

Little, Brown and Company for *A Bird* from THE POEMS OF EMILY DICKINSON, Centenary Edition, edited by Martha Dickinson Bianchi and Alfred Leete Hampson; and for *The Night Has a Thousand Eyes* by Francis William Bourdillon.

Liveright Publishing Corporation for a selection from NAPOLEON by Emil Ludwig.

John A. Lomax for *A Home on the Range* from COWBOY SONGS AND OTHER FRONTIER BALLADS.

The Macmillan Company for *The Coin* and *Blue Squills* from COLLECTED POEMS by Sara Teasdale; for selections from THE VIRGINIAN, U. S. GRANT, and THE SEVEN AGES OF WASHINGTON by Owen Wister; for *Laugh and Be Merry* from POEMS by John Masefield; for *Deirdre* from COLLECTED POEMS by James Stephens; for *Corrymeela* from SONGS FROM THE GLENS OF ANTRIM by Moira O'Neill, and for "The Crawl" from *The Song of Hugh Glass* from COLLECTED POEMS by John G. Neihardt.

The Macmillan Company and the author for *Beech Trees* and *From an Afternoon Caller* from GATES AND OTHER POEMS by Sister Mary Madeleva.

Edgar Lee Masters for *George Gray* from SPOON RIVER ANTHOLOGY.

The Nation for *Message to Siberia* by Alexander Pushkin, translated by Max Eastman.

Noble and Noble Publishers, Inc., for selections from CYRANO DE BERGERAC by Edmond Rostand, translated by Howard Thayer Kingsbury.

G. P. Putnam's Sons for *Spreading the News* from SEVEN SHORT PLAYS by Lady Gregory; for *Sing, O Sing Again,* translated by Sir John Bowring from ANTHOLOGY OF RUSSIAN LITERATURE, and for *The Riddle of America* from ANCIENT ROME AND MODERN AMERICA by Guglielmo Ferrero.

Random House, Inc., for Act II of MARCO MILLIONS by Eugene O'Neill.

Sanders and Conroy, *The Atlantic Monthly* and the author for *The Return* by Lord Dunsany.

Charles Scribner's Sons for *The Master* by Edwin Arlington Robinson; for *The Bottle Imp, The Citizen and the Traveller* from FABLES, a selection from THE STRANGE CASE OF DR. JEKYLL AND MR. HYDE, *Windy Nights, Sing Me a Song,* and *Student Song* by Robert Louis Stevenson; for *Acme* by John Galsworthy; for *The Essay Contest* from SENTIMENTAL TOMMY by J. M. Barrie; for a selection from A DOLL'S HOUSE by Henrik Ibsen; for *O World* by George Santayana; for *Little Boy Blue* by Eugene Field; for *The Old Squaw* from DIARY OF A DUDE WRANGLER by Struthers Burt; for *The Tree* by Björnsterne Björnson, and for *A Terrible Night* by Anton Chekhov.

Scribner's Magazine for *What the American Rhodes Scholar Gets from Oxford* by Frank Aydelotte.

ACKNOWLEDGMENT

John Garrett Underhill for *A Sunny Morning* by Serafín and Joaquín Alvarez Quintero, translated by Lucretia Xavier Floyd.

> Copyright, 1914, by Lucretia Xavier Floyd. *A Sunny Morning* may be performed only by arrangement with Samuel French, 25 West 45th Street, New York, N. Y.

University of California Press for *A Symphony in Gray* by Ruben Dario, *At Peace* by Amado Nervo, and *Disdain* by Leopoldo Lugones, translated by G. D. Craig in THE MODERNIST TREND.

Ann Watkins, Inc., for *The River Merchant's Wife: A Letter* by T'ai-po, translated by Ezra Pound.

H. G. Wells for a selection from EXPERIMENT IN AUTOBIOGRAPHY.

Contents

I. THE SHORT STORY

SELECTED SHORT STORIES

(Including a French translation and its retranslation into English
by Mark Twain)

II. THE PROSE TALE

SELECTED PROSE TALES

* This marks a cut version. All other selections are complete as titled.

III. THE BALLAD

XV. THE ELEGY

XVI. THE LETTER

XII. THE SONG

SELECTED SONGS

CONTENTS

XIII. THE SONNET

XIV. THE ODE

X. THE ESSAY

XI. LYRIC POETRY

CONTENTS

CONTENTS

XIX. HISTORY

XX. ORATORY AND DEBATE

Illustrations

Introduction

CAN YOU REALLY READ?

IF SOMEONE gave you the money for a tour of the world, many of you would be unable to profit fully by this opportunity because you could not speak the languages of the countries through which you must pass and could therefore enjoy only the surface sights without understanding the inner life and thought of the different peoples whom you visited.

The masterpieces in this volume which were written in foreign tongues have all been translated for you from their original language into English.[1] Are you certain, however, that even so you are fitted to travel in the Republic of Letters or to become a citizen of that intellectual democracy? Are you sure that you can read your own language with genuine skill? Some of you will be surprised to hear that many high school students cannot really read, and therefore find the doors of knowledge closed to them even when this doorway is the language they have spoken all their lives. Of course, there is no high-school student who does not know his letters and who cannot identify words on the printed page. But true reading is thinking with the author and getting the full meaning from what he writes. Tests prove that large numbers of high-school and even college students cannot do this seemingly simple thing! This explains the poor school work of countless fine boys and girls, since so much of our study must be done from books.

This also explains something of even greater importance than school success. Many men and women are handicapped in life because, although they have become adults in age, they still have reading interests and ability on the juvenile level and must always content themselves with childish books containing a childlike vocabulary, childlike sentences, and childlike ideas—even though these books may deal with the grown-up world. Thus the books and

[1] For a discussion of the difficulties of translating thoughts from one language to another, see Arnold's *On Translating Homer* (page 691) and Mark Twain's discussion of the French translation of *The Jumping Frog* (page 89).

periodicals which discuss current life and its problems in mature fashion are beyond them, and they remain throughout life uninformed about the important issues, ideas, and forces which shape their lives.

Each of you will wish to know whether you are now a child or an adult in reading ability. Perhaps your teacher will help you take a standard test to see whether you do read as skillfully as the average student of your school grade in the United States. If you find that your reading skill is below that of the average student of your age, then you will want to discover what your difficulties are and how to correct them, so that you can grow up in reading as well as in mind and body. Only thus can you qualify yourself for citizenship in the Republic of Letters and share the thoughts and relive the experiences of the intellectual leaders of the world. Only thus can you find real fun in reading books appropriate to your age and mental ability. Only thus can you read maturely like a man or woman—not immaturely like an overgrown child!

The editors of this book believe that every student has a right to grow up in reading to the full level of his mental stature; and that both textbooks and teachers should help him to outgrow childish reading habits that keep him immature and close to him the higher levels of thought. Some students have purely physical difficulties in reading. Are you sure you can see the letters clearly in each word you read or do you have to puzzle the words out if you are not to make mistakes? Can you sound the letters readily and correctly in a word you see, so that you recognize both how it is spelled and how it is pronounced? Do you use your finger to keep your place and guide your eye as you read? If so, you will read only as fast as you can move your finger and your reading will be very slow and tedious. Do you murmur words aloud to yourself as you read? If so, you will also read slowly, since the lips cannot move as quickly as the eye. Perhaps you don't actually say the words aloud, but try putting your fingers on your lips and throat to see whether you are silently moving your lips or your vocal cords and thus slowing up your progress.

If you are a slow reader, have you ever watched yourself to see whether you look at just one word at a time or whether you can see several words at a glance? As we read, we move the eye along the line, stopping every so often to get a good look. It is in these stops that we do our reading. If you can see only one word at a time, you will have to stop many times in each line, and you will be a very slow reader. If you can see several words at a time, you will need to stop seldom and can read rapidly. It is possible to train your eye to take in more and more words at a glance and so increase your speed. Sometimes people don't move their eyes steadily forward but let them waver forward and back. This also makes a slow reader.

If you find you aren't a first-class reader, perhaps you should take a test to see whether a small vocabulary is your trouble. Naturally if you have a vocabulary smaller than the average student of your age, you will not read with ease and understanding the books which average students can enjoy.

However, your vision may be good, your eye movements quick and steady, and your vocabulary reasonably large, but you may still be a poor reader because you have not learned to get the full meaning from the words, sentences and paragraphs upon the printed page. We certainly do not read just to recognize words; the facts and ideas the author is trying to convey to us are what we seek. But many of us in our reading are like the little boy with defective vision who had seen trees only as a blur of green. He had thought the trees were beautiful, but not until he had been fitted to glasses did he see the separate leaves with their lovely shapes. Likewise, many of us get only a vague notion of what an author means, and it is not till we have learned to watch for certain special things as we read, that we are able to see all the author is trying to tell us. Just as there are motions we must learn to do smoothly and skillfully in order to swim well or to play the piano, so also there are certain things we must learn to do in order to get the thought from what we read.

We read to share the experiences of others, to taste new emotions, to acquire information, to answer questions and solve problems, to form opinions and draw conclusions, to discover new problems and fresh topics for thought, and to find lines of reading that may be pursued with pleasure and profit through future years. To accomplish these results, we must learn to do the things outlined below whenever they are needed to help us understand the book in hand. One of the tricks of skillful reading is to tell which of these things *are* necessary for a special book or a special purpose, and then make just the right reading motions to get what we should out of that particular book or chapter, or to accomplish the purpose for which we are doing a special piece of reading.

SKILLS WHICH WILL GIVE YOU READING POWER

1. Find the main *topic* of a sentence, paragraph, chapter or book.
   It will help you to do this if you can:
   a. Recognize the key words that suggest the topic of the sentence.
   b. Recognize the topic sentence that states the topic discussed by a paragraph.
   c. Pick out the paragraph that explains the topic of a chapter.

2. Find the main *thought* of a paragraph, chapter or book. There is a difference between the topic discussed and the idea of the author about this topic. For instance, the topic may be censorship of the movies. But that doesn't tell whether the author is for or against it, and why. The main thought of a paragraph, book or chapter is the big thing the author says *about* the main topic. It will help you to find the main thought if you can:
   a. Predict what is to follow the events you are reading about.
   b. Note important details in a description or discussion.
   c. Outline the points taken up in explaining the main topic of a paragraph, chapter or book.
   d. Pick out general principles and recognize their illustrations.
   e. Explain figurative expressions and symbols which express the idea of a whole discussion.
   f. Interpret an allegory and figures of speech.
   g. Paraphrase or put in your own words the contents of a paragraph.
   h. Summarize the thought of a paragraph, chapter, or book.

A paraphrase does not condense a selection down to its main idea. It reproduces it in full in different words. A summary brings out merely the main thought. In writing a summary, one must exclude unimportant details, include all essential points, show the relation between them, and boil the statement down to the fewest possible words. In making a summary, see whether you can put the thought of a paragraph into two or three sentences, perhaps into a single sentence. Substitute dependent clauses for sentences, phrases for clauses, and single words for phrases.

3. Interpret what you are reading:
   a. Vitalize what you are reading by calling up things in your own experience that illustrate and explain the author's words.

b. Test what you are reading by proving or disproving it from your own experience.

c. Let your mind play over what you are reading, looking back over what you have read and forward to what you imagine is still to come.

d. Read between the lines, letting the author's words start new trains of thought in your mind, so that in a sense you collaborate with him and transform what he has written into a new literary masterpiece—part his and part yours!

4. Use what you read for your own purposes:

a. Apply ideas you gain from reading to your own conduct.

b. Learn to follow directions given in print.

c. Judge when to read with great thoroughness and when to skim through a selection.

d. Estimate the speed at which you can read each type of book with understanding.

A light story or factual reading on a subject with which you are already somewhat familiar can be read rapidly. Unfamiliar material or material which contains new and profound ideas must be read slowly. Poetry is the most condensed form of writing; the poet compresses a world of truth and meaning into a single line or phrase, and the reader must go slowly if he is to get all the hidden richness of the lines. The person who skims lightly over a great poem is like the settlers who sold their Oklahoma and Kansas farms without realizing that below the surface was untold wealth in oil.

The following books will discuss many of these reading skills more fully and give you definite exercises for their practice:

Bennett: *Translating Literature into Life*
Hovious: *Following Printed Trails*
Bessey: *Reading through Précis*
         Reading to Understand

WHAT BOOKS DO YOU MOST ENJOY?

The comfort and happiness of the citizens of any country depend on their ability to recognize and follow a high type of leader. Can you select good leaders in the intellectual Republic of Letters? In other words, can you recognize and enjoy a really good book, or like the ignorant voter who often supports corrupt and foolish political leaders, are you limited in your enjoyment of reading to second-rate stuff? The student who can use easily all the reading skills listed in this chapter will really enjoy the best books because he will not be baffled struggling to understand the great leaders in literature. The failure of many students to develop a love of good books is largely due to their lack of reading skill. The fault is not with the books! The Alps are no less magnificent because you cannot climb them. The trouble is with your climbing skill. In exploring the Republic of Letters, let us say with Arthur Guiterman:

> God give me hills to climb
> And strength for climbing.

Let us strive to learn how to recognize and enjoy great books!

Perhaps you would like to discover whether you do prefer the best literature. Here are some tests of your literary taste. In each of the following pairs of selections, each selection deals with practically the same subject. In each pair of selections, which do you really prefer and why? Be honest! You want to find out whether you at present like first-rate or third-rate reading.

Pair I

A.
> How many million Aprils came
> Before I ever knew
> How white a cherry bough could be,
> A bed of squills² how blue.
> And many a dancing April
> When life has done with me
> Will lift the blue flame of the flower,
> The white flame of the tree!

B.
> How long the world existed
> Before life showed to me
> How many lovely things there were
> For everyone to see.
> And after I am dead and gone,
> How long the world will last
> And look to all as beautiful
> As in the distant past.

Pair II

A.
> Alas, that beauty lasts but for a day;
> That happy youth should quickly slip away;
> And all our prayers can never once persuade
> Relentless time his rapid course to stay!

² *squills:* a spring flower.

B.   Yet Ah, that Spring should vanish with the Rose,
     That Youth's sweet scented manuscript should close.
     The Nightingale that in the branches sang,
     Ah, whence and whither flown again, who knows?

PAIR III

A. The melancholy days are come, the saddest of the year,
     Of wailing winds and naked woods and meadows brown
         and sere.
     Heaped in the hollows of the grove, the autumn leaves
         lie dead.
     They rustle to the eddying gust and to the rabbits' tread.

B. Where are the songs of Spring? Ay, where are they?
     Think not of them, thou hast thy music too,
     While barrèd clouds bloom the soft-dying day,
     And touch the stubble-plains with rosy hue;
     Then in a wailful choir, the small gnats mourn
     Among the river sallows, borne aloft
     Or sinking as the light wind lives or dies;
     And full-grown lambs loud bleat from hilly bourn;
     Hedge-crickets sing; and now with treble soft
     The redbreast whistles from a garden-croft,
     And gathering swallows twitter in the skies.

PAIR IV

A.   Slowly, silently, now the moon
        Walks the night in her silver shoon;
        This way, and that, she peers, and sees
        Silver fruit upon silver trees;
        One by one the casements catch
        Her beams beneath the silvery thatch;
        Couched in his kennel, like a log,
        With paws of silver sleeps the dog;
        From their shadowy cote the white breasts peep
        Of doves in a silver-feathered sleep;
        A harvest mouse goes scampering by,
        With silver claws and a silver eye;
        And moveless fish in the water gleam,
        By silver reeds in a silver stream.

B.　　　　The red flame flowers bloom and die,
　　　　　The embers puff a golden spark.
　　　　　Now and again a horse's eye
　　　　　Shines like a topaz in the dark.

　　　　　A prowling jackal jars the hush,
　　　　　The drowsy oxen chump and sigh—
　　　　　The ghost moon lifts above the bush
　　　　　And creeps across the starry sky.

　　　　　Low in the south the "Cross" [3] is bright,
　　　　　And sleep comes dreamless, undefiled,
　　　　　Here in the blue and silver night
　　　　　In the star chamber of the wild.

Pair V

A. There had been silence over in the corner; but now the man Trampas spoke again.

"And ten," said he, sliding out some chips from before him. Very strange it was to hear him, how he contrived to make those words a personal taunt. The Virginian was looking at his cards. He might have been deaf.

"And twenty," said the next player, easily.

The next threw his cards down.

It was now the Virginian's turn to bet, or leave the game, and he did not speak at once.

Therefore Trampas spoke. "Your bet, you ——."

The Virginian's pistol came out, and his hand lay on the table, holding it unaimed. And with a voice as gentle as ever, a voice that sounded almost like a caress, but drawling a very little more than usual, so that there was almost a space between each word, he issued his orders to the man Trampas: "When you call me that, smile." And he looked at Trampas across the table.

Yes, the voice was gentle. But in my ears it seemed as if somewhere the bell of death was ringing, and silence, like a stroke, fell on the large room. All men present, as if by some magnetic current, had become aware of this crisis. In my ignorance, and the total stoppage of my thoughts, I stood stock-still, and noticed various people crouching or shifting their positions.

[3] *"Cross":* the Southern Cross, a constellation of stars seen in the Southern Hemisphere.

"Sit quiet," said the dealer, scornfully to the man near me. "Can't you see he don't want to push trouble? He has handed Trampas the choice to back down or draw his steel."

Then, with equal suddenness and ease, the room came out of its strangeness. Voices and cards, the click of chips, the puff of tobacco, glasses lifted to drink—this level of smooth relaxation hinted no more plainly of what lay beneath than does the surface tell the depth of the sea.

B. Although most of the gunfire was being directed at him, the smiling young outlaw wasn't easy to hit. He kept moving and shifting, his guns held below his hips and sweeping the room in flat, deadly arcs.

The bearded desperado, Bridger, dropped to the floor, killed instantly. Both Sonny and Slim Tilden had hit him.

"Take it, yuh skunks!" Slim yelled.

Pancho Baca, smashed by another bullet, just as he was about to trigger his gun, slumped, dying, to the floor. And at that moment, Slim Tilden was hit. A slug from Smiler's guns nailed him.

Sonny saw him stagger and drop his smoking Colt, saw him reel into the wall and then go down. There was a hole above one eye, a streak of crimson below it. He'd been killed.

The death of Slim filled Sonny Tabor with white-hot fury. His nerves remained as cold as threads of ice, but his heart seemed to spin around in his chest. Diving forward through the thick smoke, he closed in at deadly range, with the shadow who was Smiler Blue. He shot him twice, driving the bullets into his belt line.

With his shirt charred and smoldering from the effects of the shots, Smiler fell heavily, his buckteeth bared in a horrible grimace.

Kelly was down, writhing hideously, his life ebbing away through a hole under the heart.

Frank Langford was getting his shots down, at last, and at the crack of his 38, Jack Dale, the last of the blackmail gang, went sprawling. He got halfway up, started to crawl toward the door, and collapsed into a motionless heap.

It was over. Slim Tilden had given his life, Sonny Tabor had a slight wound, and John Langford had been shot through the left arm. But the Box L, and the happiness of Mrs. Langford and little Betty were saved.

That ghost from the past had been quieted forever.

Pair VI

A.

My love is like a red, red rose
That's newly sprung in June;
My love is like a melody
That's sweetly played in tune.

B.

For lo, my love doth in herself contain
All this world's riches that may far be found.
If sapphires, lo, her eyes be sapphires plain,
If rubies, lo, her lips be rubies sound.
If pearls, her teeth be pearls, both pure and round;
If ivory, her forehead ivory ween;
If gold, her locks are finest gold on ground;
If silver, her fair hands are silver sheen.

Pair VII

A. Hetty walked into the Biggest Store one morning four years before with seventy-five other girls, applying for a job behind the waist department counter. The phalanx of wage earners formed a bewildering scene of beauty, carrying a total mass of blond hair sufficient to have justified the horseback gallops of a hundred Lady Godivas.

The capable, cool-eyed, impersonal, young bald-headed man, whose task it was to engage six of the contestants, was aware of a feeling of suffocation as if he were drowning in a sea of frangipanni,[4] while white clouds, hand embroidered, floated about him. And then a sail hove in sight. Hetty Pepper, homely of countenance, with small, contemptuous green eyes and chocolate-colored hair, dressed in a suit of plain woolen and a common sense hat, stood before him with every one of her twenty-nine years of life unmistakably in sight.

"You're on!" shouted the bald-headed young man, and was saved. And that is how Hetty came to be employed in the Biggest Store.

B. Mr. Garvey ground out his cigarette. His dark face flushed. "What's the matter?" he inquired bitterly. "Doesn't a legitimate business proposition interest you?"

The old gentleman below him refused to take offense. He played

---

[4] *frangipanni:* a perfume derived from, or imitating the odor of, the flower of the red jasmine.

a red six on a black seven and continued to thumb the deck with unruffled calm.

"Well?" Mr. Garvey repeated.

His aged associate in the gentle art of living like a prince on nothing a year, leaned back in his chair and wiggled his plump brown-tweed knees. "You forget my philosophy of life, my dear boy. Ha. You do indeed. At the moment, as the result of the little affair of the Countess Radeska, I am in funds. Why should I expend precious moments of leisure and vitally needed strength pitting my talents against inexperienced amateurs? Eh? Tomorrow I shall turn your share of the Affair Radeska over to you and you may——"

Mr. Uthas P. Garvey removed his well-tailored body from the table. "Bunk!" he jeered. "Twaddle! The plain truth is, Colonel Flack—that is, if you are really a colonel and your name is really Flack—that an honest dollar doesn't give you a kick."

C. Mr. Joe Poke cringed in a corner of the Jim Crow car and gazed with lackluster eyes upon the parched landscape of North Alabama. Mr. Poke was very small, very black, very weary and very broke. He had, in fact, succeeded in achieving a degree of financial decrepitude in comparison with which mere bankruptcy might be considered affluence.

The month was September; the hour, two in the afternoon. Outside, the last furnacelike blast of a scorching summer was paying final tribute to a countryside which had been burned to a crisp since July. And inside the car there were cinders—oh, innumerable cinders—each of which seemed to have a definite affinity for the abysmally miserable little traveller.

Mr. Poke's belt had been pulled so tight about his negligible waist that the buckle appeared to rest against his backbone. Hunger gnawed at him, and his only real diversion for the past two hours had been to cast longing eyes upon the fruits and confections which were being dispensed in the car by a melancholy news butch.

With a single exception, all the other dusky passengers had been prostrated by the blistering heat. That exception was a gentleman of ocher hue who sported amazing raiment, carried impressive luggage and was, apparently, impervious to climate. Mr. Poke had observed him enviously but impersonally—as a traveller in England might look upon a ceremony at Buckingham Palace gates. The debonair colored man across the car was a person from another world; superior and aloof.

And so, when this person moved across the aisle and dropped

languidly into the seat beside Mr. Poke, that attenuated gentleman blinked rapidly, rubbed his eyes and, for no apparent reason, said, "Excuse me."

The stranger remarked, "I seen you lookin' at them fruits. Hongry?"

"Mistuh, I'se so hongry I could eat my own appetite."

Pair VIII

A. Soon Jenny ceased her stitches. She ran her white hands up through the heavy dark mass of her wavy hair and dropped delicately to one side of the maroon-corduroy chair. In the mulberry gloom, her beautiful white face was whiter, an oval of thin paper against the ponderous carved woodwork.

"Annora!" cried her mother sharply.

It was too late; Jenny had fainted. Her slim body had slipped awry, hanging over the carved walnut arm of the chair; and in her beautiful face, white as whitest paper in the street lamp's shivering light, white as alabaster against the cloth of her garnet colored gown, her large eyes were closed.

B. "Let her finish her sleep!" he implored in a whisper of the police as they gathered around.

When they saw where she lay, they stood watching her, as still as the pillars around. He went to the stone slab, and bent over her, holding one poor little hand; her breathing now was quick and small, like that of a lesser creature than a woman. All waited in the growing light, their faces and hands were silvered, the remainder of their figures dark, the stones glistening a gray-green, the Plain still a mass of shade. Soon the light was strong, and a ray shone upon her unconscious form, peering under her eyelids and waking her.

"What is it, Angel?" she said, starting up. "Have they come for me?"

"Yes, dearest," he said. "They have come."

EXTRA EXERCISES

I. It is said there is no disputing about taste. But nothing is more fun or better adapted to develop one's taste. Let each member of the class take one of the following pairs of good poems for study. See whether you can tell which of the two poems is the real masterpiece. By what signs do you recognize the greater poem? The name of the poet is no guide, as great poets have often done some second-rate work. Some of the less known poems listed are in Elmo's *Home Book of Poetry and Song.*

1. Wotton's *A Happy Life* and Guest's *Thought for the Day.*
2. Guest's *Self* and Macbeth's speech beginning "My way of life" in Act V, scene 3 of Shakespeare's *Macbeth.*
3. Guest's *To a Friend* and Shakespeare's sonnet "When to the sessions of sweet silent thought."
4. Guest's *The Burdens* and Browning's *Rabbi Ben Ezra* (stanzas 4, 5, 6, 7).
5. Henley's *Invictus* and Guest's *Defeat.*
6. Aldrich's *Romance* (I) and Tennyson's *Go not, Happy Day.*
7. Morrison's *Long Time Ago* and Wordsworth's *She Dwelt Among the Untrodden Ways.*
8. Hay's *When the Boys Come Home* and Seeger's *Rendezvous with Death.*
9. Tennyson's *Tears, Idle Tears* and Guest's *Failures.*
10. Wordsworth's *Daffodils* and Montgomery's *To a Daisy.*
11. Bryant's *Robert of Lincoln* and Keats' *Ode to a Nightingale.*
12. Whittier's *My Playmate* (stanzas 1–2) and the first twelve lines of Keats' *I Stood Tiptoe.*
13. Taylor's *Shall I Wed Thee?* and Burns' *My Love Is Like a Red Red Rose.*
14. Poe's *To Helen* and Bulwer's *As Stars Look on the Sea.*
15. Hemans's *Landing of the Pilgrim Fathers* (stanzas 1–2) and Browning's *Meeting at Night.*
16. Cornwall's *The Sea* and Byron's lines from *Childe Harold* beginning "Roll on, thou dark and deep blue ocean, roll."
17. Kilmer's *Trees* and Lady Winchelsea's *The Tree.*
18. Norton's *Bingen on the Rhine* and Byron's lines from *Childe Harold* beginning "I saw before me the Gladiator lie."
19. Guest's *Heap of Living* and Wilmot's *My Little Gray Home in the West.*
20. Lowell's *My Love* (stanza 1) and Masefield's *Her Heart.*
21. Hilda Conkling's *Time* and T. S. Collier's *Time.*
22. Holland's *Lullaby* and Tennyson's *Sweet and Low.*
23. Keats' *La Belle Dame sans Merci* and Aldrich's *Sorcery.*
24. Longfellow's *Psalm of Life* and Swinburne's *Garden of Proserpine.*
25. Collins' *Ode* and Longfellow's *The Reaper and the Flowers.*
26. Whittier's *Maud Muller* and Rossetti's *Blessed Damozel.*
27. Millay's *Renascence* and Alexander's *Burial of Moses.*
28. Lang's *The Odyssey* and Keats' *On First Looking into Chapman's Homer.*
29. Lowell's *Vision of Sir Launfal* (first half of Prelude to Part II) and the early stanzas of Keats' *Eve of Saint Agnes.*
30. Hope's *Kashmiri Song* and Burns' *Bonnie Doon.*

II. Select two magazines—one of the cheap wood-pulp variety, and one a standard magazine of recognized excellence like *Harpers, The Atlantic,* etc. First compare the advertisements to see whether they appeal to the same kind of people; i.e., the same in economic condition, education, social standing, intelligence and culture. Then compare the stories and articles in the two magazines to discover whether they are adapted to the same group of readers likely to be reached by their respective advertising sections. Show why.

WHAT MAKES LITERATURE PERMANENTLY GREAT?

Now that you have tested yourself to see whether you at present really prefer the first- or second-rate in literature, let us analyze some of the preceding pairs of contrasting selections to see what are the qualities that make literature permanently great and why one of the test selections is better than the other.

UNIVERSALITY

More important than style is, of course, the content of a literary work. We like a contemporary book which seems to embody the spirit of our own times and speak our own thoughts for us. A book which rises above mere individuality and catches the general tone of its period will be a standard work in its day and age. But will it last? It will if it retains a living relation to succeeding generations by embodying thoughts, feelings, and experiences that never grow out of date, but repeat themselves age by age and are the same in ancient Troy and present-day Chicago. Why, for instance, do we still enjoy Homer, who wrote in Greece more than a thousand years before the birth of Christ? Read Homer's description (page 392) of the parting of Hector, the Trojan prince, from his wife and baby, as Hector went forth three thousand years ago to the campaign in which he met his death. What should we need to change in this touchingly human scene to make it the farewell of a soldier to his family during the World War? This poem was great in its own day since it pictured for the ancient Greek world its own ideal of heroism and the meaning of life in a warlike era. It became immortal since it also pictures the feelings which still bind together a loving family and which will be universally and eternally the same as long as the race endures.

ENRICHMENT OF LIVING

Another appeal of the really great work of literature is that it expands the reader's information or sympathy by giving him a fuller understanding of the common lot of man and the great experiences of life. For instance, Tolstoy's famous novel, *Anna Karenina*, by means of its four parallel plots, presents love and marriage from almost every possible angle. There is the loveless marriage of Anna to Karenin arranged for her in girlhood by her parents. There is her sister-in-law Dolly who sticks to a faithless husband for the sake of the children. There is Kitty's heartbreak when her tacit engagement to Vronsky dissolves in the heat of his sudden passion for Anna. There is the firm happiness of Kitty's subsequent congenial marriage to Levin. And there is the tragic effort of Anna and Vronsky to build up a life together when Anna's husband refuses her a divorce. There is even the problem of the child in the broken home, represented by Serosha, the son who had filled Anna's heart in her loveless home and for whom she yearns in spite of the new passion that seems at first to flood her life to the brim. No one who has watched this many-sided drama of human relationships unfold through this novel can fail to understand people and experience more profoundly, to meet his own life problems more intelligently, and to sympathize more keenly with the struggles and mistakes of others.

INSPIRATION

A third appeal of a great book is that it not only expresses life with rich completeness, but goes beyond the real to the ideal, and freshens the heart of the reader with youthful energy and faith in the possibility of realizing this ideal in the actual world. Every generous lad who reads the final pages of *The Tale of Two Cities* feels capable of dying like Sidney Carton for one he loves. Every reader of *Les Misérables* is sure that like Jean Valjean, he would confess his identity to save an innocent man from going to prison in his stead. Such books keep alive the noble impulses of our hearts, our highest capacities of thought and feeling. They are great leaders in the Republic of Letters.

MEMORABILITY

There are points in style, also, which mark the great work of literature and help to distinguish it from the second-rate book. The first of these is memorability.[5] A fine style warms the author's idea into reality and fixes it in the mind by expressing it in some vivid, concrete, unforgettable image. For instance, Sara Teasdale, the author of poem *A* in Pair I, is not satisfied with such vague, general expressions as *how long* and *lovely things* and *look beautiful*. She speaks of a million Aprils, of white cherry blossoms and blue squills, and refers to the dazzling colors of tree and flower as white and blue flames. Poem *B* is thoroughly commonplace; any one might have said it; and it goes in one ear and out the other. But Miss Teasdale's dancing Aprils with their cherry blooms and squills will stick in your mind after a single reading.

STIMULATION

This is because April flowers offer a good *illustration* of transient beauty, as does also poem *B* in Pair II, which is a stanza from the *Rubáiyát* of the Persian poet Omar Khayyám. Instead of the vague generalization that life is short and beauty fleeting, Omar and Teasdale call up in our mind lovely pictures of boughs of white cherry blossoms dancing in the April wind, of rose gardens in spring, of birds singing at twilight. These mind pictures fill us with a feeling of joy and regret such as our own beautiful experiences awaken, whereas the statement that life is short leaves us cold and untouched.

Moreover, you will notice that Teasdale and Omar do not draw this conclusion for you. They do not say "life is short"; they picture for you the spring season, the passing of the roses, the brief song of the nightingale. Your own mind goes on to say, "Alas, how short a time these lovely things endure!" In other words, the poets set your heart and mind to picturing, feeling, thinking. Their words start echoes within you, that warm and enrich the poet's idea. So also Dickens and Hugo do not moralize about unselfish generosity. They tell you the stories of Sidney Carton and Jean Valjean, and your own mind finishes the thought. In other words, the style of great literature is in itself stimulating to the mind and heart.

BEAUTY

The mere style of a literary masterpiece likewise often possesses a beauty and interest of its own, like that of a rich fabric which lends an extra loveliness to a charming costume design. A plaster cast may be exquisite in form, but carved in marble the statue has

---

[5] *memorability:* being easy to remember and worth remembering.

an added grace. A piece of inexpensive costume jewelry may complete satisfactorily a tasteful ensemble, but one can turn a precious jewel this way and that, watching the colors and lights of its gleaming depths. The gay colors of zinnias and peonies satisfy one when massed in great vases or garden beds, but the soft texture and fragrance of a delicate rose delights one upon nearer, longer scrutiny. So, too, the fabric of words has its beauty of texture and color and fragrance. When a clay bowl is broken, its charm is gone, but crush a crystal of quartz and its shining grains glitter splendidly in the sun. So also the crystalline substance of a book written in a beautiful style breaks into fragments we remember as unforgettable quotations.

In Pair III, the authors of both poems describe for us the autumn scene, but in item *B*, Keats far excels Bryant in the definiteness of the pictures his words suggest. *Stubble plains* is a clearer image than *meadows brown and sere*. *Barred-clouds* tells you just what kind of clouds they were. Keats' red breast *whistles;* his swallows *twitter,* and who else ever made poetry of a swarm of gnats? Not only do Keats' individual words suggest images that linger in the mind, but they combine into lines and phrases that paint with completeness scene after scene—the evening sky, the fields at sunset, the redbreast in the garden, and "the gathering swallows twittering in the skies." Moreover, the words not only fall together into perfect pictures but into a sweet and subtle rhythm which never grows monotonous like the insistent beat of Bryant's lines, because it is varied by the phrasing and by the natural pauses one makes in reading the lines.

In Pair IV, item *A*, a poem by De la Mare entitled *Silver*, is not only beautifully descriptive but is almost pure music—the magic of its melody depending upon a repetition of soft letter-sounds and a choice of musical words so arranged that one word melts into the next in a liquid flow of rhythm. Turn to pages 746-8 and 845-8 and select words, phrases, and lines that are in themselves beautiful because of their musical sound or because they suggest beautiful color, scent, sound, touch or taste, or that charm us in a different way by their humorous, original phrasing, as on pages 698-704.

FITNESS AND NATURALNESS

A final quality of style that marks the first-rate work of literature is that the style is suitable and natural. A good style is always suited to its subject; slang does not intrude into dignified passages, nor do flowery artificial expressions mar simple, touching incidents. The great writer talks grandly of grand things and simply of simple things. And he does both with naturalness and ease, yet with a dignity and restraint that keeps his grand passages from artificiality and his simple passages from triviality.

In item *B* of Pair VIII, Hardy describes only those things which help to suggest how the police who have surrounded Tess are touched by the strange mystery of sleep, and wait till she awakens to make the arrest which means her death. The author of item *A*, on the contrary, drags in the slimness of the girl's body, the carving on the chair, its upholstery, the fact that it is walnut, the color of her dress, the size of her eyes, and an elaborate set of overdone and contradictory comparisons about the whiteness of her face in the lamp light, which distract attention from any pathos or interest her fainting might have had. In the humorous items in Pair VII, the amusement over O. Henry's account of the employment manager springs naturally and easily from his situation, whereas the authors of items *B* and *C* labor hard to say something funny, and overdo it. In Pair V, Owen Wister's quiet, restrained way of describing the Virginian's first clash with Trampas creates greater tension and more frontier atmosphere than all the piled-up shooting, slam banging, and rough vocabulary of the other Western episode.

In Pair VI, while Burns and Spenser are both great poets, one feels instantly that the red rose and the sweet melody of Burns' poem are more suggestive of the fresh simple sweetness of a lovely young girl than all the elaborate comparisons by which Spenser tries to picture his sweetheart's beauty. After all, no eyes, lips, teeth, hair, and skin closely resemble jewels, gold, silver, or ivory! These comparisons are artificial, while Burns' style seems simple, suitable and natural.

As you read the world's masterpieces gathered together type by type in this book, you should therefore learn not only how races differ from and resemble each other; you should not only fill your minds with the thoughts and dreams of the great thinkers of every race and clime, but you should practice the reading skills and make the discriminations in taste between better and best that will make you feel at home in the cosmopolitan Republic of Great Books.

KEY TO TESTS OF LITERARY TASTE

Pages xxx–xxvi

Pair I A—Pair II B—Pair III B—Pair IV A—Pair V A—Pair VI A
Pair VII A—Pair VIII B

I

The Short Story

ALL the world loves a good story, especially the made-up stories which we call fiction. We turn to fiction to pass the time, to escape from ourselves and identify ourselves with more interesting persons and events, to see how other personalities meet and solve life problems like our own, and to learn about phases of life that do not come within our own experience. The most popular form of fiction is undoubtedly that literary type called the short story.

A modern short story can usually be read at a single sitting. It is built around a single episode. It has a single purpose and everything in the story has been put in by the author to bring out this purpose. It leaves you with a single strong impression. The short story is, as its name implies, condensed. It starts rapidly; includes no incidents or descriptions that do not bear on the main point; revolves around a very few characters; and comes to a quick end.

However, in this short space, the modern short story offers the reader most of the interesting features of fiction.

PLOT

In the first place, the action of the story has a *plot* or plan. This plan is based on two features which distinguish the plotted short story from the tale. The first of these is that in a plot every incident [1] or happening *causes* what happens next. Suppose I start an automobile trip, skid into a ditch five miles out of town, have a puncture several hours later, and am held up at sundown by a hitch hiker who steals my car and leaves me by the roadside. There is no causal connection between this series of incidents.[1] My skid does not cause my puncture and my puncture does not cause the hold-up. These incidents are related only because they happen one after another to me; an account of this trip would not be a causal sequence

---

[1] An incident is one happening. An episode is a short series of related incidents.

of incidents, or plot, but simply a tale. But suppose I am a student hard pressed for money: I hear of an essay contest with a large cash prize; as I am a good writer, I decide to enter it; I accidentally find an essay on the same topic; I am tempted to use this essay; I copy it and hand it in as my own; the essay wins the prize; but later my dishonesty is discovered; my prize is taken back; I am publicly disgraced. Here each incident in the story causes what comes next, and we have a causal sequence of events or plot.

In the second place, the action of a story with a plot is directed toward a definite end. The main character (hero or heroine) has an aim he wishes to accomplish,[2] and the story shows his struggle to attain this object and his final success or failure. The word *struggle* is the key to our interest in a story. Suppose John goes to a party and meets a girl named Sue. He likes Sue, dances with her and asks to call. She consents and he calls upon her repeatedly. Sue loves John, he finally proposes, her parents approve, and he and Sue are happily married. This story has a plot, since the hero accomplishes his object in marrying Sue, but the story is too tame to be interesting. John succeeds too easily.

An absorbing story contains obstacles for the leading character to contend with. This keeps up our suspense and gives the hero a chance to show his heroism in overcoming difficulties. Perhaps he has a rival, perhaps his sweetheart's family dislike him, perhaps he does not have a steady job. The lovers may belong to different churches or races. One or the other may have some personal weakness to overcome before marriage can be happy. See if you can list a dozen other obstacles that could intervene to complicate this story and furnish a little excitement. Some will be *inner* obstacles within the characters' own minds, hearts, or personalities, like prejudices, beliefs, emotions, or personal traits. Others will be *external,* like people who are hostile, circumstances in nature, accidents, or economic and social conditions. Usually the hero can overcome the difficulties in his path, and the story ends happily. But sometimes he is struggling with forces he cannot control, and he fails in his attempt. Then the end is said to be tragic. However, even in defeat the true hero is admirable, for he fights bravely to the end.

The struggle of the hero with his difficulties may be diagrammed as follows: B is the point where the hero is at the beginning of the story. E is where he wants to get. If there were no obstacles, he would move straight from B to E like John and Sue, and there

---

[2] The boy in the preceding plot has winning the prize as his aim.

would be little to hold our attention. But as the hero climbs over the mountain of obstacles before him, his progress makes a triangle with the straight line of his aim.

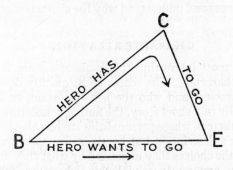

Point C is the moment when we see that the hero is going to succeed or fail but aren't quite sure how everything is going to be worked out. This is called the turning point or climax [3] of the story. The part of his line of progress from C to E is called the *resolution* or *denouement* or unraveling of the story. And E is the end or *outcome*. How would you diagram a story in which the hero failed?

SETTING

The action which makes up the plot of a story has to take place somewhere and at some definite time. The time and place of a story are called its *setting*. In reading a story, it is not enough to know just the geographical location. We must note the *social background* of the action. It may take place in New York City; but is it laid among the fashionable social set, or in the slums, or in a foreign district, or in Harlem, where the negro population of the city centers? A reader discovers where the story is laid either by the author's description of the scene or through the conversation of the characters, or from manners and customs peculiar to certain times and localities. For instance, in a story laid in an earlier period in history, the introduction of famous events and people, old-fashioned costumes, and quaint customs give us a clue to the date of the action. Some stories could have taken place at almost any time or place. Others could occur only at a given place or time or in a given social group. If this is true, ask yourself whether this

[3] Climax is the Greek word for a ladder or flight of steps. The hero has, so to speak, to climb up a steep ladder to surmount the obstacles.

essential setting is localized, historical, or social, and why it is essential. Sometimes a setting may even be symbolic and suggest the idea of the story, as in *The Silver Mine*. Usually it merely helps us to picture the scenes and understand why the characters act and think as they do.

CHARACTERIZATION

One of the most interesting things about a story is the people in it, or the characters. The reader must quickly detect who are the main characters and who the less important, or subordinate ones. Naturally in a short story, the author concentrates on a very few main characters, whose personalities are revealed to us not only by the author's description but by their own speech and actions, especially by the choices they make and by what they do in a crisis. Sometimes an apparently trivial thing, however, will give the reader a clue as to what to expect of a character.

To hold our attention, characters must seem real and consistent. It must be natural for them to do the things that are necessary to make the story, and they must belong in the setting where they are placed. The reader usually likes to get a view of all sides of a main character's personality, though occasionally, especially in a humorous story, an author will picture a person for us as a cartoonist sketches a caricature, by exaggerating some one trait or characteristic remark or habit.

It is interesting to note the types of character portrayed by the different short story writers. Each usually has a specialty. Perhaps you would like to read other stories by authors who interest you in this collection to see whether the characters in the story here included are typical of the author's major human interest.

In addition to the four w's of the short story already discussed (*who, where, when, what*), many short stories have an interesting idea or purpose behind them. Perhaps the writer wants to illustrate some truth about life, or point out a social evil, or make fun of a ridiculous custom, or paint a picture of a historic period or unfamiliar part of the world. Such an idea or purpose behind a story is called a *theme*.

Beside the basic elements of plot, setting, character, and theme, certain stories have other special points of interest. The more of these things you can notice as you read, the more fun you will get out of reading, just as the traveller who notices all the details of landscape and architecture and manners and customs in a country enjoys travelling more than the unobservant person. A certain woman who had been to Europe seventeen times could talk of nothing but the food in the hotels in which she had stayed. All the magnificent scenery, the places of historic interest, the cathedrals and castles, and quaint sights and customs had been wasted on her. There are people who travel through books and see just about as little! No wonder they are bored!

THE TITLE

The first point of added interest to notice in a short story is the title. A good title will arouse curiosity and hint what the story is about but never give away the point or outcome of the plot. A good title will often take on a deeper meaning after you have read the story. It will be phrased in an original but natural way, and will be brief and easy to pronounce and remember.

THE OPENING

If the beginning of a story is interesting, one is tempted to go on reading. Modern authors tend to start a story with action or conversation, though sometimes if the setting or characters are striking and unusual, a story may start interestingly with a description. However the story begins, the author must state as quickly as possible the setting, characters, opening situation, and anything which has happened before the plot starts which we must know about to understand the story. Sometimes it is better to tell all this antecedent action at once; sometimes it lends mystery and surprise to reveal the past of the characters gradually. To weave this explanatory matter into the opening of a story incidentally without slowing it up is a fine art; and you will be interested to see the different ways in which authors do it. In any case, the opening of the story should strike the keynote of its action, mood or theme.

POINT OF VIEW

A story may be told in either the first or third person. Sometimes the hero tells his own story. This is an excellent method if the story is highly emotional and the moods and feelings of the hero are the main interest. Sometimes a minor character tells the story. This gives a high sense of reality to the account and naturally allows for more praise of the hero than he can give himself. Stories told through letters or in the form of a diary are always in the first person. Most stories are told in the third person by the author, who can reveal to us the thoughts, feelings and actions of every person involved in the story, whereas one of the participants will have only a limited knowledge of the acts and motives of the others.

METHOD OF NARRATION

The method of narration may be either chronological or retrogressive; *i.e.*, it may start at the beginning and narrate events as they happened, or begin in the middle and then go back to earlier incidents. A mystery or detective story usually starts at the end and works backward.

SUSPENSE

Closely related to the method of narration, is the question of foreshadowing and suspense. Hints as to important future happenings in a story are called foreshadowing, but these hints must be just broad enough to create suspense without giving the secrets of the plot away. So long as we are kept in suspense, we never lay down a story voluntarily. Suspense may be created by leaving a character in a difficult situation and turning to another side of the story, by interrupting an exciting scene with description, by withholding information about which the reader's curiosity has been aroused, and by sudden, surprising, or alarming action on the part of the characters.

THE ENDING

When the climax of a short story has been reached, the end should come rapidly. The end must, however, be logical and satisfying. An illogical ending even if happy cannot satisfy an intelligent reader, since he rejects it as impossible. A tragic ending will satisfy the reader if it seems inevitable, if it seems right, if it shortens the hero's suffering, if the hero accomplishes something valuable by his suffering, or if the hero bears his defeat so nobly that the spectacle is bracing and thrilling to the onlooker.

TRUTH

Indeed, truth to life is one of the highest interests of a story. The incidents must be possible, the conversation natural, the characters and problems real, the moral teaching sound, and the philosophy of life wise and well balanced. There are, however, two kinds of truth: realism or literal truth to facts, and symbolical truth. In a fantasy or allegory, the events may be impossible but the view of life true. There never were tiny men such as appear in *Gulliver's Travels*. The diminutive size of the Lilliputians is, however, only a symbol for the pettiness of human nature—and unfortunately the pettiness thus fantastically pictured is all too real and common!

STYLE

The final interest we find in the short story is that of the author's style. His choice of words may be wide and original. His style may be realistic, imaginative, poetic, descriptive, witty, or humorous. He may be skilled at arousing in the reader emotions of sympathy, pity, fear, terror, horror or awe. Perhaps he intersperses interesting comments on life throughout the story. He may be good at creating natural, clever, or entertaining conversation which at the same time moves the story forward.

TYPES OF STORY

All of these points of interest in fiction are illustrated in one or another of the following short stories, and it will add zest to your reading if you can train yourself to look for them. You will quickly discover that oftentimes one of these interests dominates a story, so that stories can be classified as stories of action in which the plot is the main interest; stories of character which seem to be written mainly to display some striking personality; stories of setting in which the story is a study of a certain locality or period, or in which the setting powerfully influences both character and action; and stories of theme, in which the plot seems to have been created to illustrate some idea of the author. As you read, see whether you can classify the stories under these or other headings.

MARKS OF GREATNESS

The good automobile driver and the one who gets the most pleasure out of a trip is the one who has learned to coordinate all the various operations involved in driving a car so skillfully and easily that he does them all simultaneously almost without thinking. When you have trained yourself to notice almost subconsciously as you read all the items listed in this chapter, you will be able to read with equal ease and enjoyment any short story. But can you tell a good from a mediocre story? The great short story will have the following qualities not possessed by the mediocre or poor one. Can you tell how these special qualities also give a story the characteristics we earlier mentioned as marking all great literature; namely universality, enrichment of living, inspiration, and a memorable, stimulating, beautiful, fit and natural style?

1. Subject matter so chosen and handled that the story both accurately pictures and makes a worth-while comment on life as it really is.

2. A compact plot from which all distracting, irrelevant incidents, characters and description have been eliminated; whose incidents are connected in a causal sequence; which gives one dominant impression; and which has a clear central purpose.

3. A well-indicated setting which either is essential to the story or helps to explain it, or which heightens the interest of the story by the novelty or picturesqueness of the setting itself.

4. Life-like characters whose motives and reactions are so well analyzed that reading the story enlarges one's understanding of human nature in all its phases—not only in its weakness but in its capacity to triumph strongly over life and self.

5. A theme of permanent significance.

6. Such skillfully used narrative techniques as:
   (a) A beginning which is both swift, interesting and fully explanatory
   (b) A point of view and method of narration well chosen for the particular plot
   (c) Suspense and foreshadowing
   (d) Good conversation suited to the characters, interesting in itself, and so woven into the story as constantly to move the story forward
   (e) A logical, consistent, satisfying ending.

7. A sincere, natural, appropriate and interesting style.

Tales have been told since the beginning of time, but to an American reader of short stories, it is interesting to know that the short story as we know it, with its close-knit plot and other admirable technical features, was largely invented by our own Edgar Allan Poe. It was perfected by Poe's French admirers and imitators, especially by De Maupassant, and has since become the most popular literary type of modern times.

THE PURLOINED LETTER

EDGAR ALLAN POE (AMERICA)

Here we see the pattern on which most subsequent detective stories have been built, including those of Emile Gaboriot, Conan Doyle, and S. S. Van Dine.

❊　❊　❊

At Paris, just after dark one gusty evening in the autumn of 18—, I was enjoying the twofold luxury of meditation and a meer-schaum, in company with my friend C. Auguste Dupin, in his little back library, or book-closet, *au troisième, No. 33, Rue Dunnôt, Faubourg St. Germain*.[1] For one hour at least we had maintained a profound silence; while each, to any casual observer, might have seemed intently and exclusively occupied with the curling eddies of smoke that oppressed the atmosphere of the chamber. For myself, however, I was mentally discussing certain topics which had formed matter for conversation between us at an earlier period of the evening; I mean the affair of the Rue Morgue, and the mystery attending the murder of Marie Rogêt.[2] I looked upon it, therefore, as something of a coincidence, when the door of our apartment was thrown open and admitted our old acquaintance, Monsieur G——, the Prefect[3] of the Parisian police.

We gave him a hearty welcome; for there was nearly half as much of the entertaining as of the contemptible about the man, and we had not seen him for several years. We had been sitting in the dark, and Dupin now arose for the purpose of lighting a lamp, but sat down again, without doing so, upon G——'s saying that he had called to consult us, or rather to ask the opinion of my friend, about some official business which had occasioned a great deal of trouble.

"If it is any point requiring reflection," observed Dupin, as he forbore to enkindle the wick, "we shall examine it to better purpose in the dark."

"That is another of your odd notions," said the Prefect, who had a fashion of calling everything "odd" that was beyond his comprehension, and thus lived amid an absolute legion of "oddities."

"Very true," said Dupin, as he supplied his visitor with a pipe, and rolled towards him a comfortable chair.

[1] *au troisième:* on the third floor. *Rue:* street. *Faubourg St. Germain:* fashionable district in Paris.
[2] A reference to two famous detective stories, also by Poe.
[3] *Prefect:* chief.

"And what is the difficulty now?" I asked. "Nothing more in the assassination way, I hope?"

"Oh, no; nothing of that nature. The fact is, the business is *very* simple indeed, and I make no doubt that we can manage it sufficiently well ourselves; but then I thought Dupin would like to hear the details of it, because it is so excessively *odd*."

"Simple and odd," said Dupin.

"Why, yes; and not exactly that, either. The fact is, we have all been a good deal puzzled because the affair *is* so simple, and yet baffles us altogether."

"Perhaps it is the very simplicity of the thing which puts you at fault," said my friend.

"What nonsense you *do* talk!" replied the Prefect, laughing heartily.

"Perhaps the mystery is a little *too* plain," said Dupin.

"Oh, good heavens! who ever heard of such an idea?"

"A little *too* self-evident."

"Ha! ha! ha!—ha! ha! ha!—ho! ho! ho!"—roared our visitor, profoundly amused, "oh, Dupin, you will be the death of me yet!"

"And what, after all, *is* the matter on hand?" I asked.

"Why, I will tell you," replied the Prefect, as he gave a long, steady, and contemplative puff, and settled himself in his chair. "I will tell you in a few words; but, before I begin, let me caution you that this is an affair demanding the greatest secrecy; and that I should most probably lose the position I now hold, were it known that I confided it to any one."

"Proceed," said I.

"Or not," said Dupin.

"Well, then; I have received personal information, from a very high quarter, that a certain document of the last importance, has been purloined [4] from the royal apartments. The individual who purloined it is known; this beyond a doubt; he was seen to take it. It is known, also, that it still remains in his possession."

"How is this known?" asked Dupin.

"It is clearly inferred," replied the Prefect, "from the nature of the document, and from the non-appearance of certain results which would at once arise from its passing *out* of the robber's possession; —that is to say, from his employing it as he must design in the end to employ it."

"Be a little more explicit," I said.

"Well, I may venture so far as to say that the paper gives its

[4] *purloined*: stolen.

older a certain power in a certain quarter where such power is immensely valuable." The Prefect was fond of the cant of diplomacy.

"Still I do not quite understand," said Dupin.

"No? Well; the disclosure of the document to a third person, who shall be nameless, would bring in question the honor of a personage of most exalted station; and this fact gives the holder of the document an ascendancy over the illustrious personage whose honor and peace are so jeopardized."

"But this ascendancy," I interposed, "would depend upon the robber's knowledge of the loser's knowledge of the robber. Who would dare——"

"The thief," said G——, "is the Minister [5] D——, who dares all things, those unbecoming as well as those becoming a man. The method of the theft was not less ingenious than bold. The document in question—a letter, to be frank—had been received by the personage robbed while alone in the royal *boudoir*. During its perusal she was suddenly interrupted by the entrance of the other exalted personage from whom especially it was her wish to conceal it. After a hurried and vain endeavor to thrust it in a drawer, she was forced to place it, open as it was, upon a table. The address, however, was uppermost, and, the contents thus unexposed, the letter escaped notice. At this juncture enters the Minister D——. His lynx eye immediately perceives the paper, recognizes the handwriting of the address, observes the confusion of the personage addressed, and fathoms her secret. After some business transactions, hurried through in his ordinary manner, he produces a letter somewhat similar to the one in question, opens it, pretends to read it, and then places it in close juxtaposition to the other. Again he converses, for some fifteen minutes, upon the public affairs. At length, in taking leave, he takes also from the table the letter to which he had no claim. Its rightful owner saw, but, of course, dared not call attention to the act, in the presence of the third personage who stood at her elbow. The minister decamped; leaving his own letter—one of no importance—upon the table."

"Here, then," said Dupin to me, "you have precisely what you demand to make the ascendancy complete—the robber's knowledge of the loser's knowledge of the robber."

"Yes," replied the Prefect; "and the power thus attained has, for some months past, been wielded, for political purposes, to a very dangerous extent. The personage robbed is more thoroughly con-

[5] *Minister:* a cabinet minister or high government official.

vinced, every day, of the necessity of reclaiming her letter. But this of course, cannot be done openly. In fine, driven to despair, she has committed the matter to me."

"Than whom," said Dupin, amid a perfect whirl-wind of smoke "no more sagacious agent could, I suppose, be desired, or ever imagined."

"You flatter me," replied the Prefect; "but it is possible that some such opinion may have been entertained."

"It is clear," said I, "as you observe, that the letter is still in possession of the minister; since it is this possession, and not any employment of the letter, which bestows the power. With the employment the power departs."

"True," said G——; "and upon this conviction I proceeded. My first care was to make thorough search of the minister's hotel; and here my chief embarrassment lay in the necessity of searching without his knowledge. Beyond all things, I have been warned of the danger which would result from giving him reason to suspect our design."

"But," said I, "you are quite *au fait* [6] in these investigations. The Parisian police have done this thing often before."

"Oh, yes; and for this reason I did not despair. The habits of the minister gave me, too, a great advantage. He is frequently absent from home all night. His servants are by no means numerous. They sleep at a distance from their master's apartment, and, being chiefly Neapolitans, are readily made drunk. I have keys, as you know, with which I can open any chamber or cabinet in Paris. For three months a night has not passed, during the greater part of which I have not been engaged, personally, in ransacking the D—— Hôtel. [7] My honor is interested, and, to mention a great secret, the reward is enormous. So I did not abandon the search until I had become fully satisfied that the thief is a more astute man than myself. I fancy that I have investigated every nook and corner of the premises in which it is possible that the paper can be concealed."

"But is it not possible," I suggested, "that although the letter may be in possession of the minister, as it unquestionably is, he may have concealed it elsewhere than upon his own premises?"

"This is barely possible," said Dupin. "The present peculiar condition of affairs at court, and especially of those intrigues in which D—— is known to be involved, would render the instant availability of the document—its susceptibility of being produced at a moment's notice—a point of nearly equal importance with its possession."

[6] *au fait:* perfect.   [7] *Hôtel:* town house of a noble.

"I TOOK THE ENTIRE BUILDING, ROOM BY ROOM; DEVOTING THE
NIGHTS OF A WHOLE WEEK TO EACH."

"Its susceptibility of being produced?" said I.

"That is to say, of being *destroyed*," said Dupin.

"True," I observed; "the paper is clearly then upon the premises. As for its being upon the person of the minister, we may consider that as out of the question."

"Entirely," said the Prefect. "He has been twice waylaid, as if by footpads, and his person rigorously searched under my own inspection."

"You might have spared yourself this trouble," said Dupin. "D——, I presume, is not altogether a fool, and, if not, must have anticipated these waylayings, as a matter of course."

"Not *altogether* a fool," said G——, "but then he's a poet, which I take to be only one remove from a fool."

"True," said Dupin, after a long and thoughtful whiff from his meerschaum, "although I have been guilty of certain doggerel myself."

"Suppose you detail," said I, "the particulars of your search."

"Why the fact is, we took our time, and we searched *everywhere*. I have had long experience in these affairs. I took the entire building, room by room; devoting the nights of a whole week to each. We examined, first, the furniture of each apartment. We opened every possible drawer; and I presume you know that, to a properly trained police agent, such a thing as a *secret* drawer is impossible. Any man is a dolt who permits a 'secret' drawer to escape him in a search of this kind. The thing is *so* plain. There is a certain amount of bulk—of space—to be accounted for in every cabinet. Then we have accurate rules. The fiftieth part of a line could not escape us. After the cabinets we took the chairs. The cushions we probed with the fine long needles you have seen me employ. From the tables we removed the tops."

"Why so?"

"Sometimes the top of a table, or other similarly arranged piece of furniture, is removed by the person wishing to conceal an article; then the leg is excavated, the article deposited within the cavity, and the top replaced. The bottoms and tops of bedposts are employed in the same way."

"But could not the cavity be detected by sounding?" I asked.

"By no means, if, when the article is deposited, a sufficient wadding of cotton be placed around it. Besides, in our case, we were obliged to proceed without noise."

"But you could not have removed—you could not have taken to pieces *all* articles of furniture in which it would have been possible to make a deposit in the manner you mention. A letter may be compressed into a thin spiral roll, not differing much in shape or bulk from a large knitting-needle, and in this form it might be inserted into the rung of a chair, for example. You did not take to pieces all the chairs?"

"Certainly not; but we did better—we examined the rungs of every chair in the Hôtel, and, indeed, the jointings of every description of furniture, by the aid of a most powerful microscope. Had there been any traces of recent disturbance we should not have failed to detect it instantly. A single grain of gimlet-dust, for example, would have been as obvious as an apple. Any disorder in the gluing—any unusual gaping in the joints—would have sufficed to insure detection."

"I presume you looked to the mirrors, between the boards and the plates, and you probed the beds and the bed-clothes, as well as the curtains and carpets."

"That of course; and when we had absolutely completed every particle of the furniture in this way, then we examined the house itself. We divided its entire surface into compartments, which we numbered, so that none might be missed; then we scrutinized each individual square inch throughout the premises, including the two houses immediately adjoining, with the microscope, as before."

"The two houses adjoining!" I exclaimed; "you must have had a great deal of trouble."

"We had; but the reward offered is prodigious."

"You included the *grounds* about the houses?"

"All the grounds are paved with brick. They gave us comparatively little trouble. We examined the moss between the bricks, and found it undisturbed."

"You looked among D——'s papers, of course, and into the books of the library?"

"Certainly; we opened every package and parcel; we not only opened every book, but we turned over every leaf in each volume, not contenting ourselves with a mere shake, according to the fashion of some of our police officers. We also measured the thickness of every book-*cover*, with the most accurate admeasurement, and applied to each the most jealous scrutiny of the microscope. Had any of the bindings been recently meddled with, it would have been utterly impossible that the fact should have escaped observation. Some five or six volumes, just from the hands of the binder, we carefully probed, longitudinally, with the needles."

"You explored the floors beneath the carpets?"

"Beyond doubt. We removed every carpet, and examined the boards with the microscope."

"And the paper on the walls?"

"Yes."

"You looked into the cellars?"

"We did."

"Then," I said, "you have been making a miscalculation, and the letter is *not* upon the premises, as you suppose."

"I fear you are right there," said the Prefect. "And now, Dupin, what would you advise me to do?"

"To make a thorough re-search of the premises."

"That is absolutely needless," replied G——, "I am not more sure that I breathe than I am that the letter is not at the Hôtel."

"I have no better advice to give you," said Dupin. "You have, of course, an accurate description of the letter?"

"Oh, yes."—And here the Prefect, producing a memorandum-book, proceeded to read aloud a minute account of the internal, and especially of the external appearance of the missing document. Soon after finishing the perusal of this description, he took his departure, more entirely depressed in spirits than I had ever known the good gentleman before.

In about a month afterwards he paid us another visit, and found us occupied very nearly as before. He took a pipe and a chair and entered into some ordinary conversation. At length I said,——

"Well, but G——, what of the purloined letter? I presume you have at last made up your mind that there is no such thing as over-reaching the Minister?"

"Confound him, say I—yes; I made the reëxamination, however, as Dupin suggested—but it was all labor lost, as I knew it would be."

"How much was the reward offered, did you say?" asked Dupin.

"Why, a very great deal—a *very* liberal reward—I don't like to say how much, precisely; but one thing I *will* say, that I wouldn't mind giving my individual check for fifty thousand francs [8] to any one who could obtain me that letter. The fact is, it is becoming of more and more importance every day; and the reward has been lately doubled. If it were trebled, however, I could do no more than I have done."

"Why, yes," said Dupin, drawlingly, between the whiffs of his meerschaum, "I really—think, G——, you have not exerted your-

[8] 50,000 *francs:* $10,000.

self—to the utmost in this matter. You might—do a little more, I think, eh?"

"How?—in what way?"

"Why—puff, puff—you might—puff, puff—employ counsel in the matter, eh?—puff, puff, puff. Do you remember the story they tell of Abernethy?"

"No; hang Abernethy!"

"To be sure! hang him and welcome. But, once upon a time, a certain rich miser conceived the design of sponging upon this Abernethy for a medical opinion. Getting up, for this purpose, an ordinary conversation in a private company, he insinuated his case to the physician, as that of an imaginary individual."

" 'We will suppose,' said the miser, 'that his symptoms are such and such; now, doctor, what would *you* have directed him to take?' "

" 'Take!' said Abernethy, 'why, take *advice*, to be sure.' "

"But," said the Prefect, a little discomposed, "I am *perfectly* willing to take advice, and to pay for it. I would *really* give fifty thousand francs to any one who would aid me in the matter."

"In that case," replied Dupin, opening a drawer, and producing a check-book, "you may as well fill me up a check for the amount mentioned. When you have signed it, I will hand you the letter."

I was astounded. The Prefect appeared absolutely thunderstricken. For some minutes he remained speechless and motionless, looking incredulously at my friend with open mouth, and eyes that seemed starting from their sockets; then, apparently recovering himself in some measure, he seized a pen, and after several pauses and vacant stares, finally filled up and signed a check for fifty thousand francs, and handed it across the table to Dupin. The latter examined it carefully and deposited it in his pocket-book; then, unlocking an *escritoire*,[9] took thence a letter and gave it to the Prefect. This functionary grasped it in a perfect agony of joy, opened it with a trembling hand, cast a rapid glance at its contents, and then, scrambling and struggling to the door, rushed at length unceremoniously from the room and from the house, without having uttered a syllable since Dupin had requested him to fill up the check.

When he had gone, my friend entered into some explanations.

"The Parisian police," he said, "are exceedingly able in their way. They are persevering, ingenious, cunning, and thoroughly versed in the knowledge which their duties seem chiefly to demand. Thus, when G—— detailed to us his mode of searching the premises at

[9] *escritoire:* writing desk.

the Hôtel D——, I felt entire confidence in his having made a satisfactory investigation—so far as his labors extended."

"So far as his labors extended?" said I.

"Yes," said Dupin. "The measures adopted were not only the best of their kind, but carried out to absolute perfection. Had the letter been deposited within the range of their search, these fellows would, beyond a question, have found it."

I merely laughed—but he seemed quite serious in all that he said.

"The measures, then," he continued, "were good in their kind, and well executed; their defect lay in their being inapplicable to the case, and to the man. A certain set of highly ingenious resources are, with the Prefect, a sort of Procrustean [10] bed, to which he forcibly adapts his designs. But he perpetually errs by being too deep or too shallow, for the matter in hand; and many a schoolboy is a better reasoner than he. I knew one about eight years of age, whose success at guessing in the game of 'even and odd' attracted universal admiration. This game is simple, and is played with marbles. One player holds in his hand a number of these toys, and demands of another whether that number is even or odd. If the guess is right, the guesser wins one; if wrong, he loses one. The boy to whom I allude won all the marbles of the school. Of course he had some principle of guessing; and this lay in mere observation and admeasurement of the astuteness of his opponents. For example, an arrant simpleton is his opponent, and, holding up his closed hand, asks, 'are they even or odd?' Our schoolboy replies, 'odd,' and loses; but upon the second trial he wins, for he then says to himself, 'the simpleton had them even upon the first trial, and his amount of cunning is just sufficient to make him have them odd upon the second; I will therefore guess odd;'—he guesses odd, and wins. Now, with a simpleton a degree above the first, he would have reasoned thus: 'This fellow finds that in the first instance I guessed odd, and, in the second, he will propose to himself upon the first impulse, a simple variation from even to odd, as did the first simpleton; but then a second thought will suggest that this is too simple a variation, and finally he will decide upon putting it even as before. I will therefore guess even;'—he guesses even, and wins. Now this mode of reasoning in the schoolboy, whom his fellows termed 'lucky,'—what, in its last analysis, is it?"

"It is merely," I said, "an identification of the reasoner's intellect with that of his opponent."

[10] *Procrustean:* Procrustes was a giant who either cut down or stretched his visitors to fit the guest room bed.

"It is," said Dupin

"And the identification," I said, "of the reasoner's intellect with that of his opponent depends, if I understand you aright, upon the accuracy with which the opponents' intellect is admeasured."

"For its practical value it depends upon this," replied Dupin; "and the Prefect and his cohort fail so frequently, first, by default of this identification, and, secondly, by ill-admeasurement, or rather through non-admeasurement, of the intellect with which they are engaged. They consider only their *own* ideas of ingenuity; and, in searching for anything hidden, advert only to the modes in which *they* would have hidden it. They are right in this much—that their own ingenuity is a faithful representative of that of *the mass;* but when the cunning of the individual felon is diverse in character from their own, the felon foils them, of course. This always happens when it is above their own, and very usually when it is below. They have no variation of principle in their investigations; at best, when urged by some unusual emergency—by some extraordinary reward— they extend or exaggerate their old modes of *practice,* without touching their principles. What, for example, in this case of D——, has been done to vary the principle of action? What is all this boring, and probing, and sounding, and scrutinizing with the microscope, and dividing the surface of the building into registered square inches— what is it all but an exaggeration *of the application* of the one principle or set of principles of search, which are based upon the one set of notions regarding human ingenuity, to which the Prefect, in the long routine of his duty, has been accustomed? Do you not see he has taken it for granted that *all* men proceed to conceal a letter, —not exactly in a gimlet-hole bored in a chair-leg—but, at least, in *some* out-of-the-way hole or corner suggested by the same tenor of thought which would urge a man to secrete a letter in a gimlet-hole bored in a chair-leg? And do you not see also, that such *recherché* [11] nooks for concealment are adapted only for ordinary occasions and would be adopted only by ordinary intellects; for in all cases of concealment, a disposal of the article concealed—a disposal of it in this *recherché* manner,—is, in the very first instance, presumable and presumed; and thus its discovery depends, not at all upon the acumen, [12] but altogther upon the mere care, patience, and determination of the seekers. You will now understand what I mean in suggesting that, had the purloined letter been hidden anywhere within the limits of the Prefect's examination—in other words, had the principle of its concealment been

[11] *recherché:* out of the way.   [12] *acumen:* intelligence.

comprehended within the principles of the Prefect—its discovery
would have been a matter altogether beyond question. This functionary, however, has been thoroughly mystified; and the remote
source of his defeat lies in the supposition that the Minister is a
fool, because he has acquired renown as poet."

"But is this really the poet?" I asked. "There are two brothers,
I know; and both have attained reputation in letters. The Minister
I believe has written learnedly on the Differential Calculus. He is a
mathematician, and no poet."

"You are mistaken; I know him well; he is both. As poet *and*
mathematician, he would reason well; as mere mathematician, he
would have been at the mercy of the Prefect. I mean to say," continued Dupin, while I merely laughed at his last observations, "that
if the Minister had been no more than a mathematician, the Prefect would have been under no necessity of giving me this check. I
knew him, however, as both mathematician and poet,[13] and my
measures were adapted to his capacity, with reference to the circumstances by which he was surrounded. I knew him as a courtier,
too, and as a bold *intriguant*.[14] Such a man, I considered, could not
fail to be aware of the ordinary policial modes of action. He could
not have failed to anticipate—and events have proved that he did
not fail to anticipate—the waylayings to which he was subjected.
He must have foreseen, I reflected, the secret investigations of his
premises. His frequent absences from home at night, which were
hailed by the Prefect as certain aids to his success, I regarded only
as *ruses*,[15] to afford opportunity for thorough search to the police,
and thus the sooner to impress them with the conviction to which
G——, in fact, did finally arrive—the conviction that the letter was
not upon the premises. I felt, also, that the whole train of thought,
which I was at some pains in detailing to you just now, concerning
the invariable principle of policial action in searches for articles
concealed—I felt that this whole train of thought would necessarily
pass through the mind of the Minister. It would imperatively lead
him to despise all the ordinary *nooks* of concealment. *He* could not,
I reflected, be so weak as not to see that the most intricate and
remote recess of his Hôtel would be as open as his commonest closets
to the eyes, to the probes, to the gimlets, and to the microscopes of
the Prefect. I saw, in fine, that he would be driven, as a matter of
course, to *simplicity*, if not deliberately induced to it as a matter of

---

[13] *poet*: the poet will be able to imagine how other people's minds work and
devise some unusual method of foiling them.
[14] *intriguant*: intriguer.   [15] *ruses*: tricks.

choice. You will remember, perhaps, how desperately the Prefect laughed when I suggested, upon our first interview, that it was just possible this mystery troubled him so much on account of its being so *very* self-evident."

"Yes," said I, "I remember his merriment well. I really thought he would have fallen into convulsions."

"Have you ever noticed which of the street signs, over the shop doors, are the most attractive of attention?"

"I have never given the matter a thought," I said.

"There is a game of puzzles," he resumed, "which is played upon a map. One party playing requires another to find a given word— the name of town, river, state or empire—any word, in short, upon the motley and perplexed surface of the chart. A novice in the game generally seeks to embarrass his opponents by giving them the most minutely lettered names; but the adept selects such words as stretch, in large characters, from one end of the chart to the other. These, like the over-largely lettered signs and placards of the street, escape observation by dint of being excessively obvious; and here the physical oversight is precisely analogous with the moral inapprehension by which the intellect suffers to pass unnoticed those considerations which are too obtrusively and too palpably self-evident. But this is a point, it appears, somewhat above or beneath the understanding of the Prefect. He never once thought it probable, or possible, that the Minister had deposited the letter immediately beneath the nose of the whole world, by way of best preventing any portion of that world from perceiving it.

"But the more I reflected upon the daring, dashing, and discriminating ingenuity of D—— ; upon the fact that the document must always have been *at hand,* if he intended to use it to good purpose; and upon the decisive evidence, obtained by the Prefect, that it was not hidden within the limits of that dignitary's ordinary search—the more satisfied I became that, to conceal this letter, the Minister had resorted to the comprehensive and sagacious expedient of not attempting to conceal it at all.

"Full of these ideas, I prepared myself with a pair of green spectacles, and called one fine morning, quite by accident, at the Ministerial Hôtel. I found D—— at home, yawning, lounging, and dawdling, as usual, and pretending to be in the last extremity of *ennui.* He is, perhaps, the most really energetic human being now alive— but that is only when nobody sees him.

"To be even with him, I complained of my weak eyes, and lamented the necessity of the spectacles, under cover of which I cautiously and thoroughly surveyed the apartment, while seemingly intent only upon the conversation of my host.

"I paid special attention to a large writing-table near which he sat, and upon which lay confusedly, some miscellaneous letters and other papers, with one or two musical instruments and a few books. Here, however, after a long and very deliberate scrutiny, I saw nothing to excite particular suspicion.

"At length my eyes, in going the circuit of the room, fell upon a trumpery filigree card-rack of paste-board, that hung dangling by a dirty blue ribbon, from a little brass knob just beneath the middle of the mantel-piece. In this rack, which had three or four compartments, were five or six visiting cards and a solitary letter. This last was much soiled and crumpled. It was torn nearly in two (across the middle—as if a design, in the first instance, to tear it entirely up as worthless, had been altered, or stayed, in the second. It had a large black seal, bearing the D—— cipher *very* conspicuously, and was addressed, in a diminutive female hand, to D——, the minister, himself. It was thrust carelessly, and even, as it seemed, contemptuously, into one of the upper divisions of the rack.

"No sooner had I glanced at this letter, than I concluded it to be that of which I was in search. To be sure, it was, to all appearance, radically different from the one of which the Prefect had read us so minute a description. Here the seal was large and black, with the D—— cipher; there it was small and red, with the ducal arms of he S—— family. Here, the address, to the Minister, was diminutive and feminine; there the superscription, to a certain royal personage, was markedly bold and decided; the size alone formed a point of correspondence. But, then, the *radicalness* of these differences, which was excessive; the dirt; the soiled and torn condition of the paper, so inconsistent with the *true* methodical habits of D——, and so suggestive of a design to delude the beholder into an idea of the worthlessness of the document; these things, together with the hyperobtrusive situation of this document, full in the view of every visitor, and thus exactly in accordance with the conclusions to which I had previously arrived; these things, I say, were strongly corroborative of suspicion, in one who came with the intention to suspect.

"I protracted my visit as long as possible, and, while I maintained a most animated discussion with the Minister, on a topic which I knew well had never failed to interest and excite him, I kept my attention really riveted upon the letter. In this examination, I committed to memory its external appearance and arrangement in the rack; and also fell, at length, upon a discovery which set at rest whatever trivial doubt I might have entertained. In scrutinizing the edges of the paper, I observed them to be more *chafed* than seemed necessary. They presented the *broken* appearance which is manifested when a stiff paper, having been once folded and pressed with a folder, is refolded in a reversed direction, in the same creases or edges which had formed the original fold. This discovery was sufficient. It was clear to me that the letter had been turned, as a glove, inside out, re-directed, and re-sealed. I bade the Minister good morning, and took my departure at once, leaving a gold snuff-box upon the table.

"The next morning I called for the snuff-box, when we resumed, quite eagerly, the conversation of the preceding day. While thus engaged, however, a loud report, as if of a pistol, was heard immediately beneath the windows of the Hôtel, and was succeeded by a series of fearful screams, and the shoutings of a mob. D—— rushed to a casement, threw it open, and looked out. In the meantime, I stepped to the card-rack, took the letter, put it in my pocket, and replaced it by a fac-simile (so far as regards externals) which I had carefully prepared at my lodgings; imitating the D—— cipher, very readily, by means of a seal formed of bread.

"The disturbance in the street had been occasioned by the frantic behavior of a man with a musket. He had fired it among a crowd of women and children. It proved, however, to have been without ball, and the fellow was suffered to go his way as a lunatic or a drunkard. When he had gone, D—— came from the window, whither I had followed him immediately upon securing the object in view. Soon afterwards I bade him farewell. The pretended lunatic was a man in my own pay."

"But what purpose had you," I asked, "in replacing the letter by a fac-simile? Would it not have been better, at the first visit, to have seized it openly, and departed?"

"D——," replied Dupin, "is a desperate man, and a man of nerve. His Hôtel, too, is not without attendants devoted to his interests. Had I made the wild attempt you suggest, I might never have left the Ministerial presence alive. The good people of Paris might have heard of me no more. But I had an object apart from these considerations. You know my political prepossessions. In this matter, I act as a partisan of the lady concerned. For eighteen months the Minister has had her in his power. She has now him in hers; since, being unaware that the letter is not in his possession, he will proceed with his exactions as if it was. Thus will he inevitably commit himself, at once, to his political destruction. His downfall, too, will not be more precipitate than awkward. It is all very well to talk about the *facilis descensus Averni;* [16] but in all kinds of climbing, as Catalani said of singing, it is far more easy to get up than to come down. In the present instance I have no sympathy—at least no pity—for him who descends. He is that *monstrum horrendum,* [17] an unprincipled man of genius. I confess, however, that I should like very well to know the precise character of his thoughts, when, being defied by her whom the Prefect terms 'a certain personage,' he is reduced to opening the letter which I left for him in the card-rack."

"How? did you put anything particular in it?"

"Why—it did not seem altogether right to leave the interior blank —that would have been insulting. D——, at Vienna once, did me an evil turn, which I told him, quite good-humoredly, that I should remember. So, as I knew he would feel some curiosity in regard to the identity of the person who had outwitted him, I thought it a pity not to give him a clue. He is well acquainted with my MS., and I just copied into the middle of the blank sheet the words—

——Un dessein si funeste,
S'il n'est digne d'Atrée, est digne de Thyeste. [18]
They are to be found in Crébillon's *Atrée."*

A PASSION IN THE DESERT

HONORÉ DE BALZAC (FRANCE)

In an introductory section here omitted, we learn that this story is told by a man to a lady he has taken to see an animal act at the circus. She doubts that animals have affections deep enough to rely upon.

❋   ❋   ❋

During the expedition in Upper Egypt under General Desaix, a Provençal [1] soldier fell into the hands of the Mangrabins, and was taken by these Arabs into the deserts beyond the falls of the Nile.

In order to place a sufficient distance between themselves and the French army, the Mangrabins made forced marches, and rested only during the night. They camped round a well overshadowed

---

[16] *facilis descensus Averni:* the descent to the lower world is easy.

[17] *monstrum horrendum:* horrible monster.

[18] "A scheme so sinister that it is worthy not of Atreus but of Thyestes." Atreus and Thyestes are characters in a Greek story of atrocious crime.

[1] *Provençal:* from the district of Provence in France.

by palm trees under which they had previously concealed a store of provisions. Not surmising that the notion of flight would occur to their prisoner, they contented themselves with binding his hands, and after eating a few dates, and giving provender to their horses, went to sleep.

When the brave Provençal saw that his enemies were no longer watching him, he made use of his teeth to steal a scimitar, fixed the blade between his knees, and cut the cords which prevented using his hands; in a moment he was free. He at once seized a rifle and a dagger, then taking the precaution to provide himself with a sack of dried dates, oats, and powder and shot, and to fasten a scimitar to his waist, he leaped onto a horse, and spurred on vigorously in the direction where he thought to find the French army. So impatient was he to see a bivouac again that he pressed on the already tired courser at such speed that its flanks were lacerated with his spurs, and at last the poor animal died, leaving the Frenchman alone in the desert.

After walking some time in the sand with all the courage of an escaped convict, the soldier was obliged to stop, as the day had already ended. In spite of the beauty of an oriental sky at night, he felt he had not strength enough to go on. Fortunately he had been able to find a small hill, on the summit of which a few palm trees shot up into the air; it was their verdure seen from afar which had brought hope and consolation to his heart. His fatigue was so great that he lay down upon a rock of granite, capriciously cut out like a camp-bed; there he fell asleep without taking any precaution to defend himself while he slept. He had made the sacrifice of his life. His last thought was one of regret. He repented having left the Mangrabins, whose nomad life seemed to smile on him now that he was afar from them and without help. He was awakened by the sun, whose pitiless rays fell with all their force on the granite and produced an intolerable heat—for he had had the stupidity to place himself inversely to the shadow thrown by the verdant majestic heads of the palm trees. He looked at the solitary trees and shuddered—they reminded him of the graceful shafts crowned with foliage which characterize the Saracen [2] columns in the cathedral of Arles.

But when, after counting the palm trees, he cast his eye around him, the most horrible despair was infused into his soul. Before him stretched an ocean without limit. The dark sand of the desert spread farther than sight could reach in every direction, and glit-

[2] *Saracen:* Moorish or Arabic.

ered like steel struck with bright light. It might have been a sea
of looking-glass, or lakes melted together in a mirror. A fiery
vapor carried up in streaks made a perpetual whirlwind over the
quivering land. The sky was lit with an oriental splendor of insupportable purity, leaving naught for the imagination to desire.
Heaven and earth were on fire.

The silence was awful in its wild and terrible majesty. Infinity,
immensity, closed in upon the soul from every side. Not a cloud
in the sky, not a breath in the air, not a flaw on the bosom of the
sand, ever moving in diminutive waves; the horizon ended as at
sea on a clear day, with one line of light, definite as the cut of a
sword.

The Provençal threw his arms round the trunk of one of the palm
trees, as though it were the body of a friend, and then in the shelter
of the thin straight shadow that the palm cast upon the granite, he
wept. Then sitting down he remained as he was, contemplating with
profound sadness the implacable scene, which was all he had to
look upon. He cried aloud, to measure the solitude. His voice, lost
in the hollows of the hill, sounded faintly, and aroused no echo—
the echo was in his own heart. The Provençal was twenty-two years
old:—he loaded his carbine.

"There'll be time enough," he said to himself, laying on the
ground the weapon which alone could bring him deliverance.

Looking by turns at the black expanse and the blue expanse, the
soldier dreamed of France—he smelt with delight the gutters of
Paris—he remembered the towns through which he had passed, the
faces of his fellow-soldiers, the most minute details of his life. His
southern fancy soon showed him the stones of his beloved Provence,
in the play of the heat which waved over the spread sheet of the
desert. Fearing the danger of this cruel mirage, he went down the
opposite side of the hill to that by which he had come up the day
before. Great was his joy on discovering a grotto in the granite base
of the hill. The remains of a rug showed that this place of refuge
had at one time been inhabited; at a short distance he saw some
palm trees full of dates. Then the instinct which binds us to life
woke again in his heart. He hoped to live long enough to await the
passing of some Arabs, or perhaps he might hear the sound of
cannon; for at this time Bonaparte was traversing Egypt.

This thought gave him new life. The palm tree seemed to bend
with the weight of the ripe fruit. He shook some of it down. When
he tasted this unhoped-for manna, he felt sure that the palms had
been cultivated by a former inhabitant—the savory, fresh meat

of the dates was proof of the care of his predecessor. He passed suddenly from dark despair to an almost insane joy. He went up again to the top of the hill, and spent the rest of the day in cutting down one of the sterile palm trees, which the night before had served him for shelter. A vague memory made him think of the animals of the desert; and in case they might come to drink at the spring, visible from the base of the rocks but lost farther down, he resolved to guard himself from their visits by placing a barrier at the entrance of his hermitage.

In spite of his diligence, and the strength which the fear of being devoured asleep gave him, he was unable to cut the palm in pieces though he succeeded in cutting it down. At eventide the king of the desert fell; the sound of its fall resounded far and wide, like a sigh in the solitude; the soldier shuddered as though he had heard some voice predicting woe.

But like an heir who does not long bewail a deceased parent, he tore off from this beautiful tree the tall broad green leaves which are its poetic adornment, and used them to mend the mat on which he was to sleep.

Fatigued by the heat and his work, he fell asleep under the red roof of his cave.

In the middle of the night his sleep was troubled by an extraordinary noise; he sat up, and the deep silence around him allowed him to distinguish the alternative accents of a respiration whose savage energy could not belong to a human creature.

A profound terror, increased still further by the darkness, the silence, and his waking images, froze his heart within him. He almost felt his hair stand on end, when by straining his eyes to their utmost he perceived through the shadows two faint yellow lights. At first he attributed these lights to the reflection of his own pupils, but soon the vivid brilliance of the night aided him gradually to distinguish the objects around him in the cave, and he beheld a huge animal lying but two steps from him. Was it a lion, a tiger, or a crocodile?

The Provençal was not educated enough to know under what species his enemy ought to be classed; but his fright was all the greater, as his ignorance led him to imagine all terrors at once; he endured a cruel torture, noting every variation of the breathing close to him without daring to make the slightest movement. An odor, pungent like that of a fox, but more penetrating, profounder —so to speak—filled the cave, and when the Provençal became sensible of this, his terror reached its height, for he could not longer doubt the proximity of a terrible companion, whose royal dwelling served him for shelter.

Presently the reflection of the moon, descending on the horizon, lit up the den, rendering gradually visible and resplendent the spotted skin of a panther.

This lion of Egypt slept, curled up like a big dog, the peaceful possessor of a sumptuous niche at the gate of an *hôtel;* its eyes opened for a moment and closed again; its face was turned toward the man. A thousand confused thoughts passed through the Frenchman's mind; first he thought of killing it with a bullet from his gun, but he saw there was not enough distance between them for him to take proper aim—the shot would miss the mark. And if it were to wake!—the thought made his limbs rigid. He listened to his own heart beating in the midst of the silence, and cursed the too violent pulsations which the flow of blood brought on, fearing to disturb that sleep which allowed him time to think of some means of escape.

Twice he placed his hand on his scimitar, intending to cut off the head of his enemy; but the difficulty of cutting the stiff, short hair compelled him to abandon this daring project. To miss would be to die for *certain,* he thought; he preferred the chances of fair fight, and made up his mind to wait till morning. The morning did not leave him long to wait.

He could now examine the panther at ease; its muzzle was smeared with blood.

"She's had a good dinner," he thought, without troubling himself as to whether her feast might have been on human flesh. "She won't be hungry when she gets up."

It was a female. The fur on her belly and flanks was glistening white; many small marks like velvet formed beautiful bracelets round her feet; her sinuous tail was also white, ending with black rings; the overpart of her dress, yellow like unburnished gold, very lissom and soft, had the characteristic blotches in the form of rosettes, which distinguish the panther from every other feline species.

This tranquil and formidable hostess snored in an attitude as graceful as that of a cat lying on a cushion. Her blood-stained paws, nervous and well-armed, were stretched out before her face, which rested upon them, and from which radiated her straight, slender whiskers, like threads of silver.

If she had been like that in a cage, the Provençal would doubtless have admired the grace of the animal, and the vigorous contrasts of vivid color which gave her robe an imperial splendor; but just then his sight was troubled by her sinister appearance.

The presence of the panther, even asleep, could not fail to produce the effect which the magnetic eyes of the serpent are said to have on the nightingale.

For a moment the courage of the soldier began to fail before this danger, though no doubt it would have risen at the mouth of a cannon charged with shell. Nevertheless, a bold thought brought daylight to his soul and sealed up the source of the cold sweat which sprang forth on his brow. Like men driven to bay who defy death and offer their body to the smiter, so he, seeing in this merely a tragic episode, resolved to play his part with honor to the last.

"The day before yesterday the Arabs would have killed me perhaps," he said; so considering himself as good as dead already, he waited bravely, with excited curiosity, his enemy's awakening.

When the sun appeared, the panther suddenly opened her eyes; then she put out her paws with energy, as if to stretch them and get rid of cramp. At last she yawned, showing the formidable apparatus of her teeth and pointed tongue, rough as a file.

"A regular *petite maîtresse*," [3] thought the Frenchman, seeing her roll herself about so softly and coquettishly. She licked off the blood which stained her paws and muzzle, and scratched her head with repeated gestures full of prettiness. "All right, make a little toilet," the Frenchman said to himself, beginning to recover his gaiety with his courage: "we'll say good morning to each other presently," and he seized the small, short dagger which he had taken from the Mangrabins. At this moment the panther turned her head toward the man and looked at him fixedly without moving.

The rigidity of her metallic eyes and their insupportable luster made him shudder, especially when the animal walked toward him. But he looked at her caressingly, staring into her eyes in order to magnetize her, and let her come quite close to him; then with a movement both gentle and amorous he passed his hand over her whole body, from the head to the tail, scratching the flexible vertebræ which divided the panther's yellow back. The animal waved her tail voluptuously, and her eyes grew gentle; and when for the third time the Frenchman accomplished this interesting flattery, she gave forth one of those purrings by which our cats express their pleasure; but this murmur issued from a throat so powerful and so deep, that it sounded through the cave like the last vibrations of an organ in a church. The man, understanding the importance of his caresses, redoubled them in such a way as to surprise and stupefy his imperious courtesan. When he felt sure of having extinguished the ferocity

[3] *petite maîtresse:* little mistress.

f his capricious companion, whose hunger had so fortunately been atisfied the day before, he got up to go out of the cave; the panther t him go out, but when he had reached the summit of the hill she prang with the lightness of a sparrow hopping from twig to twig, nd rubbed herself against his legs, putting up her back after the nanner of all the race of cats. Then regarding her guest with eyes hose glare had softened a little, she gave vent to that wild cry hich naturalists compare to the grating of a saw.

"She is exacting," said the Frenchman, smiling.

He was bold enough to play with her ears; he caressed her belly nd scratched her head as hard as he could.

When he saw that he was successful, he tickled her skull with the oint of his dagger, watching for the right moment to kill her, but ne hardness of her bones made him tremble for his success.

The sultana of the desert showed herself gracious to her slave; ne lifted her head, stretched out her neck, and manifested her elight by the tranquillity of her attitude. It suddenly occurred to ne soldier that to kill this savage princess with one blow he must oniard her in the throat.

He raised the blade, when the panther, satisfied no doubt, laid erself gracefully at his feet, and cast up at him glances in which, in ite of their natural fierceness, was mingled confusedly a kind of ood-will. The poor Provençal ate his dates, leaning against one f the palm trees, and casting his eyes alternately on the desert in uest of some liberator and on his terrible companion to watch her ncertain clemency.

The panther looked at the place where the date stones fell, and very time that he threw one down her eyes expressed an incredible uistrust.

She examined the man with an almost commercial prudence. Iowever, this examination was favorable to him, for when he had nished his meager meal she licked his boots with her powerful ongue, brushing off with marvellous skill the dust gathered in the reases.

"Ah, but when she's really hungry!" thought the Frenchman. n spite of the shudder this thought caused him, the soldier began) measure curiously the proportions of the panther, certainly one f the most splendid specimens of her race. She was three feet high nd four feet long without counting her tail; this powerful weapon, ounded like a cudgel, was nearly three feet long. The head, large s that of a lioness, was distinguished by a rare expression of refine- ent. The cold cruelty of a tiger was dominant, it was true, but

there was also a vague resemblance to the face of a sensual woma
Indeed, the face of this solitary queen had something of the gaiet
of a drunken Nero;[4] she had satiated herself with blood, and sh
wanted to play.

The soldier tried if he might walk up and down, and the panthe
left him free, contenting herself with following him with her eye
less like a faithful dog than a big Angora cat, observing everythin
and every movement of her master.

When he looked round, he saw, by the spring, the remains of h
horse; the panther had dragged the carcass all that way; about two
thirds of it had been devoured already. The sight reassured him.

It was easy to explain the panther's absence, and the respect sh
had had for him while he slept. The first piece of good luck embol
ened him to tempt the future, and he conceived the wild hope o
continuing on good terms with the panther during the entire da
neglecting no means of taming her and remaining in her good grace

He returned to her, and had the unspeakable joy of seeing he
wag her tail with an almost imperceptible movement at his ap
proach. He sat down then, without fear, by her side, and they bega
to play together; he took her paws and muzzle, pulled her ear
rolled her over on her back, stroked her warm, delicate flanks. Sh
let him do whatever he liked, and when he began to stroke the ha
on her feet she drew her claws in carefully.

The man, keeping the dagger in one hand, thought to plunge
into the belly of the too-confiding panther, but he was afraid tha
he would be immediately strangled in her last convulsive struggle
besides, he felt in his heart a sort of remorse which bade him respe
a creature that had done him no harm. He seemed to have found
friend, in a boundless desert; half unconsciously he thought of h
first sweetheart, whom he had nicknamed "Mignonne" by way o
contrast, because she was so atrociously jealous that all the time o
her love he was in fear of the knife with which she had alway
threatened him.

This memory of his early days suggested to him the idea o
making the young panther answer to this name, now that he bega
to admire with less terror her swiftness, suppleness, and softnes
Toward the end of the day he had familiarized himself with h
perilous position; he now almost liked the painfulness of it. A
last his companion had got into the habit of looking up at him whe
ever he cried in a falsetto voice, "Mignonne."

At the setting of the sun Mignonne gave, several times runnin

[4] *Nero:* a debauched Roman emperor.

profound melancholy cry. "She's been well brought up," said ᴵe light-hearted soldier; "she says her prayers." But this mental ᴊke only occurred to him when he noticed what a pacific attitude ᴵs companion remained in. "Come, *ma petite blonde,* I'll let you ᴑ to bed first," he said to her, counting on the activity of his own ᴇgs to run away as quickly as possible, directly she was asleep, and ᴇek another shelter for the night.

The soldier waited with impatience the hour of his flight, and ᴡhen it had arrived he walked vigorously in the direction of the ᴊile; but hardly had he made a quarter of a league in the sand when ᴇ heard the panther bounding after him, crying with that saw-like ᴄry more dreadful even than the sound of her leaping.

"Ah!" he said, "then she's taken a fancy to me; she has never ᴊet any one before, and it is really quite flattering to have her first ᴊve." That instant the man fell into one of those movable quick-ᴀnds so terrible to travellers and from which it is impossible to ᴀve oneself. Feeling himself caught, he gave a shriek of alarm; ᴴe panther seized him with her teeth by the collar, and, springing ᴠigorously backward, drew him as if by magic out of the whirling ᴀnd.

"Ah, Mignonne!" cried the soldier, caressing her enthusiasti-ᴀlly; "we're bound together for life and death—but no jokes, ᴀind!" and he retraced his steps.

From that time the desert seemed inhabited. It contained a being ᴑ whom the man could talk, and whose ferocity was rendered gentle ᴊ him, though he could not explain to himself the reason for their ᴛrange friendship. Great as was the soldier's desire to stay upon ᴜard, he slept.

On awakening he could not find Mignonne; he mounted the hill, ᴀnd in the distance saw her springing toward him after the habit ᴏf these animals, who cannot run on account of the extreme flexi-ᴵlity of the vertebral column. Mignonne arrived, her jaws covered ᴠith blood; she received the wonted caress of her companion, show-ᴵng with much purring how happy it made her. Her eyes, full of ᴀnguor, turned still more gently than the day before toward the ᴾrovençal, who talked to her as one would to a tame animal.

"Ah! Mademoiselle, you are a nice girl, aren't you? Just look at ᴛhat! so we like to be made much of, don't we? Aren't you ashamed ᴏf yourself? So you have been eating some Arab or other, have you? ᴛhat doesn't matter. They're animals just the same as you are; ᴊut don't you take to eating Frenchmen, or I shan't like you any ᴏnger."

She played like a dog with its master, letting herself be rolle
over, knocked about, and stroked, alternately; sometimes she her
self would provoke the soldier, putting up her paw with a solicitin
gesture.

Some days passed in this manner. This companionship permitte
the Provençal to appreciate the sublime beauty of the desert; nov
that he had a living thing to think about, alternations of fear an
quiet, and plenty to eat, his mind became filled with contrast and hi
life began to be diversified.

Solitude revealed to him all her secrets, and enveloped him in he
delights. He discovered in the rising and setting of the sun sight
unknown to the world. He knew what it was to tremble when h
heard over his head the hiss of a bird's wing, so rarely did they pass
or when he saw the clouds, changing and many-colored travellers
melt one into another. He studied in the night time the effect of th
moon upon the ocean of sand, where the simoon made waves swit
of movement and rapid in their change. He lived the life of th
Eastern day, marvelling at its wonderful pomp; then, after havin
revelled in the sight of a hurricane over the plain where the whirlin
sands made red, dry mists and death-bearing clouds, he would wel
come the night with joy, for then fell the healthful freshness of th
stars, and he listened to imaginary music in the skies. Then solitud
taught him to unroll the treasures of dreams. He passed whole hour
in remembering mere nothings, and comparing his present life wit
his past.

At last he grew passionately fond of the panther; for some sor
of affection was a necessity.

Whether it was that his will powerfully projected had modifie
the character of his companion, or whether, because she found abun
dant food in her predatory excursions in the desert, she respecte
the man's life, he began to fear for it no longer, seeing her so wel
tamed.

He devoted the greater part of his time to sleep, but he wa
obliged to watch like a spider in its web that the moment of h
deliverance might not escape him, if any one should pass the lin
marked by the horizon. He had sacrificed his shirt to make a fla
with, which he hung at the top of a palm tree, whose foliage he ha
torn off. Taught by necessity, he found the means of keeping
spread out, by fastening it with little sticks; for the wind migl
not be blowing at the moment when the passing traveller was lool
ing through the desert.

It was during the long hours, when he had abandoned hope, tha e amused himself with the panther. He had come to learn the ifferent inflections of her voice, the expressions of her eyes; he had tudied the capricious patterns of all the rosettes which marked the old of her robe. Mignonne was not even angry when he took hold f the tuft at the end of her tail to count the rings, those graceful rnaments which glittered in the sun like jewelry. It gave him leasure to contemplate the supple, fine outlines of her form, the hiteness of her belly, the graceful pose of her head. But it was specially when she was playing that he felt most pleasure in look- ng at her; the agility and youthful lightness of her movements were continual surprise to him; he wondered at the supple way in hich she jumped and climbed, washed herself and arranged her ur, crouched down and prepared to spring. However rapid her pring might be, however slippery the stone she was on, she would lways stop short at the word "Mignonne."

One day, in a bright mid-day sun, an enormous bird coursed hrough the air. The man left his panther to look at this new guest; ut after waiting a moment the deserted sultana growled deeply.

"My goodness! I do believe she's jealous," he cried, seeing her yes become hard again.

The eagle disappeared into the air, while the soldier admired the urved contour of the panther.

But there was such youth and grace in her form! she was beau- iful as a woman! the blond fur of her robe mingled well with the elicate tints of faint white which marked her flanks.

The profuse light cast down by the sun made this living gold, hese russet markings, burn in a way to give them an indefinable ttraction.

The man and the panther looked at one another with a look full f meaning; the coquette quivered when she felt her friend stroke er head; her eyes flashed like lightning—then she shut them ightly.

"She has a soul," he said, looking at the stillness of this queen of he sands, golden like them, white like them, solitary and burning ike them.

.   .   .   .   .   .

"Well," said the lady whose escort to the circus had been telling er the preceding story, "how did two so well adapted to understand ach other end?"

"Ah, well! you see, they ended as all great passions do end—by a misunderstanding. For some reason *one* suspects the other of treason; they don't come to an explanation through pride, and quarrel and part from sheer obstinacy."

"Yet sometimes at the best moments a single word or a look is enough—but anyhow go on with your story."

"It's horribly difficult, but you will understand, after what the old villain told me over his champagne.

"He said—'I don't know if I hurt her, but she turned round, as if enraged, and with her sharp teeth caught hold of my leg—gently, I dare say; but I, thinking she would devour me, plunged my dagger into her throat. She rolled over, giving a cry that froze my heart, and I saw her dying, still looking at me without anger. I would have given all the world—my cross even, which I had not got then—to have brought her to life again. It was as though I had murdered a real person; and the soldiers who had seen my flag, and were come to my assistance, found me in tears.'

" 'Well, sir,' he said, after a moment of silence, 'since then I have been in war in Germany, in Spain, in Russia, in France; I've certainly carried my carcass about a good deal, but never have I seen anything like the desert. Ah! yes, it is very beautiful!'

" 'What did you feel there?' I asked him.

" 'Oh! that can't be described, young man. Besides, I am not always regretting my palm trees and my panther. I should have to be very melancholy for that. In the desert, you see, there is everything, and nothing.'

" 'Yes, but explain——'

" 'Well,' he said, with an impatient gesture, 'it is God without mankind.' "

THE NECKLACE
Guy de Maupassant (France)

Translated by Jonathan Sturges

She was one of those pretty and charming girls who are sometimes, as if by a mistake of destiny, born in a family of clerks. She had no dowry, no expectations, no means of being known, understood, loved, wedded, by any rich and distinguished man; and she let herself be married to a little clerk at the Ministry [1] of Public Instruction.

She dressed plainly because she could not dress well, but she was

[1] *Ministry:* department.

as unhappy as though she had really fallen from her proper station; since with women there is neither caste nor rank; and beauty, grace, and charm act instead of family and birth. Natural fineness, instinct for what is elegant, suppleness of wit, are the sole hierarchy, and make from women of the people the equals of the very greatest ladies.

She suffered ceaselessly, feeling herself born for all the delicacies and all the luxuries. She suffered from the poverty of her dwelling, from the wretched look of the walls, from the worn-out chairs, from the ugliness of the curtains. All those things, of which another woman of her rank would never even have been conscious, tortured her and made her angry. The sight of the little Breton peasant who did her humble housework aroused in her regrets which were despairing, and distracted dreams. She thought of silent ante-chambers hung with Oriental tapestry, lit by tall bronze candelabra, and of the two great footmen in knee-breeches who sleep in the big armchairs, made drowsy by the heavy warmth of the hot-air stove. She thought of the long *salons* [2] fitted up with ancient silk, of the delicate furniture carrying priceless curiosities, and of the coquettish perfumed boudoirs made for talks at five o'clock with intimate friends, with men famous and sought after, whom all women envy and whose attention they all desire.

When she sat down to dinner, before the round table covered with a table-cloth three days old, opposite her husband, who uncovered the soup tureen and declared with an enchanted air, "Ah, the good *pot-au-feu!* I don't know anything better than that," she thought of dainty dinners, of shining silverware, of tapestry which peopled the walls with ancient personages and with strange birds flying in the midst of a fairy forest; and she thought of delicious dishes served on marvelous plates, and of the whispered gallantries which you listen to with a sphinx-like smile, while you are eating the pink flesh of a trout or the wings of a quail.

She had no dresses, no jewels, nothing. And she loved nothing but that; she felt made for that. She would so have liked to please, to be envied, to be charming, to be sought after.

She had a friend, a former schoolmate at the convent, who was rich, and whom she did not like to go and see any more, because she suffered so much when she came back.

But, one evening, her husband returned home with a triumphant air, and holding a large envelope in his hand.

"There," said he, "here is something for you."

[2] *salons:* drawing rooms.

She tore the paper sharply, and drew out a printed card which bore these words:

"The Minister of Public Instruction and Mme. Georges Ramponneau request the honor of M. and Mme. Loisel's company at the palace of the Ministry on Monday evening, January 18th."

Instead of being delighted, as her husband hoped, she threw the invitation on the table with disdain, murmuring:

"What do you want me to do with that?"

"But, my dear, I thought you would be glad. You never go out, and this is such a fine opportunity. I had awful trouble to get it. Every one wants to go; it is very select, and they are not giving many invitations to clerks. The whole official world will be there."

She looked at him with an irritated eye, and she said, impatiently:

"And what do you want me to put on my back?"

He had not thought of that; he stammered:

"Why, the dress you go to the theater in. It looks very well, to me."

He stopped, distracted, seeing that his wife was crying. Two great tears descended slowly from the corners of her eyes toward the corners of her mouth. He stuttered:

"What's the matter? What's the matter?"

But, by a violent effort, she had conquered her grief, and she replied, with a calm voice, while she wiped her wet cheeks:

"Nothing. Only I have no dress, and therefore I can't go to this ball. Give your card to some colleague whose wife is better equipped than I."

He was in despair. He resumed:

"Come, let us see, Mathilde. How much would it cost, a suitable dress, which you could use on other occasions, something very simple?"

She reflected several seconds, making her calculations and wondering also what sum she could ask without drawing on herself an immediate refusal and a frightened exclamation from the economical clerk.

Finally, she replied, hesitatingly:

"I don't know exactly, but I think I could manage it with four hundred francs."

He had grown a little pale, because he was laying aside just that amount to buy a gun and treat himself to a little shooting next summer on the plain of Nanterre, with several friends who went to shoot larks down there, of a Sunday.

But he said:

"All right. I will give you four hundred francs. And try to have a pretty dress."

The day of the ball drew near, and Mme. Loisel seemed sad, uneasy, anxious. Her dress was ready, however. Her husband said to her one evening:

"What is the matter? Come, you've been so queer these last three days."

And she answered:

"It annoys me not to have a single jewel, not a single stone, nothing to put on. I shall look like distress. I should almost rather not go at all."

He resumed:

"You might wear natural flowers. It's very stylish at this time of the year. For ten francs you can get two or three magnificent roses."

She was not convinced.

"No; there's nothing more humiliating than to look poor among other women who are rich."

But her husband cried:

"How stupid you are! Go look up your friend Mme. Forestier, and ask her to lend you some jewels. You're quite thick enough with her to do that."

She uttered a cry of joy:

"It's true. I never thought of it."

The next day she went to her friend and told of her distress.

Mme. Forestier went to a wardrobe with a glass door, took out a large jewel-box, brought it back, opened it, and said to Mme. Loisel:

"Choose, my dear."

She saw first of all some bracelets, then a pearl necklace, then a Venetian cross, gold, and precious stones of admirable workmanship. She tried on the ornaments before the glass, hesitated, could not make up her mind to part with them, to give them back. She kept asking:

"Haven't you any more?"

"Why, yes. Look. I don't know what you like."

All of a sudden she discovered, in a black satin box, a superb necklace of diamonds; and her heart began to beat with an immoderate desire. Her hands trembled as she took it. She fastened it around her throat, outside her high-necked dress, and remained lost in ecstasy at the sight of herself.

Then she asked, hesitating, filled with anguish:

"Can you lend me that, only that?"

"Why, yes, certainly."

She sprang upon the neck of her friend, kissed her passionately, then fled with her treasure.

The day of the ball arrived. Mme. Loisel made a great success. She was prettier than all of them, elegant, gracious, smiling, and crazy with joy. All the men looked at her, asked her name, endeavored to be introduced. All the attachés of the Cabinet wanted to waltz with her. She was remarked by the minister himself.

She danced with intoxication, with passion, made drunk by pleasure, forgetting all, in the triumph of her beauty, in the glory of her success, in a sort of cloud of happiness composed of all this homage, of all this admiration, of all these awakened desires, and of that sense of complete victory which is so sweet to woman's heart.

She went away about four o'clock in the morning. Her husband had been sleeping since midnight, in a little deserted ante-room, with three other gentlemen whose wives were having a very good time.

He threw over her shoulders the wraps which he had brought, modest wraps of common life, whose poverty contrasted with the elegance of the ball dress. She felt this and wanted to escape so as not to be remarked by the other women, who were enveloping themselves in costly furs.

Loisel held her back.

"Wait a bit. You will catch cold outside. I will go and call a cab."

But she did not listen to him, and rapidly descended the stairs. When they were in the street they did not find a carriage; and they began to look for one, shouting after the cabmen whom they saw passing by at a distance.

They went down toward the Seine, in despair, shivering with cold. At last they found on the quay one of those ancient coupés which, exactly as if they were ashamed to show their misery during the day, are never seen round Paris until after nightfall.

It took them to their door in the Rue des Martyrs, and once more, sadly, they climbed up homeward. All was ended for her. And as to him, he reflected that he must be at the Ministry at ten o'clock.

She removed the wraps, which covered her shoulders, before the glass, so as once more to see herself in all her glory. But suddenly she uttered a cry. She had no longer the necklace around her neck!

Her husband, already half-undressed, demanded:

"What is the matter with you?"

She turned madly toward him:

"I have—I have—I've lost Mme. Forestier's necklace."

He stood up, distracted.

"What!—how?—Impossible!"

And they looked in the folds of her dress, in the folds of her cloak, in her pockets, everywhere. They did not find it.

He asked:

"You're sure you had it on when you left the ball?"

"Yes, I felt it in the vestibule of the palace."

"But if you had lost it in the street we should have heard it fall. It must be in the cab."

"Yes. Probably. Did you take his number?"

"No. And you, didn't you notice it?"

"No."

They looked, thunderstuck, at one another. At last Loisel put on his clothes.

"I shall go back on foot," said he, "over the whole route which we have taken, to see if I can't find it."

And he went out. She sat waiting on a chair in her ball dress, without strength to go to bed, overwhelmed, without fire, without a thought.

Her husband came back about seven o'clock. He had found nothing.

He went to Police Headquarters, to the newspaper offices, to offer a reward; he went to the cab companies—everywhere, in fact, whither he was urged by the least suspicion of hope.

She waited all day, in the same condition of mad fear before this terrible calamity.

Loisel returned at night with a hollow, pale face; he had discovered nothing.

"You must write to your friend," said he, "that you have broken the clasp of her necklace and that you are having it mended. That will give us time to turn round."

She wrote at his dictation.

At the end of a week they had lost all hope.

And Loisel, who had aged five years, declared:

"We must consider how to replace that ornament."

The next day they took the box which had contained it, and they went to the jeweler whose name was found within. He consulted his books.

"It was not I, madame, who sold that necklace; I must simply have furnished the case."

Then they went from jeweler to jeweler, searching for a necklace like the other, consulting their memories, sick both of them with chagrin and with anguish.

They found, in a shop at the Palais Royal, a string of diamonds which seemed to them exactly like the one they looked for. It was worth forty thousand francs. They could have it for thirty-six.

So they begged the jeweler not to sell it for three days yet. And they made a bargain that he should buy it back for thirty-four thousand francs, in case they found the other one before the end of February.

Loisel possessed eighteen thousand francs which his father had left him. He would borrow the rest.

He did borrow, asking a thousand francs of one, five hundred of another, five louis here, three louis there. He gave notes, took up ruinous obligations, dealt with usurers, and all the race of lenders. He compromised all the rest of his life, risked his signature without even knowing if he could meet it; and, frightened by the pains yet to come, by the black misery which was about to fall upon him, by the prospect of all the physical privations and of all the moral tortures which he was to suffer, he went to get the new necklace, putting down upon the merchant's counter thirty-six thousand francs.

When Mme. Loisel took back the necklace Mme. Forestier said to her, with a chilly manner:

"You should have returned it sooner, I might have needed it."

She did not open the case, as her friend had so much feared. If she had detected the substitution, what would she have thought, what would she have said? Would she not have taken Mme. Loisel for a thief?

Mme. Loisel now knew the horrible existence of the needy. She took her part, moreover, all on a sudden, with heroism. That dreadful debt must be paid. She would pay it. They dismissed their servant; they changed their lodgings; they rented a garret under the roof.

She came to know what heavy housework meant and the odious cares of the kitchen. She washed the dishes, using her rosy nails on the greasy pots and pans. She washed the dirty linen, the shirts, and the dish-cloths, which she dried upon a line; she carried the slops down to the street every morning, and carried up the water, stopping for breath at every landing. And, dressed like a woman of the people, she went to the fruiterer, the grocer, the butcher, her basket on her arm, bargaining, insulted, defending her miserable money sou by sou.

Each month they had to meet some notes, renew others, obtain more time.

Her husband worked in the evening making a fair copy of some tradesman's accounts, and late at night he often copied manuscript for five sous a page.

And this life lasted ten years.

At the end of ten years they had paid everything, everything, with the rates of usury, and the accumulations of the compound interest.

Mme. Loisel looked old now. She had become the woman of impoverished households—strong and hard and rough. With frowsy hair, skirts askew, and red hands, she talked loud while washing the floor with great swishes of water. But sometimes, when her husband was at the office, she sat down near the window, and she thought of that gay evening of long ago, of that ball where she had been so beautiful and so fêted.

What would have happened if she had not lost that necklace? Who knows? who knows? How life is strange and how changeful! How little a thing is needed for us to be lost or to be saved!

But, one Sunday, having gone to take a walk in the Champs-Élysées to refresh herself from the labors of the week, she suddenly perceived a woman who was leading a child. It was Mme. Forestier, still young, still beautiful, still charming.

Mme. Loisel felt moved. Was she going to speak to her? Yes, certainly. And now that she had paid, she was going to tell her all about it. Why not?

She went up.

"Good-day, Jeanne."

The other, astonished to be familiarly addressed by this plain good wife, did not recognize her at all, and stammered:

"But—madame!—I do not know— You must have mistaken."

"No. I am Mathilde Loisel."

Her friend uttered a cry.

"Oh, my poor Mathilde! How you are changed!"

"Yes, I have had days hard enough, since I have seen you, days wretched enough—and that because of you!"

"Of me! How so?"

"Do you remember that diamond necklace which you lent me to wear at the ministerial ball?"

"Yes. Well?"

"Well, I lost it."

"What do you mean? You brought it back."

"I brought you back another just like it. And for this we have been ten years paying. You can understand that it was not easy for us, us who had nothing. At last it is ended, and I am very glad."

Mme. Forestier had stopped.

"You say that you bought a necklace of diamonds to replace mine?"

"Yes. You never noticed it, then! They were very like."

And she smiled with a joy which was proud and naïve at once.

Mme. Forestier, strongly moved, took her two hands.

"Oh, my poor Mathilde! Why, my necklace was paste.[3] It was worth at most five hundred francs!"

THE BIRTHDAY OF THE INFANTA

Oscar Wilde (England)

This story is laid at the court of the king of Spain in the seventeenth century during the days of Spanish conquest and at the time of the Inquisition. Velasquez, the court painter of the time, made portraits of the Infanta.

❋   ❋   ❋

It was the birthday of the Infanta.[1] She was just twelve years of age, and the sun was shining brightly in the gardens of the palace.

Although she was a real Princess and the Infanta of Spain, she had only one birthday every year, just like the children of quite poor people, so it was naturally a matter of great importance to the whole country that she should have a really fine day for the occasion. And a really fine day it certainly was. The tall striped tulips stood straight up upon their stalks, like long rows of soldiers, and looked defiantly across the grass at the roses, and said: "We are quite as splendid as you are now." The purple butterflies fluttered about with gold dust on their wings, visiting each flower in turn; the little lizards crept out of the crevices of the wall, and lay basking in the white glare; and the pomegranates split and cracked with the

[3] *paste:* the stones were imitations.   [1] *Infanta:* royal Spanish princess.

heat, and showed their bleeding red hearts. Even the pale yellow lemons, that hung in such profusion from the mouldering trellis and along the dim arcades, seemed to have caught a richer color from the wonderful sunlight, and the magnolia trees opened their great globe-like blossoms of folded ivory, and filled the air with a sweet heavy perfume.

The little Princess herself walked up and down the terrace with her companions, and played at hide and seek round the stone vases and the old moss-grown statues. On ordinary days she was only allowed to play with children of her own rank, so she had always to play alone, but her birthday was an exception, and the King had given orders that she was to invite any of her young friends whom she liked to come and amuse themselves with her. There was a stately grace about these slim Spanish children as they glided about, the boys with their large-plumed hats and short fluttering cloaks, the girls holding up the trains of their long brocaded gowns, and shielding the sun from their eyes with huge fans of black and silver. But the Infanta was the most graceful of all, and the most tastefully attired, after the somewhat cumbrous fashion of the day. Her robe was of gray satin, the skirt and the wide puffed sleeves heavily embroidered with silver, and the stiff corset studded with rows of fine pearls. Two tiny slippers with big pink rosettes peeped out beneath her dress as she walked. Pink and pearl was her great gauze fan, and in her hair, which like an aureole of faded gold stood out stiffly round her pale little face, she had a beautiful white rose.

From a window in the palace the sad melancholy King watched them. Sadder even than usual was the King, for as he looked at the Infanta bowing with childish gravity to the assembling courtiers, or laughing behind her fan at the grim Duchess of Albuquerque who always accompanied her, he thought of the young Queen, her mother, who but a short time before—so it seemed to him—had come from the gay country of France, and had withered away in the somber splendor of the Spanish court, dying just six months after the birth of her child, and before she had seen the almonds blossom twice in the orchard, or plucked the second year's fruit from the old gnarled fig-tree that stood in the center of the now grass-grown courtyard. So great had been his love for her that he had not suffered even the grave to hide her from him. She had been embalmed by a Moorish physician, and her body was still lying on its tapestried bier in the black marble chapel of the Palace, just as the monks had borne her in on that windy March day nearly twelve years before. Once every month the King, wrapped in a dark cloak and with a muffled lantern in his hand, went in and knelt by her side, calling out, *"Mi-reina! Mi-reina!"* and sometimes breaking through the formal etiquette that in Spain governs every separate action of life, and sets limits even to the sorrow of a King, he would clutch at the pale jeweled hands in a wild agony of grief, and try to wake by his mad kisses the cold painted face.

His whole married life, with its fierce, fiery-colored joys and the terrible agony of its sudden ending, seemed to come back to him today as he watched the Infanta playing on the terrace. She had all the Queen's pretty petulance of manner, the same willful way of tossing her head, the same proud, curved beautiful mouth, the same wonderful smile—as she glanced up now and then at the window, or stretched out her little hand for the stately Spanish gentleman to kiss. But the shrill laughter of the children grated on his ears, and the bright, pitiless sunlight mocked his sorrow, and a dull odor of strange spices, spices such as embalmers use, seemed to taint—or was it fancy?—the clear morning air. He buried his face in his hands, and when the Infanta looked up again the curtains had been drawn, and the King had retired.

She had made a little *moue* [2] of disappointment, and shrugged her shoulders. Surely he might have stayed with her on her birthday. What did the stupid State-affairs matter? Or had he gone to that gloomy chapel, where the candles were always burning, and where she was never allowed to enter? How silly of him, when the sun was shining so brightly, and everybody was so happy! Besides, he would miss the sham bull-fight for which the trumpet was already sounding, to say nothing of the puppet show and the other wonderful things. Her uncle and the Grand Inquisitor were much more sensible. They had come out on the terrace, and paid her nice compliments. So she tossed her pretty head, and taking Don Pedro by the hand, she walked slowly down the steps toward a long pavilion of purple silk that had been erected at the end of the garden, the other children following in strict order of precedence, those who had the longest names going first.

A procession of noble boys, fantastically dressed as *toreadors,* [3] came out to meet her, and the young Count of Tierra-Nueva, a wonderfully handsome lad of about fourteen years of age, uncovering his head with all the grace of a born hidalgo and grandee of Spain, led her solemnly in to a little gilt and ivory chair that was placed on a raised dais above the arena.

It certainly was a marvelous bull-fight, and much nicer, the In-

[2] *moue:* pout. [3] *toreadors:* bull fighters.

fanta thought, than the real bull-fight that she had been brought to see at Seville, on the occasion of the visit of the Duke of Parma to her father. Some of the boys pranced about on richly caparisoned hobby-horses brandishing long javelins with gay streamers of bright ribands attached to them; others went on foot waving their scarlet cloaks before the bull, and vaulting lightly over the barrier when he charged them; and as for the bull himself he was just like a live bull, though he was only made of wickerwork and stretched hide, and sometimes insisted on running around the arena on his hind legs, which no live bull ever dreams of doing. He made a splendid fight of it, too, and the children got so excited that they stood up upon the benches, and waved their lace handkerchiefs and cried out: *Bravo toro! Bravo toro!* [4] just as sensibly as if they had been grown-up people. At last, however, after a prolonged combat, during which several of the hobby-horses were gored through and through, and their riders dismounted, the young Count of Tierra-Nueva brought the bull to his knees, and having obtained the permission from the Infanta to give the *coup de grâce*,[5] he plunged his wooden sword into the neck of the animal with such violence that the head came right off, and disclosed the laughing face of little Monsieur de Lorraine, the son of the French Ambassador at Madrid.

The arena was then cleared amidst much applause, and the dead hobby-horses dragged solemnly away by two Moorish pages in yellow and black liveries, and after a short interlude, during which a French posture-master performed upon the tight rope, some Italian puppets appeared in the semi-classical tragedy of *Sophonisba* on the stage of a small theater that had been built up for the purpose. They acted so well, and their gestures were so extremely natural, that at the close of the play the eyes of the Infanta were quite dim with tears. Indeed some of the children really cried, and had to be comforted with sweetmeats, and the Grand Inquisitor himself was so affected that he could not help saying to Don Pedro that it seemed to him intolerable that things made simply out of wood and colored wax, and worked mechanically by wires, should be so unhappy and meet with such terrible misfortunes.

An African juggler followed, who brought in a large flat basket covered with a red cloth, and having placed it in the center of the arena, he took from his turban a curious reed pipe, and blew through it. In a few moments the cloth began to move, and as the pipe grew shriller and shriller two green and gold snakes put out their strange wedge-shaped heads and rose slowly up, swaying to and fro with

[4] *Bravo toro:* brave bull.   [5] *coup de grâce:* death stroke.

the music as a plant sways in the water. The children, however, were rather frightened at their spotted hoods and quick darting tongues, and were much more pleased when the juggler made a tiny orange-tree grow out of the sand and bear pretty white blossoms and clusters of real fruit; and when he took the fan of the little daughter of the Marquess de Las-Torres, and changed it into a bluebird that flew all round the pavilion and sang, their delight and amazement knew no bounds. The solemn minuet, too, performed by the dancing boys from the church of Nuestra Señora Del Pilar, was charming. The Infanta had never before seen this wonderful cere-mony which takes place every year at May-time in front of the high altar of the Virgin, and in her honor; and, indeed, none of the royal family of Spain had entered the great cathedral of Saragossa since a mad priest, supposed by many to have been in the pay of Elizabeth of England, had tried to administer a poisoned wafer to the Prince of the Asturias.[6] So she had known only by hearsay of "Our Lady's Dance," as it was called, and it certainly was a beautiful sight. The boys wore old-fashioned court dresses of white velvet, and their curious three-cornered hats were fringed with silver and surmounted with huge plumes of ostrich feathers, the dazzling whiteness of their costumes, as they moved about in the sunlight, being still more accentuated by their swarthy faces and long black hair.

A troop of handsome Egyptians—as the gypsies were termed in those days—then advanced into the arena, and sitting down cross-legs, in a circle, began to play softly upon their zithers, moving their bodies to the tune, and humming, almost below their breath, a low, dreamy air. When they caught sight of Don Pedro they scowled at him, and some of them looked terrified, for only a few weeks before he had had two of their tribe hanged for sorcery in the marketplace at Seville, but the pretty Infanta charmed them as she leaned back peeping over her fan with her great blue eyes, and they felt sure that one so lovely as she was could never be cruel to anybody. So they played on very gently and just touching the cords of the zithers with their long pointed nails, and their heads began to nod as though they were falling asleep. Suddenly, with a cry so shrill that all the children were startled and Don Pedro's hand clutched at the agate pommel of his dagger, they leaped to their feet and whirled madly round the enclosure beating their tam-bourines, and chanting some wild love song in their strange guttural language. Then at another signal they all flung themselves again to the ground and lay there quite still, the dull strumming of the

[6] *Prince of the Asturias:* title of the heir to the Spanish throne.

zithers being the only sound that broke the silence. After they had done this several times, they disappeared for a moment and came back leading a brown shaggy bear by a chain, and carrying on their shoulders some little Barbary apes. The bear stood upon his head with the utmost gravity, and the wizened apes played all kinds of amusing tricks with two gypsy boys who seemed to be their masters, and fought with tiny swords, and fired off guns, and went through a regular soldier's drill just like the King's own bodyguard. In fact, the gypsies were a great success.

But the funniest part of the whole morning's entertainment was undoubtedly the dancing of the little Dwarf.[7] When he stumbled into the arena, waddling on his crooked legs and wagging his huge, misshapen head from side to side, the children went off into a loud shout of delight, and the Infanta herself laughed so much that the Camerera[8] was obliged to remind her that although there were many precedents in Spain for a King's daughter weeping before her equals, there were none for a Princess of the blood royal making so merry before those who were her inferiors in birth. The Dwarf, however, was really quite irresistible, and even at the Spanish Court, always noted for its cultivated passion for the horrible, so fantastic a little monster had never been seen. It was his first appearance, too. He had been discovered only the day before, running wild through the forest, by two of the nobles who happened to have been hunting in a remote part of the great cork-wood that surrounded the town, and had been carried off by them to the Palace as a surprise for the Infanta ; his father, who was only a poor charcoal-burner, being but too well pleased to get rid of so ugly and useless a child. Perhaps the most amusing thing about him was his complete unconsciousness of his own grotesque appearance. Indeed, he seemed quite happy and full of the highest spirits. When the children laughed, he laughed as freely and as joyously as any of them, and at the close of each dance he made them each the funniest of bows, smiling and nodding at them just as if he were really one of themselves, and not a little misshapen thing that Nature, in some humorous mood, had fashioned for others to mock at. As for the Infanta, she absolutely fascinated him. He could not keep his eyes off her, and seemed to dance for her alone, and when at the close of the performance, remembering how she had seen the great ladies of the Court throw

[7] *Dwarf:* In those days monstrosities were considered amusing and noblemen often kept dwarfs to entertain their company by their antics. Velasquez has painted several such royal favorites.

[8] *Camerera:* Lady of the Bed Chamber, Lady in Waiting.

bouquets to Caffarelli, the famous Italian treble, whom the Pope had sent from his own chapel to Madrid that he might cure the King's melancholy by the sweetness of his voice, she took out of her hair the beautiful white rose, and partly for a jest and partly to tease the Camerera, threw it to him across the arena with her sweetest smile; he took the whole matter quite seriously, and pressing the flower to his rough, coarse lips, he put his hand upon his heart and sank on one knee before her, grinning from ear to ear, and with his little bright eyes sparkling with pleasure.

This so upset the gravity of the Infanta that she kept on laughing long after the little Dwarf had run out of the arena, and expressed a desire to her uncle that the dance should be immediately repeated. The Camerera, however, on the plea that the sun was too hot, decided that it would be better that her Highness should return without delay to the Palace, where a wonderful feast had been already prepared for her, including a real birthday cake with her own initials worked all over it in painted sugar and a lovely silver flag waving from the top. The Infanta accordingly rose up with much dignity, and having given orders that the little Dwarf was to dance again for her after the hour of siesta, and conveyed her thanks to the young Count of Tierra-Nueva for his charming reception, she went back to her apartments, the children following in the same order in which they had entered.

Now when the little Dwarf heard that he was to dance a second time before the Infanta, and by her own express command, he was so proud that he ran out into the garden, kissing the white rose in an absurd ecstasy of pleasure, and making the most uncouth and clumsy gestures of delight. How he wished that he had gone back with her! She would have put him on her right hand, and smiled at him, and he would have never left her side, but would have made her his playmate, and taught her all kinds of delightful tricks. For though he had never been in a palace before, he knew a great many wonderful things. He could make little cages out of rushes for the grasshoppers to sing in, and fashion the long-jointed bamboo into the pipe that Pan loves to hear. He knew the cry of every bird, and could call the starlings from the tree-top, or the heron from the mere. He knew the trail of every animal, and could track the hare by its delicate footprints, and the boar by the trampled leaves. All the wind-dances he knew, the mad dance in red raiment with the autumn, the light dance in blue sandals over the corn, the dance with white snow-wreaths in winter, and the blossom-dance through the orchards in spring. He knew where the wood-pigeons built their

ests, and once when a fowler had snared the parent birds, he had
rought up the young ones himself, and had built a little dovecot
or them in the cleft of a pollard elm. They were quite tame, and
sed to feed out of his hands every morning. She would like them,
nd the rabbits that scurried about in the long fern, and the jays
vith their steely feathers and black bills, and the hedgehogs that
ould curl themselves up into prickly balls, and the great wise tor-
oises that crawled slowly about, shaking their heads and nibbling at
he young leaves. Yes, she must certainly come to the forest and
lay with him. He would give her his own little bed, and would
vatch outside the window till dawn, to see that the wild, horned
attle did not harm her, nor the gaunt wolves creep too near the
ut. And at dawn he would tap at the shutters and wake her, and
hey would go out and dance together all the day long. Certainly
here was a great deal to look at in the forest, and when she was
ired he would find a soft bank of moss for her, or carry her in his
rms, for he was very strong, though he knew that he was not tall.
Ie would make her a necklace of red bryony berries, that would be
uite as pretty as the white berries that she wore on her dress, and
vhen she was tired of them, she could throw them away, and he
vould find her others. He would bring her acorn-cups and dew-
drenched anemones, and tiny glow-worms to be stars in the pale
gold of her hair. . . .

But where was she? He asked the white rose, and it made him
o answer. The whole place seemed asleep, and even where the
shutters had not been closed, heavy curtains had been drawn across
the windows to keep out the glare.

At the end of the hall hung a richly embroidered curtain of black
velvet, powdered with suns and stars, the King's favorite devices,
and embroidered on the color he loved best. Perhaps she was hiding
behind that? He would try at any rate.

So he stole quietly across, and drew it aside. No; there was only
another room, though a prettier room, he thought, than the one
he had just left. The walls were hung with a many-figured green
arras of needle-wrought tapestry representing a hunt, the work of
some Flemish artists who had spent more than seven years in its
composition. It had once been the chamber of *Jean le Fou*, as he was
called, that mad King who was so enamoured of the chase that he
had often tried in his delirium to mount the huge rearing horses,
and to drag down the stag on which the great hounds were leaping,
sounding his hunting horn, and stabbing with his dagger at the pale
flying deer. It was now used as the council-room, and on the center

table were lying the red portfolios of the ministers, stamped wit the gold tulips of Spain, and with the arms and emblems of the hous of Hapsburg.

The little Dwarf looked in wonder all round him, and was hal afraid to go on. The strange silent horsemen that galloped so swiftl through the long glades without making any noise, seemed to hir like those terrible phantoms of whom he had heard the charcoal burners speaking—the Comprachos, who hunt only at night, an if they meet a man, turn him into a hind, and chase him. But h thought of the pretty Infanta, and took courage. He wanted to fin her alone, and to tell her that he, too, loved her. Perhaps she was i the room beyond.

He ran across the soft Moorish carpets, and opened the door. O all the rooms this was the brightest and the most beautiful. Th walls were covered with a pink-flowered Lucca damask, patterne with birds and dotted with dainty blossoms of silver ; the furnitur was of massive silver, festooned with florid wreaths, and swingin Cupids ; in front of the two large fireplaces stood great screen broidered with parrots and peacocks, and the floor, which was o sea-green onyx, seemed to stretch far away into the distance. No was he alone. Standing under the shadow of the doorway, at th extreme end of the room, he saw a little figure watching him. Hi heart trembled, a cry of joy broke from his lips, and he moved ou into the sunlight. As he did so, the figure moved out also, and he sav it plainly.

The Infanta ! It was a monster, the most grotesque monster h had ever beheld. Not properly shaped, as all other people were, bu hunchbacked, and crooked-limbed, with huge lolling head and man of black hair. The little Dwarf frowned, and the monster frowne also. He laughed, and it laughed with him, and held its hands to it sides, just as he himself was doing. He made it a mocking bow, an it returned him a low reverence. He went toward it, and it came t meet him, copying each step that he made, and stopping when h stopped himself. He shouted with amusement, and ran forward and reached out his hand, and the hand of the monster touched his and it was as cold as ice. He grew afraid, and moved his hand across and the monster's hand followed it quickly. He tried to press on but something smooth and hard stopped him. The face of the mon ster was now close to his own, and seemed full of terror. He brushe his hair off his eyes. It imitated him. He struck at it, and it re turned blow for blow. He loathed it, and it made hideous faces a him. He drew back, and it retreated.

What is it? He thought for a moment, and looked round at the rest of the room. It was strange, but everything seemed to have its double in this invisible wall of clear water. Yes, picture for picture was repeated, and couch for couch. The sleeping Faun that lay in the alcove by the doorway had its twin brother that slumbered, and the silver Venus that stood in the sunlight held out her arms to a Venus as lovely as herself.

Was it Echo? He had called to her once in the valley, and she had answered him word for word. Could she mock the eye, as she mocked the voice? Could she make a mimic world just like the real world? Could the shadows of things have color and life and movement? Could it be that——?

He started, and taking from his breast the beautiful white rose, he turned round, and kissed it. The monster had a rose of its own, petal for petal the same! It kissed it with like kisses, and pressed it to its heart with horrible gestures.

When the truth dawned upon him, he gave a wild cry of despair, and fell sobbing to the ground. So it was he who was misshapen and hunchbacked, foul to look at and grotesque. He himself was the monster, and it was at him that all the children had been laughing, and the little Princess who he thought loved him—she, too, had been merely mocking at his ugliness, and making merry over his twisted limbs. Why had they not left him in the forest, where there was no mirror to tell him how loathsome he was? Why had his father not killed him, rather than sell him to his shame? The hot tears poured down his cheeks, and he tore the white rose to pieces. The sprawling monster did the same, and scattered the faint petals in the air. It grovelled on the ground, and, when he looked at it, it watched him with a face drawn with pain. He crept away, lest he should see it, and covered his eyes with his hands. He crawled, like some wounded thing, into the shadow, and lay there moaning.

And at that moment the Infanta herself came in with her companions through the open window and, when they saw the ugly little Dwarf lying on the ground and beating the floor with his clenched hands, in the most fantastic and exaggerated manner, they went off into shouts of happy laughter, and stood all round him and watched him.

"His dancing was funny," said the Infanta; "but his acting is funnier still. Indeed he is almost as good as the puppets, only, of course, not quite so natural." And she fluttered her big fan, and applauded.

But the little Dwarf never looked up, and his sobs grew fainter and fainter, and suddenly he gave a curious gasp, and clutched his side. And then he fell back again, and lay quite still.

"That is capital," said the Infanta, after a pause; "but now you must dance for me."

"Yes," cried all the children, "you must get up and dance, for you are as clever as the Barbary apes, and much more ridiculous."

But the little Dwarf made no answer.

And the Infanta stamped her foot, and called out to her uncle, who was walking on the terrace with the Chamberlain, reading some despatches that had just arrived from Mexico. "My funny little Dwarf is sulking," she cried, "you must wake him up, and tell him to dance for me."

They smiled at each other, and sauntered in, and Don Pedro stooped down, and slapped the Dwarf on the cheek with his embroidered glove. "You must dance," he said, *"petit monstre.*[9] You must dance. The Infanta of Spain and the Indies wishes to be amused."

But the little Dwarf never moved.

"A whipping master should be sent for," said Don Pedro wearily, and he went back to the terrace. But the Chamberlain looked grave, and he knelt beside the little Dwarf, and put his hand upon his heart. And after a few moments he shrugged his shoulders, and rose up, and having made a low bow to the Infanta, he said: *"Mi bella Princesa,*[10] your funny little Dwarf will never dance again. It is a pity, for he is so ugly that he might have made the King smile."

"But why will he not dance again?" asked the Infanta, laughing.

"Because his heart is broken," answered the Chamberlain.

And the Infanta frowned, and her dainty rose-leaf lips curled in pretty disdain. "For the future let those who come to play with me have no hearts," she cried, and she ran out into the garden.

THE BOTTLE IMP

Robert Louis Stevenson (Scotland)

There was a man in the island of Hawaii, whom I shall call Keawe; for the truth is, he still lives, and his name must be kept secret. This man was poor, brave, and active; he could read and write like a schoolmaster; he was a first-rate mariner besides, sailed for some time in the island steamers, and steered a whale-boat on

[9] *petit monstre:* little monster.   [10] *Mi bella Princesa:* My pretty Princess.

Hamakua coast. At length it came in Keawe's mind to have a ght of the great world and foreign cities, and he shipped on a vessel und to San Francisco.

This is a fine town, with a fine harbor, and rich people uncount-le; and, in particular, there is one hill which is covered with laces. Upon this hill Keawe was one day taking a walk, with his cket full of money, viewing the great houses upon either hand th pleasure. "What fine houses they are!" he was thinking, "and w happy must these people be who dwell in them, and take no re for the morrow!" The thought was in his mind when he came reast of a house that was smaller than some others, but all finished d beautified like a toy; the steps of that house shone like silver, d the borders of the garden bloomed like garlands, and the win-ws were bright like diamonds; and Keawe stopped and wondered the excellence of all he saw. So stopping, he was aware of a man at looked forth upon him through a window, so clear that Keawe uld see him as you see a fish in a pool upon the reef. The man was derly, with a bald head and a black beard; and his face was heavy ith sorrow, and he bitterly sighed. And the truth of it is, that as eawe looked in upon the man, and the man looked out upon eawe, each envied the other.

All of a sudden the man smiled and nodded, and beckoned Keawe enter, and met him at the door of the house.

"This is a fine house of mine," said the man, and bitterly sighed. Would you not care to view the chambers?"

So he led Keawe all over it, from the cellar to the roof, and there as nothing there that was not perfect of its kind, and Keawe was stonished.

"Truly," said Keawe, "this is a beautiful house; if I lived in the ke of it, I should be laughing all day long. How comes it, then, at you should be sighing?"

"There is no reason," said the man, "why you should not have a ouse in all points similar to this, and finer, if you wish. You have me money, I suppose?"

"I have fifty dollars," said Keawe; "but a house like this will cost ore than fifty dollars."

The man made a computation. "I am sorry you have no more," aid he, "for it may raise you trouble in the future; but it shall be ours at fifty dollars."

"The house?" asked Keawe.

"No, not the house," replied the man; "but the bottle. For, I must ell you, although I appear to you so rich and fortunate, all my fortune, and this house itself and its garden, came out of a bottle no much bigger than a pint. This is it."

And he opened a lock-fast place, and took out a round-bellie bottle with a long neck; the glass of it was white like milk, wit changing rainbow colors in the grain. Withinsides something ol scurely moved, like a shadow and a fire.

"This is the bottle," said the man; and, when Keawe laughe "You do not believe me?" he added. "Try, then, for yourself. Se if you can break it."

So Keawe took the bottle up and dashed it on the floor till he wa weary; but it jumped on the floor like a child's ball, and was no injured.

"This is a strange thing," said Keawe. "For by the touch of it, a well as by the look, the bottle should be of glass."

"Of glass it is," replied the man, sighing more heavily than ever "but the glass of it was tempered in the flames of hell. An imp live in it, and that is the shadow we behold there moving; or, so I sup pose. If any man buys this bottle the imp is at his command; a that he desires—love, fame, money, houses like this house, ay, or city like this city—all are his at the word uttered. Napoleon ha this bottle, and by it he grew to be the king of the world; but he sol it at the last and fell. Captain Cook had this bottle, and by it h found his way to so many islands; but he, too, sold it, and wa slain upon Hawaii. For, once it is sold, the power goes and the pro tection; and unless a man remain content with what he has, ill wil befall him."

"And yet you talk of selling it yourself?" Keawe said.

"I have all I wish, and I am growing elderly," replied the man "There is one thing the imp cannot do—he cannot prolong life; and it would not be fair to conceal from you there is a drawback to th bottle; for if a man die before he sells it, he must burn in hell fo ever."

"To be sure, that is a drawback and no mistake," cried Keawe "I would not meddle with the thing. I can do without a house, than God; but there is one thing I could not be doing with one particle and that is to be damned."

"Dear me, you must not run away with things," returned the man. "All you have to do is to use the power of the imp in modera tion, and then sell it to someone else, as I do to you, and finish you life in comfort."

"Well, I observe two things," said Keawe. "All the time you keep sighing like a maid in love, that is one; and, for the other, you sel this bottle very cheap."

"I have told you already why I sigh," said the man. "It is because my health is breaking up; and, as you said yourself, to die and go to the devil is a pity for anyone. As for why I sell so cheap, I must explain to you there is a peculiarity about the bottle. Long ago, when the devil brought it first upon earth, it was extremely expensive; but it cannot be sold at all, unless sold at a loss. If you sell it for as much as you paid for it, back it comes to you again like a homing pigeon. It follows that the price has kept falling in these centuries, and the bottle is now remarkably cheap. I bought it myself from one of my great neighbors on this hill, and the price I paid was ninety dollars. I could sell it for as high as eighty-nine dollars and ninety-nine cents, but not a penny dearer, or back the thing must come to me. Now, about this there are two bothers. First, when you offer a bottle so singular for eighty-odd dollars, people suppose you to be jesting. And second—but there is no hurry about that—and I need not go into it. Only remember it must be coined money that you sell it for."

"How am I to know that this is all true?" asked Keawe.

"Some of it you can try at once," replied the man. "Give me your fifty dollars, take the bottle, and wish your fifty dollars back into your pocket. If that does not happen, I pledge you my honor I will cry off the bargain and restore your money."

"You are not deceiving me?" said Keawe.

The man bound himself with a great oath.

"Well, I will risk that much," said Keawe, "for that can do no harm," and he paid over his money to the man, and the man handed him the bottle.

"Imp of the bottle," said Keawe, "I want my fifty dollars back." And sure enough, he had scarce said the word before his pocket was as heavy as ever.

"To be sure this is a wonderful bottle," said Keawe.

"And now good-morning to you, my fine fellow, and the devil go with you," said the man.

"Hold on," said Keawe, "I don't want any more of this fun. Here, take your bottle back."

"You have bought it for less than I paid for it," replied the man, rubbing his hands. "It is yours now; and, for my part, I am only concerned to see the back of you." And with that he rang for his Chinese servant, and had Keawe shown out of the house.

Now, when Keawe was in the street, with the bottle under his arm, he began to think. "If all is true about this bottle, I may have made a losing bargain," thinks he. "But, perhaps the man was only fooling me." The first thing he did was to count his money; the sum

was exact—forty-nine dollars American money, and one Chili piec
"That looks like the truth," said Keawe. "Now I will try anoth
part."

Keawe set the bottle in the gutter and turned a corner; but |
had scarce done so, when something knocked upon his elbow, ar
behold! it was the long neck sticking up; and as for the rour
belly, it was jammed into the pocket of his pilot-coat.

"And that looks like the truth," said Keawe.

The next thing he did was to buy a corkscrew in a shop, and g
apart into a secret place in the fields. And there he tried to draw tl
cork, but as often as he put the screw in, out it came again, and tl
cork was as whole as ever.

"This is some new sort of cork," said Keawe, and all at once I
began to shake and sweat, for he was afraid of that bottle.

On his way back to the port-side he saw a shop where a man so
shells and clubs from the wild islands, old heathen deities, o
coined money, pictures from China and Japan, and all manner (
things that sailors bring in their sea-chests. And here he had a
idea. So he went in and offered the bottle for a hundred dollar
The man of the shop laughed at him at first, and offered him fiv
but, indeed, it was a curious bottle, such glass was never blown i
any human glassworks, so prettily the colors shone under the milk
white, and so strangely the shadow hovered in the midst; so, afte
he had disputed a while after the manner of his kind, the shopma
gave Keawe sixty silver dollars for the thing and set it on a shelf i
the midst of his window.

"Now," said Keawe, "I have sold that for sixty which I bougl
for fifty. I shall know the truth upon another point."

So he went back on board his ship, and when he opened his ches
there was the bottle, come more quickly than himself. Now Keaw
had a mate on board whose name was Lopaka.

"What ails you?" said Lopaka, "that you stare in your chest?"

They were alone in the ship's forecastle, and Keawe bound hir
to secrecy, and told all.

"This is a very strange affair," said Lopaka; "and I fear you wil
be in trouble about this bottle. But there is one point very clear—
that you are sure of the trouble, and you had better have the profi
in the bargain. Make up your mind what you want with it; give th
order, and if it is done as you desire, I will buy the bottle myself
for I have an idea of my own to get a schooner, and go tradin;
through the islands."

"That is not my idea," said Keawe; "but to have a beautifu

use and garden on the Kona Coast, where I was born, the sun ining in at the door, flowers in the garden, glass in the windows, ctures on the walls, and toys and fine carpets on the table, for all e world like the house I was in this day—only a story higher, and th balconies all about like the King's palace; and to live there thout care and make merry with my friends and relatives."

"Well," said Lopaka, "let us carry it back with us to Hawaii; d if all comes true, as you suppose, I will buy the bottle, as I said, d ask a schooner."

Upon that they were agreed, and it was not long before the ship turned to Honolulu, carrying Keawe and Lopaka, and the bottle. hey were scarce come ashore when they met a friend upon the each, who began at once to condole with Keawe.

"I do not know what I am to be condoled about," said Keawe.

"Is it possible you have not heard," said the friend, "your uncle— at good old man—is dead, and your cousin—that beautiful boy— as drowned at sea?"

Keawe was filled with sorrow, and, beginning to weep and to ment, he forgot about the bottle. But Lopaka was thinking to mself, and presently, when Keawe's grief was a little abated, "I ve been thinking," said Lopaka, "had not your uncle lands in awaii, in the district of Kaü?"

"No," said Keawe; "not in Kaü: they are on the mountain side -a little be-south Hookena."

"These lands will now be yours?" asked Lopaka.

"And so they will," says Keawe, and began again to lament for s relatives.

"No," said Lopaka, "do not lament at present. I have a thought my mind. How if this should be the doing of the bottle? For here the place ready for your house."

"If this be so," cried Keawe, "it is a very ill way to serve me by lling my relatives. But it may be, indeed; for it was in just such a ation that I saw the house with my mind's eye."

"The house, however, is not yet built," said Lopaka.

"No, nor like to be!" said Keawe; "for though my uncle has some ffee and ava and bananas, it will not be more than will keep me in mfort; and the rest of that land is the black lava."

"Let us go to the lawyer," said Lopaka; "I have still this idea in y mind."

Now, when they came to the lawyer's, it appeared Keawe's uncle d grown monstrous rich in the last days, and there was a fund of oney.

"And here is the money for the house!" cried Lopaka.

"If you are thinking of a new house," said the lawyer, "here is t
card of a new architect of whom they tell me great things."

"Better and better!" cried Lopaka. "Here is all made plain
us. Let us continue to obey orders."

So they went to the architect, and he had drawings of houses
his table.

"You want something out of the way?" said the architect. "He
do you like this?" and he handed a drawing to Keawe.

Now, when Keawe set eyes on the drawing, he cried out alou
for it was the picture of his thought exactly drawn.

"I am in for this house," thought he. "Little as I like the way
comes to me, I am in for it now, and I may as well take the go
along with the evil."

So he told the architect all that he wished; and he asked the m
plainly for how much he would undertake the whole affair.

The architect put many questions, and took his pen and made
computation; and when he had done he named the very sum th
Keawe had inherited.

Lopaka and Keawe looked at one another and nodded.

"It is quite clear," thought Keawe, "that I am to have this hous
whether or no. It comes from the devil, and I fear I will get litt
good by that; and of one thing I am sure, I will make no mo
wishes as long as I have this bottle. But with the house I am saddle
and I may as well take the good along with the evil."

The house was built on the mountain side, visible to ships. Abov
the forest ran up into the clouds of rain; below, the black lava fe
in cliffs, where the kings of old lay buried. A garden bloomed abo
that house with every hue of flowers; and there was an orchard
papaia on the one hand and an orchard of breadfruit on the othe
and right in front, toward the sea, a ship's mast had been rigged
and bore a flag. As for the house, it was three stories high, wi
great chambers and broad balconies on each. The windows were
glass, so excellent that it was as clear as water and as bright as da
All manner of furniture adorned the chambers. Pictures hung up
the wall in golden frames—pictures of ships, and men fighting, ar
of the most beautiful women, and of singular places; nowhere in t
world are there pictures of so bright a color as those Keawe foun
hanging in his house. As for the knick-knacks, they were extraord
narily fine: chiming clocks and musical boxes, little men with no
ding heads, books filled with pictures, weapons of price from a
quarters of the world, and the most elegant puzzles to entertain t

isure of a solitary man. And as no one would care to live in such
ıambers, only to walk through and view them, the balconies were
ıade so broad that a whole town might have lived upon them in
elight; and Keawe knew not which to prefer, whether the back
orch, where you got the land breeze and looked upon the orchards
ınd the flowers, or the front balcony, where you could drink the
ind of the sea, and look down the steep wall of the mountain and
ıe the schooners plying up the coast for wood and ava and bananas.

When they had viewed all, Keawe and Lopaka sat on the porch.

"Well," asked Lopaka, "is it all as you designed?"

"Words cannot utter it," said Keawe. "It is better than I dreamed,
ınd I am sick with satisfaction."

"There is but one thing to consider," said Lopaka, "all this may
ıe quite natural, and the bottle imp have nothing whatever to say to
. If I were to buy the bottle, and got no schooner after all, I should
ave put my hand in the fire for nothing. I gave you my word, I
now; but yet I think you would not grudge me one more proof."

"I have sworn I would take no more favors," said Keawe. "I
ave gone already deep enough."

"This is no favor I am thinking of," replied Lopaka. "It is only to
ıe the imp himself. There is nothing to be gained by that, and so
ıothing to be ashamed of, and yet, if I once saw him, I should be
ıure of the whole matter. So indulge me so far, and let me see the
ınp; and, after that, here is the money in my hand, and I will
ıuy it."

"There is only one thing I am afraid of," said Keawe. "The imp
ıay be very ugly to view, and if you once set eyes upon him you
ıight be very undesirous of the bottle."

"I am a man of my word," said Lopaka. "And here is the money
ıetwixt us."

"Very well," replied Keawe, "I have a curiosity myself. So come,
ıt us have one look at you, Mr. Imp."

Now as soon as that was said, the imp looked out of the bottle,
ınd in again, swift as a lizard; and there sat Keawe and Lopaka
ıurned to stone. The night had quite come, before either found a
hought to say or voice to say it with; and then Lopaka pushed the
ıoney over and took the bottle.

"I am a man of my word," said he, "and had need to be so, or I
ould not touch this bottle with my foot. Well, I shall get my
chooner and a dollar or two for my pocket; and then I will be rid
ıf this devil as fast as I can. For to tell you the plain truth, the look
ıf him has cast me down."

So Lopaka went down the mountain; and Keawe stood in 1 front balcony, and listened to the clink of the horse's shoes, a watched the lantern go shining down the path, and along the cliff caves where the old dead are buried; and all the time he trembl and clasped his hands, and prayed for his friend, and gave glory God that he himself was escaped out of that trouble.

But the next day came very brightly, and that new house of 1 was so delightful to behold that he forgot his terrors. One day fo lowed another, and Keawe dwelt there in perpetual joy. He had 1 place on the back porch; it was there he ate and lived, and read t stories in the Honolulu newspapers; but when any one came by th would go in and view the chambers and the pictures. And the fan of the house went far and wide. As for Keawe himself, he could n walk in the chambers without singing; and when ships sailed 1 upon the sea, he would fly his colors on the mast.

So time went by, until one day Keawe went upon a visit as far Kailua to certain of his friends. A little beyond Honaunau, lookii far ahead, he was aware of a woman bathing in the edge of the se: and she seemed a well-grown girl, but he thought no more of Then he saw her white shift flutter as she put it on, and then her r holoku; and by the time he came abreast of her she was done wi her toilet, and had come up from the sea, and stood by the trac side in her red holoku, and she was all freshened with the bath, ar her eyes shone and were kind. Now Keawe no sooner beheld h than he drew rein.

"I thought I knew every one in this country," said he. "Ho comes it that I do not know you?"

"I am Kokua, daughter of Kiano," said the girl, "and I have ju returned from Oahu. Who are you?"

"I will tell you who I am in a little," said Keawe, dismountin from his horse, "but not now. For I have a thought in my mind, an if you knew who I was, you might have heard of me, and would no give me a true answer. But tell me, first of all, one thing: are yo married?"

At this Kokua laughed out aloud. "It is you who asks questions, she said. "Are you married yourself?"

"Indeed, Kokua, I am not," replied Keawe, "and never though to be until this hour. But here is the plain truth. I have met yo here at the road-side, and I saw your eyes, which are like the star: and my heart went to you as swift as a bird. And so now, if you want none of me, say so, and I will go on to my own place; but if yo think me no worse than any other young man, say so, too, and I wi

n aside to your father's for the night, and tomorrow I will talk
th the good man."

Kokua said never a word, but they looked at the sea and laughed.

"Kokua," said Keawe, "if you say nothing, I will take that for
e good answer; so let us be stepping to your father's door."

The next day he had a word with Kiano, and found the girl alone.
is was the wooing of Keawe. Things had gone fast, but they had
ne far also, and the thought of Keawe rang in the maiden's head;
e heard his voice in the breach of the surf upon the lava, and for
is young man that she had seen but twice she would have left
ther and mother and her native islands. As for Keawe himself, his
rse flew up the path of the mountain under the cliff of tombs,
d the sound of the hoofs, and the sound of Keawe singing to him-
lf for pleasure, echoed in the caverns of the dead. He came to the
right House, and still he was singing. He sat and ate in the broad
lcony, and his Chinese servant wondered, to hear how he sang
tween the mouthfuls. The sun went down into the sea, and the
ght came; and Keawe walked the balconies by lamplight, high
the mountains, and the voice of his singing startled men on ships.

"Here am I now upon my high place," he said to himself. "Life
ay be no better; this is the mountain top; and all shelves about
e towards the worse. For the first time I will light up the cham-
rs, and bathe in my fine bath with the hot water and the cold, and
eep above in the bed of my bridal chamber."

So the Chinaman had word, and he must rise from sleep and light
e furnaces; and as he walked below, beside the boilers, he heard
is master singing and rejoicing above him in the lighted chambers.
Then the water began to be hot the Chinaman cried to his master;
d Keawe went into the bathroom; and the Chinaman heard him
ng as he filled the marble basin; and heard him sing, and the
nging broken, as he undressed; until of a sudden, the song ceased.
he Chinaman listened, and listened; he called up the house to
eawe to ask if all were well, and Keawe answered him "Yes,"
nd bade him go to bed; but there was no more singing in the
right House; and all night long the Chinaman heard his master's
eet go round and round the balconies without repose.

Now, the truth of it was this: as Keawe undressed for his bath, he
pied upon his flesh a patch like a patch of lichen on a rock, and
t was then that he stopped singing. For he knew the likeness of
hat patch, and knew that he was fallen in the leprosy.

Now you are to observe what sort of a man Keawe was, for he
night have dwelt there in the Bright House for years, and no one

been the wiser of his sickness; but he reckoned nothing of that, he must lose Kokua. And again he might have wed Kokua even he was; and so many would have done, because they have the so of pigs; but Keawe loved the maid manfully, and he would do h no hurt and bring her in no danger.

A little beyond the midst of the night, there came in his mind t recollection of that bottle. He called to memory the day when t devil had looked forth; and at the thought ice ran in his veins.

"A dreadful thing is the bottle," thought Keawe, "and dreadf is the imp, and it is a dreadful thing to risk the flames of hell. B what other hope have I to cure my sickness or to wed Koku. What!" he thought, "would I beard the devil once, only to get n a house, and not face him again to win Kokua?"

Thereupon he called to mind it was the next day the ship wei by on her return to Honolulu. "There must I go first," he though "and see Lopaka. For the best hope that I have now is to find th. same bottle I was so pleased to be rid of."

(In Honolulu, he found that the bottle had changed hands man times, and he traced it with difficulty.)

But at last he was recommended to a man in Beritania Stree When he came to the door, about the hour of the evening meal, the were the usual marks of the new house, and the young garden, an the electric light shining in the windows; but when the owne came, a shock of hope and fear ran through Keawe; for here was young man, white as a corpse, and black about the eyes, the hai shedding from his head, and such a look in his countenance as man may have when he is waiting for the gallows.

"Here it is, to be sure," thought Keawe, and so with this man h noways veiled his errand. "I am come to buy the bottle," said he.

At the word, the young man of Beritania Street reeled against th wall.

"The bottle!" he gasped. "To buy the bottle!"

"Yes," he said, "I am come to buy the bottle. What is the pric by now?"

At that word the young man looked upon Keawe like a ghost.

"The price," says he; "the price! You do not know the price?

"It is for that I am asking you," returned Keawe. "But why ar you so much concerned? Is there anything wrong about the price?

"It has dropped a great deal in value since your time, Mr Keawe," said the young man, stammering.

"Well, well I shall have the less to pay for it," says Keawe. "How much did it cost you?"

The young man was as white as a sheet. "Two cents," said he.

"What?" cried Keawe, "two cents? Why, then, you can only sell for one. And he who buys it——" The words died upon Keawe's tongue; he who bought it could never sell it again, the bottle and the bottle imp must abide with him until he died, and when he died must carry him to the red end of hell.

The young man of Beritania Street fell upon his knees. "For God's sake, buy it!" he cried. "You can have all my fortune in the bargain. I was mad when I bought it at that price. I had embezzled money at my store; I was lost else; I must have gone to jail."

"Poor creature," said Keawe, "you would risk your soul upon so desperate an adventure, and to avoid the proper punishment of your own disgrace; and you think I could hesitate with love in front of me. Give me the bottle, and the change which I make sure you have all ready. Here is a five-cent piece."

It was as Keawe supposed; the young man had the change ready in a drawer; the bottle changed hands, and Keawe's fingers no sooner clasped upon the stalk than he had breathed his wish to be a clean man. And, sure enough, when he got to his room, and stripped himself before a glass, his flesh was whole like an infant's. And here was the strange thing: he had no sooner seen this miracle than his mind was changed within him, and he cared naught for the leprosy, and little enough for Kokua; and had but the one thought, that here he was bound to the bottle imp for time and for eternity, and had no better hope but to be a cinder for ever in the flames of hell. Away ahead of him he saw them blaze with his mind's eye, and his soul shrank, and darkness fell upon the light.

When Keawe came to himself a little, he was aware it was the night when the band played at the hotel. Of a sudden the band played a song that he had sung with Kokua, and at the strain courage returned to him.

"It is done now," he thought, "and once more let me take the good along with the evil."

So it befell that as soon as it could be managed he was wedded to Kokua, and carried her up the mountain side to the Bright House.

Now when they were together Keawe's heart was stilled; but as soon as he was alone he fell into a brooding horror, and heard the flames crackle, and saw the red fire burn in the bottomless pit. The girl, indeed, had come to him wholly; her heart leaped in her side at sight of him, her hand clung to his; and she was so fashioned,

from the hair upon her head to the nails upon her toes, that no
could see her without joy. She was pleasant in her nature. She ha
the good word always. Full of song she was, and went to and fr
in the Bright House, the brightest thing in its three stories, carc
ling like the birds. And Keawe beheld and heard her with deligh
and then must shrink upon one side, and weep and groan to thin
upon the price that he had paid for her; and then he must dry h
eyes, and wash his face, and go and sit with her on the broad ba
conies, joining in her songs, and, with a sick spirit, answering h
smiles.

(However, love has sharp eyes. Kokua saw his wretchedness an
believed that she was at fault and had failed to make him happy. O
day Keawe came upon her weeping bitterly, and to comfort her, to
her the true source of his trouble. Kokua suggested to him that ther
were countries with coins smaller than a cent. They went to Frenc
Tahiti, where five centimes make a cent, and as soon as they coul
speak the language, they began to try to sell the bottle.)

But it was not easy to persuade people that you were in earnes
when you offered to sell them for four centimes the spring of healt
and riches inexhaustible. It was necessary besides to explain th
dangers of the bottle; and either people disbelieved the whole thin
and laughed, or they thought the more of the darker part, becam
overcast with gravity, and drew away from Keawe and Koku
as from persons who had dealings with the devil.

Depression fell upon their spirits. They would sit at night, afte
a day's weariness, and not exchange one word.

One night Kokua awoke. Keawe was gone. She felt in the be
and his place was cold. Then fear fell upon her, and she sat up. /
little moonshine filtered through the shutters. The room was brigh
and she could spy the bottle on the floor. Outside it blew high, th
great trees of the avenue cried aloud, and the fallen leaves rattle
in the verandah. In the midst of this Kokua was aware of anothe
sound; whether of a beast or of man she could scarce tell, but it wa
as sad as death, and cut her to the soul. Softly she arose, set th
door ajar, and looked forth into the moonlit yard. There, under th
bananas, lay Keawe, his mouth in the dust, and as he lay he moane

It was Kokua's first thought to run forward and console him; he
second potently withheld her. Keawe had borne himself before hi
wife like a brave man; it became her little in the hour of weaknes
to intrude upon his shame. With the thought she drew back into
the house.

"Heaven," she thought, "how careless have I been—how weak! is he, not I, that stands in this eternal peril; it was he, not I, that ok the curse upon his soul. It is for my sake, and for the love of a eature of so little worth and such poor help, that he now beholds close to him the flames of hell. Am I so dull of spirit that never ll now I surmised my duty, or have I seen it before and turned ide? A love for a love, and let mine be equalled with Keawe's! soul for a soul, and be it mine to perish!"

She was a deft woman with her hands, and was soon apparelled. e took in her hands the change—the precious centimes they kept er at their side. When she was forth in the avenue clouds came on e wind, and the moon was blackened. The town slept, and she ew not whither to turn till she heard one coughing in the shadow the trees.

"Old man," said Kokua, "what do you here abroad in the cold ght?"

The old man could scarce express himself for coughing, but she ade out that he was old and poor, and a stranger in the island.

"Sit down here," said Kokua, "and let me tell you a tale." And e told him the story of Keawe from the beginning to the end.

"And now," said she, "I am his wife, whom he bought with his ul's welfare. And what should I do? If I went to him myself and ffered to buy it, he would refuse. But if you go, he will sell it agerly; I will await you here; you will buy it for four centimes, nd I will buy it again for three. And the Lord strengthen a poor irl!"

"If you meant falsely," said the old man, "I think God would rike you dead."

"He would!" cried Kokua. "Be sure he would. I could not be so eacherous; God would not suffer it."

"Give me the four centimes and await me here," said the old man.

Now, when Kokua stood alone in the street, her spirit died. The ind roared in the trees, and it seemed to her the rushing of the ames of hell; the shadows towered in the light of the street lamp, nd they seemed to her the snatching hands of evil ones. If she had ad the strength, she must have run away, and if she had had the reath, she must have screamed aloud; but, in truth, she could do either, and stood and trembled in the avenue, like an affrighted hild.

Then she saw the old man returning, and he had the bottle in his and.

"I have done your bidding," said he, "I left your husband weep-

ing like a child; tonight he will sleep easy." And he held the bott
forth.

"Before you give it me," Kokua panted, "take the good with t
evil—ask to be delivered from your cough."

"I am an old man," replied the other, "and too near the gate
the grave to take a favor from the devil. But what is this? W
do you not take the bottle? Do you hesitate?" The old man look
upon Kokua kindly. "Poor child!" said he, "you fear: your so
misgives you. Well, let me keep it. I am old, and can never mo
be happy in this world, and as for the next——"

"Give it me!" gasped Kokua. "There is your money. Do y
think I am so base as that? Give me the bottle."

"God bless you, child," said the old man.

Kokua concealed the bottle under her holoku, said farewell to t
old man, and walked off along the avenue, she cared not whithe
For all roads were now the same to her, and led equally to hell.

Near day she came to her mind again, and returned to the hous
It was even as the old man said—Keawe slumbered like a chil
Kokua stood and gazed upon his face.

"Now, my husband," said she, "it is your turn to sleep. When yo
wake it will be your turn to sing and laugh. But for poor Koku
alas! that meant no evil—for poor Kokua no more sleep, no mo
singing, no more delight, whether in earth or heaven."

With that she lay down in the bed by his side, and her misery wa
so extreme that she fell in a deep slumber instantly.

Late in the morning her husband woke her and gave her the goo
news. It seemed he was silly with delight, for he paid no heed to h
distress, ill though she dissembled it. The words stuck in her mout
it mattered not; Keawe did the speaking. She ate not a bite, b
who was to observe it? For Keawe cleared the dish. Kokua sa
and heard him, like some strange thing in a dream; there were time
when she forgot or doubted, and put her hands to her brow; t
know herself doomed and hear her husband babble, seemed s
monstrous.

"O my husband!" said Kokua. "Is it not a terrible thing to sav
oneself by the eternal ruin of another? It seems to me I could n
laugh. I would be humbled. I would be filled with melancholy.
would pray for the poor holder."

Then Keawe, because he felt the truth of what she said, gre
angry. "Heighty-teighty!" cried he. "You may be filled wit
melancholy if you please. It is not the mind of a good wife. If yo
thought at all of me, you would sit shamed."

Thereupon he went out, and Kokua was alone.

What chance had she to sell that bottle at two centimes? None, she perceived. And here—on the morrow of her sacrifice—was her husband leaving and blaming her.

She would not even try to profit by what time she had, but sat in the house, and now had the bottle out and viewed it with unutterable fear, and now, with loathing, hid it out of sight.

By and by, Keawe came back, and would have her take a drive.

"My husband, I am ill," she said. "I am out of heart. Excuse me, I can take no pleasure."

Then was Keawe more wroth than ever. With her, because he thought she was brooding over the case of the old man; and with himself, because he thought she was right and was ashamed to be so happy.

"This is your truth," cried he, "and this your affection! Your husband is just saved from eternal ruin, which he encountered for the love of you—and you can take no pleasure! Kokua, you have a disloyal heart."

He went forth again furious, and wandered in the town all day. He met friends, and drank with them; they hired a carriage and drove into the country, and there drank again.

Now there was an old brutal sailor drinking with him, one that had been a boatswain of a whaler—a runaway, a digger in gold mines, a convict in prisons. He had a low mind and a foul mouth; he loved to drink and to see others drunken; and he pressed the glass upon Keawe. Soon there was no more money in the company.

"Here, you!" says the boatswain, "you are rich, you have been always saying. You have a bottle or some foolishness."

"Yes," says Keawe, "I am rich; I will go back and get some money from my wife, who keeps it."

"That's a bad idea, mate," said the boatswain. "Never you trust a petticoat with dollars. They're all as false as water; you keep an eye on her."

Now this word struck in Keawe's mind; for he was muddled with what he had been drinking.

"I should not wonder but she was false, indeed," thought he. "Why else should she be so cast down at my release? But I will show her I am not the man to be fooled. I will catch her in the act."

Accordingly, when they were back in town, Keawe bade the boatswain wait for him at the corner and went forward up the avenue alone to the door of his house. The night had come again; there was a light within, but never a sound; and Keawe crept about the corner, opened the back door softly, and looked in.

There was Kokua on the floor, the lamp at her side; before her

was a milk-white bottle, with a round belly and a long neck; a
as she viewed it, Kokua wrung her hands.

A long time Keawe stood and looked in the doorway. At first
was struck stupid; and then fear fell upon him that the bargain h:
been made amiss, and the bottle had come back to him as it car
at San Francisco; and at that his knees were loosened, and t.
fumes of the wine departed from his head like mists off a river
the morning. And then he had another thought; and it was
strange one, that made his cheeks to burn.

"I must make sure of this," thought he.

So he closed the door, and went softly round the corner agai
and then came noisily in, as though he were but now returned. An
lo! by the time he opened the front door no bottle was to be seer
and Kokua sat in a chair and started up like one awakened out
sleep.

"I have been drinking all day and making merry," said Keaw
"I have been with good companions, and now I only came back f
money, and return to drink and carouse with them again."

Both his face and voice were as stern as judgment, but Kok
was too troubled to observe.

"You do well to use your own, my husband," said she, and h
words trembled.

"Oh, I do well in all things," said Keawe, and he went straight
the chest and took out money. But he looked besides in the corn
where they kept the bottle, and there was no bottle there.

At that the chest heaved upon the floor like a sea-billow, and t
house span about him like a wreath of smoke, for he saw she w:
lost now, and there was no escape. "It is what I feared," he though
"It was she who bought it."

And then he came to himself a little and rose up; but the swe:
streamed on his face as thick as the rain and as cold as the wel
water.

"Kokua," said he, "I said to you today what ill became me. No
I return to my jolly companions," and at that he laughed a litt
quietly. "I will take more pleasure in the cup if you forgive me."

She clasped his knees in a moment, she kissed his knees wit
flowing tears.

"Oh," she cried, "I ask but a kind word!"

"Let us never think hardly of the other," said Keawe, and wa
gone out of the house.

Now, the money that Keawe had taken was only some of tha
store of centime pieces they had laid in at their arrival. It was ver
sure he had no mind to be drinking. His wife had given her sou

for him, now he must give his for hers; no other thought was in the world with him.

At the corner, there was the boatswain waiting.

"My wife has the bottle," said Keawe, "and, unless you help me to recover it, there can be no more money and no more liquor tonight."

"You do not mean to say you are serious about that bottle?" cried the boatswain.

"There is the lamp," said Keawe. "Do I look as if I was jesting?"

"That is so," said the boatswain. "You look as serious as a ghost."

"Well, then," said Keawe, "here are two centimes; you just go to my wife in the house, and offer her these for the bottle, which (if I am not much mistaken) she will give you instantly. Bring it to me here, and I will buy it back from you for one; for that is the law with this bottle that it still must be sold for a less sum. But whatever you do, never breathe a word to her that you have come from me."

"Mate, I wonder are you making a fool of me?" asked the boatswain.

"It will do you no harm if I am," returned Keawe.

"That is so, mate," said the boatswain.

"And if you doubt me," added Keawe, "you can try. As soon as you are clear of the house, wish to have your pocket full of money, or a bottle of the best rum, or what you please, and you will see the virtue of the thing."

"Very well, Kanaka," says the boatswain. "I will try; but if you are having your fun out of me, I will take my fun out of you with a belaying-pin."

So the whaler-man went off up the avenue; and Keawe stood and waited. It was near the same spot where Kokua had waited the night before; but Keawe was more resolved, and never faltered in his purpose; only his soul was bitter with despair.

It seemed a long time he had to wait before he heard a voice singing in the darkness of the avenue. He knew the voice to be the boatswain's; but it was strange how drunken it appeared upon a sudden.

Next the man himself came stumbling into the light of the lamp. He had the devil's bottle buttoned in his coat; another bottle was in his hand; and even as he came in view he raised it to his mouth and drank.

"You have it," said Keawe. "I see that."

"Hands off!" cried the boatswain, jumping back. "Take a step near me, and I'll smash your mouth. You thought you could make a catspaw of me, did you?"

"What do you mean?" cried Keawe.

"Mean?" cried the boatswain. "This is a pretty good bottle, this is; that's what I mean. How I got it for two centimes I can't make out; but I am sure you sha'nt have it for one."

"You mean you won't sell?" gasped Keawe.

"No, sir," cried the boatswain. "But I'll give you a drink of the rum, if you like."

"I tell you," said Keawe, "the man who has that bottle goes to hell."

"I reckon I'm going anyway," returned the sailor; "and this bottle's the best thing to go with I've struck yet. No, sir!" he cried again, "this is my bottle now, and you can go and fish for another."

"Can this be true?" Keawe cried. "For your own sake, I beseech you, sell it me!"

"I don't value any of your talk," replied the boatswain. "You thought I was a flat, now you see I'm not; and there's an end. If you won't have a swallow of the rum, I'll have one myself. Here's your health, and good-night to you!"

So off he went down the avenue towards town, and there goes the bottle out of the story.

But Keawe ran to Kokua light as the wind; and great was their joy that night; and great, since then, has been the peace of all their days in the Bright House.

HIS WEDDED WIFE

Rudyard Kipling (England)

His Wedded Wife was written when Kipling was a young reporter on a newspaper in India. It is one of the earliest of his long series of soldier's stories of life in the Orient—some of them as humorous as others are dramatic or pathetic. Many of these tales are written in the cockney dialect of the uneducated London soldier, which Kipling has made famous both in his *Soldiers Three* stories and in his *Barrack Room Ballads*. The hero of the following yarn has just left military school to join his regiment in India.

❊　❊　❊

Shakespeare says something about worms turning if you tread on them too severely. The safest plan is never to tread on a worm

—not even on the last new subaltern [1] from Home,[2] with his buttons hardly out of their tissue paper, and the red of sappy English beef in his cheeks. This is the story of the worm that turned. For the sake of brevity, we will call Henry Augustus Ramsay Faizanne, "The Worm," although he really was an exceedingly pretty boy, without a hair on his face, and with a waist like a girl's, when he came out to the Second "Shikarris" and was made unhappy in several ways. The "Shikarris" are a high-caste regiment, and you must be able to do things well—play a banjo, or ride more than little, or sing, or act—to get on with them.

The Worm did nothing except fall off his pony, and knock chips out of gate-posts with his trap.[3] Even that became monotonous after a time. He objected to whist, cut the cloth at billiards, sang out of tune, kept very much to himself, and wrote to his Mamma and sisters at Home. Four of these five things were vices which the "Shikarris" objected to and set themselves to eradicate. Every one knows how subalterns are, by brother-subalterns, softened and not permitted to be ferocious. It is good and wholesome, and does no one any harm, unless tempers are lost; and then there is trouble.

The "Shikarris" shikarred The Worm very much, and he bore everything without winking. He was so good and so anxious to learn, and flushed so pink, that his education was cut short, and he was left to his own devices by every one except the Senior Subaltern [4] who continued to make life a burden to The Worm. The Senior Subaltern meant no harm; but his chaff was coarse, and he didn't quite understand where to stop. He had been waiting too long for his Company; [5] and that always sours a man. Also he was in love, which made him worse.

One day, after he had borrowed The Worm's trap for a lady who never existed, had used it himself all the afternoon, had sent a note to The Worm, purporting to come from the lady, and was telling the Mess all about it, The Worm rose in his place and said, in his quiet, lady-like voice: "That was a very pretty sell; but I'll lay you a month's pay to a month's pay when you get your step,[6] that I work a sell on you that you'll remember for the rest of your days, and the Regiment after you when you're dead or broke." The Worm wasn't angry in the least, and the rest of the Mess shouted.

---

[1] *subaltern:* an army officer below captain.   [2] *Home:* England.
[3] *trap:* a light buggy.
[4] *Senior Subaltern:* the senior first lieutenant in the regiment.
[5] *for his Company:* for his promotion to captain, when he would command a company.
[6] *step:* promotion.

Then the Senior Subaltern looked at The Worm from the boot upwards, and down again and said: "Done, Baby." The Worm took the rest of the Mess to witness that the bet had been taken, and retired into a book with a sweet smile.

Two months passed, and the Senior Subaltern still educated The Worm, who began to move about a little more as the hot weather came on. I have said that the Senior Subaltern was in love. The curious thing is that a girl was in love with the Senior Subaltern. Though the Colonel said awful things, and the Majors snorted, and married Captains looked unutterable wisdom, and the juniors scoffed, those two were engaged.

The Senior Subaltern was so pleased with getting his Company and his acceptance at the same time that he forgot to bother The Worm. The girl was a pretty girl, and had money of her own. She does not come into this story at all.

One night, at the beginning of the hot weather, all the Mess, except The Worm, who had gone to his own room to write Home letters, were sitting on the platform outside the Mess House. The Band had finished playing, but no one wanted to go in. And the Captains' wives were there also. The folly of a man in love is unlimited. The Senior Subaltern had been holding forth on the merits of the girl he was engaged to, and the ladies were purring approval, while the men yawned, when there was a rustle of skirts in the dark, and a tired, faint voice lifted itself.

"Where's my husband?"

I do not wish in the least to reflect on the morality of the "Shikarris"; but it is on record that four men jumped up as if they had been shot. Three of them were married men. Perhaps they were afraid that their wives had come from Home unbeknownst. The fourth said that he had acted on the impulse of the moment. He explained this afterwards.

Then the voice cried "Oh, Lionel!" Lionel was the Senior Subaltern's name. A woman came into the little circle of light by the candles on the peg-tables, stretching out her hands to the dark where the Senior Subaltern was, and sobbing. We rose to our feet, feeling that things were going to happen and ready to believe the worst. In this bad, small world of ours, one knows so little of the life of the next man—which, after all, is entirely his own concern— that one is not surprised when a crash comes. Anything might turn up any day for any one. Perhaps the Senior Subaltern had been trapped in his youth. Men are crippled that way occasionally. We didn't know; we wanted to hear; and the Captains' wives were as anxious as we. If he had been trapped, he was to be excused; for the woman from nowhere, in the dusty shoes and gray travelling dress, was very lovely, with black hair and great eyes full of tears. She was tall, with a fine figure, and her voice had a running sob in it pitiful to hear. As soon as the Senior Subaltern stood up, she threw her arms round his neck, and called him "my darling," and said she could not bear waiting alone in England, and his letters were so short, and cold, and she was his to the end of the world, and would he forgive her? This did not sound quite like a lady's way of speaking. It was too demonstrative.

Things seemed black indeed, and the Captains' wives peered under their eyebrows at the Senior Subaltern, and the Colonel's face set like the Day of Judgment framed in gray bristles, and no one spoke for a while.

Next the Colonel said, very shortly: "Well, Sir?" and the woman sobbed afresh. The Senior Subaltern was half choked with the arms round his neck, but he gasped out: "It's a d—d lie! I never had a wife in my life!" "Don't swear," said the Colonel. "Come into the Mess. We must sift this clear somehow," and he sighed to himself, for he believed in his "Shikarris," did the Colonel.

We trooped into the ante-room, under the full lights, and there we saw how beautiful the woman was. She stood up in the middle of us all, sometimes choking with crying, then hard and proud, and then holding out her arms to the Senior Subaltern. It was like the fourth act of a tragedy. She told us how the Senior Subaltern had married her when he was Home on leave eighteen months before; and she seemed to know all that we knew, and more too, of his people and his past life. He was white and ashy gray, trying now and again to break into the torrent of her words; and we, noting how lovely she was and what a criminal he looked, esteemed him a beast of the worst kind. We felt sorry for him, though.

I shall never forget the indictment of the Senior Subaltern by his wife. Nor will he. It was so sudden, rushing out of the dark, unannounced, into our dull lives. The Captains' wives stood back; but their eyes were alight, and you could see that they had already convicted and sentenced the Senior Subaltern. The Colonel seemed five years older. One Major was shading his eyes with his hand and watching the woman from underneath it. Another was chewing his mustache and smiling quietly as if he were witnessing a play. Full in the open space in the center, by the whist-tables, the Senior Subaltern's terrier was hunting for fleas. I remember all this as clearly as though a photograph were in my hand. I remember the

look of horror on the Senior Subaltern's face. It was rather like
seeing a man hanged; but much more interesting. Finally, the
woman wound up by saying that the Senior Subaltern carried a
double F.M. in tattoo on his left shoulder. We all knew that, and to
our innocent minds it seemed to clinch the matter. But one of the
Bachelor Majors said very politely: "I presume that your marriage
certificate would be more to the purpose?"

That roused the woman. She stood up and sneered at the Senior
Subaltern for a cur, and abused the Major and the Colonel and all
the rest. Then she wept, and then she pulled a paper from her
breast, saying imperially: "Take that! And let my husband—my
lawfully wedded husband—read it aloud—if he dare!"

There was a hush, and the men looked into each other's eyes as
the Senior Subaltern came forward in a dazed and dizzy way, and
took the paper. We were wondering, as we stared, whether there
was anything against any one of us that might turn up later on.
The Senior Subaltern's throat was dry; but, as he ran his eye over
the paper, he broke out into a hoarse cackle of relief, and said to the
woman: "You young blackguard!"

But the woman had fled through a door, and on the paper was
written: "This is to certify that I, The Worm, have paid in full my
debts to the Senior Subaltern, and, further, that the Senior Subaltern is my debtor, by agreement on the 23d of February, as by the
Mess attested, to the extent of one month's Captain's pay, in the
lawful currency of the India Empire."

Then a deputation set off for The Worm's quarters and found
him, betwixt and between, unlacing his stays, with the hat, wig,
serge dress, etc., on the bed. He came over as he was, and the
"Shikarris" shouted till the Gunners' Mess sent over to know if
they might have a share of the fun. I think we were all, except the
Colonel and the Senior Subaltern, a little disappointed that the
scandal had come to nothing. But that is human nature. There
could be no two words about The Worm's acting. It leaned as near
to a nasty tragedy as anything this side of a joke can. When most
of the Subalterns sat upon him with sofa-cushions to find out why
he had not said that acting was his strong point, he answered very
quietly: "I don't think you ever asked me. I used to act at Home
with my sisters." But no acting with girls could account for The
Worm's display that night. Personally, I think it was in bad taste.
Besides being dangerous. There is no sort of use in playing with
fire, even for fun.

The "Shikarris" made him President of the Regimental Dra

matic Club; and, when the Senior Subaltern paid up his debt, which he did at once, The Worm sank the money in scenery and dresses. He was a good Worm; and the "Shikarris" are proud of him. The only drawback is that he has been christened "Mrs. Senior Subaltern"; and, as there are now two Mrs. Senior Subalterns in the Station, this is sometimes confusing to strangers.

TONY KYTES, THE ARCH DECEIVER

Thomas Hardy (England)

"I shall never forget Tony's face. 'Twas a little, round, firm, tight face, with a seam here and there left by the small-pox, but not enough to hurt his looks in a woman's eye, though he'd had it baddish when he was a boy. So very serious-looking and unsmiling 'a was, that young man, that it really seemed as if he couldn't laugh at all without great pain to his conscience. He looked very hard at a small speck in your eye when talking to 'ee. And there was no more sign of a whisker or beard on Tony Kytes's face than on the palm of my hand. He used to sing 'The Tailor's Breeches' with a religious manner, as if it were a hymn. He was quite the women's favorite, and in return for their likings he loved 'em in shoals.

"But in course of time Tony got fixed down to one in particular, Milly Richards—a nice, light, small, tender little thing; and it was soon said that they were engaged to be married. One Saturday he had been to market to do business for his father, and was driving home the wagon in the afternoon. When he reached the foot of the very hill we shall be going over in ten minutes, who should he see waiting for him at the top but Unity Sallet, a handsome girl, one of the young women he'd been very tender towards before he'd got engaged to Milly.

"As soon as Tony came up to her she said, 'My dear Tony, will you give me a lift home?'

"'That I will, darling,' said Tony. 'You don't suppose I could refuse 'ee?'

"She smiled a smile, and up she hopped, and on drove Tony.

"'Tony,' she says, in a sort of tender chide, 'why did ye desert me for that other one? In what is she better than I? I should have made 'ee a fine wife, and a more loving one, too. 'Tisn't girls that are so easily won at first that are the best. Think how long we've known each other—ever since we were children almost—now haven't we, Tony?'

" 'Yes, that we have,' says Tony, a-struck with the truth o't.

" 'And you've never seen anything in me to complain of, have ye, Tony? Now tell the truth to me.'

" 'I never have, upon my life,' says Tony.

" 'And—can you say I'm not pretty, Tony? Now look at me!'

"He let his eyes light upon her for a long while. 'I really can't,' says he. 'In fact, I never knowed you was so pretty before!'

" 'Prettier than she?'

"What Tony would have said to that nobody knows, for before he could speak, what should he see ahead, over the hedge past the turning, but a feather he knew well—the feather in Milly's hat— she to whom he had been thinking of putting the question as to giving out the banns that very week.

" 'Unity,' says he, as mild as he could, 'here's Milly coming. Now I shall catch it mightily if she sees 'ee riding here with me; and if you get down she'll be turning the corner in a moment, and, seeing 'ee in the road, she'll know we've been coming on together. Now, dearest Unity, will ye, to avoid all unpleasantness, which I know ye can't bear any more than I, will ye lie down in the back part of the wagon, and let me cover you over with the tarpaulin till Milly has passed? It will all be done in a minute. Do!—and I'll think over what we've said; and perhaps I shall put a loving question to you after all, instead of to Milly. 'Tisn't true that it is all settled between her and me.'

"Well, Unity Sallet agreed, and lay down at the back end of the wagon, and Tony covered her over, so that the wagon seemed to be empty but for the loose tarpaulin; and then he drove on to meet Milly.

" 'My dear Tony!' cries Milly, looking up with a little pout at him as he came near. 'How long you've been coming home! Just as if I didn't live at Upper Longpuddle at all! And I've come to meet you as you asked me to do, and to ride back with you, and talk over our future home—since you asked me, and I promised. But I shouldn't have come else, Mr. Tony!'

" 'Ay, my dear, I did ask ye—to be sure I did, now I think of it— but I had quite forgot it. To ride back with me, did you say, dear Milly?'

" 'Well, of course! What can I do else? Surely you don't want me to walk, now I've come all this way?'

" 'Oh, no, no! I was thinking you might be going on to town to meet your mother. I saw her there—and she looked as if she might be expecting 'ee.'

" 'Oh, no ; she's just home. She came across the fields, and so got back before you.'

" 'Ah ! I didn't know that,' says Tony. And there was no help for it but to take her up beside him.

"They talked on very pleasantly, and looked at the trees and beasts and birds and insects, and at the plowmen at work in the fields, till presently who should they see looking out of the upper window of a house that stood beside the road they were following but Hannah Jolliver, another young beauty of the place at that time, and the very first woman that Tony had fallen in love with—before Milly and before Unity, in fact—the one that he had almost arranged to marry instead of Milly. She was a much more dashing girl than Milly Richards, though he'd not thought much of her of late. The house Hannah was looking from was her aunt's.

" 'My dear Milly—my coming wife, as I may call 'ee,' says Tony in his modest way, and not so loud that Unity could overhear, 'I see a young woman looking from a window who I think may accost me. The fact is, Milly, she had a notion that I was wishing to marry her, and since she's discovered I've promised another, and prettier than she, I'm rather afeared of her temper if she sees us together. Now, Milly, would you do me a favor—my coming wife, as I may say ?'

" 'Certainly, dearest Tony,' says she.

" 'Then would ye creep under the tarpaulin just here in the front of the wagon, and hide there out of sight till we've passed the house ? She hasn't seen us yet. You see, we ought to live in peace and good-will since 'tis almost Christmas, and 'twill prevent angry passions rising, which we always should do.'

" 'I don't mind, to oblige you, Tony,' Milly said ; and though she didn't care much about doing it, she crept under, and crouched down just behind the seat, Unity being snug at the other end. So they drove on till they got near the roadside cottage. Hannah had soon seen him coming, and waited at the window, looking down upon him. She tossed her head a little disdainful and smiled off-hand.

" 'Well, aren't you going to be civil enough to ask me to ride home with you ?' she says, seeing that he was for driving past with a nod and a smile.

" 'Ah, to be sure ! What was I thinking of ?' said Tony, in a flut-ter. 'But you seem as if you was staying at your aunt's ?'

" 'No, I am not,' she said. 'Don't you see I have my bonnet and jacket on ? I have only called to see her on my way home. How can you be so stupid, Tony ?'

" 'In that case—ah—of course you must come along wi' me,' says Tony, feeling a dim sort of sweat rising up inside his clothes. And he reined in the horse, and waited till she'd come downstairs, and then helped her up beside him. He drove on again, his face as long as a face that was a round one by nature well could be.

"Hannah looked round sideways into his eyes. 'This is nice, isn't it, Tony?' she says. 'I like riding with you.'

"Tony looked back into her eyes. 'And I with you,' he said, after a while. In short, having considered her, he warmed up, and the more he looked at her the more he liked her, till he couldn't for the life of him think why he had ever said a word about marriage to Milly or Unity while Hannah Jolliver was in question. So they sat a little closer and closer, their feet upon the foot-board and their shoulders touching, and Tony thought over and over again how handsome Hannah was. He spoke tenderer and tenderer, and called her 'dear Hannah' in a whisper at last.

" 'You've settled it with Milly by this time, I suppose,' said she.

" 'N—no, not exactly.'

" 'What? How low you talk, Tony.'

" 'Yes—I've a kind of hoarseness. I said, not exactly.'

" 'I suppose you mean to?'

" 'Well, as to that—' His eyes rested on her face, and hers on his. He wondered how he could have been such a fool as not to follow up Hannah. 'My sweet Hannah!' he bursts out, taking her hand, not being really able to help it, and forgetting Milly and Unity and all the world besides. 'Settled it? I don't think I have!'

" 'Hark!' says Hannah.

" 'What?' says Tony, letting go her hand.

" 'Surely I heard a sort of little screaming squeak under that tar-cloth? Why, you've been carrying corn, and there's mice in this wagon, I declare!' She began to haul up the tails of her gown.

" 'Oh, no; 'tis the axle,' said Tony, in an assuring way. 'It do go like that sometimes in dry weather.'

" 'Perhaps it was. . . . Well, now, to be quite honest, dear Tony, do you like her better than me? Because—because, although I've held off so independent, I'll own at last that I do like 'ee, Tony, to tell the truth; and I wouldn't say no if you asked me—you know what.'

"Tony was so won over by this pretty offering mood of a girl who had been quite the reverse (Hannah had a backward way with her at times, if you can mind) that he just glanced behind, and then whispered very soft, 'I haven't quite promised her, and I think I can get out of it, and ask you that question you speak of.'

" 'Throw over Milly?—all to marry me! How delightful!' broke out Hannah, quite loud, clapping her hands.

"At this there was a real squeak—an angry, spiteful squeak, and afterwards a long moan, as if something had broke its heart, and a movement of the wagon cloth.

" 'Something's there!' said Hannah, starting up.

" 'It's nothing, really,' says Tony, in a soothing voice, and praying inwardly for a way out of this. 'I wouldn't tell 'ee at first because I wouldn't frighten 'ee. But, Hannah, I've really a couple of ferrets in a bag under there, for rabbiting, and they quarrel sometimes. I don't wish it knowed, as 'twould be called poaching. Oh, they can't get out, bless ye!—you are quite safe. And—and—what a fine day it is, isn't it, Hannah, for this time of year? Be you going to market next Saturday? How is your aunt now?' And so on, says Tony, to keep her from talking any more about love in Milly's hearing.

"But he found his work cut out for him, and wondering again how he should get out of this ticklish business, he looked about for a chance. Nearing home he saw his father in a field not far off, holding up his hand as if he wished to speak to Tony.

" 'Would you mind taking the reins a moment, Hannah,' he said, much relieved, 'while I go and find out what father wants?'

"She consented, and away he hastened into the field, only too glad to get breathing-time. He found that his father was looking at him with rather a stern eye.

" 'Come, come, Tony,' says old Mr. Kytes, as soon as his son was alongside him, 'this won't do, you know.'

" 'What?' says Tony.

" 'Why, if you mean to marry Milly Richards, do it, and there's an end o't. But don't go driving about the country with Jolliver's daughter and making a scandal. I won't have such things done.'

" 'I only asked her—that is, she asked me—to ride home.'

" 'She? Why, now, if it had been Milly, 'twould have been quite proper; but you and Hannah Jolliver going about by yourselves—'

" 'Milly's there, too, father.'

" 'Milly? Where?'

" 'Under the tarpaulin! Yes; the truth is, father, I've got rather into a nunny-watch, I'm afeard! Unity Sallet is there, too—yes, under the other end of the tarpaulin. All three are in that wagon, and what to do with 'em I know no more than the dead. The best plan is, as I'm thinking, to speak out loud and plain to one of 'em before the rest, and that will settle it; not but what 'twill cause 'em to kick up a bit of a miff, for certain. Now, which would you marry, father, if you was in my place?'

"'Whichever of 'em did *not* ask to ride with thee.'

"'That was Milly, I'm bound to say, as she only mounted by my invitation. But Milly——'

"'Then stick to Milly, she's the best. . . . But look at that!'

"His father pointed towards the wagon. 'She can't hold that horse in. You shouldn't have left the reins in her hands. Run on and take the horse's head, or there'll be some accident to them maids!'

"Tony's horse, in fact, in spite of Hannah's tugging at the reins, had started on his way at a brisk walking pace, being very anxious to get back to the stable, for he had had a long day out. Without another word, Tony rushed away from his father to overtake the horse.

"Now, of all things that could have happened to wean him from Milly, there was nothing so powerful as his father's recommending her. No; it could not be Milly, after all. Hannah must be the one, since he could not marry all three. This he thought while running after the wagon. But queer things were happening inside it.

"It was, of course, Milly who had screamed under the tarpaulin, being obliged to let off her bitter rage and shame in that way at what Tony was saying, and never daring to show, for very pride and dread o' being laughed at, that she was in hiding. She became more and more restless, and in twisting herself about, what did she see but another woman's foot and white stocking close to her head. It quite frightened her, not knowing that Unity Sallet was in the wagon likewise. But after the fright was over she determined to get to the bottom of all this, and she crept and crept along the bed of the wagon, under the cloth, like a snake, when lo and behold she came face to face with Unity.

"'Well, if this isn't disgraceful!' says Milly, in a raging whisper, to Unity.

"''Tis,' says Unity, 'to see you hiding in a young man's wagon like this, and no great character belonging to either of ye!'

"'Mind what you are saying!' replied Milly, getting louder. 'I am engaged to be married to him, and haven't I a right to be here? What right have you, I should like to know? What has he been promising you? A pretty lot of nonsense, I expect! But what Tony says to other women is all mere wind, and no concern to me!'

"'Don't you be too sure!' says Unity. 'He's going to have Hannah, and not you, nor me either; I could hear that.'

"Now, at these strange voices sounding from under the cloth

Hannah was thunderstruck a'most into a swound; and it was just at this time that the horse moved on. Hannah tugged away wildly, not knowing what she was doing; and as the quarrel rose louder and louder Hannah got so horrified that she let go the reins altogether. The horse went on at his own pace, and coming to the corner where we turn round to drop down the hill to Lower Longpuddle he turned too quick, the off-wheels went up the bank, the wagon rose sideways till it was quite on edge upon the near axles, and out rolled the three maidens into the road in a heap.

"When Tony came up, frightened and breathless, he was relieved enough to see that neither of his darlings was hurt, beyond a few scratches from the brambles of the hedge. But he was rather alarmed when he heard how they were going on at one another.

" 'Don't ye quarrel, my dears—don't ye!' says he, taking off his hat out of respect to 'em. And then he would have kissed them all round, as fair and square as a man could, but they were in too much of a taking to let him, and screeched and sobbed till they was quite spent.

" 'Now, I'll speak out honest, because I ought to,' says Tony, as soon as he could get heard. 'And this is the truth,' says he: 'I've asked Hannah to be mine, and she is willing, and we are going to put up the banns next——'

"Tony had not noticed that Hannah's father was coming up behind, nor had he noticed that Hannah's face was beginning to bleed from the scratch of a bramble. Hannah had seen her father, and had run to him, crying worse than ever.

" 'My daughter is *not* willing, sir,' says Mr. Jolliver, hot and strong. 'Be you willing, Hannah? I ask ye to have spirit enough to refuse him.'

" 'I have spirit, and I do refuse him!' says Hannah, partly because her father was there, and partly, too, in a tantrum because of the discovery and the scratch on her face. 'Little did I think when I was so soft with him just now that I was talking to such a false deceiver!'

" 'What, you won't have me, Hannah?' says Tony, his jaw hanging down like a dead man's.

" 'Never; I would sooner marry no—nobody at all!' she gasped out, though with her heart in her throat, for she would not have refused Tony if he had asked her quietly, and her father had not been there, and her face had not been scratched by the bramble. And having said that, away she walked upon her father's arm, thinking and hoping he would ask her again.

"Tony didn't know what to say next. Milly was sobbing her hear
out; but as his father had strongly recommended her he couldn'
feel inclined that way. So he turned to Unity.

" 'Well, will you, Unity dear, be mine?' he says.

" 'Take her leavings? Not I!' says Unity. 'I'd scorn it!' And
away walks Unity Sallet likewise, though she looked back when
she'd gone some way, to see if he was following her.

"So there at last were left Milly and Tony by themselves, she
crying in watery streams, and Tony looking like a tree struck by
lightning.

" 'Well, Milly,' he says at last, going up to her, 'it do seem as i
fate had ordained that it should be you and I, or nobody. And wha
must be must be, I suppose. Hey, Milly?'

" 'If you like, Tony. You didn't really mean what you said t
them?'

" 'Not a word of it,' declares Tony, bringing down his fist upon
his palm.

"And then he kissed her, and put the wagon to rights, and they
mounted together; and their banns were put up the very nex
Sunday."

A SERVICE OF LOVE

O. Henry (America)

When one loves one's Art no service seems too hard.

That is our premise. This story shall draw a conclusion from it
and show at the same time that the premise is incorrect. That wil
be a new thing in logic, and a feat in story-telling somewhat olde
than the great wall of China.

Joe Larrabee came out of the post-oak flats of the Middle Wes
pulsing with a genius for pictorial art. At six he drew a picture o
the town pump with a prominent citizen passing it hastily. Thi
effort was framed and hung in the drug-store window by the side o
the ear of corn with an uneven number of rows. At twenty he lef
for New York with a flowing necktie and a capital tied up some
what closer.

Delia Caruthers did things in six octaves so promisingly in a pine
tree village in the South that her relatives chipped in enough fo
her to go "North" and "finish." They could not see her f——, bu
that is our story.

Joe and Delia met in an atelier where a number of art and music students had gathered to discuss chiaroscuro,[1] Wagner, music, Rembrandt's works, pictures, Waldteufel, wall paper, Chopin, and Oolong.

Joe and Delia became enamored one of the other, or each of the other, as you please, and in a short time were married—for (see above), when one loves one's Art no service seems too hard.

Mr. and Mrs. Larrabee began housekeeping in a flat. It was a lonesome flat—something like the A sharp way down at the left-hand end of the keyboard. And they were happy; for they had Art, and they had each other. And my advice to the rich young man would be—sell all thou hast, and give it to the poor—janitor for the privilege of living in a flat with your Art and your Delia.

Flat-dwellers shall indorse my dictum that theirs is the only true happiness. If a home is happy it cannot fit too close—let the dresser collapse and become a billiard table; let the mantel turn to a rowing machine, the escritoire [2] to a spare bedchamber, the washstand to an upright piano; let the four walls come together, if they will, so you and your Delia are between. But if home be the other kind, let it be wide and long—enter you at the Golden Gate, hang your hat on Hatteras, your cape on Cape Horn, and go out by the Labrador.

Joe was painting in the class of the great Magister—you know his fame. His fees are high; his lessons are light—his high-lights have brought him renown. Delia was studying under Rosenstock—you know his repute as a disturber of the piano keys.

They were mighty happy as long as their money lasted. So is every—but I will not be cynical. Their aims were very clear and defined. Joe was to become capable very soon of turning out pictures that old gentlemen with thin side-whiskers and thick pocketbooks would sandbag one another in his studio for the privilege of buying. Delia was to become familiar and then contemptuous with Music, so that when she saw the orchestra seats and boxes unsold she could have sore throat and lobster in a private dining room and refuse to go on the stage.

But the best, in my opinion, was the home life in the little flat—the ardent, voluble chats after the day's study; the cozy dinners and fresh, light breakfasts; the interchange of ambitions—ambitions interwoven each with the other's or else inconsiderable—the mutual help and inspiration; and—overlook my artlessness—stuffed olives and cheese sandwiches at 11 P.M.

[1] *chiaroscuro:* light and shade.   [2] *escritoire:* desk.

But after a while Art flagged. It sometimes does, even if some switchman doesn't flag it. Everything going out and nothing coming in, as the vulgarians say. Money was lacking to pay Mr. Magister and Herr Rosenstock their prices. When one loves one's Art no service seems too hard. So, Delia said she must give music lessons to keep the chafing dish bubbling.

For two or three days she went out canvassing for pupils. One evening she came home elated.

"Joe, dear," she said, gleefully, "I've a pupil. And, oh, the loveliest people. General—General A. B. Pinkney's daughter—on Seventy-first street. Such a splendid house, Joe—you ought to see the front door! Byzantine I think you would call it. And inside! Oh, Joe, I never saw anything like it before.

"My pupil is his daughter Clementina. I dearly love her already. Shes' a delicate thing—dresses always in white; and the sweetest, simplest manners! Only eighteen years old. I'm to give three lessons a week; and, just think, Joe! $5 a lesson. I don't mind it a bit; for when I get two or three more pupils I can resume my lessons with Herr Rosenstock. Now, smooth out that wrinkle between your brow, dear, and let's have a nice supper."

"That's all right for you, Dele," said Joe, attacking a can of peas with a carving knife and a hatchet, "but how about me? Do you think I'm going to let you hustle for wages while I philander [3] in the regions of high art? Not by the bones of Benvenuto Cellini! [4] I guess I can sell papers or lay cobblestones, and bring in a dollar or two."

Delia came and hung about his neck.

"Joe, dear, you are silly. You must keep on at your studies. It is not as if I had quit my music and gone to work at something else. While I teach I learn. I am always with my music. And we can live as happily as millionaires on $15 a week. You mustn't think of leaving Mr. Magister."

"All right," said Joe, reaching for the blue scalloped vegetable dish. "But I hate for you to be giving lessons. It isn't Art. But you're a trump and a dear to do it."

"When one loves one's Art no service seems too hard," said Delia.

"Magister praised the sky in that sketch I made in the park," said Joe. "And Tinkle gave me permission to hang two of them in his window. I may sell one if the right kind of a moneyed idiot sees them."

[3] *philander:* flirt.
[4] *Cellini:* a famous sculptor.

"I'm sure you will," said Delia, sweetly. "And now let's be thankful for Gen. Pinkney and this veal roast."

During all of the next week the Larrabees had an early breakfast. Joe was enthusiastic about some morning-effect sketches he was doing in Central Park, and Delia packed him off breakfasted, coddled, praised and kissed at 7 o'clock. Art is an engaging mistress. It was most times 7 o'clock when he returned in the evening.

At the end of the week Delia, sweetly proud but languid, triumphantly tossed three five-dollar bills on the 8 x 10 (inches) centre table of the 8 x 10 (feet) flat parlor.

"Sometimes," she said, a little wearily, "Clementina tries me. I'm afraid she doesn't practice enough, and I have to tell her the same things so often. And then she always dresses entirely in white, and that does get monotonous. General Pinkney is the dearest old man! I wish you could know him, Joe. He comes in sometimes when I am with Clementina at the piano—he is a widower, you know—and stands there pulling his white goatee. 'And how are the semiquavers and the demisemiquavers progressing?' he always asks.

"I wish you could see the wainscoting in that drawing room, Joe! And those Astrakhan rug portieres. And Clementina has such a funny little cough. I hope she is stronger than she looks. Oh, I really am getting attached to her, she is so gentle and high bred. Gen. Pinkney's brother was once Minister to Bolivia."

And then Joe, with the air of Monte Cristo, drew forth a ten, a five, a two and a one—all legal tender notes—and laid them beside Delia's earnings.

"Sold that watercolor of the obelisk to a man from Peoria," he announced, overwhelmingly.

"Don't joke with me," said Delia—"not from Peoria!"

"All the way. I wish you could see him, Dele. Fat man with a woolen muffler and a quill toothpick. He saw the sketch in Tinkle's window and thought it was a windmill at first. He was game, though, and bought it anyhow. He ordered another—an oil sketch of the Lackawanna freight depot—to take back with him. Music lessons! Oh, I guess Art is still in it."

"I'm so glad you've kept on," said Delia, heartily. "You're bound to win, dear. Thirty-three dollars! We never had so much to spend before. We'll have oysters tonight."

"And filet mignon with champignons," said Joe. "Where is the olive fork?"

On the next Saturday evening Joe reached home first. He spread

his $18 on the parlor table and washed what seemed to be a gre:
deal of dark paint from his hands.

Half an hour later Delia arrived, her right hand tied up in
shapeless bundle of wraps and bandages.

"How is this?" asked Joe after the usual greetings. Delia laughe
but not very joyously.

"Clementina," she explained, "insisted upon a Welsh rabbit aft
her lesson. She is such a queer girl. Welsh rabbits at 5 in the afte
noon. The General was there. You should have seen him run f
the chafing dish, Joe, just as if there wasn't a servant in the hous
I know Clementina isn't in good health; she is so nervous. In ser
ing the rabbit she spilled a great lot of it, boiling hot, over my har
and wrist. It hurt awfully, Joe. And the dear girl was so sorry
But General Pinkney! Joe, that old man nearly went distracted. I
rushed downstairs and sent somebody—they said the furnace ma
or somebody in the basement—out to a drug store for some oil ar
things to bind it up with. It doesn't hurt so much now."

"What's this?" asked Joe, taking the hand tenderly and pullir
at some white strands beneath the bandages.

"It's something soft," said Delia, "that had oil on it. Oh, Joe, d
you sell another sketch?" She had seen the money on the table.

"Did I?" said Joe; "just ask the man from Peoria. He got b
depot today, and he isn't sure but he thinks he wants another parl
scape and a view on the Hudson. What time this afternoon did yc
burn your hand, Dele?"

"Five o'clock, I think," said Dele, plaintively. "The iron—
mean the rabbit came off the fire about that time. You ought
have seen General Pinkney, Joe, when . . ."

"Sit down here a moment, Dele," said Joe. He drew her to tl
couch, sat beside her and put his arm across her shoulders.

"What have you been doing for the last two weeks, Dele?" I
asked.

She braved it for a moment or two with an eye full of love ar
stubbornness, and murmured a vague phrase or two of Gener
Pinkney; but at length down went her head and out came the trut
and tears.

"I couldn't get any pupils," she confessed. "And I couldn't bea
to have you give up your lessons; and I got a place ironing shir
in that big Twenty-fourth Street laundry. And I think I did ver
well to make up both General Pinkney and Clementina, don't yo
Joe? And when a girl in the laundry set down a hot iron on my han
this afternoon I was all the way home making up that story abou

he Welsh rabbit. You're not angry, are you, Joe? And if I hadn't
ot the work you mightn't have sold your sketches to that man
rom Peoria."

"He wasn't from Peoria," said Joe, slowly.

"Well, it doesn't matter where he was from. How clever you are,
oe—and—kiss me, Joe—and what made you ever suspect that I
vasn't giving music lessons to Clementina?"

"I didn't," said Joe, "until tonight. And I wouldn't have then,
nly I sent up this cotton waste and oil from the engine-room this
fternoon for a girl upstairs who had her hand burned with a
moothing-iron. I've been firing the engine in that laundry for the
ast two weeks."

"And then you didn't——"

"My purchaser from Peoria," said Joe, "and General Pinkney are
)oth creations of the same art—but you wouldn't call it either paint-
ng or music."

And then they both laughed, and Joe began:

"When one loves one's Art no service seems——"

But Delia stopped him with her hand on his lips. "No," she said
—"just 'When one loves.'"

THE JUMPING FROG OF CALAVERAS COUNTY

Mark Twain (America)

As half the selections in this volume have been translated from a
oreign language, you will be interested in the following plaintive pro-
est made by Mark Twain against what happened to his famous story
)f *The Jumping Frog* when it was translated into French. The same
)oint is raised by Arnold in his essay *On Translating Homer* (see
)age 691). Twain writes: "Even a criminal is entitled to fair play;
ind certainly when a man who has done no harm has been unjustly
reated, he is privileged to do his best to right himself. My attention
ias just been called to an article some three years old in a French
nagazine entitled, *Revue des Deux Mondes* (Review of Some Two
Vorlds), wherein the writer treats of "Les Humoristes Americaines"
These Humorists Americans). I am one of these humorists Ameri-
:ans dissected by him, and hence the complaint I am making.

"This gentleman's article is an able one (as articles go, in the
French, where they always tangle up everything to that degree that
vhen you start into a sentence you never know whether you are going
o come out alive or not). It is a very good article, and the writer says
ill manner of kind and complimentary things about me—for which I

am sure I thank him with all my heart; but then why should he g
and spoil all his praise by one unlucky experiment? What I refer t
is this: he says my *Jumping Frog* is a funny story, but still he can
see why it should ever really convulse any one with laughter—an
straightway proceeds to translate it into French in order to prove t
his nation that there is nothing so very extravagantly funny about it
Just there is where my complaint originates. He has not translate
it at all; he has simply mixed it all up; it is no more like *The Jumpin*
Frog when he gets through with it than I am like a meridian of longi
tude. But my mere assertion is not proof; wherefore I print the Frenc
version, that all may see that I do not speak falsely; furthermore, i
order that even the unlettered may know my injury and give me the
compassion, I have been at infinite pains and trouble to retranslat
this French version back into English; and to tell the truth I hav
well-nigh worn myself out at it, having scarcely rested from my wor
during five days and nights. I cannot speak the French language, bu
I can translate very well, though not fast, I being self-educated. I as
the reader to run his eye over the original English version of *Th*
Jumping Frog and then read the French or my retranslation, an
kindly take notice how the Frenchman has riddled the grammar.
think it is the worst I ever saw; and yet the French are called a pol
ished nation. If I had a boy that put sentences together as they do
I would polish him to some purpose. Without further introduction
The Jumping Frog, as I originally wrote it, was as follows (after i
will be found part of the French version, and after the latter my re
translation from the French)."

❋   ❋   ❋

In compliance with the request of a friend of mine, who wrot
me from the East, I called on good-natured, garrulous old Simor
Wheeler, and inquired after my friend's friend, Leonidas W
Smiley, as requested to do, and I hereunto append the result. I have
a lurking suspicion that *Leonidas W.* Smiley is a myth; that my
friend never knew such a personage; and that he only conjecture
that if I asked old Wheeler about him, it would remind him of hi
infamous *Jim* Smiley, and he would go to work and bore me to
death with some exasperating reminiscence of him as long and a
tedious as it should be useless to me. If that was the design, i
succeeded.

I found Simon Wheeler dozing comfortably by the bar-room stov
of the dilapidated tavern in the decaying mining camp of Angel's
and I noticed that he was fat and bald-headed, and had an expres
sion of winning gentleness and simplicity upon his tranquil counte

ance. He roused up, and gave me good-day. I told him a friend of
1ine had commissioned me to make some inquiries about a cher-
shed companion of his boyhood named *Leonidas W.* Smiley—*Rev.*
.eonidas W. Smiley, a young minister of the Gospel, who he had
eard was at one time a resident of Angel's Camp. I added that if
Ir. Wheeler could tell me anything about this Rev. Leonidas W.
miley, I would feel under many obligations to him.

Simon Wheeler backed me into a corner and blockaded me there
7ith his chair, and then sat down and reeled off the monotonous nar-
ative which follows this paragraph. He never smiled, he never
rowned, he never changed his voice from the gentle-flowing key
o which he tuned his initial sentence, he never betrayed the slight-
st suspicion of enthusiasm; but all through the interminable narra-
ive there ran a vein of impressive earnestness and sincerity, which
howed me plainly that, so far from his imagining that there was
nything ridiculous or funny about his story, he regarded it as a
eally important matter, and admired its two heroes as men of
ranscendent genius in *finesse*. I let him go on in his own way, and
ever interrupted him once.

"Rev. Leonidas W. H'm, Reverend Le—well, there was a feller
ere once by the name of *Jim* Smiley, in the winter of '49—or maybe
. was the spring of '50—I don't recollect exactly, somehow, though
7hat makes me think it was one or the other is because I remember
he big flume warn't finished when he first come to the camp; but
nyway, he was the curiousest man about always betting on any-
hing that turned up you ever see, if he could get anybody to bet on
he other side; and if he couldn't he'd change sides. Any way that
uited the other man would suit *him*—any way just so's he got a
et, *he* was satisfied. But still he was lucky, uncommon lucky; he
nost always come out winner. He was always ready and laying for
chance; there couldn't be no solit'ry thing mentioned but that
eller'd offer to bet on it, and take ary side you please, as I was just
elling you. If there was a horse-race, you'd find him flush or you'd
ind him busted at the end of it; if there was a dog-fight, he'd bet
n it; if there was a cat-fight, he'd bet on it; if there was a chicken-
ight, he'd bet on it; why, if there was two birds setting on a fence,
e would bet you which one would fly first; or if there was a camp-
neeting, he would be there reg'lar to bet on Parson Walker, which
e judged to be the best exhorter about here, and so he was, too, and
. good man. If he even see a straddle-bug start to go anywheres, he
vould bet you how long it would take him to get to—to wherever
e was going to, and if you took him up, he would foller that

straddle-bug to Mexico but what he would find out where he wa
bound for and how long he was on the road. Lots of the boys her
has seen that Smiley, and can tell you about him. Why, it neve
made no difference to *him*—he'd bet on *any* thing—the dangde
feller. Parson Walker's wife laid very sick once, for a good whil
and it seemed as if they warn't going to save her; but one mornir
he come in, and Smiley up and asked him how she was, and he sa
she was consid'able better—thank the Lord for his inf'nite merc
—and coming on so smart that with the blessing of Prov'dence she
get well yet; and Smiley, before he thought, says: 'Well, I'll res
two-and-a-half she don't anyway.'

"Thish-yer Smiley had a mare—the boys called her the fiftee
minute nag, but that was only in fun, you know, because, of cours
she was faster than that—and he used to win money on that hors
for all she was so slow and always had the asthma, or the distempe
or the consumption, or something of that kind. They used to giv
her two or three hundred yards start, and then pass her under way
but always at the fag end of the race she'd get excited and despera
like, and come cavorting and straddling up, and scattering her le
around limber, sometimes in the air, and sometimes out to one sic
among the fences, and kicking up m-o-r-e dust and raising m-o-r
racket with her coughing and sneezing and blowing her nose—an
always fetch up at the stand just about a neck ahead, as near as yo
could cipher it down.

"And he had a little small bull-pup, that to look at him you'
think he warn't worth a cent but to set around and look ornery an
lay for a chance to steal something. But as soon as money was u
on him he was a different dog; his under-jaw'd begin to stick ou
like the fo'castle of a steamboat, and his teeth would uncover an
shine like the furnaces. And a dog might tackle him and bully-ra
him, and bite him, and throw him over his shoulder two or thre
times, and Andrew Jackson—which was the name of the pup–
Andrew Jackson would never let on but what *he* was satisfied, an
hadn't expected nothing else—and the bets being doubled an
doubled on the other side all the time, till the money was all up
and then all of a sudden he would grab that other dog jest by th
j'int of his hind leg and freeze to it—not chaw, you understand, bu
only just grip and hang on till they throwed up the sponge, if i
was a year. Smiley always come out winner on that pup, till h
harnessed a dog once that didn't have no hind legs, because they'
been sawed off in a circular saw, and when the thing had gone alon
far enough, and the money was all up, and he come to make a snatc
for his pet holt, he see in a minute how he'd been imposed on, an

ow the other dog had him in the door, so to speak, and he 'peared
irprised, and then he looked sorter discouraged-like and didn't
y no more to win the fight, and so he got shucked out bad. He
ive Smiley a look, as much as to say his heart was broke, and it
as *his* fault, for putting up a dog that hadn't no hind legs for him
) take holt of, which was his main dependence in a fight, and then
e limped off a piece and laid down and died. It was a good pup, was
iat Andrew Jackson, and would have made a name for hisself if
e'd lived, for the stuff was in him and he had genius—I know it,
ecause he hadn't no opportunities to speak of, and it don't stand
) reason that a dog could make such a fight as he could under them
ircumstances if he hadn't no talent. It always makes me feel sorry
hen I think of that last fight of his'n, and the way it turned out.

"Well, thish-yer Smiley had rat-tarriers, and chicken cocks, and
omcats, and all them kind of things, till you couldn't rest, and you
ouldn't fetch nothing for him to bet on but he'd match you. He
etched a frog one day, and took him home, and said he cal'lated to
lucate him; and so he never done nothing for three months but set
a his back yard and learn that frog to jump. And you bet you he
id learn him, too. He'd give him a little punch behind, and the
ext minute you'd see that frog whirling in the air like a doughnut—
ee him turn one summerset, or maybe a couple, if he got a good
tart, and come down flat-footed and all right, like a cat. He got
im up so in the matter of ketching flies, and kep' him in practice so
onstant, that he'd nail a fly every time as fur as he could see him.
miley said all a frog wanted was education, and he could do 'most
nything—and I believe him. Why, I've seen him set Dan'l Webster
own here on this floor—Dan'l Webster was the name of the frog
—and sing out, 'Flies, Dan'l, flies!' and quicker'n you could wink
e'd spring straight up and snake a fly off'n the counter there, and
op down on the floor ag'in as solid as a gob of mud, and fall to
cratching the side of his head with his hind foot as indifferent as
he hadn't no idea he'd been doin' any more'n any frog might do.
ou never see a frog so modest and straightfor'ard as he was, for
ll he was so gifted. And when it come to fair and square jumping
n a deal level, he could get over more ground at one straddle than
ny animal of his breed you ever see. Jumping on a deal level was
is strong suit, you understand; and when it come to that, Smiley
ould ante up money on him as long as he had a red. Smiley was
aonstrous proud of his frog, and well he might be, for fellers that
ad travelled and been everywheres all said he laid over any frog
aat ever *they* see.

"Well, Smiley kep' the beast in a little lattice box, and he used to

fetch him down-town sometimes and lay for a bet. One day a felle
—a stranger in the camp, he was—come acrost him with his box
and says: " 'What might it be that you've got in the box?'

"And Smiley says, sorter indifferent-like: 'It might be a parro
or it might be a canary, maybe but it ain't—it's only just a frog.'

"And the feller took it, and looked at it careful, and turned i
round this way and that, and says: 'H'm—so 'tis. Well, what's h
good for?'

" 'Well,' Smiley says, easy and careless, 'he's good enough for on
thing, I should judge—he can outjump any frog in Calavera
county.'

"The feller took the box again, and took another long, particula
look, and give it back to Smiley, and says, very deliberate, 'Well
he says, 'I don't see no p'ints about that frog that's any better'
any other frog.'

" 'Maybe you don't,' Smiley says. 'Maybe you understand frog
and maybe you don't understand 'em; maybe you've had experi
ence, and maybe you ain't only a amature, as it were. Anyways, I'v
got *my* opinion, and I'll resk forty dollars that he can outjump an
frog in Calaveras county.'

"And the feller studied a minute, and then says, kinder sad like
'Well, I'm only a stranger here, and I ain't got no frog; but if I ha
a frog, I'd bet you.'

"And then Smiley says, 'That's all right—that's all right—i
you'll hold my box a minute, I'll go and get you a frog.' And so th
feller took the box, and put up his forty dollars along with Smiley'
and set down to wait.

"So he set there a good while thinking and thinking to hisself, an
then he got the frog out and prized his mouth open and took a tea
spoon and filled him full of quail shot—filled him pretty near u
to his chin—and set him on the floor. Smiley he went to the swam
and slopped around in the mud for a long time, and finally h
ketched a frog, and fetched him in, and give him to this feller, an
says:

" 'Now, if you're ready, set him alongside of Dan'l, with his fore
paws just even with Dan'l's, and I'll give the word.' Then he says
'One—two—three—*git!*' and him and the feller touched up th
frogs from behind, and the new frog hopped off lively, but Dan
give a heave, and hysted up his shoulders—so—like a Frenchmar
but it warn't no use—he couldn't budge; he was planted as solid a
a church, and he couldn't no more stir than if he was anchored ou
Smiley was a good deal surprised, and he was disgusted too, but h
didn't have no idea what the matter was, of course.

"The feller took the money and started away; and when he was
going out at the door, he sorter jerked his thumb over his shoulder—
so—at Dan'l, and says again, very deliberate, 'Well,' he says, '*I
don't see no p'ints about that frog that's any better'n any other
frog.*'

"Smiley he stood scratching his head and looking down at Dan'l
long time, and at last he says, 'I do wonder what in the nation that
frog throw'd off for—I wonder if there ain't something the matter
with him—he 'pears to look mighty baggy, somehow.' And he
ketched Dan'l by the nap of the neck, and hefted him, and says,
Why, blame my cats if he don't weigh five pound;' and turned him
upside down and he belched out a double handful of shot. And then
he see how it was, and he was the maddest man—he set the frog
down and took out after that feller, but he never ketched him.
And——"

Here Simon Wheeler heard his name called from the front yard,
and got up to see what was wanted. And turning to me as he
moved away, he said: "Just set where you are, stranger, and rest
easy—I ain't going to be gone a second."

But, by your leave, I did not think that a continuation of the
history of the enterprising vagabond *Jim* Smiley would be likely
to afford me much information concerning the Rev. *Leonidas W.*
Smiley, and so I started away.

At the door I met the sociable Wheeler returning, and he button-
holed me and re-commenced:

"Well, thish-yer Smiley had a yeller one-eyed cow that didn't
have no tail, only just a short stump like a bannanner, and——"

However, lacking both time and inclination, I did not wait to
hear about the afflicted cow, but took my leave.

"Now," says Mark Twain, "look upon this picture and say if
iconoclasm can farther go."

(From the *Revue des Deux Mondes* of July 15, 1872)

LA GRENOUILLE SAUTEUSE DU COMTE
DE CALAVERAS

Se Smiley avait un petit bouledogue qui, à le voir, ne valait pas un sou;
on aurait cru que parier contre lui c'était voler, tant il était ordinaire; mais
aussitôt les enjeux faits, il devenait un autre chien. Sa mâchoire inférieure
commençait à ressortir comme un gaillard d'avant, ses dents se découvraient
brillantes commes des fournaises, et un chien pouvait le taquiner, l'exciter,
le mordre, le jeter deux au trois fois par-dessus son épaule, André
Jackson, c'etait le nom du chien, André Jackson prenait cela tranquillement,

comme s'il ne fût jamais attendu à autre chose, et quand les paris étaie
doublés et redoublés contre lui, il vous saisissait l'autre chien juste à l'artic
lation de la jambe de derrière, et il ne la lâchait plus, non pas qu'il la mâch
vous concevez, mais il s'y serait tenu pendu jusqu'à ce qu'on jetât l'épon
en l'air, fallût-il attendre un an. Smiley gagnait toujours avec cette bête-l
malheureusement ils ont fini par dresser un chien qui n'avait pas de patt
de derrière, parce qu'on les avait sciées, et quand les choses furent au poi
qu'il voulait, et qu'il en vint a set jeter sur son morceau favori, le pauv
chien comprit en un instant qu'on s'etait moqué de lui, et que l'autre
tenait. Vous n'avez jamais vu personne avoir l'air plus penaud et pl
découragé; il ne fit aucun effort pour gagner le combat et fut rudeme
secoué, de sorte que, regardant Smiley comme pour lui dire:—Mon cœ
est brisé, c'est ta faute; pourquoi m'avoir livré à un chien qui n'a pas
pattes de derrière, puisque c'est par là que je les bats?—il s'en alla en clo
nant, et se coucha pour mourir. Ah! c'était un bon chien, cet André Jacks
et il se serait fait un nom, s'il avait vécu, car il y avait de l'etoffe en lui,
avait du génie, je la sais, bien que de grandes occasions lui aient manqu
mais il est impossible de supposer qu'un chien capable de se battre com
lui, certaines circonstances étant données, ait manqué de talent. Je m
sens triste toutes les fois que je pense à son dernier combat et au dénoûme
qu'il a eu. Eh bien! ce Smiley nourrissait des terriers à rats, et des coqs
combat, et des chats, et toute sorte de choses, au point qu'il était toujo
en mesure de vous tenir tête, et qu'avec sa rage de paris on n'avait p
de repos. Il attrapa un jour une grenouille et l'emporta chez lui, disa
qu'il prétendait faire son éducation; vous me croirez si vous voulez, m
pendant trois mois il n'a rien fait que lui apprendre à sauter dans une co
retirée de sa maison. Et je vous réponds qu'il avait réussi. Il lui donnait
petit coup par derrière, et l'instant d'après vous voyiez la grenouille tourr
en l'air comme un beignet au-dessus de la poêle, faire une culbute, quelqu
fois deux, lorsqu'elle était bien partie, et retomber sur ses pattes comme
chat. Il l'avait dressée dans l'art de gober des mouches, et l'y exerçait co
tinuellement, si bien qu'une mouche, du plus loin qu'elle apparaissait, ét
une mouche perdue. Smiley avait coutume de dire que tout ce qui manqu
à une grenouille, c'était l'éducation, qu'avec l'éducation elle pouvait fa
presque tout, et je le crois. Tenez, je l'ai vu poser Daniel Webster là s
se plancher,—Daniel Webster était le nom de la grenouille,—et lui chant
—Des mouches! Daniel, des mouches!—En un clin d'oeil, Daniel av
bondi et saisi une mouche ici sur le comptoir, puis sauté denouveau par ter
où il restait vraiment à se gratter la tête avec sa patte de derrière, com
s'il n'avait pas eu la moindre ideé de sa supériorité. Jamais vous n'av
grenouille vu de aussi modeste, aussi naturelle, douée comme elle l'éta
Et quand il s'agissait de sauter purement et simplement sur terrain pl
elle faisait plus de chemin en un saut qu'aucune bête de son espéce q
vous puissiez connaître. Sauter à plat, c'était son fort! Quand il s'agiss
de cela, Smiley entassait les enjeux sur elle tant qu'il lui, restait un rou
liard. Il faut le reconnaître, Smiley était monstrueusement fier de
grenouille, et il en avait le droit, car des gens qui avaient voyagé, c
avaient tout vu, disaient qu'on lui ferait injure de la comparer à une autr
de façon que Smiley gardait Daniel dans une petite boîte à claire-voie qu
emportait parfois à la ville pour quelque pari.

Un jour, un individu étranger au camp l'arrête avec sa boîte et lui d
"Qu'est-ce que vous avez donc serré là dedans?"

Smiley, dit d'un air différent: "Cela pourrait être un perroquet ou un serin, mais ce n'est rien de pareil, ce n'est qu'une grenouille."

L'individu la prend, la regarde avec soin, la tourne d'un côté et de l'autre puis il dit: "Tiens! en effet! A quoi est-elle bonne?"

"—Mon Dieu!" répond Smiley, toujours d'un air dégagé, "elle est bonne pour une chose à mon avis; elle peut battre en sautant toute grenouille du comté de Calaveras."

L'individu reprend la boîte, l'examine de nouveau longuement, et la rend à Smiley en disant d'un air délibéré: "Eh bien! je ne vois pas que cette grenouille ait rien de mieux qu'aucune grenouille."

"—Possible que vous ne le voyiez paz, dit Smiley, possible que vous en-tendiez en grenouilles, possible que vous ne vous y entendiez point, possible que vous ayez de l'expérience, et possible que vous ne soyez qu'un amateur. De toute manière, je parie quarante dollars qu'elle battra en sautant n'im-porte quelle grenouille du comté de Calaveras."

L'individu réfléchit une seconde et dit comme attristé: "Je ne suis qu'un étranger ici, je n'ais pas de grenouille; mais si j'en avais une, je tiendrais le pari."

"—Fort bien!" repond Smiley. "Rien de plus facile. Si vous voulez tenir ma boîte une minute, j'irai vous chercher une grenouille."—Voilà donc l'indi-vidu qui garde la boîte, qui met ses quarante dollars sur ceux de Smiley et qui attend. Il attend assez longtemps, réfléchissant tout seul, et figurez-vous qu'il prend Daniel, lui ouvre la bouche de force at avec une cuiller à thé l'emplit de menu plomb de chasse, mais l'emplit jusqu'au menton, puis il le pose par terre. Smiley pendant ce temps était à barboter dans une mare. Finalement il attrape une grenouille, l'apporte à cet individu et dit: "Maintenant, si vous êtes prêt, mettez-la tout contre Daniel, avec leurs pattes de devant sur la même ligne, et je donnerai le signal." Puis il ajoute: "Un, deux, trois, sautez!"

Lui et l'individu touchent leurs grenouilles par derriére, et la grenouille neuve se met à sautiller, mais Daniel se soulève lourdement, hausse les épaules ainsi, comme un Français; à quoi bon? il ne pouvait bouger, il était planté solide comme une enclume, il n'avançait pas plus que si on eût mis à l'ancre. Smiley fut surpris et dégoûté, mais il ne se doutait pas du tour, bien entendu. L'individu empoche l'argent, s'en va, et en s'en allant est-ce qu'il ne donne pas un coup de pouce pardessus l'épaule, comma ça, au pauvre Daniel, en disant de son air délibéré: "Eh bien! je ne vois pas que cette grenouille ait rien de mieux qu'une autre."

Smiley se gratta longtemps la tête, les yeux fixés sur Daniel jusqu'à ce qu'enfin il dit: "Je me demande comment diable il se fait que cette bête ait refusé. . . . Est-ce qu'elle aurait quelque chose? . . . On croirait qu'elle est enflée."

Il empoigne Daniel par la peau du cou, le souléve et dit: "Le loup me croque, s'il ne pèse pas cinq livres."

Il le retourne, et le malheureux crache deux poignées de plomb. Quand Smiley reconnut ce qui en était, il fut comme fou. Vous le voyez d'ici poser la grenouille par terre et courir après cet individu, mais il ne le rattrapa jamais, et. . . .

Now behold *The Jumping Frog* as Mark Twain says, "clawed back into a civilized language once more by patient unremunerative toil."

THE FROG JUMPING OF THE COUNTY OF CALAVERAS

This Smiley had a small bulldog (bouledogue!) who, to him see, no value not a cent; one would believe that to bet against him it was to steal, so much he was ordinary; but as soon as the game made, he becomes another dog. Her jaw inferior commence to project like a deck of before, his teeth themselves discover brilliant like some furnaces, and a dog could him tackle (le taquiner), him excite, him murder (le mordre), him throw two or three times over his shoulder, André Jackson—this was the name of the dog—André Jackson takes that tranquilly, as if he not himself was never expecting other thing, and when the bets were doubled and redoubled against him, he you seize the other dog just at the articulation of the leg of behind, and he not it leave more, not that he it masticate, you conceive but he himself there shall be holding during until that one throws the sponge in the air, must he wait a year. Smiley gained always with this beast-là; unhappily they have finished by elevating a dog who no had not of feet of behind, because one them had sawed; and when things were at the point that he would, and that he came to himself throw upon his morsel favorite, the poor dog comprehended in an instant that he himself was deceived in him, and that the other dog him had. You no have never seen person having the air more penaud and more discouraged; he not made no effort to gain the combat, and was rudely shucked.

Eh bien! this Smiley nourished some terriers à rats, and some cocks of combat, and some cats, and all sorts of things; and with his rage of betting one no had more of repose. He trapped one day a frog and him imported with him (et l'emporta chez lui) saying that he pretended to make his education. You me believe if you will, but during three months he not has nothing done but to him apprehend to jump (apprendre à sauter) in a court retired of her mansion (de sa maison). And I you respond that he have succeeded. He him gives a small blow by behind, and the instant after you shall see the frog turn in the air like a grease-biscuit, make one summer sault, sometimes two, when she was well started, and refall upon his feet like a cat. He him had accomplished in the art of to gobble the flies (gobe des mouches), and him there exercised continually—so well that a fly at the most far that she appeared was a fly lost. Smiley had custom to say that all which lacked to a frog it was the education, but with the education she could do nearly all—and I I im believe. Tenez, I him have seen pose Daniel Webster there upon this plank—Daniel Webster was the name of the frog —and to him sing, "Some flies, Daniel, some flies"—in a flash of the eye Daniel had bounded and seized a fly here upon the counter, then jumped anew at the earth, where he rested truly to himself scratch the head with his behind foot, as if he no had not the least idea of his superiority. Never you not have seen frog as modest, as natural, sweet as she was. And when he himself agitated to jump purely and simply upon plain earth, she does more ground in one jump than any beast of his species than you can know To jump plain—this was his strong. When he himself agitated for that Smiley multiplied the bets upon her as long as there to him remained a red It must to know, Smiley was monstrously proud of his frog, and he of it was right, for some men who were traveled, who had all seen, said that the o him would be injurious to him compare to another frog. Smiley guarded Daniel in a little box latticed which he carried bytimes to the village for some bet.

One day an individual stranger at the camp him arrested with his box and him said: "What is this that you have them shut up there within?"

Smiley said, with an air indifferent: "That could be a paroquet, or a syringe (ou un serin), but this no is nothing of such, it not is but a frog."

The individual it took, it regarded with care, it turned from one side and from the other, then he said: "Tiens! in effect! At what is she good?"

"My God!" respond Smiley, always with an air disengaged, "she is good for one thing, to my notice she can batter in jumping all frogs of the county of Calaveras."

The individual retook the box, it examined of new longly, and it rendered to Smiley in saying with an air deliberate: "Eh bien! I no saw not that that frog had nothing of better than each frog." (If that isn't grammar gone to seed then I count myself no judge.—M. T.)

"Possible that you not it saw not," said Smiley, "possible that you—you comprehend frogs; possible that you not you there comprehend nothing; possible that you had of the experience, and possible that you not be but an amateur. Of all manner I bet forty dollars that she batter in jumping no matter which frog of the county of Calaveras."

The individual reflected a second, and said like sad: "I not am but a stranger here, I no have not a frog; but if I of it had one, I would embrace the bet."

"Strong well!" respond Smiley: "nothing of more facility. If you will hold my box a minute, I go you to search a frog."

Behold, then, the individual, who guards the box, who puts his forty dollars upon those of Smiley, and who attends. He attended enough longtimes, reflecting all solely. And figure you that he takes Daniel, him opens the mouth by force and with a teaspoon him fills with shot of the hunt, even him fills just to the chin, then he him puts by the earth. Smiley during these times was at slopping in a swamp. Finally he trapped a frog, him carried to that individual, and said: "Now if you be ready, put him all against Daniel, with their before feet upon the same line, and I give the signal"—then he added: "One, two, three—advance!"

Him and the individual touched their frogs by behind, and the frog new put to jump smartly, but Daniel himself lifted ponderously, exalted the shoulders thus, like a Frenchman—to what good? he not could budge, he is planted solid like a church, he not advance no more than if one him had put at the anchor.

Smiley was surprised and disgusted, but he not himself doubted not of the turn being intended (mais il ne se doutait pas du tour, bien entendu). The individual empocketed the silver, himself with it went, and of it himself in going is it that he no gives not a jerk of thumb over the shoulder—like that—at the poor Daniel, in saying with his air deliberate: "Eh bien! I no see not that that frog has nothing of better than another."

Smiley himself scratched longtimes the head, the eyes fixed upon Daniel, until that which at last he said: "I me demand how the devil it makes itself that this beast has refused. Is it that she had something? One would believe that she is stuffed."

He grasped Daniel by the skin of the neck, him lifted and said: "Th wolf me bite if he no weigh not five pounds."

He him reversed and the unhappy belched two handfuls of shot. Whe Smiley recognized how it was, he was like mad. He deposited his fro by the earth and ran after the individual, but he not him caught never.

"Such," concludes Twain, "is *The Jumping Frog,* to the distorte French eye. I claim that I never put together such an odious mixtu of bad grammar and delirium tremens in my life. And what has a po foreigner like me done, to be abused and misrepresented like this When I say, 'Well I don't see no p'ints about that frog that's an better'n any other frog,' is it kind, is it just, for this Frenchman t try to make it appear that I said, 'Eh bien! I no saw not that tha frog had nothing of better than each frog?' I have no heart to wri more. I never felt so about anything before."

A TERRIBLE NIGHT

Anton Chekhov (Russia)

Ivan Petrovitch Requiemov became pallid, put out the lamp an began in an agitated voice:

"Not a glimmer of light pierced the thick darkness that hung ov the earth on Christmas Eve, 1883. I was returning home from th house of a friend, who is now dead, where we had all remained la holding a spiritistic séance.[1] For some reason the small by-street through which I had to go, were dark, and I had to make my wa by groping. I was living at the time in Moscow, near the church the Assumption on the Tombtsa, in a house belonging to the gover ment official Cadaverov, one of the most obscure parts of the Arba My thoughts as I walked home were sad and depressing.

" 'Your life is drawing to an end. . . . Repent. . . .'

"These were the words Spinoza,[2] whose spirit we had been ab to call up, had addressed to me at the séance. I had asked for the again, and the saucer had not only repeated them, but had adde 'tonight.' I am no believer in spiritism, but the thought of deat makes me gloomy. Ladies and gentlemen, death is unavoidable, a daily occurrence, but nevertheless to man's nature it is a subje abhorrent. Now, when I was surrounded by cold, impenetrab darkness, when before my eyes I could only see torrents of rai

[1] *séance:* a meeting at which spirits of the departed are supposedly called fro the after world.

[2] *Spinoza:* a great philosopher.

ops, when the wind howled plaintively above my head, and there
as not a single living soul anywhere near me, nor was a human
ound to be heard, my soul became filled with an undefined, unac-
ountable dread. I, a man free from prejudices, hastened along,
aring to look back, or to the side. It seemed to me if I looked
ack I would inevitably see death like a spectre behind me."

Requiemov breathed heavily, he gulped down a glass of water,
nd continued:

"This undefined dread, you will understand, did not leave me
even when having mounted to the fourth story of Cadaverov's house
opened the door and entered my room. It was dark in my modest
dwelling. The wind moaned in the stove as if begging to be let into
he warmth, and knocked at the door of the ventilator.

" 'If Spinoza is to be believed,' I said to myself, smiling, 'I am to
be tonight amid this lamentation. It certainly is eerie!'

"I lit a match. . . . A furious gust of wind passed over the roof
f the house. The gentle wailing changed into wrathful roars. Some-
here below a half-detached shutter clattered and the door of my
entilator squeaked plaintively for help. . . .

" 'It's bad for the houseless on a night like this,' I thought.

"But it was no time to give oneself up to such reflections. When
he sulphur on the match I had lighted gave out a blue flame, and I
ast my eyes round the room, I saw an unexpected and terrible
ght. . . . What a pity the gust of wind had not reached my
match! Then, perhaps I would have seen nothing and my hair
ould not have stood on end. I shrieked, I made a step toward the
oor, and filled with horror, despair and amazement I closed my
yes.

"There was a coffin in the middle of the room.

"The blue light burnt but a short time; still I had been able to
iscern the outlines of the coffin. . . . I saw the pink glimmer and
parkle of the brocade, I saw the gold galloon cross on the lid. There
re things, ladies and gentlemen, that stamp themselves on your
memory, though you have seen them only for an instant. So it was
vith this coffin. I only saw it for a second, but I can remember it in
ll its smallest details. It was a coffin for a person of middle height,
nd judging by its pink color it was for a young girl. The rich bro-
ade, the feet, the bronze handles—all denoted that the corpse was
ich.

"I rushed headlong out of my room and without reasoning, with-
ut thinking, only feeling an inexpressible dread, I tore down the
tairs. The corridors and the staircase were dark, my legs got en-

tangled in the skirts of my long fur coat, and it was a marvel that
did not fall down and break my neck. When I found myself in th
street I leaned against a wet lamp-post and began to get calm. M
heart palpitated, my breathing was heavy . . ."

One of the listeners turned up the lamp and moved closer to th
narrator, who continued:

"I would not have been surprised if I had found my room on fir
if a robber or a mad dog had been there. . . . I would not have bee
surprised if the ceiling had fallen down, if the floor had collapsed
if the walls had fallen in. . . . All that is natural and compreher
sible. But how could a coffin have got into my room? Where did
come from? An expensive, a woman's coffin, evidently made fo
some young aristocrat—how could it have found its way into th
wretched room of a small government official? Was it empty, or di
it contain a corpse? . . . Who was she, this rich girl who had die
so inopportunely, and was now paying me this strange and terrib
visit? A painful secret!

" 'If this is no miracle it must be a crime,' shot through m
head.

"I was lost in conjectures. During my absence the door had bee
locked and the place where I hid the key was known only to my mos
intimate friends. My friends could not have placed the coffi
there! . . . It might also be supposed that the coffin had bee
brought to me by the undertakers owing to some error. They migh
have mistaken the house or gone to the wrong story or the wron
door, and had carried the coffin into the wrong flat. But who does no
know that our coffin-makers will never leave a room until they hav
been paid for their work, or at least have received a good tip?

" 'The spirits have foretold my death,' I thought. 'Can it be the
who have taken the trouble to provide me with a coffin in due time?

"Ladies and gentlemen, I do not believe nor have I ever believe
in spiritism, but such a coincidence might even plunge a philosophe
into a mystical frame of mind.

" 'All this is stupid, and I am as cowardly as a schoolboy,' I de
cided at last. 'It was only an optical illusion—nothing more! Whil
walking home my frame of mind had been so gloomy that it is no
surprising that my unstrung nerves made me see a coffin. . . . O
course, it was only an optical illusion! What else could it be?'

"The rain beat in my face, and the wind tore fiercely at my coa
and cap. . . . I was cold and wet through and through. I had to g
somewhere—but where? To return to my own room would expos
me to the risk of again seeing the coffin, and it would be beyond my

trength to bear that sight. Without a single living soul near me, iot hearing a single human sound, left alone face to face with that :offin in which perhaps a corpse was lying, I might lose my senses. On the other hand, to remain in the street under the torrents of rain ind in the cold was impossible.

"I decided to go and pass the night at my friend Restov's room, who, as you all know, afterwards shot himself. At the time he was iving in furnished rooms in the house belonging to the merchant Skullov, situated in the Dead Lane."

Requiemov wiped away the cold sweat that had appeared on his pale face, and, heaving a deep sigh, continued:

"I did not find my friend in. I knocked at his door, and at last being convinced that he was out, I felt about on the transom for the key, opened the door and went in. I threw my wet fur-coat on the floor, groped about in the darkness for the sofa and sat down to rest. It was dark. . . . The wind hummed sadly in the window ventilator. The cricket was singing its monotonous song in the stove. The bells in the Kremlin [3] were ringing for the Christmas matins. I hastened to strike a match. But the light did not relieve me of my gloomy mood; on the contrary, a terrible, an inexpressible horror mastered me once more. I shrieked, staggered and rushed out of the room almost beside myself.

"In my friend's room, as in my own, I also saw a coffin!

"My friend's coffin was nearly twice the size of mine, and the brown material with which it was covered gave it an especially gloomy appearance. How had it got there? It could only be an optical illusion—how was it possible to doubt it? . . . There could not be coffins in every room! My nerves were evidently diseased. . . . I had hallucinations. Wherever I might go now I would always see before me the terrible dwelling of the dead. Consequently I was mad, I was infected with something like 'coffin-mania' and the cause of my mental derangement was not far to seek: it was only necessary to remember the spiritistic séance and Spinoza's words. . . .

" 'I am going mad!' I thought in terror, seizing my head in my hands. 'My God! My God! What am I to do?'

"My head was ready to burst, my legs failed me. . . . The rain poured down as if out of buckets, the wind pierced me through and through, and I had neither a fur-coat nor a cap. I could not go back to fetch them from the room . . . that was beyond my strength. . . . Dread clasped me firmly in its cold embrace. My hair stood

[3] *Kremlin:* the Russian royal palace, long the seat of the Tzarist rule.

on end, cold perspiration streamed down my face, although I believed that it was only hallucinations.

"What was I to do?" Requiemov continued. "I was out of my mind, and I risked catching a severe cold. Fortunately, I remembered that my good friend Godsacreov, who had but lately received his doctor's degree, was living not far from the Dead Lane. He had also been with us at the spiritistic séance. I hastened to him. . . . At that time he had not yet married the rich merchant's daughter, and was living in the fifth story of the house belonging to the State Councillor Graveyardin.

"At Godsacreov's my nerves were destined to be subjected to further torture. As I was mounting to the fifth story I heard a terrible noise. Somebody was running about upstairs, stamping heavily with his feet and slamming doors.

" 'Help!' I heard somebody cry in a voice that pierced the very soul. 'Help! Porter!'

"A moment later a dark figure in a fur-coat and a crushed silk hat rushed down the stairs toward me.

" 'Godsacreov,' I cried, recognizing my friend. 'Is it you? What is the matter?'

"When Godsacreov reached the landing on which I was standing, he stopped and seized me convulsively by the hand. He was pale, he breathed heavily and trembled. His eyes wandered restlessly around, his chest heaved. . . .

" 'Is that you, Requiemov?' he asked in a hoarse voice. 'Is it really you? You are pale, like one risen from the grave. . . . But no, are you not a hallucination? My God. . . . You look terrible! . . .'

" 'But what's the matter with you? You look like a ghost!'

" 'Och! wait, my dear fellow, let me recover my breath. . . . I am glad to have met you, if it really is you and not an optical illusion. That damned spiritistic séance. . . . It has so upset my nerves that, would you believe it, just now, when I came home, I saw in my room . . . a coffin!'

"I could not believe my own ears, and asked him to repeat what he had said.

" 'A coffin, a real coffin!' the doctor repeated, sitting down on the steps quite exhausted. 'I am no coward, but the devil himself would be frightened if, after a spiritistic séance, he ran up against a coffin.'

"Stammering and confusedly I told the doctor about the coffins I had seen. . . .

"For a minute we looked at each other with staring eyes, and open-mouthed with astonishment. Then to convince ourselves that we were not dreaming we began pinching each other.

" 'We both feel pain,' the doctor said, 'so at the present moment we are not asleep, and we are not dreaming of each other. Therefore, my coffin and both your coffins were not optical illusions, but something that exists. What are we to do now, old man?'

"We stood for a whole hour on the cold staircase, lost in guesses and conjectures; we got terribly cold and at last decided to conquer our cowardly fear, arouse the man-servant on duty and go with him to the doctor's room. So we went. We entered the room, lit a candle and we really saw a coffin covered with white silver brocade with gold fringe and tassels. The man-servant piously crossed himself.

" 'Now we can find out,' the doctor said, still trembling in every limb, 'if the coffin is empty or if it is . . . inhabited!'

"After long and quite comprehensible hesitation, the doctor bent over the coffin and, pressing his lips together from fright and expectation, he tore off the lid.

"We looked into the coffin and . . .

"The coffin was empty. . . .

"There was no corpse in it, but instead we found the following letter:

"Dear Godsacreov,

"You know that my father-in-law's business has got into a terrible mess. He is over head and ears in debt. Tomorrow or the day after there will be an execution in his house, and this would entirely ruin his family and mine, and would ruin our honor too, which is more precious than anything else for me. At a family council we held yesterday we decided to hide everything valuable or of worth. As the whole of my father-in-law's property consists of coffins (he is, as you doubtless know, the best undertaker in town), we decided to hide away all the best coffins. I entreat you, as a friend, to save our property and our honor! Hoping that you will help us to save our goods, I send you, dear old fellow, one coffin, with the request that you will hide it in your rooms, and keep it till called for. Without the assistance of our friends and acquaintances we are ruined. I hope that you will not refuse me this assistance, all the more as the coffin will not remain with you for more than a week. To everyone whom I consider as our sincere friend, I have sent a coffin, trusting in their magnanimity and nobility.

"Your affectionate,

"Ivan Jawin."

"For three months after that I had to undergo a cure for my shattered nerves, while our friend, the undertaker's son-in-law, saved both his honor and his property, and is now the owner of an under-

taker's business; he arranges funeral processions, sells monument
and gravestones. His business, however, is not getting on very wel
and every evening when I come home I always expect to find next t
my bed a white marble monument or a catafalque." [4]

THE SILVER MINE

SELMA LAGERLÖF (SWEDEN)

Translated by Velma Swanston Howard

King Gustaf the Third [1] was traveling through Dalecarlia. H
was pressed for time, and all the way he wanted to drive like light
ning. Although they drove with such speed that the horses were ex
tended like stretched rubber bands and the coach cleared the turn
on two wheels, the King poked his head out of the window and
shouted to the postilion: "Why don't you go ahead? Do you thin
you are driving over eggs?"

Since they had to drive over poor country roads at such a mad
pace, it would have been almost a miracle had the harness and
wagon held together! And they didn't, either; for at the foot of a
steep hill the pole broke—and there the King sat! The courtiers
sprang from the coach and scolded the driver, but this did not lessen
the damage done. There was no possibility of continuing the jour
ney until the coach was mended.

When the courtiers looked round to try to find something with
which the King could amuse himself while he waited, they noticed a
church spire looming high above the trees in a grove a short distance
ahead. They intimated to the King that he might step into one of
the coaches in which the attendants were riding and drive up to the
church. It was a Sunday, and the King might attend service to pass
the time until the royal coach was ready.

The King accepted the proposal and drove toward the church.
He had been traveling for hours through dark forest regions, but
here it looked more cheerful, with fairly large meadows and villages,
and with the Dal River gliding on, light and pretty, between thick
rows of alder bushes.

But the King had ill-luck to this extent: the bellringer took up
the recessional chant just as the King was stepping from the coach
on the church knoll and the people were coming out from the serv-

---

[4] *catafalque*: stand to support a coffin.   [1] *King Gustaf the Third*: 1771–1792.

e. But when they came walking past him, the King remained standing, with one foot in the wagon and the other on the foot-step. He did not move from the spot—only stared at them. They were the finest lot of folk he had ever seen. All the men were above the average height, with intelligent and earnest faces, and the women were dignified and stately, with an air of Sabbath peace about them.

The whole of the preceding day the King had talked only of the desolate tracts he was passing through, and had said to his courtiers again and again, "Now I am certainly driving through the very poorest part of my kingdom!" But now, when he saw the people, garbed in the picturesque dress of this section of the country, he forgot to think of their poverty; instead his heart warmed, and he remarked to himself: "The King of Sweden is not so badly off as his enemies think. So long as my subjects look like this, I shall probably be able to defend both my faith and my country."

He commanded the courtiers to make known to the people that the stranger who was standing amongst them was their King, and that they should gather around him, so he could talk to them.

And then the King made a speech to the people. He spoke from the high steps outside the vestry, and the narrow step upon which he stood is there even today.

The King gave an account of the sad plight in which the kingdom was placed. He said that the Swedes were threatened with war, both by Russians and Danes. Under ordinary circumstances it wouldn't be such a serious matter, but now the army was filled with traitors, and he did not dare depend upon it. Therefore there was no other course for him to pursue than to go himself into the country settlements and ask his subjects if they would be loyal to their King and help him with men and money, so he could save the Fatherland.

The peasants stood quietly while the King was speaking, and when he had finished they gave no sign either of approval or disapproval.

The King himself thought that he had spoken very well. The tears had sprung to his eyes several times while he was speaking. But when the peasants stood there all the while, troubled and undecided, and could not make up their minds to answer him, the King frowned and looked displeased.

The peasants understood that it was becoming monotonous for the King to wait, and finally one of them stepped out from the crowd.

"Now, you must know, King Gustaf, that we were not expecting

a royal visit in the parish today," said the peasant, "and therefor
we are not prepared to answer you at once. I advise you to go in
the vestry and speak with our pastor, while we discuss among ou
selves this matter which you have laid before us."

The King apprehended that a more satisfactory response was n
to be had immediately, so he felt that it would be best for him t
follow the peasant's advice.

When he came into the vestry, he found no one there but a ma
who looked like a peasant. He was tall and rugged, with big hand
toughened by labor, and he wore neither cassock nor collar, bi
leather breeches and a long white homespun coat, like all the othe
men.

He arose and bowed to the King when the latter entered.

"I thought I should find the parson in here," said the King.

The man grew somewhat red in the face. He thought it annoyin
to mention the fact that he was the parson of this parish, when h
saw that the King had mistaken him for a peasant. "Yes," said he
"the parson is usually on hand in here."

The King dropped into a large armchair which stood in the vestr
at that time, and which stands there today, looking exactly lik
itself, with this difference: the congregation has had a gilded crow
attached to the back of it.

"Have you a good parson in this parish?" asked the King, wh
wanted to appear interested in the welfare of the peasants.

When the King questioned him in this manner, the parson fel
that he couldn't possibly tell who he was. "It's better to let him g
on believing that I'm only a peasant," thought he, and replied tha
the parson was good enough. He preached a pure and clear gospe
and tried to live as he taught.

The King thought that this was a good commendation, but he hac
a sharp ear and marked a certain doubt in the tone. "You sound as
if you were not quite satisfied with the parson," said the King.

"He's a bit arbitrary," said the man, thinking that if the Kin
should find out later who he was, he would not think that the parso
had been standing here and blowing his own horn, therefore h
wished to come out with a little fault-finding also. "There are some
no doubt, who say the parson wants to be the only one to counse
and rule in this parish," he continued.

"Then, at all events, he has led and managed in the best possibl
way," said the King. He didn't like it that the peasant had com
plained of one who was placed above him. "To me it appears as
though good habits and old-time simplicity were the rule here."

"The people are good enough," said the curate, "but then they live in poverty and isolation. Human beings here would certainly be no better than others if this world's temptations came closer to them."

"But there's no fear of anything of the sort happening," said the King with a shrug.

He said nothing further, but began thrumming on the table with his fingers. He thought he had exchanged a sufficient number of gracious words with this peasant and wondered when the others would be ready with their answer.

"These peasants are not very eager to help their King," thought he. "If I only had my coach, I would drive away from them and their palaver!"

The pastor sat there troubled, debating with himself as to how he should decide an important matter which he must settle. He was beginning to feel happy because he had not told the King who he was. Now he felt that he could speak with him about matters which otherwise he could not have placed before him.

After a while the parson broke the silence and asked the King if it was an actual fact that enemies were upon them and that the kingdom was in danger.

The King thought this man ought to have sense enough not to trouble him further. He simply glared at him and said nothing.

"I ask because I was standing in here and could not hear very well," said the parson. "But if this is really the case, I want to say to you that the pastor of this congregation might perhaps be able to procure for the King as much money as he will need."

"I thought you said just now that every one here was poor," said the King, thinking that the man didn't know what he was talking about.

"Yes, that is true," replied the rector, "and the parson has no more than any of the others. But if the King would condescend to listen to me for a moment, I will explain how the pastor happens to have the power to help him."

"You may speak," said the King. "You seem to find it easier to get the words past your lips than your friends and neighbors out there, who never will be ready with what they have to tell me."

"It is not so easy to reply to the King! I'm afraid that, in the end, it will be the parson who must undertake this on behalf of the others."

The King crossed his legs, folded his arms, and let his head sink down on his breast. "You may begin now," he said in the tone of one already asleep.

"Once upon a time there were five men from this parish who were

out on a moose hunt," began the clergyman. "One of them was tl
parson of whom we are speaking. Two of the others were soldier
named Olaf and Eric Svärd; the fourth man was the innkeeper i
this settlement, and the fifth was a peasant named Israel Po
Persson."

"Don't go to the trouble of mentioning so many names," muttere
the King, letting his head droop to one side.

"Those men were good hunters," continued the parson, "wl
usually had luck with them; but that day they had wandered lon
and far without getting anything. Finally they gave up the hur
altogether and sat down on the ground to talk. They said there wa
not a spot in the whole forest fit for cultivation; all of it was onl
mountain and swamp land. 'Our Lord has not done right by us i
giving us such a poor land to live in,' said one. 'In other localitie
people can get riches for themselves in abundance, but here, with a
our toil and drudgery, we can scarcely get our daily bread.'"

The pastor paused a moment, as if uncertain that the King hear
him, but the latter moved his little finger to show that he was awake

"Just as the hunters were discussing this matter, the parson sa
something that glittered at the base of the mountain, where he ha
kicked away a moss-tuft. 'This is a queer mountain,' he though
as he kicked off another moss-tuft. He picked up a sliver of ston
that came with the moss and which shone exactly like the other. 'I
can't be possible that this stuff is lead,' said he. Then the other
sprang up and scraped away the turf with the butt end of thei
rifles. When they did this, they saw plainly that a broad vein o
ore followed the mountain. 'What do you think this might be i
asked the parson. The men chipped off bits of stone and bit int
them. 'It must be lead, or zinc at least,' said they. 'And the whol
mountain is full of it,' added the innkeeper."

When the parson had got thus far in his narrative, the King's hea
was seen to straighten up a little and one eye opened. "Do you know
if any of those persons knew anything about ore and minerals?" he
asked.

"They did not," replied the parson.

Then the King's head sank and both eyes closed.

"The clergyman and his companions were very happy," continued
the speaker, without letting himself be disturbed by the King's in
difference; "they fancied that now they had found that which would
give them and their descendants wealth. 'I'll never have to do any
more work,' said one. 'Now I can afford to do nothing at all the
whole week through, and on Sundays I shall drive to church in a
golden chariot!' They were otherwise sensible men, but the grea

find had gone to their heads and they talked like children. Still they had enough presence of mind to put back the moss-tufts and conceal the vein of ore. Then they carefully noted the place where it was, and went home. Before they parted company, they agreed that the parson should travel to Falun and ask the mining expert what kind of ore this was. He was to return as soon as possible, and until then they promised one another on oath not to reveal to a single soul where the ore was to be found."

The King's head was raised again a trifle, but he did not interrupt the speaker with a word. It appeared as though he was beginning to believe that the man actually had something of importance he wished to say to him, since he didn't allow himself to be disturbed by his indifference.

"Then the parson departed with a few samples of ore in his pocket. He was just as happy in the thought of becoming rich as the others were. He was thinking of rebuilding the parsonage, which at present was no better than a peasant's cottage, and then he would marry a dean's daughter whom he liked. He had thought that he might have to wait for her many years! He was poor and obscure and knew that it would be a long while before he should get any post that would enable him to marry.

"The parson drove over to Falun in two days, and there he had to wait another whole day because the mining expert was away. Finally, he ran across him and showed him the bits of ore. The mining expert took them in his hand. He looked at them first, then at the parson. The parson related how he had found them in a mountain at home in his parish, and wondered if it might not be lead.

" 'No, it's not lead,' said the mining expert.

" 'Perhaps it is zinc, then?' asked the parson.

" 'Nor is it zinc,' said the mineralogist.

"The parson thought that all the hope within him sank. He had not been so depressed in many a long day.

" 'Have you many stones like these in your parish?' asked the mineralogist.

" 'We have a whole mountain full,' said the parson.

"Then the mineralogist came up closer, slapped the parson on the shoulder, and said, 'Let us see that you make such good use of this that it will prove a blessing both to yourselves and to the country, for this is silver.'

" 'Indeed?' said the parson, feeling his way. 'So it is silver!'

"The mineralogist began telling him how he should go to work to get legal rights to the mine and gave him many valuable suggestions; but the parson stood there dazed and didn't listen to what he was saying. He was only thinking of how wonderful it was that at home in his poor parish stood a whole mountain of silver ore, waiting for him."

The King raised his head so suddenly that the parson stopped short in his narrative. "It turned out, of course, that when he got home and began working the mine, he saw that the mineralogist had only been stringing him," said the King.

"Oh, no, the mineralogist had not fooled him," said the parson.

"You may continue," said the King, as he settled himself more comfortably in the chair to listen.

"When the parson was at home again and was driving through the parish," continued the clergyman, "he thought that first of all he should inform his partners of the value of their find. And as he drove alongside the Innkeeper Sten Stensson's place, he intended to drive up to the house and tell him they had found silver. But when he stopped outside the gate, he noticed that a broad path of evergreen was strewn all the way up to the doorstep.

" 'Who has died in this place?' asked the parson of a boy who stood leaning against the fence.

" 'The innkeeper himself,' answered the boy. Then he let the clergyman know that the innkeeper had drunk himself full every day for a week. 'Oh, so much brandy, so much brandy has been drunk here!'

" 'How can that be?' asked the parson. 'The innkeeper used never to drink himself full.'

" 'Oh,' said the boy, 'he drank because he said he had found a mine. He was very rich. He should never have to do anything now but drink, he said. Last night he drove off, full as he was, and the wagon turned over and he was killed.'

"When the parson heard this, he drove homeward. He was distressed over what he had heard. He had come back so happy, rejoicing because he could tell the great good news.

"When the parson had driven a few paces, he saw Israel Per Persson walking along. He looked about as usual, and the parson thought it was well that fortune had not gone to his head too. Him he would cheer at once with the news that he was a rich man.

" 'Good day!' said Per Persson. 'Do you come from Falun now?'

" 'I do,' said the parson. 'And now I must tell you that it has turned out even better than we had imagined. The mineralogist said it was silver ore that we had found.'

"That instant Per Persson looked as though the ground under him had opened! 'What are you saying, what are you saying? Is it silver?'

" 'Yes,' answered the parson. 'We'll all be rich men now, all of us, and can live like gentlemen.'

" 'Oh, is it silver!' said Per Persson once again, looking more and more mournful.

" 'Why, of course it is silver,' replied the parson. 'You mustn't think that I want to deceive you. You musn't be afraid of being happy.'

" 'Happy!' said Per Persson. 'Should I be happy? I believed it was only glitter that we had found, so I thought it would be better to take the certain for the uncertain: I have sold my share in the mine to Olaf Svärd for a hundred dollars.' He was desperate, and when the parson drove away from him, he stood on the highway and wept.

"When the clergyman got back to his home, he sent a servant to Olaf Svärd and his brother to tell them that it was silver they had found. He thought that he had had quite enough driving around and spreading the good news.

"But in the evening, when the parson sat alone, his joy asserted itself again. He went out in the darkness and stood on a hillock upon which he contemplated building the new parsonage. It should be imposing, of course, as fine as a bishop's palace. He stood out there long that night; nor did he content himself with rebuilding the parsonage! It occurred to him that, since there were such riches to be found in the parish, throngs of people would pour in and, finally, a whole city would be built around the mine. And then he would have to erect a new church in place of the old one. Toward this object a large portion of his wealth would probably go. And he was not content with this, either, but fancied that when his church was ready, the King and many bishops would come to the dedication. Then the King would be pleased with the church, but he would remark that there was no place where a king might put up, and then he would have to erect a castle in the new city."

Just then one of the King's courtiers opened the door of the vestry and announced that the big royal coach was mended.

At the first moment the King was ready to withdraw, but on second thought he changed his mind. "You may tell your story to the end," he said to the parson. "But you can hurry it a bit. We know all about how the man thought and dreamed. We want to know how he acted."

"But while the parson was still lost in his dreams," continued the clergyman, "word came to him that Israel Per Persson had made away with himself. He had not been able to bear the disappointment of having sold his share in the mine. He had thought, no doubt, that he could not endure to go about every day seeing another enjoying the wealth that might have been his."

The King straightened up a little. He kept both eyes open. "Upon my word," he said, "if I had been that parson, I should have had enough of the mine!"

"The King is a rich man," said the parson. "He has quite enough, at all events. It is not the same thing with a poor curate who possesses nothing. The unhappy wretch thought instead, when he saw that God's blessing was not with his enterprise: 'I will dream no more of bringing glory and profit to myself with these riches; but I can't let the silver lie buried in the earth! I must take it out, for the benefit of the poor and needy. I will work the mine, to put the whole parish on its feet.'

"So one day the parson went out to see Olaf Svärd, to ask him and his brother as to what should be done immediately with the silver mountain. When he came in the vicinity of the barracks, he met a cart surrounded by armed peasants, and in the cart sat a man with his hands tied behind him and a rope around his ankles.

"When the parson passed by, the cart stopped, and he had time to regard the prisoner, whose head was tied up so it wasn't easy to see who he was. But the parson thought he recognized Olaf Svärd. He heard the prisoner beg those who guarded him to let him speak a few words with the parson.

"The parson drew nearer, and the prisoner turned toward him. 'You will soon be the only one who knows where the silver mine is,' said Olaf.

" 'What are you saying, Olaf?' asked the parson.

" 'Well, you see, parson, since we have learned that it was a silver mine we had found, my brother and I could no longer be as good friends as before. We were continually quarreling. Last night we got into a controversy over which one of us five it was who first discovered the mine. It ended in strife between us, and we came to blows. I have killed my brother and he has left me with a souvenir across the forehead [2] to remember him by. I must hang now, and then you will be the only one who knows anything about the mine; therefore I wish to ask something of you.'

" 'Speak out!' said the parson. 'I'll do what I can for you.'

[2] A reference to Cain's murder of his brother Abel, *Gen.* iv, 3-15.

" 'You know that I am leaving several little children behind me,' began the soldier, but the parson interrupted him.

" 'As regards this, you can rest easy. That which comes to your hare in the mine, they shall have, exactly as if you yourself were living.'

" 'No,' said Olaf Svärd, 'it was another thing I wanted to ask you. Don't let them have any portion of that which comes from the mine!'

"The parson staggered back a step. He stood there dumb and could not answer.

" 'If you do not promise me this, I cannot die in peace,' said the prisoner.

" 'Yes,' said the parson slowly and painfully. 'I promise you what you ask of me.'

"Thereupon the murderer was taken away, and the parson stood on the highway thinking how he should keep the promise he had given him. On the way home he thought of the wealth which he had been so happy over. But if it really were true that the people in this community could not stand riches?—Already four were ruined, who hitherto had been dignified and excellent men. He seemed to see the whole community before him, and he pictured to himself how this silver mine would destroy one after another. Was it befitting that he, who had been appointed to watch over these poor human beings' souls, should let loose upon them that which would be their destruction?"

All of a sudden the King sat bolt upright in his chair. "I declare!" said he, "you'll make me understand that a parson in this isolated settlement must be every inch a man."

"Nor was it enough with what had already happened," continued the parson, "for as soon as the news about the mine spread among the parishioners, they stopped working and went about in idleness, waiting for the time when great riches should pour in on them. All the ne'er-do-wells there were in this section streamed in, and drunkenness and fighting were what the parson heard talked of continually. A lot of people did nothing but tramp round in the forest searching for the mine, and the parson marked that as soon as he left the house people followed him stealthily to find out if he wasn't going to the silver mountain and to steal the secret from him.

"When matters were come to this pass, the parson called the peasants together to vote. To start with, he reminded them of all the misfortunes which the discovery of the mountain had brought upon them, and he asked them if they were going to let themselves be

ruined or if they would save themselves. Then he told them tha
they must not expect him, who was their spiritual adviser, to help
on their destruction. Now he had decided not to reveal to any one
where the silver mine was, and never would he himself take riche
from it. And then he asked the peasants how they would have i
henceforth. If they wished to continue their search for the mine and
wait upon riches, then he would go so far away that not a hearsay of
their misery could reach him; but if they would give up thinking
about the silver mine and be as heretofore, he would remain with
them. 'Whichever way you may choose,' said the parson, 'remem
ber this, that from me no one shall ever know anything about th
silver mountain!'"

"Well," said the King, "how did they decide?"

"They did as their pastor wished," said the parson. "They under
stood that he meant well by them when he wanted to remain poo
for their sakes. And they commissioned him to go to the forest and
conceal the vein of ore with evergreen and stone, so that no on
would be able to find it—neither they themselves nor their pos
terity."

"And ever since the parson has been living here just as poor a
the rest?"

"Yes," answered the curate, "he has lived here just as poor as th
rest."

"He has married, of course, and built himself a new parsonage?"
said the King.

"No, he couldn't afford to marry, and he lives in the old cabin."

"It's a pretty story that you have told me," said the King. Afte
a few seconds he resumed: "Was it of the silver mountain that you
were thinking when you said that the parson here would be abl
to procure for me as much money as I need?"

"Yes," said the other.

"But I can't put the thumb-screws on him," said the King. "O
how would you that I should get such a man to show me the moun
tain—a man who has renounced his sweetheart and all the allure
ments of life?"

"Oh, that's a different matter," said the parson. "But if it's th
Fatherland that is in need of the fortune, he will probably give in."

"Will you answer for that?" asked the King.

"Yes, that I will answer for," said the clergyman.

"Doesn't he care, then, what becomes of his parishioners?"

"That can rest in God's hand."

The King rose from the chair and walked over to the window. H stood for a moment and looked upon the group of people outside. The longer he looked, the clearer his large eyes shone, and his figure seemed to grow. "You may greet the pastor of this congregation, and say that for Sweden's King there is no sight more beautiful than to see a people such as this!"

Then the King turned from the window and looked at the clergyman. He began to smile. "Is it true that the pastor of this parish is so poor that he removes his black clothes as soon as the service is over and dresses himself like a peasant?" asked the King.

"Yes, so poor is he," said the curate, and a crimson flush leaped into his rough-hewn face.

The King went back to the window. One could see that he was in his best mood. All that was noble and great within him had been quickened into life. "You must let that mine lie in peace," said the King. "Inasmuch as you have labored and starved a lifetime to make this people such as you would have it, you may keep it as it is."

"But if the kingdom is in danger?" said the parson.

"The kingdom is better served with men than with money," remarked the King. When he had said this, he bade the clergyman farewell and went out from the vestry.

Without stood the group of people, as quiet and taciturn as they were when he went in. As the King came down the steps, a peasant stepped up to him.

"Have you had a talk with our pastor?" said the peasant.

"Yes," said the King. "I have talked with him."

"Then of course you have our answer?" said the peasant. "We asked you to go in and talk with our parson, that he might give you an answer from us."

"I have the answer," said the King.

THE LOST DAY

GIOVANNI PAPINI (ITALY)

Translated by Alethea Graham

I know a good many lovely old princesses, but they are all so poor that they can hardly afford one little maid in black, and have to live in Tuscany in some tumble-down country house, one of those secret houses where two dusty cypresses stand guard over a gate in the high wall.

If ever you should meet one of these princesses at the house of a
dowager countess whose receptions are no longer fashionable, call
her "Highness," and speak to her in French—the cosmopolitan,
classical, colorless sort of French you can learn in L'Abbé Mar-
montel's *Contes Moraux,* which is spoken by *gens de qualité.*[1] My
princesses nearly always answer with polite profusion, and when
you have succeeded in penetrating their poor little souls (souls
as little and dusty and full of pretty trifles as a seventeenth-century
chapel), you will come to the conclusion that life, after all, is worth
living, and that your mother was not as stupid as you might think
when she brought you into the world.

What amazing secrets my lovely old princesses have whispered to
me! Though they love powder, they love talking even more; and
although they are all German (there is only one Russian), the delightful *ancien régime* [2] French still gives me a delicate and unusual
emotion, so that my heart flutters, and I confess I sometimes find
myself sighing softly as a lover sighs.

One evening, when it was still quite early, I was sitting silent near
the oldest and most beautiful of my princesses. We were in the
drawing-room of a Tuscan country house; I sat in an Empire chair
near the table, where I had been given a little cup of weak tea.

My princess wore black; her face was covered by a black veil, and
her hair (it was white, I knew, and still rather curly) was covered
by a black hat. There seemed to be a halo of darkness all around
her. I tried to believe that she was nothing but a fantastic creature
called up by my imagination; it was not difficult to believe this
because the room was almost dark; a single candle shed a feeble
light on her powdered face, the only white thing in the surrounding
shadow. Everything else melted into the gloom, so that I could
imagine I had nothing but a head hanging in front of me, detached
from its body, and floating a yard or so above the ground.

"So you insist," she said, "on my telling you my last secret. I have
always kept it a secret because it's a far less likely story than any of
my other ones. But I know that in a month or two I must die, before
the winter is out; and I can never be sure of finding another man
as interested as you are in absurd sorts of stories. . . . Well, this
secret began when I was twenty-two. At that time I was the prettiest
princess in Vienna—but I've told you that story before. *Passons!*
Well, it happened that at the end of my twenty-second year I had a
call from an old gentleman, decorated and clean-shaven, and h

---

[1] *gens de qualité:* people of high birth and position.
[2] *ancien régime:* the old régime or aristocratic social system which long ag
passed away.

ked whether he could speak to me alone for just one moment. As
on as we were alone he said : 'I have a daughter I love very dearly,
d she is seriously ill. I must give her back life and strength; so I
n going round everywhere looking for years of youth to buy or
rrow. If you will lend me one year of your life, I will give it back
you, day by day, before your life is finished. So when you finish
ur twenty-second year, instead of being twenty-three you will
ip a year and be twenty-four. But you'll still be so young, you
ill hardly notice the gap; and then, of course, I'll give you back
l your three hundred and sixty-five days right up to the last one,
vo or three at a time, so that, when you're old, you can have back
oments of genuine youth, a sudden return of freshness and beauty.
ou must not think I am laughing at you. I am just a poor father
ho has prayed God so long and so fervently that a gift is vouch-
fed to me which others cannot be given. I have succeeded in col-
cting three years already, but I need several more. Give me one of
urs, and you will surely never be sorry for it!'

"I had always been used to strange adventures, and in the almost
perial society in which I moved nothing was really considered
possible. So I agreed to the amazing loan, and in a few days I be-
me a year older. Hardly any one noticed; and until I was forty
went on living perfectly happily without ever wanting back the
ar that I had given on trust and which was still owing to me.

"The old gentleman had left me his address with the contract. He
d asked me always to let him know a month beforehand when I
ould want a day or a week of my youth back, and he promised that
should always get what I asked for on the appointed day.

"After my fortieth year, when my beauty was beginning to fade,
retired to one of the few castles that still belonged to my family,
d only went to Vienna once or twice in the year. I used to write
good time to my old gentleman, and then I used to go to the Court
lls in the great houses of the capital, as young and lovely as I had
en at twenty-three; and I used to amaze all the people who had
en my beauty fading. How strange the days before my appear-
nce must have been! In the evening I went to bed tired and
née [3] and the next morning I woke up gay and light-hearted as a
ird that has just learnt to fly, and ran to the looking-glass to see.
ll my wrinkles had gone, my body was fresh and plump, my hair
as golden again, and my lips red—so red that I could have kissed
em myself. At Vienna all my admirers came crowding around me,
xclaiming at my wonderful beauty and accusing me of witchcraft;
ut really they had no idea what had really happened. As soon as

[3] *fanée:* faded.

my little lease of youth was about to elapse, I got back into my ca riage and was rushed back to my castle, where I refused to see an one. One day a young Bohemian count, who had fallen violently love with me when I was in Vienna, managed to get into my room— can't imagine how he did it—and nearly fainted when he saw ho much uglier and older I was (although I was still very much lil her) than the woman who had won his heart in the streets of Vienn

"After that no one ever managed to break into my self-impos retreat; the terrible course of my hourly decay was only broken no and then by my rare hours of youth, with their strange joy and awf melancholy. Can you imagine what an odd life I lived—long mont of lonely old age interspersed with the thrill of a day or two's beau and love?

"To begin with, those three hundred and sixty-five days seem absolutely inexhaustible, and it seemed as if I could never come the end of them. So I was rather careless about them, and wrote to often to my mysterious Debtor of Life. But he is a most terrib accurate person. One day I went to his house and saw all h account-books; you know I am by no means the only person he h made this sort of contract with, and I am quite sure he keeps all h accounts most accurately. I saw his daughter too—a very pa creature, sitting on a veranda and all surrounded with flowers.

"I have never been able to find out exactly from where he gets tl life that he gives back so punctually, in daily instalments; but rather think he incurs new debts to pay back the old ones. I wond who the women are who gave him the days he's passed on to m . . . I should like to know one of them; but I have never been ab to find out anything, although I've often made discreet inquirie *Mais, peut-être elles ne seraient pas si étranges que je crois. . .*

"At any rate, he is a most extraordinarily interesting man, and l works out his system beautifully. You can't imagine, though, ho terrible my life became when he told me, calmly—like a banke don't you know!—that now he only had eleven of my days left. Fe a whole year I never wrote to him, and once I felt inclined to mal him a present of my remaining days and never to bother myself ar more worrying about them. I'm sure you know why I felt like that Every time I became young again, the more painful was my re awakening to age, because there was a bigger difference each tin between my real age and twenty-three.

"But it was impossible to hold out much longer. You don't thin surely, that a lonely old woman could ever refuse her privilege day or two of beauty and love and charm and joy, now and then

---

[4] But perhaps they are not as unknown to me as I think.

o be loved for a day—desired for an hour—happy for a moment!
ous êtes trop jeune pour comprendre tout mon ravissement.[5]

"But my days are almost finished—I shall soon close my account
r ever. Think; I've only one more day to ask for. After that I
all be definitely an old woman, consecrated to death. One day of
ht, and then everlasting darkness. . . . You see . . . the unex-
cted tragedy of my life. Before I ask for that one day . . .

"But when shall I ask for it? What shall I do with it? I haven't
en young for three whole years, and now hardly any one remem-
rs me at Vienna; my beauty would seem ghostly. . . . But I feel
eed a lover, an ardent, passionate lover. . . . My poor, wrinkled,
d face will be fresh and rosy again, and my lips will breathe desire
r the very last time. Poor, pale, cracked lips! They long to be red
d warm just once agair only for one day—just for a last lover,
r a last kiss!

"But I can't make up my mind! I haven't got the strength of
ind to spend the last little penny of my youth—I don't know how
spend it—but I have a wild longing to spend it. . . ."

Poor, charming princess! She had raised her little veil and the
ars were making little channels on her powdered face. Her sobs—
though she tried to restrain them politely—prevented her going on.
hen I felt I must do all I could to console this adorable old lady,
d I fell at her feet—the feet of a withered old princess all dressed
black—and assured her that I would love her more ardently than
y lover; and I begged her, softly and insistently, to give the last
y of her youth to me and to me alone.

I cannot quite remember everything I said, but it must have
oved her profoundly, because she promised, rather melodramati-
lly, that in a month's time I might be her last lover—for a day.
e agreed to meet at the same house; then I kissed her pale, thin
nds, and bade her farewell.

While I was walking back toward the town that night, the moon,
t quite full, looked at me persistently, pityingly sarcastic; but I
as thinking of my princess so hard that I did not take the moon
riously in the least.

That month was terribly long, quite the longest month in my life.
had promised my future mistress not to try to see her until the
pointed day, and I kept my promise faithfully. However, at last
e day arrived; it seemed the longest of all that long month.
inally the evening came, and after I had dressed with great care, I
t off for the country house, my heart beating and my steps uneasy.

[5] You are too young to understand completely my joy.

I saw the windows of the house from far off; I had never see[n] them so brilliantly lighted. When I got nearer I found the ga[te] open and the balcony heavy with flowers. I went in and through the drawing-room, where all the candles of two elaborate chand[e]liers were burning.

I was asked to wait; I waited and no one came. The house wa[s] perfectly quiet. The lights burned softly and the flowers filled th[e] silence with their perfume. After waiting restlessly for an hour, [I] could bear it no longer and went into the dining-room. The tab[le] was laid for two, and there were masses of fruit and flowers. The[n] I went through into a little drawing-room, dimly lit and deserte[d.] At last I came to a door which I knew led into the princess's room. [I] knocked once or twice, but no one answered. Then I plucked up m[y] courage—I knew a lover can neglect the rules of etiquette—an[d] opened the door; then I stopped on the threshold.

The room was full of beautiful clothes, thrown about anyhow, [as] if the place had been sacked. Four chandeliers threw a stron[g] flickering light around. The princess was reclining in an arm-cha[ir] in front of the mirror; she was wearing one of the loveliest dress[es] I have ever seen.

I called her; she did not answer.

I went up to her, touched her, but she did not move. Then [I] noticed that her face was thin and white, just as I had always see[n] it, but perhaps a little more frightened, a little sadder than usual. [I] put my hand over her mouth, but I could feel no breath; I put it o[n] her breast, but I could feel no heart-beat.

The poor princess was dead—she had died, quietly and suddenl[y] while she was in front of the mirror watching for her youth to com[e] back.

A letter I found near her on the ground explained her sudde[n] death. There were only a few lines of stiff, military handwritin[g,] which said:

My Dear Princess,

I am extremely sorry I cannot give you back at once the last day of you[th] I owe you. I have not been able to find any woman who was sensible enoug[h] to believe my almost unbelievable promise, and my daughter's life is [in] danger.

I will do my best, however, and I will let you know whether I am succes[s-] ful; I should like to be able to satisfy you to the last.

Believe me,

Yours sincerely . . .

The signature was illegible.

ADIÓS,[1] CORDERA

LEOPOLDO ALAS (SPAIN)

Translated by Charles B. McMichael

There were three; always the three! Rosa, Pinin and Cordera.

The Somonte meadow was a triangular cutting of velvety green, retched like a tapestry, down hill across the mountains. The rail-ad from Obiedo to Gijon cut off one of its corners, the lower one. telegraph pole, planted there like a standard of conquest, with its ttle white cups, and its parallel wires to right and to left, repre-nted to Rosa and Pinin the wide world, unexplored, mysterious, vful, forever unknown.

Mornings without end; beneath the passing of the sun, some-mes, amid the humming of the insects, the cow and the children waited the approach of midday to go to the house. And finally ernal evenings of sweet, silent sadness, in the same meadow, before ie coming of the night, with the evening star as a mute witness on igh. The clouds rolled by there overhead. The shadows of the ees and of the rocks lengthened on the hill and in the dale; the irds went to bed; some stars began to shine in the darkest part f the blue sky, and Pinin and Rosa, the twin children of Anton e Chinta, their souls possessed by all the sweet, dreamy serenity of plemn and serious Nature, were quiet for hours and hours, seated ear Cordera, who accompanied the august silence with the soft pund of her lazy bell.

In this quiet, in this inactive calm, there was love. The brother nd sister loved each other and Pinin and Rosa loved Cordera, their irge, dun-colored grandmother cow. Cordera, as well as it is pos-ible to guess those things, said that she loved the twins, whose duty t was to look after her. She had little gift of expression, but the atience with which she suffered them to use her as a hiding place, nd for a mount, and for other things which caught the fancy of the outhful shepherds, tacitly showed the affection of the pacific and houghtful animal. In hard times Pinin and Rosa had given to Cor-lera the very limit of solicitude and care. Anton de Chinta had not lways rented the Somonte meadow. That luxury was compara-ively new. Years before, Cordera had to go out on the Common, hat is, to graze as she could, in the roads and lanes, upon the nouthfuls of scant herbage which occupied so much of the highways

[1] *Adiós:* Goodbye.

as pasturage. Pinin and Rosa in those days of want spied out t
best croppings in the neighborhood, the least disturbed, and guard
her from the thousand ills which cattle that must get their living
the public roads are subject to. In the days of hunger in the stab
where hay was scarce and straw to make a warm bed for the c
was not to be had, Cordera owed to the labors of Pinin and Rosa t
alleviation of her misery. And in the heroic days of maternity, wh
her calf arrived, and when the necessary struggle ensued betwe
the feeding and prosperity of the little one and the nourishi
of the Chintas, which consisted of robbing from the mother c
every drop which was not necessary for the life of the new-bo
calf, Rosa and Pinin were always on the side of Cordera.

Anton de Chinta knew that he had been born to poverty, wh
he realized the impossibility of accomplishing that gilded dream
keeping a "corral" of his own with a yoke of oxen, at least. I
owned, thanks to a thousand economies, which caused rivulets
sweat and purgatories of privation—yes, he owned one cow, Co
dera; and he never got beyond that. Before he was able to buy a
other, he found himself in arrears to the overseer, who was the lan
lord of the cottage which he rented, and to pay them he was oblige
to take to the market, though it wrung his heart, Cordera, t
darling of his children. Chinta's wife had died two years after Anto
had brought Cordera to their home. The stable and the marriag
bed had a partition wall between, if you can call a web of chestn
branches and cornstalks a wall. Chinta's wife, the muse of econom
in that hovel, looking at the cow through a chink in the broken wa
of branches, pointed her out as the salvation of her family.

"Take care of her. She is your support," appeared to say the eye
of the poor, dying woman, who perished, exhausted by hunger an
work. The love of the twin children had been centered on Corder
As the lap of a mother, which the father could not replace, was th
warmth of Cordera in the stable and there in Somonte. All th
Anton understood in his own way, confusedly. Of the sale that wa
necessary, he did not say a word to the children.

On Saturday, at dawn of day, in bad humor, Anton began to wal
to Gijon, driving Cordera ahead of him, without more gear than he
bell collar. Pinin and Rosa were asleep. On other days, he used t
wake them at daybreak. When they got up, they found themselve
without Cordera. When at dusk Anton and Cordera came up th
lane, fretful, tired and covered with dust, the father gave no ex
planations, but the children guessed that there was danger.

He had not sold her because no one was willing to give the pric

had put on her head—a price made excessive by a sophistry [2] of
fection; he asked much so that no one might dare to bid. Those
no had come near to try their luck had soon taken their departure,
wearing at him while he looked with eyes of hate and distrust on
my one who dared to insist on going near the price fixed. Up to the
st moment, Anton de Chinta stood in the market place of Humedal
fying fate.

"They can't say I do not want to sell, only I cannot get for Cor-
ra what she is worth." Thus he deceived himself, and finally sigh-
g, as though not quite satisfied, he took his way for the high road
Canadas, amidst the confusion and noise of pigs and bullocks,
en and cows which the country people of many parishes were
iving, just as it was of old with masters and their beasts.

In Nataoyo, at the crossing of two roads, Chinta again ran the
sk of losing Cordera; a neighbor from Carvio who had hung
ound all day offering only a little less than Chinta asked, made a
nal attack; somewhat drunk he raised his bid higher and higher,
ruggling between covetousness and desire to get the cow.

They stood motionless, their hands clasped in the middle of the
ghway, stopping the traffic. At last covetousness won the day;
e small amount of fifty centimos kept them apart, like an abyss;
ey let go their hands, and each went his way, Anton by a little lane
hich led through honeysuckles which were not in bloom and
owering bramble berries to his home.

From the day on which they suspected danger, Pinin and Rosa
ere never pacified. In the middle of the week the superintendent
me himself to the corral of Anton. He was a countryman of the
me parish, ill-tempered and cruel to servants who were in debt.
he landlord would not wait any longer. The cow would have to be
ld at a low price. He must pay or get out into the street. On the
aturday following Pinin went to Humedal with his father. The boy
ooked with horror at the meat contractors, tyrants of the market.
ordera was sold at a fair price to the highest bidder, a man from
astile. They made a brand on her skin, and sent her back to her
table, mournfully tinkling her bell. Behind her walked Anton de
hinta in silence and Pinin, with eyes like fists. When Rosa heard
f the sale, she threw her arms around the neck of Cordera, who
ubmitted to her embraces as she used to do to the yoke. "That is
he way the old woman went," thought the despondent Anton. "She
elongs to the race of beasts, but her children have no other mother
r grandmother."

[2] *sophistry*: subterfuge.

Some days afterwards, in the green field of Somonte, the silen[ce] was funereal. Cordera, who was ignorant of her fate, was resti[ng] *sub specie aeternitatis,*[3] as she will rest and sob when the cru[el] blow shall strike her dead. But Rosa and Pinin remained desola[te] stretched on the grass, hopeless of the future. They looked wi[th] anger at the trains which passed and at the telegraph wires. It w[as] that unknown world, on the one side and on the other, which w[as] taking their beloved Cordera away from them. Friday at dusk w[as] the time of departure. There came an agent of the buyer of Cast[ile] for the cattle. Anton and the commissionaire went into the cotta[ge] for Cordera. Anton had been plying the bottle, and was excite[d.] The weight of the money in his purse cheered him up, however. [He] liked to rattle on. He talked much, praised the excellences of t[he] cow. The other smiled, for the praises of Anton were of no conce[rn] to him. "How the cow gave so many liters of milk, how obedie[nt] she was under the yoke, how strong under a burden. And that in [a] few days she would be cut up into steaks and other savory bits[.] Anton did not like to think of that. He figured her alive and wor[k]ing, serving some other working man, forgetful of him and his chi[l]dren, but alive and happy. Pinin and Rosa, seated on a moun[d,] thinking of nothing but Cordera and her troubles, their han[ds] clasped, looked at the enemy with terror-stricken eyes. At the la[st] moment they threw themselves upon their friend with kisses. Th[e] children followed for quite a distance through the lane of hig[h] hedges Cordera and the commissionaire, the former going agains[t] her will with a stranger, and at such an unusual hour. At last the[y] had to separate. Anton called from the house.

"Bah, children, come here; I tell you there has been enough o[f] trifles," he called, with tears in his voice.

The night was falling, and the long lane growing dark beneath th[e] vault of high hedges. The form of Cordera became black in th[e] distance. Then there remained nothing but the slow tinkle of th[e] bell, vanishing in the distance amidst the melancholy chirrups o[f] countless crickets.

"Adiós, Cordera, good-bye, Cordera!"

"Good-bye, Cordera of my soul!"

"Good-bye," repeated Pinin, more excited than Rosa.

"Good-bye," answered last of all the bell, in its own way, until it[s] sad lament was lost among the many sounds of a July evening in [a] country village.

On the following morning at the usual hour, very early, Pinin an[d]

[3] *sub specie aeternitatis:* without sense of time.

Rosa were at the Somonte meadow. That lonely spot never before had seemed desolate to them, but that day, Somonte, without Cordera, was like the desert.

On a sudden a locomotive whistled, steam appeared, an instant later the train. In an inclosed box car with tall narrow windows or air vents, were dimly seen the twin heads of mated cows, placidly looking through the ventilators.

"Adiós, Cordera," shouted Rosa guessing that her friend, the grandmother cow, was there.

"Adiós, Cordera," shrieked Pinin, in the same belief, shaking his fist at the train which was flying by on its way to Castile. And weeping, the lad cried out, more acquainted than his sister with the ways of the world:

"They are taking her to the butcher so that gentlemen and Indians may eat meat."

"Adiós, Cordera."

"Adiós, Cordera."

Both Rosa and Pinin looked with anger at the railway and the telegraph, the symbols of that enemy, the world, which was carrying off and would devour the companion of so many lonely hours, and the sharer of tenderness so great, so silent, in order to convert her into tid-bits for rich gluttons.

"Adiós, Cordera; Adiós, Cordera. . . ."

ACME

John Galsworthy (England)

In these days no man of genius need starve. The following story of my friend Bruce may be taken as proof of this assertion. Nearly sixty when I first knew him, he must have written already some fifteen books, which had earned him the reputation of "a genius" with the few who know. He used to live in York Street, Adelphi, where he had two rooms up the very shaky staircase of a house chiefly remarkable for the fact that its front door seemed always open. I suppose there never was a writer more indifferent to what people thought of him. He profoundly neglected the press—not with one of those neglects which grow on writers from reading reviews of their own works; he seemed never to read criticism—but with the basic neglect of "an original," a nomadic spirit, a stranger in modern civilization, who would leave his attics for long months of

wandering and come back there to hibernate and write a book. He
was a tall, thin man, with a face rather like Mark Twain's, black
eyebrows which bristled and shot up, a bitten, drooping, gray moustache, and fuzzy gray hair; but his eyes were like owl's eyes, piercing, melancholy, dark brown, and gave to his rugged face the
extraordinary expression of a spirit remote from the flesh which had
captured it. He was a bachelor, who seemed to avoid women; perhaps they had taught him that; for he must have been very attractive to them.

The year of which I write had been to my friend Bruce the devil
monetarily speaking. With his passion for writing that for which
his age had no taste—what could he expect? His last book had been
a complete frost. He had undergone, too, an operation which had
cost him much money and left him very weak. When I went to see
him that October I found him stretched out on two chairs, smoking
the Brazilian cigarettes which he affected—and which always affected me, so black and strong they were, in their yellow maize-leaf
coverings. He had a writing-pad on his knee, and sheets of paper
scattered all around. The room had a very meager look. I had not
seen him for a year and more, but he looked up at me as if I'd been
in yesterday.

"Hallo!" he said. "I went into a thing they call a cinema [1] last
night. Have you ever been?"

"Ever been? Do you know how long the cinema has been going?
Since about 1900."

"Well! What a *thing!* I'm writing a skit [2] on it!"

"How—a skit?"

"Parody—wildest yarn you ever read."

He took up a sheet of paper and began chuckling to himself.

"My heroine," he said, "is an Octoroon. [3] Her eyes swim, and her
lovely bosom heaves. Everybody wants her, and she's more virtuous than words can say. The situations she doesn't succumb to
would freeze your blood; they'll roast your marrow. She has a perfect devil of a brother with whom she was brought up, and who
knows her deep dark secret and wants to trade her off to a millionaire who also has a deep dark secret. All together, there are four
deep dark secrets in my yarn. It's a corker."

"What a waste of your time!" I said.

"My time!" he answered fiercely. "What's the use of my time?
Nobody buys my books."

[1] *cinema:* motion picture.   [2] *skit:* a humorous, critical "take-off."
[3] *Octoroon:* a person with some Negro blood.

"Who's attending you?"

"Doctors! They take your money, that's all. I've got no money.
on't talk about me!" Again he took up a sheet of manuscript, and
uckled.

"Last night—at that place—they had—good God!—a race be-
een a train and a motor-car. Well, I've got one between a train,
motor-car, a flying machine, and a horse."

I sat up.

"May I have a look at your skit," I said, "when you've finished
?"

"It *is* finished. Wrote it straight off. D'you think I could stop and
en go on again with a thing like that?" He gathered the sheets and
ld them out to me. "Take the thing—it's amused me to do it.
he heroine's secret is that she isn't an Octoroon at all; she's a
e La Casse—purest Creole blood of the South; and her villainous
other isn't her brother; and the bad millionaire isn't a million-
re; and her penniless lover is. It's rich, I tell you!"

"Thanks," I said dryly, and took the sheets.

I went away concerned about my friend, his illness and his pov-
ty, especially his poverty, for I saw no end to it.

After dinner that evening I began languidly to read his skit. I had
ot read two pages of the thirty-five before I started up, sat down
ain, and feverishly read on. Skit! By George! He had written
perfect scenario—or, rather, that which wanted the merest profes-
onal touching-up to be perfect. I was excited. It was a little gold-
ine if properly handled. Any good film company, I felt convinced,
ould catch at it. Yes! But how to handle it? Bruce was such
unaccountable creature, such a wild old bird. Imagine his having
ly just realized the cinema! If I told him his skit was a serious
m, he would say: "Good God!" and put it in the fire, priceless
ough it was. And yet, how could I market it without *carte
anche,* and how get *carte blanche* without giving my discovery
vay? I was deathly keen on getting some money for him; and this
ing, properly worked, might almost make him independent. I
lt as if I had a priceless museum piece which a single stumble
ight shatter to fragments. The tone of his voice when he spoke
the cinema—"What a *thing!*"—kept coming back to me. He was
ickly proud, too—very difficult about money. Could I work it
ithout telling him anything? I knew he never looked at a news-
per. But should I be justified in taking advantage of that—in
tting the thing accepted and produced without his knowing? I
volved the question for hours, and went to see him again next day.

He was reading.

"Hallo! You again? What do you think of this theory—that t‍ Egyptians derive from a Saharan civilization?"

"I don't think," I said.

"It's nonsense. This fellow——"

I interrupted him.

"Do you want that skit back, or can I keep it?"

"Skit? What skit?"

"The thing you gave me yesterday."

"That! Light your fire with it. This fellow——"

"Yes," I said; "I'll light a fire with it. I see you're busy."

"Oh, no! I'm not," he said. "I've nothing to do. What's the go‍ of my writing? I earn less and less with every book that comes o‍ I'm dying of poverty."

"That's because you won't consider the public."

"How can I consider the public when I don't know what th‍ want?"

"Because you won't take the trouble to find out. If I suggest‍ a way to you of pleasing the public and making money, you'd ki‍ me out of the room."

And the words: "For instance, I've got a little gold-mine of you‍ in my pocket," were on the tip of my tongue, but I choked the‍ back. "Daren't risk it!" I thought. "He's given you the thin‍ *Carte blanche—cartes serrés!*" [4]

I took the gold-mine away and promptly rough-shaped it for t‍ film. It was perfectly easy, without any alteration of the stor‍ Then I was faced with the temptation to put his name to it. T‍ point was this: If I took it to a film company as an authorless sc‍ nario, I should get only authorless terms; whereas, if I put his nan‍ to it, with a little talking I could double the terms at least. T‍ film public didn't know his name, of course, but the inner litera‍ public did, and it's wonderful how you can impress the market wi‍ the word "genius" judiciously used. It was too dangerous, ho‍ ever; and at last I hit on a middle course. I would take it to the‍ with no name attached, but tell them it was by "a genius" and su‍ gest that they could make capital out of the incognito. I knew the‍ would feel it *was* by a genius.

I took it to an excellent company next day with a covering no‍ saying: "The author, a man of recognized literary genius, for ce‍ tain reasons prefers to remain unknown." They took a fortnig‍ in which to rise, but they rose. They had to. The thing was t‍

[4] *Carte blanche—cartes serrés:* without restrictions and with the cards shuffl‍

ood in itself. For a week I played them over terms. Twice I delivered an ultimatum—twice they surrendered; they knew too well
what they had got. I could have made a contract with two thousand
pounds down which would have brought at least another two thousand pounds before the contract term closed; but I compounded for
one that gave me three thousand pounds down as likely to lead to
less difficulty with Bruce. The terms were not a whit too good for
what was really the "acme" [5] of scenarios. If I could have been
quite open I could certainly have done better. Finally, however, I
signed the contract, delivered the manuscript and received a check
for the price. I was elated, and at the same time knew that my
troubles were just beginning. With Bruce's feeling about the film,
now the deuce should I get him to take the money? Could I go to
his publishers and conspire with them to trickle it out to him gradually as if it came from his books? That meant letting them into the
secret; besides, he was too used to receiving practically nothing
from his books; it would lead him to make inquiry, and the secret
was bound to come out. Could I get a lawyer to spring an inheritance on him? That would mean no end of lying and elaboration,
even if a lawyer would consent. Should I send him the money in
Bank of England notes with the words: "From a lifelong admirer
of your genius"? I was afraid he would suspect a trick, or stolen
notes, and go to the police to trace them. Or should I just go, put
the check on the table, and tell him the truth?

The question worried me terribly, for I didn't feel entitled to
consult others who knew him. It was the sort of thing that, if talked
over, would certainly leak out. It was not desirable, however, to
delay cashing a big check like that. Besides, they had started on
the production. It happened to be a slack time, with a dearth of
good films, so that they were rushing it on. And in the meantime
here was Bruce—starved of everything he wanted, unable to get
away for want of money, depressed about his health and his future.
And yet so completely had he always seemed to me different,
strange, superior to this civilization of ours, that the idea of going
to him and saying simply: "This is yours, for the film you wrote,"
scared me. I could hear his: "I? Write for the cinema? What do
you mean?"

When I came to think of it, I had surely taken an extravagant
liberty in marketing the thing without consulting him. I felt he
would never forgive that, and my feeling toward him was so affectionate, even reverential, that I simply hated the idea of being

[5] *acme:* the most perfect.

wiped out of his good books. At last I hit on a way that by intro
ducing my own interest might break my fall. I cashed the check
lodged the money at my bank, drew my own check on it for th
full amount, and, armed with that and the contract, went to see him

He was lying on two chairs smoking his Brazilians and playin
with a stray cat which had attached itself to him. He seemed rathe
less prickly than usual, and, after beating about the bushes of hi
health and other matters, I began:

"I've got a confession to make, Bruce."

"Confession!" he said. "What confession?"

"You remember that skit on the film you wrote and gave m
about six weeks ago?"

"No."

"Yes, you do—about an Octoroon."

He chuckled. "Oh! ah! That!"

I took a deep breath, and went on:

"Well, I sold it; and the price of course belongs to you."

"What? Who'd print a thing like that?"

"It isn't printed. It's been made into a film—super-film, the
call it."

His hand came to a pause on the cat's back, and he glared at me
I hastened on:

"I ought to have told you what I was doing, but you're so prickly
and you've got such confounded superior notions. I thought if
did you'd be biting off your nose to spite your own face. The fac
is it made a marvelous scenario. Here's the contract, and here's a
check on my bank for the price—three thousand pounds. If yo
like to treat me as your agent, you owe me three hundred pounds
I don't expect it, but I'm not proud like you, and I shan't sneeze.

"Good God!" he said.

"Yes, I know. But it's all nonsense, Bruce. You can carry
scruples to altogether too great length. Tainted source! Every
thing's tainted, if you come to that. The film's a quite justified
expression of modern civilization—a natural outcome of the age
It gives amusement; it affords pleasure. It may be vulgar, it may
be cheap, but we *are* vulgar, and we *are* cheap, and it's no use pre
tending we're not—not you, of course, Bruce, but people at large
A vulgar age wants vulgar amusement, and if we can give it that
amusement we ought to; life's not too cheery, anyway."

The glare in his eyes was almost paralyzing me, but I managed to
stammer on:

"You live out of the world—you don't realize what humdrum

people want; something to balance the grayness, the—the banality of their lives. They want blood, thrill, sensation of all sorts. You didn't mean to give it them, but you have, you've done them a benefit, whether you wish to or not, and the money's yours and you've got to take it."

The cat suddenly jumped down. I waited for the storm to burst.

"I know," I dashed on, "that you hate and despise the film——"

Suddenly his voice boomed out:

"Bosh! What are you talking about? Film! I go there every other night."

It was my turn to say: "Good God!" And ramming contract and check into his empty hand, I bolted, closely followed by the cat.

THE INFANT PRODIGY

THOMAS MANN (GERMANY)

Translated by H. T. Lowe-Porter

The infant prodigy entered. The hall became quiet.

It became quiet and then the audience began to clap, because somewhere at the side a leader of mobs, a born organizer, clapped first. The audience had heard nothing yet, but they applauded; for a mighty publicity organization had heralded the prodigy and people were already hypnotized, whether they knew it or not.

The prodigy came from behind a splendid screen embroidered with Empire garlands and great conventionalized flowers, and climbed nimbly up the steps to the platform, diving into the applause as into a bath; a little chilly and shivering, but yet as though into a friendly element. He advanced to the edge of the platform and smiled as though he were about to be photographed; he made a shy, charming gesture of greeting, like a little girl.

He was dressed entirely in white silk, which the audience found enchanting. The little white jacket was fancifully cut, with a sash underneath it, and even his shoes were made of white silk. But against the white socks his bare little legs stood out quite brown; for he was a Greek boy.

He was called Bibi Saccellaphylaccas. And such indeed was his name. No one knew what Bibi was the pet name for, nobody but the impresario,[1] and he regarded it as a trade secret. Bibi had

[1] *impresario:* a promoter who brings players before the public.

smooth black hair reaching to his shoulders; it was parted on the side and fastened back from the narrow domed forehead by a little silk bow. His was the most harmless childish countenance in the world, with an unfinished nose and guileless mouth. The area beneath his pitch-black mouselike eyes was already a little tired and visibly lined. He looked as though he were nine years old but was really eight and given out for seven. It was hard to tell whether to believe this or not. Probably everybody knew better and still believed it, as happens about so many things. The average man thinks that a little falseness goes with beauty. Where should we get any excitement out of our daily life if we were not willing to pretend a bit? And the average man is quite right, in his average brains!

The prodigy kept on bowing until the applause died down, then he went up to the grand piano, and the audience cast a last look at its programs. First came a *Marche Solennelle*,[2] then a *Reverie*, and then *Le Hibou et les Moineaux*[3]—all by Bibi Saccellaphylaccas. The whole program was by him, they were all his compositions. He could not score them, of course, but he had them all in his extraordinary little head and they possessed real artistic significance, or so it said, seriously and objectively, in the program. The program sounded as though the impresario had wrested these concessions from his critical nature after a hard struggle.

The prodigy sat down upon the revolving stool and felt with his feet for the pedals, which were raised by means of a clever device so that Bibi could reach them. It was Bibi's own piano, he took it everywhere with him. It rested upon wooden trestles and its polish was somewhat marred by the constant transportation—but all that only made things more interesting.

Bibi put his silk-shod feet on the pedals; then he made an artful little face, looked straight ahead of him, and lifted his right hand. It was a brown, childish little hand; but the wrist was strong and unlike a child's, with well-developed bones.

Bibi made his face for the audience because he was aware that he had to entertain them a little. But he had his own private enjoyment in the thing too, an enjoyment which he could never convey to anybody. It was that prickling delight, that secret shudder of bliss, which ran through him every time he sat at an open piano—it would always be with him. And here was the keyboard again, these seven black and white octaves, among which he had so often lost himself in abysmal and thrilling adventures—and yet it always

[2] *Marche Solennelle:* Solemn March.
[3] *Le Hibou et les Moineaux:* The Owl and the Sparrows.

ooked as clean and untouched as a newly washed blackboard. This
was the realm of music that lay before him. It lay spread out like
an inviting ocean, where he might plunge in and blissfully swim,
where he might go under in night and storm, yet keep the mastery:
control, ordain—he held his right hand poised in the air.

A breathless stillness reigned in the room—the tense moment
before the first note came. . . . How would it begin? It began so.
And Bibi, with his index finger, fetched the first note out of the
piano, a quite unexpectedly powerful first note in the middle regis-
er, like a trumpet blast. Others followed, an introduction developed—the audience relaxed.

The concert was held in the palatial hall of a fashionable first-
class hotel. The walls were covered with mirrors framed in gilded
arabesques, between frescoes of the rosy and fleshly school. Orna-
mental columns supported a ceiling that displayed a whole universe
of electric bulbs, in clusters darting a brilliance far brighter than
day and filling the whole space with thin, vibrating golden light.
Not a seat was unoccupied, people were standing in the side aisles
and at the back. The front seats cost twelve marks; [4] for the impresario believed that anything worth having was worth paying
for. And they were occupied by the best society, for it was in the
upper classes, of course, that the greatest enthusiasm was felt.
There were even some children, with their legs hanging down
demurely from their chairs and their shining eyes staring at their
gifted little white-clad contemporary.

Down in front on the left side sat the prodigy's mother, an
extremely obese woman with a powdered double chin and a feather
on her head. Beside her was the impresario, a man of oriental
appearance with large gold buttons on his conspicuous cuffs.

Bibi ended in a grand climax. With what power this wee manikin
belabored the keyboard! The audience could scarcely trust its
ears. The march theme, an infectious, swinging tune, broke out
once more, fully harmonized, bold and showy; with every note Bibi
flung himself back from the waist as though he were marching in a
triumphal procession. He ended *fortissimo*, [5] bent over, slipped
sideways off the stool, and stood with a smile awaiting the applause.

And the applause burst forth, unanimously, enthusiastically; the
child made his demure little maidenly curtsy and people in the
front seat thought: "Look what slim little hips he has! Clap, clap!
Hurrah, bravo, little chap, Saccophylax or whatever your name is!
Wait, let me take off my gloves—what a little devil of a chap he is!"

Bibi had to come out three times from behind the screen before

[4] *mark*: a German coin worth then about a quarter. [5] *fortissimo*: very loud.

they would stop. Some late-comers entered the hall and move about looking for seats. Then the concert continued. Bibi's *Reveri* murmured its numbers, consisting almost entirely of arpeggio above which a bar of melody rose now and then, weak-winged. The came *Le Hibou et les Moineaux*. This piece was brilliantly suc cessful, it made a strong impression; it was an effective childhoo fantasy, remarkably well envisaged. The bass represented the ow sitting morosely rolling his filmy eyes; while in the treble th impudent, half-frightened sparrows chirped. Bibi received an ova tion when he finished, he was called out four times. A hotel pag with shiny buttons carried up three great laurel wreaths onto th stage and proffered them from one side while Bibi nodded and expressed his thanks.

Ah, the knowing little creature understood how to make peopl clap! He stopped behind the screen, they had to wait for him lingered a little on the steps of the platform, admired the lon streamers on the wreaths—although actually such things bore him stiff by now. He bowed with the utmost charm, he gave th audience plenty of time to rave itself out, because applause is valu able and must not be cut short. "*Le Hibou* is my drawing card," he thought—this expression he had learned from the impresario "Now I will play the fantasy, it is a lot better than *Le Hibou*, o course, especially the C-sharp passage. But you idiots dote on th *Hibou*, though it is the first and the silliest thing I wrote." He continued to bow and smile.

Next came a *Méditation* and then an *Étude* [6]—the program was quite comprehensive. The *Méditation* was very like the *Reverie*—which was nothing against it—and the *Étude* displayed all of Bibi's virtuosity, which naturally fell a little short of his inventiveness. And then the *Fantaisie*. This was his favorite; he varied it a little each time, giving himself free rein and sometimes surprising even himself, on good evenings, by his own inventiveness.

He sat and played, so little, so white and shining, against the great black grand piano, elect [7] and alone, above that confused sea of faces, above the heavy, insensitive mass soul, upon which he was laboring to work with his individual, differentiated soul. His lock of soft black hair with the white silk bow had fallen over his forehead, his trained and bony little wrists pounded away, the muscles stood out visibly on his brown childish cheeks.

Sitting there he sometimes had moments of oblivion and solitude,

[6] *Étude:* Study.   [7] *elect:* chosen from the mass.

when the gaze of his strange little mouselike eyes with the big rings beneath them would lose itself and stare through the painted stage into space that was peopled with strange vague life. Then out of the corner of his eye he would give a quick look back into the hall and be once more with his audience.

"Joy and pain, the heights and the depths—that is my *Fantaisie*," he thought lovingly. "Listen, here is the C-sharp passage." He lingered over the approach, wondering if they would notice anything. But no, of course not, how should they? And he cast his eyes up prettily at the ceiling so that at least they might have something to look at.

All these people sat there in their regular rows, looking at the prodigy and thinking all sorts of things in their regular brains. An old gentleman with a white beard, a seal ring on his finger and a bulbous swelling on his bald spot, a growth if you like, was thinking to himself: "Really, one ought to be ashamed." He had never got any further than "Ah, thou dearest Augustin" on the piano, and here he sat now, a gray old man, looking on while this little hop-o'-my-thumb performed miracles. Yes, yes, it is a gift of God, we must remember that, God grants His gifts, or He withholds them, and there is no shame in being an ordinary man. As with the Christ Child.—Before a child one may kneel without feeling ashamed. Strange that thoughts like these should be so satisfying—he would even say so sweet, if it were not too silly for a tough old man like him to use the word. That was how he felt, anyhow.

Art . . . the business man with the parrot-nose was thinking. Yes, it adds something cheerful to life, a little good white silk and a little tumty-ti-ti-tum. Really he does not play so badly. Fully fifty seats, twelve marks apiece, that makes six hundred marks—and everything else besides. Take off the rent of the hall, the lighting and the programs, you must have fully a thousand marks profit. That is worth while."

"That was Chopin [8] he was just playing," thought the piano-teacher, a lady with a pointed nose; she was of an age when the understanding sharpens as the hopes decay. "But not very original—I will say that afterwards, it sounds well. And his hand position is entirely amateur. One must be able to lay a coin on the back of the hand—I would use a ruler on him."

Then there was a young girl, at that self-conscious and chlorotic [9] time of life when the most ineffable ideas come into the mind. She

---

[8] *Chopin:* a great Polish composer. The teacher means Bibi imitates passages from other musicians, no doubt unconsciously. [9] *chlorotic:* colorful.

was thinking to herself: "What is it he is playing? It is expressiv
of passion, yet he is a child. If he kissed me, it would be as thoug
my little brother kissed me—no kiss at all. Is there such a thing a
passion all by itself, without any earthly object, a sort of child's
play of passion? What nonsense! If I were to say such thing
aloud they would just be at me with some more codliver oil. Suc
is life."

An officer was leaning against a column. He looked on at Bibi'
success and thought: "Yes, you are something and I am something
each in his own way." So he clapped his heels together and paid t
the prodigy the respect which he felt to be due to all the power
that be.

Then there was a critic, an elderly man in a shiny black coat an
turned-up trousers splashed with mud. He sat in his free seat an
thought: "Look at him, this young beggar of a Bibi. As an indi
vidual he has still to develop, but as a type he is already quite com
plete, the artist *par excellence*.[10] He has in himself all the artist'
exaltation and his utter worthlessness, his charlatanry and his sa
cred fire, his burning contempt and his secret raptures. Of course
can't write all that, it is too good. Of course, I should have been a
artist myself if I had not seen through the whole business s
clearly."

Then the prodigy stopped playing and a perfect storm arose i
the hall. He had to come out again and again from behind hi
screen. The man with the shiny buttons carried up more wreaths
four laurel wreaths, a lyre made of violets, a bouquet of roses. H
had not arms enough to convey all these tributes, the impresari
himself mounted the stage to help him. He hung a laurel wreatl
round Bibi's neck, he tenderly stroked the black hair—and suddenl
as though overcome he bent down and gave the prodigy a kiss, a
resounding kiss, square on the mouth. And then the storm becam
a hurricane. That kiss ran through the room like an electric shock
it went direct to people's marrow and made them shiver down thei
backs. They were carried away by a helpless compulsion of shee
noise. Loud shouts mingled with the hysterical clapping of hands
Some of Bibi's commonplace little friends down there waved thei
handkerchiefs. But the critic thought: "Of course that kiss had t
come—it's a good old gag. Yes, good Lord, if only one did not se
through everything quite so clearly—"

And so the concert drew to a close. It began at half past sever
and finished at half past eight. The platform was laden with

[10] *par excellence:* to the highest degree, completely.

reaths and two little pots of flowers stood on the lamp-stands of
ie piano. Bibi played as his last number his *Rhapsodie Grecque,*
hich turned into the Greek national hymn at the end. His fellow-
ountrymen in the audience would gladly have sung it with him if
ie company had not been so august. They made up for it with a
owerful noise and hullabaloo, a hot-blooded national demonstra-
on. And the aging critic was thinking: "Yes, the hymn had to
ome too. They have to exploit every vein—publicity cannot afford
o neglect any means to its end. I think I'll criticize that as inar-
istic. But perhaps I am wrong, perhaps that is the most artistic
hing of all. What is the artist? A jack-in-the-box. Criticism is on
 higher plane. But I can't say that." And away he went in his
uddy trousers.

THE RETURN

LORD DUNSANY (IRELAND)

Can you all hear me? I am speaking on the wireless.[1] And I
elieve that I am in touch with you.

I thought that perhaps you might care to hear a ghost story. An
ctual personal experience, with nothing secondhand about it. A
hing that occurred actually to myself, perhaps the most personal
host story that any of you may have heard.

Well, to begin with, I was a long way away, when there came over
ie very suddenly an irresistible feeling to return to the old haunts
hat I had known a long while ago. I say "to begin with," for one
nust begin somewhere; and my long wanderings, and the remote
arts to which I had come, are not much concerned with this tale.
Sufficient that I turned at once for home, borne by a longing so
strong that it seemed to leave me no choice, and I came in the course
of time to that very village whose every chimney I knew. Every
oath I knew there too, and every little track running off from the
oaths the width of a single footstep, by which children ran to gardens of their own that they had found or made among weeds; but
some of these paths had altered in the long time since I was there.
It was a long, long time. The old public house was the same, the
Green Man at the corner. And there I drifted, almost aimlessly,
and yet with a feeling that there as much as anywhere I might find
the life of the old village throbbing away. It was as I passed over

[1] *wireless:* the radio.

the fields on the way to the Green Man that I first heard people talking about a ghost. I was passing a wheat field, over the stubble, brushing by a line of sheaves, when two men at work there, taking the sheaves away, began to talk of the ghost all of a sudden. "They say it comes every hundred years," said one.

"Yes," said the other, looking up at the leaves turning with the earliest touch of autumn, "and it should be about the very day."

"It is," said the first; and I heard them say no more, and passed on feeling sure I should hear more at the inn. At the inn I knew none of them, not one; and, where once I thought I did, it was only some old family likeness. So I sat all by myself in a corner beside a curtain and listened to what they said. And, just as I came in, their talk took the same turn as what I had heard in the cornfield. There was a ghost, it seemed, that came to that village once in a hundred years, and the hundred years were up. "Might be coming soon," said one, who looked like a gamekeeper.

"Aye, if there's any truth in it," said a farmer.

"True enough, by all accounts," said some.

"And there's been a look about the shadows lately," the keeper said, "like what my grandmother told me of."

"Your grandmother?" one of them asked.

"Yes, she saw it," he said.

"Must have been an old woman," said a man, looking round from the bar, on which he was leaning.

"Saw it as a child," said the keeper.

"I wouldn't walk near the stream tonight," said another, "not if any mist was rising. You'd meet it, all damp in the mist."

I sat there quietly in the shade of the curtain listening to all they said.

"Wonder where it comes from," said the farmer.

"Ah," they all said, and shook their heads, and no one even ventured to guess about that.

"Drifts over the fields where it used to walk, I expect, and up to the old house," said the bartender. "But as to where it comes from —ah."

And then their talk died away, as though it were somehow chilled by a draft blowing out of eternity. And when I saw I should get no more of this story from them I slipped quietly out of the room.

Two women were talking on a doorstep as I passed the next house; they seemed to be talking about the price of tea. And suddenly I heard one say: "It will be about the hundred years."

"Aye," said the other one, "I shouldn't wonder." And one of

em went inside the house at that, and the other hurried away
ong the street, and I was all alone once more.

I passed a group of children in the road; and saw from a certain
ish that came over their playing, and from the way that a few
them put their heads together and glanced up toward the old
use, that they too were talking of the ghost. It left no doubt that
at house was the seat of the mystery, and that there these ends
tales one heard in the village would be all gathered together. But
hen would it be? Was it the hundred years? It hardly seemed
me that it could be yet. The air seemed somehow not quite suffi-
ently haunted, though it hardly seems worth telling you so airy a
ncy. Partly to see the old village again, and partly to get more
cts, if I could, about this tale of the ghost, I hung about the vil-
ge. I went to the village green. It delighted me to see the calm
d space again—altered, but not out of knowledge; and there were
ese on it, just as of old. And then a young man and a girl came by,
ing along a path that slanted across the green, the same path that
ere had been in my time. And by some strange chance they too, as
on as they came within hearing, began to speak of the end of the
undred years, and that visitor that all of them were expect-
g. Half believing and half wondering, they passed away out of
aring.

One is moved by impulses more than by reason when one comes
old haunts that one knew. Had reason moved me alone, I should
ave gone at once to the old house on the hill beyond the village,
d satisfied my curiosity there. But stronger than curiosity,
ronger than any other emotion within me, I found the lure of the
eat willows, standing in their strange attitudes by the long-
emembered stream. To them I went as evening began to draw in.
white mist rose as I came, and began to creep slowly through fields
at sloped to the stream. I went with it, glad of its company, and
itered about those fields whose every boundary was unchanged
y even a yard since the days when I knew them. And there the old
aystacks stood, dark in the same corners, as though they had never
een used since last I saw them; and the mist came up and touched
em, and flowed about them, till they stood amongst it like islands.
seemed to know every one of them, not only by their positions,
ut by the size of them. You see, nothing could ever have happened
the years since I was there to make each field give more hay, or
ny less, or to find a better place for the haystack to stand in each
eld. It was this that made me see, what I already profoundly felt,
hat I still had my share in this village. Much had changed, but the

fundamental things were there as ever. Indeed, it could not hav
been otherwise. And it made me feel more friendly with the mis
with which I was sauntering amongst these remembered nooks, t
reflect that it was another of those things that would be in tha
valley always. Or if it wandered away in the warm weather, cai
ried off by some stray wind, it would return like myself.

Couples walking late, or men traveling lonely, turned now awa
from the mist, as though they found something ominous in it
waving and wandering whiteness; they turned suddenly for th
uplands, and we were left quite alone. And I knew they were righ
to avoid the stream at this hour, for there was a most haunted fee
ing about it, and that feeling slowly increased as the evening gre
stiller and later. Rooks passed, and all the singing birds were asleer
A few wild ducks came over, and circled once, and dropped pas
me down to their home in a patch of irises; they alone seeming ur
perturbed by whatever was making the mist so unmistakably eeri
And then a silence fell that nothing disturbed at all, and all the whil
the eeriness was increasing.

It was like that till the moon rose. But when the moon came hug
and yellow and magical and very nearly full, almost with a leap ove
a ridge of the downland that showed just clear of the osiers, I suc
denly knew that the hundred years were up, and that whateve
haunted the old house over the meadows, on the opposite side fror
the moon, would be now on its way if ever. So I left the stream a
once and turned for the hill, to see what was to be seen. I went, a
the way, over fields every one of which I had carried so long in m
memory that I knew my way unmistakably. Sometimes they di
fered from the picture of them that I had treasured so long, bu
only by being a little duller, by shining a little less vividly, as mus
be the way with heavy solid earth when compared with an old men
ory. Voices were rising now in the village behind me, as thoug
the large moon coming over the ridges, or the end of the hundre
years, had awaked all of a sudden uneasy apprehensions; and nc
only human voices rose in a hum, but there came sharply throug
them the outcry of dogs, which clearly shared the vague fear tha
seemed haunting their masters. The sound of the voices grew lo
as I moved away from them, but never ceased to fill the night wit
fear. At what moment the hundred years would end I knew not, bu
it seemed to me that as the moon rose higher the very last hours c
the century were falling away.

I crossed a road, and a couple walking down it paused suddenl
and looked up to the old house on the hill. I saw the shape of i

dark, with no windows lit, though now and then the moon flashed curiously upon panes. And this bulk in the night, with flashes upon the windows, I knew for the end of my journey. In this house my life had begun, and to it I returned. It was this house that had called me, through all the length of my wanderings, and that I felt drawing me now, as the Pole draws the needles of magnets. I paid no heed any more to that uneasy hum that came quavering up from voices astir in the village, but left them to whatever troubled them in the mist, and made straight for that house. Far down below me now were the mist and its fears, and the slope of the hill steepened. I swept up it; and just as I came to the edge of the lawns I knew as I know no other lawns, I found a high wall before me. They had built it since the days when I knew those lawns. There seemed something about the moon and about the hour that told me not to loiter before this wall, and I pressed on to the house.

The lawns were the same as ever, and all the dew was glittering under the moon, and a hush was heavy upon them, and the house was deep in sleep. Not a sound came from the black bulk of the house, not a movement of door or window, though I had returned to my home from so far and after so long. It stood there black and silent, but the chill and the hush and the darkness of the house were to stop me no more than the wall. I had come from so far to see those lawns again, and the old house standing amongst them. I went round to the door, and the glass which there was in its panels stared blankly at me, with shutters behind them; and all the bolts were locked. There a dog saw me. It had been lying down in a barrel, guarding the door, when it suddenly saw me and howled. But still no sound or movement came from the house.

I knew I was very near to the end of my long journey now, the old wainscot of oak on an upper landing, carved with the curious heads of ancient kings, dark with the years and darkening all the corridor, that ran to the door of a room that was once my nursery. I knew now that this carved oak was the end of my journey. I entered the house, and the dog howled once more. Before me, all in the dark, were the stairs I knew. I needed no light. I knew every turn of those stairs, and every step of them, and the very flight of the echoes that used to rise from the creak of each different board. I sped up them, and the dog was howling now with one long quivering howl. I came to the landing, and there was the old dark corridor, and there were the ancient heads with their curious faces that semed to look at me with the first welcome I had had since my long journey began. The howling of the dog, which was louder now, seemed at last to disturb the house, for far away I heard the thudding of footsteps. And the steps were coming toward me.

Can you hear me? I feel that you can. I believe I am near you. A door opened some way off. The steps were nearer. A woman came along the corridor, holding a candle, walking slowly, and looking about her anxiously as she came. And just then clearly out of the tower of the old church of the village the notes of midnight floated over the mist; and it felt to me at that moment that the hundred years were over. And all of a sudden the woman holding the candle saw me. She seemed to see me more clearly than any had done in the village: I noticed that in her eyes as her mouth opened slowly. And then she screamed.

This is a personal experience. Nothing secondhand, as so often there is in such stories. I turned from the woman's white face to the dark of the old carved wainscot, whose every panel and every figure I knew; and, sinking far into that venerable timber, sinking home to the deeps of the oak, I knew that *I* was the ghost.

READING PROBLEMS ON THE SHORT STORY

1. *The Purloined Letter:* Why does Poe introduce the friend of Dupin into the story? What was the minister's purpose in stealing the letter? What obstacle defeated the police in their search for it? What principle guided Dupin in his search for the letter? Why does he succeed where the police fail? What part of the story is told chronologically and what part retrogressively? Why?

2. *A Passion in the Desert:* Could this story have taken place in any other setting? What is the dominant interest—character, setting, emotion? Explain the aptness of the title. Stop at "She examined the man with an almost commercial prudence," and guess the outcome of the story. Finish it to test your guess. Then go back over the story to see how many hints or foreshadowings of coming events Balzac gives us. Can you remember actions of your pets which parallel those of this panther? What is the aim of the hero in this story? Does he achieve it? Where is the turning point or climax? Is the end logical?

3. *The Necklace:* What is the aim of the heroine in this story? In how many ways is the character of the heroine revealed? How is her character changed by the loss of the necklace? Point out details which will suggest the poverty and struggle of the years of repayment. Why does the author keep the fact that the necklace was paste till the end? What relation has this fact to the theme of the story? What happened afterward? Does this matter?

4. *The Birthday of the Infanta:* In how many ways are the time, place and social background of this story indicated? Contrast the appearance

and the character of the Dwarf. How is suspense created as the Dwarf starts his trip through the palace seeking the Infanta? At what point during this trip do you begin to guess the outcome? Is the main interest in this story in setting, plot, character, theme, or emotion? Does the behavior of the Infanta seem to you natural or unnatural? Prove from your own observation of children. Does it fit the infantas pictured by Velasquez?

5. *The Bottle Imp:* Separate what is possible in this story from what is impossible and fantastic. Do these fantastic events symbolize real truths about life, and if so, what? What in particular is symbolized by the rules as to the sale of the bottle? What does Stevenson mean to suggest by the way in which Keawe's wish for his house was fulfilled? Outline some possible story which will show what Stevenson means by wishing on a bottle and then regretting the consequences. What choices made by the characters reveal their true natures? Did Keawe and his wife deserve to get rid of the bottle at the end? Why?

6. *His Wedded Wife:* How does The Worm prove his real worth, good sense, and character during the months when he was being initiated by his brother officers? What was particularly appropriate in the moment when the supposed wife appeared on the verandah? Did you at any point suspect the identity of the wife? Why? Do any of the onlookers do so? Check over the hints as to "her" identity which the author gives. Did the Senior Subaltern deserve his punishment? Why did The Worm select that particular form of revenge? What effect did The Worm's performance have on his standing in the regiment? Compare the hero of this story with the Boy in Kipling's story entitled *Thrown Away.*

7. *Tony Kytes:* What are the contending parties in this story and for what are they struggling? Look back over this story and pick out hints which indicate whether Tony really got the girl he liked best. Was she the one who loved him most? Did she lack pride? self-respect? initiative? quick wit? Why was she willing to take him under the circumstances? In what does the humor of the story lie—in situation, character, diction, incident?

8. *A Service of Love:* Give examples from this story of humorous exaggeration; of amusingly worded phrases. Show that the setting of this story is composed of more than the place where it happens. Do you think the marriage of Joe and Delia will be a permanent success? Why? Which is the cleverer in his pretense—Joe or Delia? What part does coincidence play in the story? Why is the ending so effective?

9. *The Jumping Frog:* The ancient Greek anecdote from which this story grew did not develop the characters at all. Why does Twain go into so much detail about Smiley and his previous adventures? How does Simon Wheeler's conversational style add reality to the story? Students of French should compare the French translation with the original to see whether they think it has caught the Mark Twain flavor. Has Mark's retranslation done justice to the French? All students should ask themselves what differences between the languages Mark Twain's retranslation emphasizes. Why is this

retranslation so funny, and even though it is, of course, a burlesque, what light does it throw on the difficulty of translating a masterpiece from one language to another? Pick out special phrases which seem extraordinarily *un*successful. Why are they so?

10. *A Terrible Night:* What series of incidents causes the heroes of this story to be so unnerved by the sight of the coffins? Did you suspect before the end that the story was a hoax? Is the speaker serious or ironical in saying that his friend the undertaker saved "his honor" by secreting the coffins?

11. *The Silver Mine:* Why did the parson conceal his identity? What impression does the King form of the parson from the story of the mine? Does he recognize the parson? Prove or disprove from the story that the King and parson are right in their final decision. Of what is the mine a symbol? Summarize in a paragraph the theme of the story. What is effective about the style in which the whole story is told? Does the author ever intrude himself into the story? Why?

12. *The Lost Day:* Do her days of returning youth make the princess really happy? What, on the other hand, has she missed in her old age? Note facts that show the immaturity of the princess' attitude toward life. What does the author mean to symbolize by the lost day? Why does the princess' death coincide with the loss of the day? State what you consider the theme of this story.

13. *Adiós, Cordera:* Why are the railroad and the telegraph mentioned at the beginning and end of the story? Is the loss of the cow more than a financial tragedy? What did the cow mean in the life of the children? Why? How is the style in which this story is written appropriate to the subject? In what way does it heighten the pathos? Would the loss of a city child's pet have been as great a tragedy?

14. *Acme:* Summarize in your own words the criticisms of the average movie plot contained in Bruce's skit. How are these criticisms conveyed to the reader? Are they fair? Does Bruce despise the movies as much as his friend? Why does he go there every other night? Was Bruce a genius?

15. *The Infant Prodigy:* Analyze the character of the child, the effect on him of publicity, and the attitude of the audience. Was Bibi a talented musician? Have the audience come because of the music? Pick out all the details in the story which satirize the methods by which public attention is secured and exploited? What do the comments of individual members of the audience at the end add to the story?

16. *The Return:* Why does the speaker use the radio? How is each detail of the setting of this story made to create a mysterious feeling that something supernatural is to happen? Why is not the whole setting described at once? What is the order of description? What other devices are used to create suspense? When did you first guess the identity of the ghost? After finishing the story, go back over it to see in how many places this identity is hinted or foreshadowed.

FURTHER READINGS IN THE SHORT STORY

Eaton: *Short Stories for Reading and Enjoyment*
Mikels: *Short Stories for English Courses*
Schweikert: *Short Stories*
Galsworthy: *Caravan*
Maclaren: *Beside the Bonnie Briar Bush*
De Maupassant: *The Odd Number*
Poe: *Tales of Imagination*
Stevenson: *New Arabian Nights*
Adam: *Torture by Hope*
Bunner: *A Sisterly Scheme*
Chekhov: *Vanko*
Verotchka
Coppée: *The Substitute*
Daudet: *The Siege of Berlin*
Doyle: *The Three Garridebs*
Ferber: *The Gay Old Dog*

Gerould: *Vain Oblations*
Harte: *Luck of Roaring Camp*
Outcasts of Poker Flat
Kipling: *His Majesty the King*
Baa, Baa, Black Sheep
The Bridge Builders
The Brushwood Boy
William the Conqueror
The Tomb of His Ancestors
Drums of the Fore and Aft
Only a Subaltern
O. Henry: *The Gift of the Magi*
Makes the Whole World Kin
The Lonesome Road
The Ransom of Red Chief
Ouida: *A Dog of Flanders*
Terhune: *The Grudge*
Twain: *The Man Who Corrupted Hadleyburg*

SUGGESTIONS FOR ORIGINAL NARRATIVES

1. The Mystery of the Hidden Library Book. 2. Making Friends with a New Pet. 3. The Lost Suit Case. 4. You Can't Judge People by Their Looks. 5. A Repented Victory. 6. A Freshman Outwits the Senior Bully. 7. He Asked Two Girls to One Party. 8. Self-Sacrifice for One's Chum. 9. Teaching My Dog to Do Tricks. 10. A Clever Hallowe'en Prank That Destroyed No Property. 11. The Invention That Was Never Marketed. 12. How Someone I Know Grew Old Gracefully. 13. Losing a Favorite Pet. 14. A Parody of a Popular Motion Picture. 15. Infant Prodigies I Have Known. 16. Revisiting Grandfather's Old Home.

II

The Prose Tale

THE highly perfected short story of modern days has not sprung into existence in a moment. Even so brilliant a writer as Poe could not invent its technique out of his own head. The immediate predecessor of the short story with a plot was the plotless tale written by Washington Irving, Nathaniel Hawthorne, and earlier authors. The tale has all the interest of the short story except that it is held together not by a causal sequence of events centering around a hero's struggle against obstacles to achieve some aim, but by a central character to whom a series of amusing or exciting things happen one after another quite independently and more or less by accident. The interest centers in the single incidents; long-sustained suspense and the excitement and satisfaction of reaching a climax in the action are missing. But a character can be drawn, a setting depicted, an atmosphere created, significant incidents brilliantly told, and a theme set forth with a finish and perfection of style equal to that of the modern short story. The tale lends itself especially well to a string of detached humorous adventures such as the Spanish were fond of spinning about their favorite clever rascals, like Lazarillo de Tormes. Old legends usually fall into tale form, like Irving's romantic *Tales of the Alhambra*. Certain modern writers still prefer the tale to the story form.

Of the six already mentioned features of the short story [1] which are also found in the tale, the skill with which the incidents are told is perhaps the surest mark of a fine tale. An incident is a single happening. We often relate single incidents in conversation to entertain our friends. Such an incident, related alone, is called an anecdote. A well-told anecdote starts quickly, giving the *who, when* and *where* almost in the opening sentence. The action itself must also be told rapidly, including just the essential facts and moving swiftly to the point. The point must under no circumstances be revealed before the end. And a neat concluding remark to give

[1] Characterization, setting, atmosphere, significant incident, theme, style.

148

the incident a finished effect must round off the anecdote. The skillful tale-teller employs this technique both in his separate incidents
and in the tale as a whole. Moreover, the incidents narrated must be
appropriate to the characters and setting and of genuine significance
in enlarging our understanding of life.

THE FALCON

GIOVANNI BOCCACCIO (ITALY)

Translated by Thomas Roscoe

The modern short story is often traced back to Boccaccio, who
made a famous collection of retold tales entitled *The Decameron*.
These tales are strung together by Boccaccio in a novel manner. He
tells how, to escape the plague, a party of aristocratic young Floren-
tines isolated themselves in a remote country house. Here they
amused each other day by day reciting interesting tales, one of which
follows.

❋   ❋   ❋

There once lived in Florence a youth called Federigo, son of
Messer Philippo Alberighi, who for feats of arms and accomplish-
ments was held in higher esteem than any cavalier of his age in
Tuscany. This young man became deeply enamored of a lady called
Monna Giovanna, reputed in her time one of the most beautiful and
agreeable women in Florence; and in order to win her affections he
gave a succession of tournaments, feasts, and banquets, and spared
no expense in his entertainments. But this lady, not less discreet
than beautiful, paid no regard to all that was done in her honor, nor
condescended to notice the author of it.

Federigo, thus spending all his property and acquiring none in
return, was soon stripped of his wealth, and became suddenly impoverished, having nothing now remaining but a small farm, on the
produce of which he found a bare subsistence; yet he still retained
a favorite falcon, which for her rare qualities was nowhere to be
matched. Being thus unable to live any longer in the city in the
style he was accustomed to, and being more than ever enamored
of the lady, he departed to his little estate in the country, and there
without inviting any one to his house, he amused himself with his
falcon, and endured his poverty with tranquil patience.

It happened that when Federigo was reduced to this extremity, the husband of Monna Giovanna fell sick, and feeling the approach of death, made his will, leaving his possessions, which were very great, to an only son now growing up, and in the event of the son's death, to Monna Giovanni, whom he dearly loved; and he had no sooner subscribed his will than he died. Monna Giovanni, having thus become a widow, went according to the custom of our ladies to pass her year of mourning in retirement, removing to one of her estates very near to the farm of Federigo. Hereupon it happened that her son was accustomed to visit Federigo, and taking great delight in hawks and dogs, and having often seen Federigo's falcon, he became wonderfully fond of it and ardently longed to possess it, but did not venture to ask for it, as he well knew how dear it was to its owner.

Within a short time after this the boy fell sick. His mother, who had no other child, and loved him to excess, stood over him the whole day to tend and comfort him, often asking him and entreating him to tell her if there were anything in the world he desired, as, if it were possible to procure it, he should have it. The youth, after a repetition of these questions, at length said, "My dear mother, if you could by any means procure me Federigo's falcon, I think I should recover from my sickness." The lady, hearing a request so far out of her power, began to consider what she might do to gratify her son's wish. She knew that Federigo had long loved her, but had never received from her so much as a single glance in return. How then (she reflected) shall I send or go to beg this falcon, which from all I hear is the best bird that ever flew, and moreover is now Federigo's sole maintenance; and how can I be guilty of so great a rudeness as to deprive a gentleman who has no other pleasure remaining, of this his only recreation?

Thus troubled in her thoughts, she knew not what to reply to her son. Her maternal love, however, at last prevailed, and she determined to attempt to gratify his wishes, but resolved not to send, but to go herself to Federigo. She then said to her son, "My dear son, be comforted, and get well, for I promise you that the first thing in the morning, I will go myself for the falcon, and bring it to you." This promise brought a beam of joy into the boy's countenance, and the same day he showed evident signs of amendment.

The next morning Monna Giovanna, taking with her another lady as a companion, proceeded to Federigo's humble habitation, and inquired for him. As it happened not to be a day fit for hawking, he was in his garden, and desired one of his people to go to the gate. He was beyond measure surprised when he heard that Monna Giovanna was asking for him, and ran in great joy to meet her. As soon as she saw him approach she gracefully moved to meet him, and respectfully saluting him, said, "Federigo, I am come to recompense you in some sort for the evil you have received at my hands, at a time when you loved me more than was wise on your part, and the recompense I intend is to make myself and my companion your guests at dinner today." To which Federigo with great humility replied, "Alas! madam, I do not recollect to have received any evil at your hands, but so much good that, if it were ever in my power, I should be happy, for the love I have borne you, and more so for the honor of this visit, to expend my fortune a second time in your honor"; and thus speaking, he respectfully led her into his house, and thence conducted her into his garden, and there, not having any other person to introduce her to, said, "Madam, this good woman, the wife of my husbandman, will wait on you whilst I prepare our table."

Living in extreme poverty, Federigo was seldom in a state to receive any one in his house, and this morning being less prepared than usual, and finding nothing to show respect to a lady in whose honor he had entertained such numbers of people, he was grieved beyond measure, and stood in great perplexity, inveighing against his evil fortune as a man bereft of his senses, and running hither and thither, and finding neither money nor provision; and the hour being late, and his desire being great to show the lady some mark of attention, happening to cast his eyes on his favorite falcon, which was resting on its perch in his chamber, and seeing no other resource, he seized the poor bird, and finding it fat and in good condition, thought it would be a dish worthy of the lady, without further hesitation he wrung its neck, and giving it to a girl, ordered her to pluck it and place it on the spit and carefully roast it. He then spread on his table a napkin of snowy whiteness, one of the few things which yet remained to him of his former possessions, and after some time, with a cheerful aspect, returned into the garden to the lady, and told her that a dinner, the best he could provide, was prepared for her. On this the lady with her companion went and seated themselves at the table, where Federigo with great courtesy waited on them, whilst they unknowingly ate his favorite bird.

When they had risen from table, after some agreeable conversation, it seemed to the lady to be now a proper time to make known the purpose of her visit, and turning politely to Federigo, she thus spoke: "Calling to recollection your past life, Federigo, and remembering my reserve, which you perhaps esteemed hard-heartedness and cruelty, I doubt not that you will wonder at my presumption when you learn the object of my visit; but if you now had, or ever had had children, and knew the strength of a parent's affection, feel assured that you would in some measure pardon me; an though you have none, I, who have a dear and beloved son, cannc yet forego the common affections of a mother. I am, then, by mater nal love and duty compelled to ask of you the gift of a possessio which I know is indeed very dear to you, and justly so, since you evil fortune has left you no other comfort in your adversity. Th gift then I ask is your falcon, which my son is so desirous of posses ing, that if I do not obtain it for him, I fear it will so far aggravat the illness under which he labors, that I shall lose him. On thi account, therefore, I entreat you, not by the love which you profes for me (by which you ought in no degree to be governed), but b the magnanimity of your character, which is better manifested in courtesy of this kind than in any other way, that you would do m the favor to bestow it on me, so that by this gift I may be enable to preserve the life of my dear and only son, and I shall myself b for ever indebted to you."

Federigo thus hearing the request of the lady, and seeing it ou of his power to gratify her, as he had served his falcon for dinne began in her presence to weep most bitterly, and became unable t utter a word in reply. The lady, supposing that Federigo's grie arose from his affection to his falcon, and his regret to part with i and expecting a refusal, prepared herself for the worst. "Since th hour, most honored lady," began Federigo, "that I first fixed m affection on you, I have always found Fortune most perverse an cruel to me, but all her blows I consider light in comparison wit the one she has now dealt me, seeing that you have condescende to visit my house, which when I was rich you would not deign t enter, and entreat me for so small a gift; for she has so contrive that it is not in my power to grant it you, and why it is not, yo shall briefly hear. When you informed me that you meant to hono me with your company to dinner, considering your rank, and tha it was only proper that I should pay you due honor by procurin every delicacy in my power, as is becoming on such occasions, an recollecting the falcon which you now request of me, and its man excellent qualities, I considered it a dish not unworthy to be place before you, and I therefore this morning served it up to you roaste at dinner, a thing which at the time I considered most opportun but finding now that you wish to possess the falcon alive for you sick son, my inability to gratify you grieves me so far that I thin I shall never know happiness more."

In confirmation of his words he then produced the feathers an beak and talons of the poor bird. Monna Giovanna at this recita eprehended him for killing so fine a falcon for a lady's dinner, at he same time, however, highly commending in her own mind his magnanimity, which it had not been in the power of Fortune to base. The lady having thus lost all chance of possessing the falcon, nd despairing of the recovery of her son, thanked Federigo for the onor done her, and for his intended good-will, and departed very much dejected. Her son, either through pining for the falcon, or from his complaint being aggravated by disappointment, died a few ays after, to the great grief of his mother. After having for some me indulged her sorrow and tears, her brothers, seeing that she was left extremely rich and was still young, entreated her to marry gain. This she was not desirous of doing, but finding herself constantly assailed by their request, and recollecting the noble conduct f Federigo, and this last instance of his magnanimity in having sacrificed the finest falcon in the world out of respect to her, she aid to her brothers, "I should willingly, if it were agreeable to ou, remain in my present state, but if you insist that I marry, I will ssuredly take no one for my husband but Federigo de gli lberighi."

On which her brothers, smiling, replied, "What folly is this? Would you marry a man who is a beggar?" To this she answered, Brothers, I well know that the matter is as you state it, but I noose rather a man that hath need of wealth, than wealth that hath eed of a man." The brothers, seeing her fixed determination, and nowing the genuine worth of Federigo, notwithstanding his poverty, bestowed their sister on him with all her fortune. Federigo nus unexpectedly found himself united to a beautiful lady whom e had long dearly loved, and passed the remainder of his days in eace and happiness.

THE LEGEND OF THE ROSE OF THE ALHAMBRA

Washington Irving (America)

During the Dark Ages, Spain was conquered by the Moors (or racens) who built at Granada a royal palace called the Alhambra, hose ruins are one of the most beautiful architectural sights in Spain.

❈ ❈ ❈

For some time after the surrender of Granada by the Moors, that lightful city was a frequent and favorite residence of the Spanish vereigns, until they were frightened away by successive shocks

of earthquakes, which toppled down various houses and made th
old Moslem towers rock to their foundation.

Many, many years then rolled away, during which Granada wa
rarely honored by a royal guest. The palaces of the nobility re
mained silent and shut up; and the Alhambra, like a slighte
beauty, sat in mournful desolation among her neglected gardens
The Tower of the Infantas,[1] once the residence of the three beautifu
Moorish princesses, partook of the general desolation. The spide
spun her web athwart the gilded vault, and bats and owls nestle
in those chambers that had been graced by the presence of Zayda
Zorayda, and Zorahayda. The neglect of the tower may have bee
partly owing to some superstitious notions of the neighbors. It wa
rumored that the spirit of the youthful Zorahayda, who had per
ished in that tower, was often seen by moonlight seated beside th
fountain in the hall, or moaning about the battlements, and tha
the notes of her silver lute would be heard at midnight by wayfarer
passing along the glen.

At length the city of Granada was once more enlivened by th
royal presence. All the world knows that Philip V was the firs
Bourbon[2] that swayed the Spanish scepter. All the world know
that he married, in second nuptials, Elizabetta or Isabella (for the
are the same), the beautiful princess of Parma; and all the worl
knows that by this chain of circumstances a French prince and a
Italian princess were seated together on the Spanish throne. Fo
the reception of this illustrious pair the Alhambra was repaired an
fitted up with all possible expedition.

The arrival of the court changed the whole aspect of the latel
deserted place. The clangor of drum and trumpet, the tramp o
steed about the avenues and outer court, the glitter of arms an
display of banners about barbican[3] and battlement, recalled th
ancient and warlike glories of the fortress. A softer spirit, howeve
reigned within the royal palace. There was the rustling of robes
and the cautious tread and murmuring voice of reverential courtier
about the antechambers, a loitering of pages and maids of hono
about the gardens, and the sound of music stealing from ope
casements.

Among those who attended in the train of the monarchs was
favorite page of the queen, named Ruyz de Alarcon. He was jus
turned of eighteen, light and lithe of form, and graceful as a youn
Antinous.[4] To the queen, he was all deference and respect, yet h

[1] *Infantas:* royal princesses.   [2] King of Spain, 1700–1746.
[3] *barbican:* the outwork of the castle.
[4] *Antinous:* a beautiful favorite of the Emperor Hadrian.

vas at heart a roguish stripling, petted and spoiled by the ladies bout the court.

This loitering page was one morning rambling about the groves f the Generaliffe,[5] which overlook the grounds of the Alhambra. He had taken with him for his amusement a favorite gyrfalcon of he queen. In the course of his rambles, seeing a bird rising from a thicket, he unhooded the hawk and let him fly. The falcon towred high in the air, made a swoop at his quarry, but missing it, oared away regardless of the calls of the page. The latter followed he truant bird with his eye, until he saw it alight upon the battlements of a remote and lonely tower, in the outer wall of the Alhambra, built on the edge of a ravine that separated the royal fortress rom the grounds of the Generaliffe. It was, in fact, the "Tower f the Princesses."

The page descended into the ravine and approached the tower, but it had no entrance from the glen, and its lofty height rendered any attempt to scale it fruitless. Seeking one of the gates of the ortress, therefore, he made a wide circuit to that side of the tower acing within the walls.

A small garden inclosed by a trellis-work of reeds overhung with myrtle lay before the tower. Opening a wicket, the page passed between beds of flowers and thickets of roses to the door. It was closed and bolted. A crevice in the door gave him a peep into the interior. There was a small Moorish hall with fretted walls, light marble columns, and an alabaster fountain surrounded with flowers. In the center hung a gilt cage containing a singing bird. Beneath it, on a chair, lay a tortoise-shell cat among reels of silk; and a guitar, decorated with ribands, leaned against the fountain.

Ruyz de Alarcon was struck with these traces of female taste and elegance in a lonely, and, as he had supposed, deserted tower. They reminded him of the tales of enchanted halls in the Alhambra; and he tortoise-shell cat might be some spellbound princess.

He knocked gently at the door. A beautiful face peeped out from a little window above, but was instantly withdrawn. He waited, expecting that the door would be opened; but he waited in vain. No footstep was to be heard within—all was silent. Had his senses deceived him, or was this beautiful apparition the fairy of the tower? He knocked again, and more loudly. After a little while the beaming face once more peeped forth. It was that of a blooming damsel of fifteen.

The page immediately doffed his plumed bonnet, and entreated

---

[5] *Generaliffe:* The summer palace of the Moorish princes.

in the most courteous accents to be permitted to ascend the tow
in pursuit of his falcon.

"I dare not open the door, Señor," replied the little damsel, blus
ing; "my aunt has forbidden it."

"I do beseech you, fair maid; it is the favorite falcon of the quee
I dare not return to the palace without it."

"Are you then one of the cavaliers of the court?"

"I am, fair maid; but I shall lose the queen's favor and my pla
if I lose this hawk."

"Santa Maria! It is against you cavaliers of the court that m
aunt has charged me especially to bar the door."

"Against wicked cavaliers, doubtless; but I am none of thos
only a simple, harmless page, who will be ruined and undone if yo
deny me this small request."

The heart of the little damsel was touched by the distress of th
page. It was a thousand pities he should be ruined for the want o
so trifling a boon. Surely, too, he could not be one of those dange
ous beings whom her aunt had described as a species of canniba
He was gentle and modest, and stood so entreatingly with cap i
hand, and looked so charming!

The sly page redoubled his entreaties in such moving terms tha
it was not in the nature of mortal maiden to deny him; so the blus
ing little warder of the tower descended and opened the door wit
a trembling hand. The page was charmed by the portrait now re
vealed to him. Her Andalusian [6] bodice and trim basquiña set o
the round but delicate symmetry of her form. Her glossy hair wa
parted on her forehead with scrupulous exactness, and decorate
with a fresh plucked rose, according to the universal custom of th
country. It is true, her complexion was tinged by the ardor of
southern sun, but it served to give richness to the bloom of he
cheek, and to heighten the luster of her eyes.

Ruyz de Alarcon beheld all this with a single glance, for it becam
him not to tarry. He merely murmured his acknowledgments, an
then bounded lightly up the spiral staircase in quest of his falco

He soon returned with the truant bird upon his fist. The damse
in the meantime had seated herself by the fountain in the hall an
was winding silk; but in her agitation she let fall the reel upon th
pavement. The page sprang, picked it up, then dropping gracefull
on one knee, presented it to her. Seizing the hand extended to re
ceive it, he imprinted on it a kiss more fervent and devout than h
had ever imprinted on the fair hand of his sovereign.

[6] *Andalusia:* a province in southern Spain.

"AVE MARIA, SEÑOR!" EXCLAIMED THE DAMSEL, BLUSHING
STILL DEEPER WITH CONFUSION AND SURPRISE.

"Ave Maria, Señor!" exclaimed the damsel, blushing still deeper with confusion and surprise.

The modest page made a thousand apologies, assuring her it was the way at court of expressing the most profound homage and respect. She sat blushing, with her eyes cast down upon her work, entangling the silk which she attempted to wind.

Suddenly a shrill voice was heard at a distance.

"My aunt is returning from mass!" cried the damsel in affright. "I pray you, Señor, depart."

"Not until you grant me that rose from your hair as a remembrance."

She hastily untwisted the rose from her raven locks.

"Take it," cried she, "but pray begone."

The page took the rose, and at the same time kissed the fair hand that gave it. Then, placing the flower in his bonnet, and taking the falcon upon his fist, he bounded off through the garden, bearing away with him the heart of the gentle Jacinta.

When the vigilant aunt arrived at the tower, she remarked the agitation of her niece, and an air of confusion in the hall; but a word of explanation from Jacinta sufficed.

"A gyrfalcon had pursued his prey into the hall."

"Mercy on us!" said the aunt. "To think of a falcon flying into the tower. Did ever one hear of so saucy a hawk? Why, the very bird in the cage is not safe."

The vigilant Fredegonda was one of the most wary of ancient spinsters. The niece was the orphan of an officer who had fallen in the wars. She had been educated in a convent, and had recently been transferred from her sacred asylum to the immediate guardianship of her aunt. Her fresh and dawning beauty had caught the public eye, even in her seclusion, and, with that poetical turn common to the people of Andalusia, the peasantry of the neighborhood had given her the appellation of "The Rose of the Alhambra."

The wary aunt continued to keep a faithful watch over her little niece as long as the court continued at Granada, and flattered herself that her vigilance had been successful. At length King Philip cut short his sojourn at Granada, and suddenly departed with all his train. The vigilant Fredegonda watched the royal pageant as it issued forth from the Gate of Justice and descended the great avenue leading to the city. When the last banner disappeared from her sight, she returned exulting to her tower, for all her cares were over.

To her surprise, a light Arabian steed pawed the ground at the wicket gate of the garden. To her horror she saw through the thickets of roses a youth, in gayly embroidered dress, at the feet her niece. At the sound of her footsteps he gave a tender adie bounded lightly over the barrier of reeds and myrtles, sprang up his horse, and was out of sight in an instant.

The tender Jacinta in the agony of her grief lost all thought of h aunt's displeasure. Throwing herself into her arms, she broke for into sobs and tears.

"Oh!" cried she, "he is gone! he is gone! and I shall never s him more!"

"Gone! who is gone? what youth is this I saw at your feet?"

"A queen's page, aunt, who came to bid me farewell."

"A queen's page, child!" echoed the vigilant Fredegonda faintl "and when did you become acquainted with a queen's page?"

"The morning that the gyrfalcon flew into the tower. It was tl queen's gyrfalcon, and he came in pursuit of it."

"Ah, silly, silly girl! know that there are no gyrfalcons half s dangerous as these prankling pages, and it is precisely such simp birds as thee that they pounce upon."

Days, weeks, months elapsed, and nothing more was heard of tl page. The pomegranate ripened, the vine yielded up its fruit, tl autumn rains descended in torrents from the mountains; the Sierr Nevada [7] became covered with a snowy mantle, and wintry blast howled through the halls of the Alhambra. Still he came not. Th winter passed away. Again the genial spring burst forth with son and blossoms and balmy zephyr. The snows melted from the mour tains, until none remained but on the lofty summit of the Nevada glistening through the sultry summer air. Still nothing was hear of the forgetful page.

In the meantime the poor little Jacinta grew pale and thoughtfu Her former occupations and amusements were abandoned, her sil lay entangled, her guitar unstrung, her flowers were neglected, th notes of her bird unheeded, and her eyes, once so bright, wer dimmed with weeping.

"Alas, silly child!" would the staid Fredegonda say, when sh found her niece in one of her desponding moods. "What coulds thou expect from one of a haughty and aspiring family, thou, a orphan, the descendant of a fallen line? Be assured, if the yout were true, his father, who is one of the proudest nobles about th court, would prohibit his union with one so humble and portionles as thou. Pluck up thy resolution, therefore, and drive these idl notions from thy mind."

[7] *Sierra Nevada:* a mountain range.

The words of Fredegonda only served to increase the melancholy f her niece.

At a late hour one midsummer night, after her aunt had retired o rest, she remained alone in the hall of the tower, seated beside he alabaster fountain. The poor little damsel's heart was overladen vith sad and tender recollections, her tears began to flow, and lowly fell drop by drop into the fountain. By degrees the crystal vater became agitated, and bubble—bubble—bubble, boiled up and vas tossed about until a female figure, richly clad in Moorish robes, lowly rose to view.

• Jacinta was so frightened that she fled from the hall, and did not enture to return. The next morning, she related to her aunt what he had seen, but the good lady treated it as a fantasy of her roubled mind, or supposed she had fallen asleep and dreamed eside the fountain.

"Thou hast been thinking of the story of the three Moorish prinesses that once inhabited the tower," said she, "and it has entered nto thy dreams."

"What story, aunt? I know nothing of it."

"Thou hast certainly heard of the three princesses, Zayda, Zoayda, and Zorahayda, who were confined in this tower by the king, heir father, and agreed to fly with three Christian cavaliers. The rst two accomplished their escape, but the third failed in resolution nd remained, and, it is said, died in this tower."

"I now recollect to have heard of it," said Jacinta, "and to have vept over the fate of the gentle Zorahayda."

"Thou mayst well weep over her fate," continued the aunt, "for he lover of Zorahayda was thy ancestor. He long bemoaned his Ioorish love, but time cured him of his grief, and he married a panish lady, from whom thou art descended."

Jacinta pondered upon these words.

"That what I have seen is no fantasy of the brain," said she to erself, "I am confident. If indeed it be the spirit of the gentle orahayda, which I have heard lingers about this tower, of what hould I be afraid? I'll watch by the fountain tonight—perhaps the isit will be repeated."

Toward midnight, when everything was quiet, she again took er seat in the hall. As the bell on the distant watch-tower of the lhambra struck the midnight hour, the fountain was again agied, and bubble—bubble—bubble, it tossed about the waters until ie Moorish female again rose to view. She was young and beautiul. Her dress was rich with jewels, and in her hand she held a silver

lute. Jacinta trembled and was faint, but was reassured by the so
and plaintive voice of the apparition, and the sweet expression o
her pale, melancholy countenance.

"Daughter of mortality," said she, "what aileth thee? Why d
thy tears trouble my fountain, and thy sighs disturb the quie
watches of the night?"

"I weep because of the faithlessness of man, and I bemoan m
solitary and forsaken state."

"Take comfort. Thy sorrows may yet have an end. Thou be
holdest a Moorish princess, who, like thee, was unhappy in her love
A Christian knight, thy ancestor, won my heart, and would hav
borne me to his native land. But I lacked courage equal to my fait
and lingered till too late. For this, the evil genii are permitted t
have power over me, and I remain enchanted in this tower, unti
some pure Christian will deign to break the magic spell. Wilt tho
undertake the task?"

"I will!" replied the damsel, trembling.

"Come hither, then, and fear not. Dip thy hand in the fountair
sprinkle the water over me, and baptize me after the manner o
thy faith. So shall the enchantment be dispelled, and my trouble
spirit have repose."

The damsel advanced with faltering steps, dipped her hand in th
fountain, collected water in the palm, and sprinkled it over the pa
face of the phantom.

The latter smiled with benignity. She dropped her silver lute a
the feet of Jacinta, crossed her white arms, and melted from sight
so that it seemed merely as if a shower of dewdrops had fallen int
the fountain.

Jacinta retired from the hall, filled with awe and wonder. Sh
scarcely closed her eyes that night. But when she awoke at day
break out of a troubled slumber, the whole appeared to her like a
dream. On descending into the hall, however, the truth of the visio
was established; for, beside the fountain she beheld the silver lute
glittering in the morning sunshine.

She hastened to her aunt, related all that had befallen her, an
called her to behold the lute as a testimonial of the reality of he
story. If the good lady had any lingering doubts, they were remove
when Jacinta touched the instrument, for she drew forth such rap
turous tones as to thaw even the frigid heart of Fredegonda. Noth
ing but supernatural melody could have produced such an effect.

The extraordinary power of the lute became every day more an
more apparent. The wayfarer passing by the tower was detained

and, as it were, spellbound, in breathless ecstasy. The very birds gathered in the neighboring trees, and, hushing their own strains, listened in charmed silence. Rumor soon spread the news abroad. The inhabitants of Granada thronged to the Alhambra to catch a few notes of the transcendent music that floated about the tower of Las Infantas.

The lovely little minstrel was at length drawn forth from her retreat. The rich and powerful of the land contended who should entertain and do honor to her. Wherever she went, her vigilant aunt kept a dragon watch at her elbow, awing the throngs of admirers who hung in raptures on her strains. The report of her wonderful powers spread from city to city. Malaga, Seville, Cordova, all became successively mad on the theme. Nothing was talked of throughout Andalusia but the beautiful minstrel of the Alhambra. How could it be otherwise among a people so musical and gallant as the Andalusians?

While all Andalusia was thus music mad, a different mood prevailed at the court of Spain. Philip V, as is well known, was subject to all kinds of fancies. Sometimes he would keep to his bed for weeks together, groaning under imaginary complaints. At other times he would insist upon abdicating his throne, to the great annoyance of his royal spouse, who had a strong relish for the splendors of a court and the glories of a crown and guided the scepter of her imbecile lord with an expert and steady hand.

Nothing was found to be so effective in dispelling the king's fits of melancholy as the powers of music; the queen took care, therefore, to have the best performers, both vocal and instrumental, at hand, and retained the famous Italian singer Farinelli about the court as a kind of royal physician.

At the moment we treat of, however, a freak had come over the mind of this illustrious Bourbon that surpassed all former moods. After a long spell of imaginary illness, which set all the strains of Farinelli and the consultations of a whole orchestra of court fiddlers at defiance, the monarch fairly, in idea, gave up the ghost, and considered himself absolutely dead.

This would have been harmless enough, and even convenient both to his queen and courtiers, had he been content to remain in the quietude befitting a dead man. But to their annoyance, he insisted upon having the funeral ceremonies performed over him, and began to grow impatient and to revile bitterly at them for negligence and disrespect in leaving him unburied. What was to be done? To disobey the king's positive commands was monstrous in the eyes

of the obsequious [8] courtiers,—but to obey him, and bury him aliv
would be downright regicide!

In the midst of this fearful dilemma, a rumor reached the cou
of the female minstrel who was turning the brains of all Andalusi
The queen dispatched missives in all haste, to summon her to S
Ildefonso, where the court at that time resided.

Within a few days, as the queen with her maids of honor wa
walking in those stately gardens, intended, with their avenue an
terraces and fountains, to eclipse the glories of Versailles,[9] tl
far-famed minstrel was conducted into her presence. The imperia
Elizabetta gazed with surprise at the youthful and unpretendin
appearance of the little being that had set the world madding. Sh
was in her picturesque Andalusian dress, her silver lute was in he
hand, and she stood with modest and downcast eyes, but with
simplicity and freshness of beauty that still bespoke her "the Ros
of the Alhambra."

As usual, she was accompanied by the ever-vigilant Fredegonda
who gave the whole history of her parentage and descent to the in
quiring queen. If the stately Elizabetta had been interested by th
appearance of Jacinta, she was still more pleased when she learne
that her father had bravely fallen in the service of the crown.

"If thy powers equal their renown," said she, "and thou cans
cast forth this evil spirit that possesses thy sovereign, thy fortun
shall henceforth be my care, and honors and wealth attend thee."

Impatient to make trial of her skill, the queen led the way at onc
to the apartment of the moody monarch.

Jacinta followed with downcast eyes through files of guards and
crowds of courtiers. They arrived at length at a great chambe
hung in black. The windows were closed to exclude the light o
day. A number of yellow wax tapers in silver sconces diffused a
mournful light, and dimly revealed the figures of mutes in mourn
ing dresses, and courtiers, who glided about with noiseless step and
woebegone visage. In the midst of a funeral bier, his hands folded
on his breast, and the tip of his nose just visible, lay extended this
would-be-buried monarch.

The queen entered the chamber in silence, and, pointing to a
footstool in an obscure corner, beckoned to Jacinta to sit down and
commence.

At first she touched her lute with a faltering hand, but gathering
confidence and animation as she proceeded, drew forth such soft,
aerial harmony that all present could scarce believe it mortal. As to

[8] *Obsequious:* attentive.   [9] *Versailles:* the French royal country palace.

ιe monarch, who had already considered himself in the world of
ɔirits, he set it down for some angelic melody or the music of the
ɔheres.

By degrees the theme was varied, and the voice of the minstrel
ccompanied the instrument. She poured forth one of the legendary
allads treating of the ancient glories of the Alhambra and the
chievements of the Moors. Her whole soul entered into the theme,
ɔr with the recollections of the Alhambra was associated the story
f her love. The funereal chamber resounded with the animating
train. It entered into the gloomy heart of the monarch. He raised
is head and gazed around. He sat up on his couch. His eye began
ɔ kindle; at length, leaping upon the floor, he called for sword and
uckler.

The triumph of music, or rather of the enchanted lute, was com-
ɔlete. The demon of melancholy was cast forth, and, as it were, a
ead man brought to life. The windows of the apartment were
hrown open; the glorious splendor of Spanish sunshine burst into
he late sorrowful chamber. All eyes sought the lovely enchantress,
ɔut the lute had fallen from her hand. She had sunk upon the earth,
nd the next moment was clasped to the heart of Ruyz de Alarcon.

DAVID SWAN

NATHANIEL HAWTHORNE (AMERICA)

We have nothing to do with David Swan until we find him, at the
ge of twenty, on the high road from his native place to the city of
3oston, where his uncle, a small dealer in the grocery line, was to
ake him behind the counter. Be it enough to say that he was a
ɩative of New Hampshire, born of respectable parents, and had re-
·eived an ordinary school education with a classic finish by a year
ɩt Gilmanton Academy. After journeying on foot from sunrise till
ɩearly noon of a summer's day, his weariness and the increasing
ɩeat determined him to sit down in the first convenient shade and
ɩwait the coming up of the stage-coach. As if planted on purpose
·or him, there soon appeared a little tuft of maples with a delightful
·ecess in the midst, and such a fresh bubbling spring that it seemed
ɩever to have sparkled for any wayfarer but David Swan. Virgin
ɔr not, he kissed it with his thirsty lips and then flung himself along
:he brink, pillowing his head upon some shirts and a pair of panta-
.oons tied up in a striped cotton handkerchief. The sunbeams could

not reach him; the dust did not yet rise from the road after the heavy rain of yesterday, and his grassy lair suited the young man better than a bed of down. The spring murmured drowsily beside him; the branches waved dreamily across the blue sky overhead, and a deep sleep, perchance hiding dreams within its depths, fell upon David Swan. But we are to relate events which he did not dream of.

While he lay sound asleep in the shade other people were wide awake, and passed to and fro, afoot, on horseback and in all sorts of vehicles, along the sunny road by his bed-chamber. Some looked neither to the right hand nor the left and knew not that he was there; some merely glanced that way without admitting the slumberer among their busy thoughts; some laughed to see how soundly he slept; and several whose hearts were brimming full of scorn ejected their venomous superfluity on David Swan. A middle-aged widow, when nobody else was near, thrust her head a little way into the recess, and vowed that the young fellow looked charming in his sleep. A temperance lecturer saw him, and wrought poor David into the texture of his evening's discourse as an awful instance of dead drunkenness by the roadside.

But censure, praise, merriment, scorn and indifference were all one—or, rather, all nothing—to David Swan. He had slept only a few moments when a brown carriage drawn by a handsome pair of horses bowled easily along and was brought to a standstill nearly in front of David's resting-place. A linch-pin had fallen out and permitted one of the wheels to slide off. The damage was slight and occasioned merely a momentary alarm to an elderly merchant and his wife, who were returning to Boston in the carriage. While the coachman and a servant were replacing the wheel the lady and gentleman sheltered themselves beneath the maple trees, and there espied the bubbling fountain and David Swan asleep beside it. Impressed with the awe which the humblest sleeper usually sheds around him, the merchant trod as lightly as the gout would allow, and his spouse took good heed not to rustle her silk gown lest David should start up all of a sudden.

"How soundly he sleeps!" whispered the old gentleman. "From what a depth he draws that easy breath! Such sleep as that, brought on without an opiate, would be worth more to me than half my income, for it would suppose health and an untroubled mind."

"And youth besides," said the lady. "Healthy and quiet age does not sleep thus. Our slumber is no more like his than our wakefulness."

The longer they looked, the more did this elderly couple feel interested in the unknown youth to whom the wayside and the maple shade were as a secret chamber with the rich gloom of damask curtains brooding over him. Perceiving that a stray sunbeam glimmered down upon his face, the lady contrived to twist a branch aside so as to intercept it, and, having done this little act of kindness, she began to feel like a mother to him.

"Providence seems to have laid him here," whispered she to her husband, "and to have brought us hither to find him, after our disappointment in our cousin's son. Methinks I can see a likeness to our departed Henry. Shall we waken him?"

"To what purpose?" said the merchant, hesitating. "We know nothing of the youth's character."

"That open countenance!" replied his wife, in the same hushed voice, yet earnestly. "This innocent sleep!"

While these whispers were passing, the sleeper's heart did not throb, nor his breath become agitated, nor his features betray the least token of interest. Yet fortune was bending over him, just ready to let fall a burden of gold. The old merchant had lost his only son, and had no heir to his wealth except a distant relative with whose conduct he was dissatisfied. In such cases people sometimes do stranger things than to act the magician and awaken a young man to splendor who fell asleep in poverty.

"Shall we not waken him?" repeated the lady, persuasively.

"The coach is ready, sir," said the servant, behind.

The old couple started, reddened and hurried away, mutually wondering that they should ever have dreamed of doing anything so very ridiculous. The merchant threw himself back in the carriage and occupied his mind with the plan of a magnificent asylum for unfortunate men of business. Meanwhile, David Swan enjoyed his nap.

The carriage could not have gone above a mile or two when a pretty young girl came along with a tripping pace which showed precisely how her little heart was dancing in her bosom. Perhaps it was this merry kind of motion that caused—is there any harm in saying it?—her garter to slip its knot. Conscious that the silken girth—if silk it were—was relaxing its hold, she turned aside into the shelter of the maple trees and there found a young man asleep by the spring. Blushing as red as any rose that she should have intruded into a gentleman's bedchamber, and for such a purpose, too, she was about to make her escape on tiptoe. But there was peril near the sleeper. A monster of a bee had been wandering overhead—buzz, buzz, buzz—now among the leaves, now flashing through the strips of sunshine, and now lost in the dark shade, till finally he appeared to be settling on the eyelid of David Swan. The sting of a bee is sometimes deadly. As freehearted as she was innocent, the girl attacked the intruder with her handkerchief, brushed him soundly and drove him from beneath the maple shade. How sweet a picture! This good deed accomplished, with quickened breath and a deeper blush she stole a glance at the youthful stranger for whom she had been battling with a dragon in the air.

"He is handsome!" thought she, and blushed redder yet.

How could it be that no dream of bliss grew so strong within him that, shattered by its very strength, it should part asunder and allow him to perceive the girl among its phantoms? Why, at least, did not a smile of welcome brighten upon his face? She was come, the maid whose soul, according to the old and beautiful idea, had been severed from his own, and whom in all his vague but passionate desires he yearned to meet. Her only could he love with a perfect love, him only could she receive into the depths of her heart, and now her image was faintly blushing in the fountain by his side; should it pass away, its happy luster would never gleam upon his life again.

"How sound he sleeps!" murmured the girl. She departed, but did not trip along the road so lightly as when she came.

Now, this girl's father was a thriving country merchant in the neighborhood, and happened at that identical time to be looking out for just such a young man as David Swan. Had David formed a wayside acquaintance with the daughter, he would have become the father's clerk, and all else in natural succession. So here, again, had good fortune—the best of fortunes—stolen so near that her garments brushed against him, and he knew nothing of the matter.

The girl was hardly out of sight when two men turned aside beneath the maple shade. Both had dark faces set off by cloth caps, which were drawn down aslant over their brows. Their dresses were shabby, yet had a certain smartness. These were a couple of rascals who got their living by whatever the devil sent them, and now in the interim of other business had staked the joint profits of their next piece of villainy on a game of cards which was to have been decided here under the trees. But finding David asleep by the spring one of the rogues whispered to his fellow:

"Hist! Do you see that bundle under his head?"

The other villain nodded, winked and leered.

"I'll bet you a horn of brandy," said the first, "that the chap has either a pocketbook or a snug little hoard of small change stowed away among his shirts. And if not there we will find it in his pantaloons pocket."

"But how if he wakes?" said the other.

His companion thrust aside his waistcoat, pointed to the handle of a dirk, and nodded.

"So be it!" muttered the second villain.

They approached the unconscious David, and, while one pointed the dagger toward his heart, the other began to search the bundle beneath his head. Their two faces grim, wrinkled and ghastly with guilt and fear bent over their victim, looking horrible enough to be mistaken for fiends should he suddenly awake. Nay, had the villains glanced aside into the spring, even they would hardly have known themselves as reflected there. But David Swan had never worn a more tranquil aspect, even when asleep on his mother's breast.

"I must take away the bundle," whispered one.

"If he stirs I'll strike," muttered the other.

But at this moment a dog, scenting along the ground, came in beneath the maple trees and gazed alternately at each of these wicked men, and then at the quiet sleeper. He then lapped out of the fountain.

"Pshaw!" said one villain. "We can do nothing now. The dog's master must be close behind."

"Let's take a drink and be off," said the other.

The man with the dagger thrust back the weapon into his bosom and drew forth a pocket-pistol, but not of that kind which kills by a single discharge. It was a flask of liquor with a block-tin tumbler screwed upon the mouth. Each drank a comfortable dram, and left the spot with so many jests and such laughter at their unaccomplished wickedness that they might be said to have gone on their way rejoicing. In a few hours they had forgotten the whole affair, nor once imagined that the recording angel had written down the crime of murder against their souls in letters as durable as eternity. As for David Swan, he still slept quietly, neither conscious of the shadow of death when it hung over him, nor of the glow of renewed life when that shadow was withdrawn. He slept, but no longer so quietly as at first. An hour's repose had snatched from his elastic frame the weariness with which many hours of toil had burdened it. Now he stirred, now moved his lips without a sound, now talked in an inward tone to the noonday specters of his dream. But a noise of wheels came rattling louder and louder along the road, until it dashed through the dispersing mist of David's slumber; and there was the stage-coach. He started up with all his ideas about him.

"Halloo, driver! Take a passenger?" shouted he.

"Room on top!" answered the driver.

Up mounted David, and bowled away merrily toward Boston without so much as a parting glance at that fountain of dreamlike vicissitude. He knew not that a phantom of wealth had thrown a golden hue upon its waters, nor that one of love had sighed softly to their murmur, nor that one of death had threatened to crimson them with his blood, all in the brief hours since he lay down to sleep. Sleeping or waking, we hear not the airy footsteps of the strange things that almost happen. Does it not argue a superintending providence that, while viewless and unexpected events thrust themselves continually athwart our path, there should still be regularity enough in mortal life to render foresight even partially available?

READING PROBLEMS ON THE PROSE TALE

1. *The Falcon:* What is the dominant incident of this tale? Prove that Boccaccio tells only the barely essential facts in narrating this incident. In what does the interest of the incident lie?

2. *The Rose of the Alhambra:* Detached from its setting, why would this story lose in interest and point? List details which build up the atmosphere of romance which surrounds the Alhambra. How many incidents are narrated? Examine each to see how skillfully it is brought to a neat end.

3. *David Swan:* Does Hawthorne give us a complete picture of David Swan's character? Why? How does he cast about the story the sense of the mystery of sleep? What is the general theme of the story? What phase of this theme does each passer-by or group of passers-by represent? Would it be better or worse for us if we could be conscious of all the forces and chances in motion about us?

FURTHER READINGS IN THE TALE

Anderson: *Fairy Tales and Stories*
Anonymous: *The Arabian Nights' Entertainment*
Bible: *Tales of Gideon, Jacob, and Moses*

Collins: *The Terribly Strange Bed*
Grimm: *Domestic Tales*
Münchhausen: *Adventures*
Tolstoy: *Twenty Three Tales*
Unamuno: *Solitude*

SUGGESTIONS FOR ORIGINAL TALES

1. A Useless Sacrifice. 2. Moving Away. 3. Reunited by Radio. 4. Unrecognized Opportunity. 5. The Catastrophe That Did Not Happen.

III

The Ballad

STORIES have been told ever since man began to speak, and oddly enough the oldest stories we know were told in verse—perhaps because in the days before writing had been invented, when tales had to be handed on by word of mouth and repeated from memory, it was easier to remember poetry than prose.

Be that as it may, the prose tale developed from the metrical tale (or tale in verse) and the ballad (or short verse tale in song form). Both the metrical tale and the ballad arose before the invention of printed books, and were intended to be chanted or sung, not to be read.

Ballads were composed by professional story-tellers called in different languages scops, bards, minstrels, and troubadours. Before the days of written or printed books, these minstrels and troubadours were the traveling libraries of the ancient world. As the minstrels handed their tales and ballads on from generation to generation, and as these ballads were sung and resung by minstrel after minstrel, they were altered and polished until no one could say who had really composed a given ballad.

The form of the ballad, too, was perfected, and a special rhythm and stanza were gradually selected as most appropriate to the story in song form. The earliest ballads were written in rhymed couplets (two rhyming lines standing side by side). The most common ballad stanza, however, was composed of four lines in march rhythm, the first and third having four beats, and the second and fourth having usually three beats.

O whó	is hé	has dóne	this déed
And tóld	the kíng	of mé	
To sénd	us fórth	this tíme	of yéar
To sáil	upón	the séa?	

Lines two and four always rhyme. Sometimes, lines one and three rhyme, also. The stanza is often followed by a chorus or refrain, in which the listeners can join with the minstrel.

progs toit

THE BALLAD

If the short story is to be told in the brief form of a song, it will have to be told somewhat differently from the modern prose short story or tale. In the first place, it must be even more condensed, only the high points of the story being included and the rest left to the listener's imagination. The main incident alone can be dwelt upon, and even that very slightly. Description is reduced to a minimum. Moreover, a song is more emotional than a prose narrative, and the ballad tends to deal largely with thrilling and sentimental topics. Furthermore, a song must be simple to impress a mixed group of listeners. The ballad story, therefore, is simple, the events little complicated, and the characters more or less naïve and child-hearted. Indeed, so simple are ballad characters and one hero or heroine is so like another that certain stock expressions descriptive of their appearance and character recur in ballad after ballad.

The European ballads which have survived to our own time by having been written down in the seventeenth and eighteenth centuries, were almost all first composed in the eleventh, twelfth and thirteenth centuries—the days of feudalism, knighthood, and chivalry—and they tell the stories of popular heroes and beautiful maidens of that early time. They bring to us the freshness of a younger world. But so well are they written, that even today they move us to excitement, to laughter, and to tears as they did the unlettered listeners who gathered about the ballad singers in castle halls, in smoky taverns, and on village greens eight hundred years ago.

Modern poets often imitate old ballads in telling their own stories in verse, and some of the most spirited pieces of recent narrative poetry are in ballad form.

The ballad form is marked by the following characteristics, some of which have been already discussed.

1. The ballad stanza, with the accent on certain words sometimes forced to fit the rhythm.
2. Refrain.
3. Repetition of a line in succeeding stanzas with something new added.
4. Parallelism of line structure.
5. Stock phrases or epithets descriptive of people and things.
6. Dialogue, especially of the question and answer type.
7. Condensation and omission of easily imagined incidents.
8. A stock sequence of relatives to whom messages are to be sent after the hero's death.

9. The leaving of a list of legacies by a dying hero.
10. A spirited or sentimental tone.

Some or all of these qualities will be readily noted in the following selections, which add the charm of a marked rhythm and musical accompaniment to a moving tale.

THE FOLK BALLAD

HIND HORN

ANONYMOUS (SCOTLAND)

"Hind Horn fair, and Hind Horn free,
O where were you born, in what countrie?"

"In gude green-wood, there I was born,
And all my forbears me beforn.

"O seven years I served the king, 5
And as for wages, I never gat nane;

"But ae sight o' his ae daughter.

 . . . .

"My love ga'e me a siller wand,
'Twas to rule ower a' Scotland. 10

"And she ga'e me a gay gowd ring,
The virtue o't was above a' thing.

" 'As lang's this ring it keeps the hue,
Ye'll know I am a lover true:

" 'But when the ring turns pale and wan, 15
Ye'll know I love another man.' "

He hoist up sails, and awa' sailed he,
And sailed into a far countrie.

And when he looked upon his ring,
He knew she loved another man. 20

7. *ae:* one. 9. *ga'e:* gave.

He hoist up sails and hame came he,
Hame unto his ain countrie.

The first he met on his own land,
It chanced to be a beggar man.

"What news, what news, my gude auld man?
What news, what news ha'e ye to me?"

"Nae news, nae news," said the auld man,
"The morn's our queen's wedding day."

"Will ye lend me your begging weed?
And I'll lend you my riding steed."

"My begging weed will ill suit thee,
And your riding steed will ill suit me."

But part be right, and part be wrang,
Frae the beggar man the cloak he wan.

"Auld man, come tell to me your leed;
What news ye gi'e when ye beg your bread."

"As ye walk up unto the hill,
Your pike staff ye lend ye till.

"But whan ye come near by the yett,
Straight to them ye will upstep.

"Take nane frae Peter, nor frae Paul,
Nane frae high or low o' them all.

"And frae them all ye will take nane,
Until it comes frae the bride's ain hand."

He took nane frae Peter nor frae Paul,
Nane frae the high nor low o' them all,

22. *ain:* own. 31. *weed:* costume. 34. *Frae:* from. *wan:* won. 35. *leed:* tecnique of begging. 39. *yett:* gate. 41. *nane:* none.

"OUT O' THE CUP HE DRANK THE WINE,
AND INTO THE CUP HE DROPT THE RING."

And frae them all he would take nane,
Until it came frae the bride's ain hand.

The bride came tripping down the stair,
The combs o' red gowd in her hair,   50

A cup o' red wine in her hand,
And that she ga'e to the beggar man.

Out o' the cup he drank the wine,
And into the cup he dropt the ring.

"O got ye't by sea, or got ye't by land,   55
Or got ye't on a drowned man's hand?"

"I got it not by sea, nor got it by land,
Nor got I it on a drowned man's hand.

"But I got it at my wooing gay,
And I'll gi'e't you on your wedding day."   60

"I'll take the red gowd frae my head,
And follow you, and beg my bread.

"I'll take the red gowd frae my hair,
And follow you for evermair."

Atween the kitchen and the ha',   65
He loot his cloutie cloak down fa',

And wi' red gowd shone ower them a',
And frae the bridegroom the bride he sta'.

EDWARD, EDWARD
Anonymous (Scotland)

"Why does your brand sae drop wi' blude,
    Edward, Edward?
Why does your brand sae drop wi' blude,
    And why sae sad gang ye, O?"
"O I hae killed my hawk sae gude,   5
    Mither, Mither;
O I hae killed my hawk sae gude,
    And I had nae mair but he, O."

66. *cloutie:* dirty and ragged. 68. *sta':* stole. 1. *blude:* blood.

"Your hawk's blude was never sae red,
   Edward, Edward;   10
Your hawk's blude was never sae red.
  My dear son I tell thee, O."
"O I hae killed my red-roan steed,
   Mither, Mither;
O I hae killed my red-roan steed,   15
  That erst was sae fair and free, O."

"Your steed was auld and ye hae got mair,
   Edward, Edward;
Your steed was auld and ye hae got mair;
  Some other dule ye dree, O."   20
"O I hae killed my father dear,
   Mither, Mither;
O I hae killed my father dear.
  Alas and wae is me, O."

"And whatten penance will ye dree for that, 25
   Edward, Edward?
Whatten penance will ye dree for that,
  My dear son now tell me, O."
"I'll set my foot in yonder boat,
   Mither, Mither;   30
I'll set my foot in yonder boat,
  And I'll fare o'er the sea, O."

"And what will you do with your tow'rs and you ha',
   Edward, Edward?
And what will you do with your tow'rs and your ha' 35
  That were sae fair to see, O?"
"I'll let them stand till down they fa',
   Mither, Mither;
I'll let them stand till down they fa',
  For here never mair maun I be, O." 40

"And what will ye leave to your bairns and your wife,
   Edward, Edward?
And what will ye leave to your bairns and your wife,
  When ye gang owre the sea, O?"

17. *mair:* more. 20. *dule ye dree:* grief you suffer. 24. *wae:* woe. 33–37. *ha',
fa':* hall, fall. 40. *maun:* must.

"The world's room: let them beg through life, 45
      Mither, Mither.
The world's room: let them beg through life,
      For them never mair will I see, O."

"And what will ye leave to your ain mither dear,
      Edward, Edward? 50
And what will ye leave to your ain mither dear,
      My dear son now tell me, O?"
"The curse of hell frae me sall you bear,
      Mither, Mither;
The curse of hell frae me sall ye bear: 55
      Sic counsels ye gave to me, O."

FAIR HELEN

Anonymous (Scotland)

I wish I were where Helen lies;
Night and day on me she cries;
O that I were where Helen lies
      On fair Kirconnell lea!

Curst be the heart that thought the thought, 5
And curst the hand that fired the shot,
When in my arms burd Helen dropt,
      And died to succor me!

O think na but my heart was sair
When my Love dropt down and spak' nae mair! 10
I laid her down wi' meikle care
      On fair Kirconnell lea.

As I went down the water-side,
None but my foe to be my guide,
None but my foe to be my guide, 15
      On fair Kirconnell lea;

53. *sall:* shall. 56. *sic:* such. 7. *burd:* maiden. 9. *na:* not. 11. *meikle:* great.

I lighted down my sword to draw,
I hackèd him in pieces sma',
I hackèd him in pieces sma',
    For her sake that died for me.   20

O Helen fair, beyond compare!
I'll make a garland of thy hair
Shall bind my heart for evermair
    Until the day I die.

O that I were where Helen lies!   25
Night and day on me she cries;
Out of my bed she bids me rise,
    Says, "Haste and come to me!"

O Helen fair! O Helen chaste!
If I were with thee, I were blest,
Where thou lies low and takes thy rest   30
    On fair Kirconnell lea.

I wish my grave were growing green,
A winding-sheet drawn ower my een,
And I in Helen's arms lying,
    On fair Kirconnell lea.   35

I wish I were where Helen lies;
Night and day on me she cries;
And I am weary of the skies,
    Since my Love died for me.   40

IN THE CLEAR FOUNTAIN

TRADITIONAL (FRANCE)

Translated by Ruth Mary Weeks

In the clear fountain
My hands I shall dip.

La hi tra la la la.

On the leaves of the oak
Dry each wet fingertip.   5

On its uppermost branch
Does the nightingale sing.

Sing on, happy bird,
Light-heartedly sing!

My heart is not so   10
Since my lover has gone.

For a rosebud refused
He has left me alone.

I would that the rosebud
Were still on the tree;   15

That even the rose tree
Unplanted could be;

That the birth of the planter
Again could we see;

And that Pierre my beloved   20
Had yet to love me.

THE KING RENAUD

TRADITIONAL (FRANCE)

Translated by Ruth Mary Weeks

King Renaud from the war came back;
A mortal wound he bore, alack.
His mother from the turret saw
The coming of her son Renaud.

"Renaud, Renaud, I give you joy;   5
Your wife has borne to you a boy."
"Nor wife, nor son, my mother, dear,
Can give me joy tonight, I fear.

"Come, Mother, quickly come below;
Make up my bed with sheets of snow. 10
Short time to live have I, alas!
My soul must ere the midnight pass.

"But let a place for me be found
Wherefrom my wife shall hear no sound."
At midnight as himself had said,
The King Renaud was lying dead.

Ere the hour of matin had been kept,
Each servant in the castle wept.
Before the breakfast hour was done,
The maids were weeping every one.

"Tell me, Mother, tell me right,
Why should our valets weep tonight."
"In the stream they rubbed our horses down
And let the finest stallion drown."

"But why, my Mother, do you know
For the finest horse should they weep so?
When King Renaud again comes back,
Much finer horses shall not lack.

"And tell me why my maidens, too,
Weep even as the valets do."
"My child, the sheets they washed today
And let the newest float away."

"But over linen, Mother dear,
Why should the maidens shed a tear?
When Renaud comes, right sure am I
More lovely linen will he buy.

"And tell me, Mother, why I hear
This tapping, tapping somewhere near."
"My daughter, 'tis the joiner's man
Who mends the floor as best he can."

"Tell me, tell me, Mother dear,
What priestly chant is this I hear?"
"My child, the priests can do no less
Than all the house securely bless."

Then when at length she left her bed,
She wished to hear the masses said;
And when her eight long days had passed,
Her devotions must be paid at last.

"Tell me, tell me, Mother, pray,
What color shall I choose today?"   50
"Lay out the gray, lay out the green,
Lay out the black to choose between."

"Tell, oh Mother, tell me why
The black. What should it signify?"
"A woman who has borne a son   55
A dress of black may well become."

When to the chapel they were nigh,
They saw three priests come passing by.
"There is the wife of the great lord
Whose body we so late interred."   60

"Tell me, tell me, Mother pray,
What is it that these priests do say?"
"They say we quickly on must pass
If we expect to hear the mass."

Into the church at last she went;   65
To her the taper they present.
She kneeled, and saw beneath the pew
The earth was freshly turned anew.

"Tell me, Mother, tell me why
The earth thus freshly turned doth lie."   70
"My child, the truth must now be said.
Beneath this earth Renaud lies dead."

"If 'neath this earth Renaud doth rest,
Take the keys of my treasure chest;
Take my jewels every one;   75
Rear thou well King Renaud's son.

"Cleave, earth, and yield an opening!
I go to join Renaud, my king."
The earth was cleft, a gulf yawned there—
And vanished had the lady fair.   80

THE THREE HUSSARS

ANONYMOUS (FRANCE)

Translated by Percy Allen

They were three Hussars of the Guard,
Returning from war that day,
And gaily they sang and they sparred
Free and easy down the way.
"I shall see my love again,
She is Margoton," sang one.
"She is Jeanneton." "She's Madeleine
The one girl under the sun."

But a man is across their way:
" 'Tis old bell-ringer John, I swear:
What news in the village to-day?"
"Oh, nought ever happens down there."
"But Margoton, I used to meet?"
"I rang for her vows last year;
She is Sister Marguerite
In the convent a league from here."

"And Jeanneton, mine of old time?"
"Before last December's cold,
I was ringing her wedding chime;
Her firstborn is ten days old."
"My Madeleine," the third said, "say
She is happy?" "Most happy of all.
Three months ago this very day
I was tolling her burial."

"Ringer, when next you meet Marguerite
In the convent of Sacred Head,
Lay my blessing down at her feet,
And tell her I'm off to wed."
"Ringer, when next you see Jeanneton
In her home; tell her, in my name,
That I am a captain now and gone
A hunting, for bigger game!"

"Ringer, when you see my mother again,
Bend low the white head before;
Then tell her I still at the wars remain,   35
And that I return no more."

THE BRIDAL OF ANDALLA

Anonymous (Spain)

Translated by John G. Lockhart

This story is based on a legend of Moorish days in Granada.

❋   ❋   ❋

'Rise up, rise up, Xarifa! lay the golden cushion down;
Rise up, come to the window, and gaze with all the town!
From gay guitar and violin the silver notes are flowing,
And the lovely lute doth speak between the trumpets' lordly
    blowing;
And banners bright from lattice light are waving everywhere,   5
And the tall, tall plume of our cousin's bridegroom floats proudly
    in the air:
Rise up, rise up, Xarifa! lay the golden cushion down;
Rise up, come to the window, and gaze with all the town!

"Arise, arise, Xarifa! I see Andalla's face;
He bends him to the people with a calm and princely grace: 10
Through all the land of Xeres and banks of Guadalquivir
Rode bridegroom forth so brave as he, so brave and lovely, never.
Yon tall plume waving o'er his brow, of purple mixed with white,
'Twas wreathèd by Queen Zara, whom he will wed to-night.
Rise up, rise up, Xarifa! lay the golden cushion down;   15
Rise up, come to the window, and gaze with all the town!

"What aileth thee, Xarifa? what makes thine eyes look down?
Why stay ye from the window far, nor gaze with all the town?
I've heard you say on many a day—and sure you said the truth—
Andalla rides without a peer 'mong all Granada's youth;   20
Without a peer he rideth, and yon milk-white horse doth go,
Beneath his stately master, with a stately step and slow.
Then rise—oh rise, Xarifa! lay the golden cushion down:
Unseen here through the lattice, you may gaze with all the town!"

The Zegri lady rose not, nor laid her cushion down,　　　　25
Nor came she to the window to gaze with all the town;
But though her eyes dwelt on her knee, in vain her fingers strove,
And though her needle pressed the silk, no flower Zarifa wove:
One bonny rosebud she had traced before the noise drew nigh,—
That bonny bud a tear effaced, slow dropping from her eye.　　30
"No—no," she sighs: "bid me not rise, nor lay my cushion down,
To gaze upon Andalla with all the gazing town!—"

"Why rise ye not, Xarifa, nor lay your cushion down?
Why gaze ye not, Xarifa, with all the gazing town?
Hear, hear the trumpet how it swells, and how the people cry!　35
He stops at Zara's palace-gate;—why sit ye still—oh why?"—
"At Zara's gate stops Zara's mate: in him shall I discover
The dark-eyed youth pledged me his truth with tears, and was my
　　　lover?
I will not rise, with weary eyes, nor lay my cushion down,
To gaze on false Andalla with all the gazing town!"　　　40

SING, O SING AGAIN

ANONYMOUS (RUSSIA)

Translated by Sir John Bowring

Sing, O sing again, lovely lark of mine,
Sitting there alone amidst the green of May!

In the prison-tower the lad sits mournfully;
To his father writes, to his mother writes:
Thus he wrote, and these, these were the very words:　　5
"O good father mine, thou belovèd sir!
O good mother mine, thou belovèd dame!
Ransom me, I pray, ransom the good lad,—
He is your beloved, is your only son!"
Father, mother,—both,—both refused to hear,　　10
Cursed their hapless race, cursed their hapless seed:
"Never did a thief our honest name disgrace,—
Highwayman or thief never stained the name!"

Sing, O sing again, lovely lark of mine,
Sitting there alone in the green of May!　　15

From the prison-tower thus the prisoner wrote,
Thus the prisoner wrote to his belovèd maid:
"O thou soul of mine! O thou lovely maid!
Truest love of mine, sweetest love of mine!
Save, O save, I pray, save the prisoned lad!"   20
Swiftly then exclaimed that belovèd maid:
"Come, attendant! Come! Come, my faithful nurse!
Servant faithful, you that long have faithful been,
Bring the golden key, bring the key with speed!
Ope the treasure chests, open them in haste;   25
Golden treasures bring, bring them straight to me:
Ransom him, I say, ransom the good lad,
He is my beloved, of my heart beloved."

Sing, O sing again, lovely lark of mine,
Sitting there alone amidst the green of May!   30

THE BALLAD OF MULAN

Anonymous (China)

Translated by Arthur Whaley

Written in northern China during the domination of the Wei Tartars,
fifth century A. D.

❋   ❋   ❋

Click, click, forever click, click;
Mulan sits at the door and weaves.
Listen, and you will not hear the shuttle's sound,
But only hear a girl's sobs and sighs.
"Oh tell me, lady, are you thinking of your love,   5
Oh tell me, lady, are you longing for your dear?"
"Oh no, oh no, I am not thinking of my love,
Oh no, oh no, I am not longing for my dear.
But last night I read the battle-roll;
The Khan has ordered a great levy of men.   10
The battle-roll was written in twelve books,
And in each book stood my father's name.
My father's sons are not grown men.
And of all my brothers, none is older than me.

Oh let me to the market to buy saddle and horse, 15
And ride with the soldiers to take my father's place."
In the eastern market she's bought a gallant horse,
In the western market she's bought saddle and cloth.
In the southern market she's bought snaffle and reins,
In the northern market she's bought a tall whip. 20
In the morning she stole from her father's and mother's house;
At night she was camping by the Yellow River's side.
She could not hear her father and mother calling to her by her name,
But only the song of the Yellow River as its hurrying waters hissed
    and swirled through the night. 25
At dawn they left the River and went on their way;
At dusk they came to the Black Water's side.
She could not hear her father and mother calling to her by her name,
She could only hear the muffled voices of Scythian horsemen riding
    on the hills of Yen.
A thousand leagues she tramped on the errands of war, 30
Frontiers and hills she crossed like a bird in flight.
Through the northern air echoed the watchman's tap;
The wintry light gleamed on coats of mail.
The captain had fought a hundred fights, and died;
The warriors in ten years had won their rest. 35

They went home; they saw the Emperor's face;
The Son of Heaven was seated in the Hall of Light.
To the strong in battle lordships and lands he gave;
And of prize money a hundred thousand strings.
Then spoke the Khan and asked her what she would take. 40
"Oh, Mulan asks not to be made
A counsellor at the Khan's court;
She only begs for a camel that can march
A thousand leagues a day,
To take her back to her home." 45

When her father and mother heard that she had come,
They went out to the wall and led her back to the house.
When her little sister heard that she had come,
She went to the door and rouged her face afresh.
When her little brother heard that his sister had come, 50
He sharpened his knife and darted like a flash
Towards the pigs and sheep.

She opened the gate that leads to the eastern tower,
And sat on her bed that stood in the western tower.
She cast aside her heavy soldier's cloak,   55
And wore again her old-time dress.
She stood at the window and bound her cloudy hair;
She went to the mirror and fastened her yellow combs.
She left the house and met her messmates in the road;
Her messmates were startled out of their wits.   60
They had marched with her for twelve years of war
And never known that Mulan was a girl.
For the male hare has a lilting lolloping gait,
And the female hare has a wild and roving eye;
But set them both scampering side by side,   65
And who so wise could tell you "This is he"?

READING PROBLEMS ON THE FOLK BALLAD

1. *Hind Horn:* What parts of this story are left to the reader's imagination? Do you think the most interesting incidents have been selected for telling? Why does Hind Horn go in disguise to the wedding? Compare this story with that of *Lochinvar* by Sir Walter Scott.

2. *Edward, Edward:* What is the effectiveness of the questions and answers used in this ballad? What does the repetition of lines with something new at the end add to the emotional tone of the story? Which of the ten ballad characteristics mentioned in the introduction to the Ballad are illustrated in this story? What do you think has led up to the murder of Edward's father? Picture the domestic situation indicated in the poem. What is Edward's real character?

3. *Fair Helen:* How does the stanza form of this ballad differ from that of the usual ballad? Supply imaginary reasons for the shooting which resulted in Helen's death. Is this ballad written to tell a story or to convey some other point?

4. *In the Clear Fountain:* Which ballad expresses to you most fully the grief of the bereaved lover—this song or *Fair Helen?* Why? What is the difference between the French and Scottish methods of expressing emotion? Why are the last four stanzas of *In the Clear Fountain* so appealing?

5. *The King Renaud:* Which ballad most effectively postpones knowledge of the tragedy, this ballad or *Edward, Edward?* Compare the reasons why this knowledge is held back in each poem. The characters in this ballad are more fully revealed than in any so far presented. How is this done? Why is the ending so effective?

6. *The Three Hussars:* How are the three hussars differentiated in character? Which one loved his lost sweetheart the most? Has this ballad a theme?

7. *The Bridal of Andalla:* How is the story behind this ballad gradually suggested by the principal speaker, so that Xarifa's final answer comes merely as a summary of what we already guess? How is the picturesque Moorish background of the story also suggested?

8. *Sing, O Sing Again:* What question should you like to ask the author of this poem? Does the sweetheart stop to ask it? Why? Compare this poem with the chapter from *Vanity Fair* on page 279. What does the refrain add to this ballad?

9. *The Ballad of Mulan:* Has the author of this ballad selected the most significant episodes for inclusion? Are there points about which you should like to know more? How are the events of her military career suggested? Explain the poetic effectiveness of the things she does upon her return.

THE IMITATION BALLAD

THE ELF-KING

Johann Wolfgang von Goethe (Germany)

Translated by Ruth Mary Weeks

This ballad is based on the old legend of the fairy folk who can steal the souls of mortals or spirit them completely away to fairy land.

❊   ❊   ❊

Who gallops so late through wind and wild?
It is a father with his child.
Closely he shields the boy in his arm;
He holds him fast; he folds him warm.

"My Son, why hide you your face in fear?"
"See you not the Elf-King, Father dear—
The King of the Elves with his crown and train?"
"My Son, 'tis only the mist and the rain."

"Thou lovely child, come go with me!
The gayest games I'll play with thee;
The brightest blooms in our garden spring;
My mother will deck you in gold like a king."

"My Father, my Father, can you not hear
What the Elf-King whispers bending near?"
"Hush, my child, in my arms entwined!
'Tis the withered leaves in the sighing wind."

"Beautiful boy, come go with me,
My daughters fair shall wait on thee.
They nightly dance in a fairy ring;
They'll rock thee and dance for thee and sing."

"My Father, my Father, see you not where
The Elf-King's daughter beckons there?"
"My Son, my Son, naught can I see
"But the glimmer gray of the willow tree."

"I love you, beautiful boy, and so
I'll force you to come if you say me no."

"He clutches me, Father!" cries out the son,
"A hurt to me the Elf-King's done."

The father shudders; he gallops amain;
He clasps the child as it moans in pain.
He reaches the courtyard in anguished dread.
Within his arms, the boy—was dead.

LA BELLE DAME SANS MERCI

JOHN KEATS (ENGLAND)

Another tale of the supernatural is this story of a wandering knight
bewitched and abandoned by a soulless sorceress. It, too, is based on
a medieval legend.

❅ ❅ ❅

"O what can ail thee, knight-at-arms,
    Alone and palely loitering?
The sedge has withered from the lake,
    And no birds sing.

"Oh what can ail thee, knight-at-arms!   5
    So haggard and so woebegone?
The squirrel's granary is full,
    And the harvest's done.

"I see a lily on thy brow
    With anguish moist and fever-dew,   10
And on thy cheeks a fading rose
    Fast withereth, too."

Title: The Lovely Merciless Lady.

"I met a lady in the meads,
　　Full beautiful—a faëry's child;
Her hair was long, her foot was light,   15
　　And her eyes were wild.

"I made a garland for her head,
　　And bracelets, too, and fragrant zone;
She looked at me as she did love,
　　And made sweet moan.   20

"I set her on my pacing steed
　　And nothing else saw all day long,
For sidelong would she bend, and sing
　　A faëry's song.

"She found me roots of relish sweet,   25
　　And honey wild and manna-dew,
And sure in language strange she said,
　　'I love thee true.'

"She took me to her elfin grot,
　　And there she wept and sighed full sore;   30
And there I shut her wild, wild eyes
　　With kisses four.

"And there she lullèd me asleep,
　　And there I dreamed—Ah! woe betide!
The latest dream I ever dreamed   35
　　On the cold hill's side.

"I saw pale kings and princes, too,
　　Pale warriors, death-pale were they all;
They cried—'La belle Dame sans Merci
　　Hath thee in thrall!'   40

"I saw their starved lips in the gloam
　　With horrid warning gapèd wide,
And I awoke and found me here
　　On the cold hill's side.

"And this is why I sojourn here,   45
　　Alone and palely loitering,
Though the sedge is withered from the lake,
　　And no birds sing."

THE LORELEI

HEINRICH HEINE (GERMANY)

Translated by Ruth Mary Weeks

As the Greek ocean had its Sirens who lured sailors to death on the
rocks by their singing, so the Rhine had its fabled Lorelei.

❊   ❊   ❊

I know not why at eventime
My heart so sad should be.
A legend of the olden time
Comes strangely back to me.

The air is cool in the twilight;   5
Calmly the Rhine doth flow;
And the mountain summits still are bright
With the rosy afterglow.

Yonder a maid is sitting,
Young and wondrous fair.   10
Her golden raiment glistening,
She combs her golden hair.

With a golden comb she's combing,
And as she combs she sings.
How sweetly through the gloaming   15
Her magic music rings.

The ravished sailor drifting
Sees not the treacherous shoal.
To her his eyes are lifting;
To her he sends his soul.   20

O'er boat and sailor swelling
The rushing billows run.
This with her fatal singing
The Lorelei has done.

THE ASRA

HEINRICH HEINE (GERMANY)

Translated by Ruth Mary Weeks

Daily in the palace garden
Roamed the Sultan's lovely daughter
In the evening by the fountain
Where the crystal water plashes.

Daily stood a youthful captive
In the evening by the fountain;
By the crystal waters plashing
Daily grew he pale and paler.

Till one evening turned the princess
To the slave with sudden question:
"Tell thy name to me, I bid thee;
What thy home and what thy kindred."

And the slave then spoke in answer:
"Mohammed am I of Arabia,
From the race of those same Asra
Who, when they love, must perish."

A LITTLE TAVERN

ALEXANDER PETÖFI (HUNGARY)

Translated by Alice Stone Blackwell

Petöfi has been called "the Burns of Hungary." Many of his poems
illustrate Hungarian life and character.

❊ ❊ ❊

Where the village ends, a little tavern
Stands beside the Szamos, flowing clear.
It could see its image in the water,
Only that the night is drawing near.

Night is falling, with its dim gray shadows;
All the world is growing hushed and still.

By the shore the ferry boat is resting,
Darkness fills it, silent, mute and chill.

But the inn is noisy, and the player
Smites the cimbalon with might and main,   10
And the lads so lustily are shouting
That the windows quake in every pane.

"O my hostess, golden flower of women!
Bring me your best wine, that brightest flows.
Let it be as aged as my grandsire,   15
And as ardent as my youthful rose!

"Play up, gipsy, play up louder, better!
I am in the mood to dance today.
Madly now I dance away my money,
Madly now I dance my soul away!"   20

Somebody comes knocking at the window:
"Don't make such a noise! More quiet keep.
'Tis his lordship sends this message to you;
He has gone to bed and wants to sleep."

"Oh, I say, the devil take his lordship!   25
You may follow, too, the selfsame way.
Never heed him, gipsy, keep on playing,
Even if I sell my shirt to pay!"

"Lads, God bless you!"—Somebody comes tapping
Once again before the hour takes flight—   30
"Please amuse yourselves a bit more softly;
My poor mother is not well tonight."

No one answers, but they drain their glasses,
And they bid the music cease to play;
And, as quickly as their wine is finished,   35
All the lads are on their homeward way.

17. *gipsy:* In Hungary the gipsies are the musicians of the people.

THE WRECK OF THE HESPERUS

Henry Wadsworth Longfellow (America)

This describes the wreck of a schooner belonging to the Gloucester fishing fleet.

❈ ❈ ❈

It was the schooner *Hesperus*,
   That sailed the wintry sea;
And the skipper had taken his little daughter,
   To bear him company.

Blue were her eyes as the fairy-flax,
   Her cheeks like the dawn of day,
And her bosom white as the hawthorn buds,
   That ope in the month of May.

The skipper he stood beside the helm,
   His pipe was in his mouth,
And he watched how the veering flaw did blow
   The smoke now west, now south.

Then up and spake an old sailòr,
   Had sailed to the Spanish Main,
"I pray thee, put into yonder port,
   For I fear a hurricane.

"Last night the moon had a golden ring,
   And tonight no moon we see!"
The skipper, he blew a whiff from his pipe,
   And a scornful laugh laughed he.

Colder and louder blew the wind,
   A gale from the northwest;
The snow fell hissing in the brine,
   And the billows frothed like yeast.

Down came the storm, and smote amain
   The vessel in its strength;
She shuddered and paused, like a frightened steed,
   Then leaped her cable's length.

10

15

20

25

"Come hither! come hither! my little daughtèr,
  And do not tremble so;   30
For I can weather the roughest gale
  That ever wind did blow."

He wrapped her warm in his seaman's coat
  Against the stinging blast;
He cut a rope from a broken spar,   35
  And bound her to the mast.

"O father! I hear the church-bells ring,
  Oh, say, what may it be?"
" 'Tis the fog-bell on a rock-bound coast!"—
  And he steered for the open sea.   40

"O father! I hear the sound of guns,
  Oh, say, what may it be?"
"Some ship in distress, that cannot live
  In such an angry sea!"

"O father! I see a gleaming light,   45
  Oh, say, what may it be?"
But the father answered never a word—
  A frozen corpse was he.

Lashed to the helm, all stiff and stark,
  With his face turned to the skies,
The lantern gleamed through the gleaming snow   50
  On his fixed and glassy eyes.

Then the maiden clasped her hands and prayed
  That savèd she might be;
And she thought of Christ, who stilled the wave,   55
  On the Lake of Galilee.

And fast through the midnight dark and drear,
  Through the whistling sleet and snow,
Like a sheeted ghost, the vessel swept
  Tow'rd the reef of Norman's Woe.

And ever the fitful gusts between   61
  A sound came from the land;

It was the sound of the trampling surf
   On the rocks and the hard sea-sand.

The breakers were right beneath her bows;   65
   She drifted a dreary wreck;
And a whooping billow swept the crew
   Like icicles from her deck.

She struck where the white and fleecy waves
   Looked soft as carded wool,   70
But the cruel rocks, they gored her side
   Like the horns of an angry bull.

Her rattling shrouds, all sheathed in ice,
   With the masts went by the board;
Like a vessel of glass, she stove and sank,   75
   Ho! ho! the breakers roared!

At daybreak, on the bleak sea-beach,
   A fisherman stood aghast,
To see the form of a maiden fair
   Lashed close to a drifting mast.   80

The salt sea was frozen on her breast,
   The salt tears in her eyes;
And he saw her hair, like the brown seaweed,
   On the billows fall and rise.

Such was the wreck of the *Hesperus*,   85
   In the midnight and the snow!
Christ save us from a death like this,
   On the reef of Norman's Woe!

THE DIVERTING HISTORY OF JOHN GILPIN
Showing How He Went Farther Than He Intended, and Came Home Safe Again

William Cowper (England)

This is a mock ballad or burlesque. A burlesque makes fun of something by imitating its style closely but with a touch of exaggeration. This poem is made even funnier by the choice of an everyday, undignified subject.

John Gilpin was a citizen
  Of credit and renown;
A trainband captain eke was he
  Of famous London town.

John Gilpin's spouse said to her dear,   5
  "Though wedded we have been
These twice ten tedious years, yet we
  No holiday have seen.

"Tomorrow is our wedding day,
  And we will then repair   10
Unto the Bell at Edmonton
  All in a chaise and pair.

"My sister, and my sister's child,
  Myself, and children three,
Will fill the chaise; so you must ride   15
  On horseback after we."

He soon replied, "I do admire
  Of womankind but one,
And you are she, my dearest dear;
  Therefore it shall be done.   20

"I am a linendraper bold,
  As all the world doth know,
And my good friend the calender
  Will lend his horse to go."

Quoth Mrs. Gilpin, "That's well said;   25
  And for that wine is dear,
We will be furnished with our own,
  Which is both bright and clear."

John Gilpin kissed his loving wife;
  O'erjoyed was he to find,   30
That, though on pleasure she was bent,
  She had a frugal mind.

3. *trainband:* militia. 11. *Bell:* an inn. 21. *linendraper:* a retailer of iinens.
23. *calender:* a presser of cloth.

The morning came, the chaise was brought,
　　But yet was not allowed
To drive up to the door, lest all　　　　　　35
　　Should say that she was proud.

So three doors off the chaise was stayed,
　　Where they did all get in ;
Six precious souls, and all agog
　　To dash through thick and thin.　　　40

Smack went the whip, round went the wheels,
　　Were never folks so glad ;
The stones did rattle underneath,
　　As if Cheapside were mad.

John Gilpin at his horse's side　　　　　　45
　　Seized fast the flowing mane,
And up he got, in haste to ride,
　　But soon came down again ;

For saddletree scarce reached had he
　　His journey to begin,　　　　　　　　50
When, turning round his head, he saw
　　Three customers come in.

So down he came ; for loss of time,
　　Although it grieved him sore,
Yet loss of pence, full well he knew,　　55
　　Would trouble him much more.

'Twas long before the customers
　　Were suited to their mind,
When Betty screaming came downstairs,
　　"The wine is left behind !"　　　　　60

"Good lack !" quoth he—"yet bring it me,
　　My leathern belt likewise,
In which I bear my trusty sword
　　When I do exercise."

44. *Cheapside:* one of the chief business streets of London.

Now Mistress Gilpin (careful soul!)   65
    Had two stone bottles found,
To hold the liquor that she loved,
    And keep it safe and sound.

Each bottle had a curling ear,
    Through which the belt he drew,   70
And hung a bottle on each side,
    To make his balance true.

Then over all, that he might be
    Equipped from top to toe,
His long red cloak, well brushed and neat,   75
    He manfully did throw.

Now see him mounted once again
    Upon his nimble steed,
Full slowly pacing o'er the stones,
    With caution and good heed.   80

But finding soon a smoother road
    Beneath his well-shod feet,
The snorting beast began to trot,
    Which galled him in his seat.

So, "Fair and softly," John he cried,   85
    But John he cried in vain;
That trot became a gallop soon,
    In spite of curb and rein.

So stooping down, as needs he must
    Who cannot sit upright,   90
He grasped the mane with both his hands,
    And eke with all his might.

His horse, who never in that sort
    Had handled been before,
What thing upon his back had got   95
    Did wonder more and more.

Away went Gilpin, neck or nought;
   Away went hat and wig;
He little dreamt, when he set out,
   Of running such a rig.

The wind did blow, the cloak did fly,
   Like streamer long and gay,
Till, loop and button failing both,
   At last it flew away.

Then might all people well discern
   The bottles he had slung;
A bottle swinging at each side,
   As hath been said or sung.

The dogs did bark, the children screamed,
   Up flew the windows all:
And every soul cried out, "Well done!"
   As loud as he could bawl.

Away went Gilpin—who but he?
   His fame soon spread around—
"He carries weight! he rides a race!
   'Tis for a thousand pound!"

And still as fast as he drew near,
   'Twas wonderful to view
How in a trice the turnpike men
   Their gates wide open threw.

And now, as he went bowing down,
   His reeking head full low,
The bottles twain behind his back
   Were shattered at a blow.

Down ran the wine into the road,
   Most piteous to be seen,
Which made his horse's flanks to smoke
   As they had basted been.

115. *He carries weight:* the weight of jockeys in a race is equalized by adding artificial weight to the lighter men. 119. *turnpike:* tollgate. 128. *basted:* as one wets a roast in the oven to keep it moist and tender.

At Edmonton his loving wife
　　From the balcony espied   130
Her tender husband, wondering much
　　To see how he did ride.

"Stop, stop, John Gilpin! Here's the house!"
　　They all at once did cry.
"The dinner waits and we are tired."   135
　　Said Gilpin, "So am I."

But yet his horse was not a whit
　　Inclined to tarry there;
For why? his owner had a house
　　Full ten miles off, at Ware.   140

So like an arrow swift he flew,
　　Shot by an archer strong;
So did he fly—which brings me to
　　The middle of my song.

Away went Gilpin, out of breath,   145
　　And sore against his will,
Till at his friend the calender's
　　His horse at last stood still.

The calender, amazed to see
　　His neighbor in such trim,   150
Laid down his pipe, flew to the gate,
　　And thus accosted him:

"What news? what news? your tidings tell,
　　Tell me you must and shall.
Say why bareheaded you are come,   155
　　Or why you come at all?"

Now Gilpin had a pleasant wit,
　　And loved a timely joke;
And thus unto the calender
　　In merry guise he spoke;   160

"I came because your horse would come;
  And, if I well forbode,
My hat and wig will soon be here—
  They are upon the road."

The calender, right glad to find
  His friend in merry pin,
Returned him not a single word,
  But to the house went in;

Whence straight he came with hat and wig—
  A wig that flowed behind,
A hat not much the worse for wear,
  Each comely in its kind.

He held them up, and in his turn
  Thus showed his ready wit:
"My head is twice as big as yours,
  They therefore needs must fit.

"But let me scrape the dirt away
  That hangs upon your face;
And stop and eat, for well you may
  Be in a hungry case."

Said John, "It is my wedding day,
  And all the world would stare,
If wife should dine at Edmonton,
  And I should dine at Ware."

So turning to his horse, he said,
  "I am in haste to dine;
'Twas for your pleasure you came here,
  You shall go back for mine."

Ah luckless speech, and bootless boast!
  For which he paid full dear;
For, while he spake, a braying ass
  Did sing most loud and clear;

166. *pin*: mood.

Whereat his horse did snort, as he
   Had heard a lion roar,
And galloped off with all his might,   195
   As he had done before.

Away went Gilpin, and away
   Went Gilpin's hat and wig;
He lost them sooner than at first.
   For why?—they were too big.   200

Now Mistress Gilpin, when she saw
   Her husband posting down
Into the country far away,
   She pulled out half-a-crown;

And thus unto the youth she said,   205
   That drove them to the Bell,
"This shall be yours, when you bring back
   My husband safe and well."

The youth did ride, and soon did meet
   John coming back amain;   210
Whom in a trice he tried to stop,
   By catching at his rein.

But not performing what he meant,
   And gladly would have done,
The frighted steed he frighted more,   215
   And made him faster run.

Away went Gilpin, and away
   Went postboy at his heels,
The postboy's horse right glad to miss
   The lumbering of the wheels.   220

Six gentlemen upon the road,
   Thus seeing Gilpin fly,
With postboy scampering in the rear,
   They raised the hue and cry:

"Stop thief! stop thief! a highwayman!"
  Not one of them was mute;
And all and each that passed that way
  Did join in the pursuit.

And now the turnpike gates again
  Flew open in short space,
The toll-men thinking as before,
  That Gilpin rode a race.

And so he did, and won it too,
  For he got first to town,
Nor stopped till where he had got up
  He did again get down.

Now let us sing, "Long live the king,
  And Gilpin, long live he";
And when he next doth ride abroad.
  May I be there to see!

FATHER WILLIAM

LEWIS CARROLL (ENGLAND)

Father William appears in *Alice in Wonderland,* a fantastic tale i
which original people do and say exactly what they please and thin
instead of following the conventional pattern of behavior. Fathe
William certainly refuses to follow the aged-parent-pattern believe
in by many young people.

❀ ❀ ❀

"You are old, Father William," the young man said,
  "And your hair has become very white;
And yet you incessantly stand on your head—
  Do you think, at your age, it is right?"

"In my youth," Father William replied to his son,
  "I feared it might injure the brain;
But, now that I'm perfectly sure I have none,
  Why, I do it again and again."

"You are old," said the youth, "as I mentioned before,
  And have grown most uncommonly fat;
Yet you turned a back-somersault in at the door—
  Pray, what is the reason of that?"

"In my youth," said the sage, as he shook his grey locks,
    "I kept all my limbs very supple
By the use of this ointment—one shilling the box—   15
    Allow me to sell you a couple?"

"You are old," said the youth, "and your jaws are
        too weak
    For anything tougher than suet;
Yet you finished the goose, with the bones and the beak—
    Pray, how did you manage to do it?"   20

"In my youth," said his father, "I took to the law,
    And argued each case with my wife;
And the muscular strength which it gave to my jaw
    Has lasted the rest of my life."

"You are old," said the youth, "one would hardly suppose   25
    That your eye was as steady as ever;
Yet you balanced an eel on the end of your nose—
    What made you so awfully clever?"

"I have answered three questions, and that is enough,"
    Said his father. "Don't give yourself airs!   30
Do you think I can listen all day to such stuff?
    Be off, or I'll kick you down-stairs!"

READING PROBLEMS ON IMITATION BALLADS

1. *The Elf-King:* How is the dramatic power of the story heightened by putting it largely in dialog? Make sure who is making each speech.

2. *La Belle Dame Sans Merci:* How does Keats suggest the autumn scene in so few words? What peculiarity of the stanza form gives a minor tone to the rhythm? What touches add a supernatural air to the story? What effect is produced by the repetition at the end?

3. *The Lorelei:* How does Heine surround his story with an atmosphere in which the incident seems credible? How does he convey the charm of the Lorelei's song? Why does he give the sailor no individuality?

4. *The Asra:* Tell the unspoken story behind this song. Why does Heine use unrhymed verse in this ballad?

5. *A Little Tavern:* Ballads are called the voice of the people. How many sides of popular feeling does this ballad reflect?

6. *The Wreck of the Hesperus:* Find as many as possible of the popular ballad devices which Longfellow has imitated in this poem. Like the movie

directors, Longfellow felt his story needed a sentimental interest and added the shipman's daughter. Does this enhance the effectiveness of the poem?

7. *John Gilpin:* Point out passages in which Cowper imitates the ballad style with ludicrous effect. Note particularly the adjectives and adverbs we often see in serious ballads. Point out also the humorous nature of Gilpin's various predicaments. Can you find quotable lines in the poem?

8. *Father William:* What gives this poem a more galloping movement than any other ballad we have so far read? Why does Carroll make this poem gallop? The ballad is a take-off on the surprise of youth that old people still have plenty of snap and vigor. On whom is the joke—the father or son? It contains also side hits at other things, among them three major professions? Can you find them all?

FURTHER READINGS IN THE BALLAD

Lomax and Allen: *American Ballads and Folk Songs*
Pound: *American Ballads and Songs*
Strempel: *A Book of Ballads Old and New*
Witham: *English and Scottish Popular Ballads*
Anonymous: *Barbara Allen*
    Gentle River, Gentle River
    The Two Corbies
    Saint Olaf

Browning: *How They Brought the Good News*
Kipling: *The Ballad of East and West*
Masefield: *Spanish Waters Ballad of John Silver*
Scott: *Rosabelle*
Service: *The Shooting of Dan McGrew*
Southey: *Inchcape Rock*
Yeats: *The Ballad of Father Gilligan*
Whittier: *Skipper Ireson's Ride*

SUGGESTIONS FOR ORIGINAL BALLADS

1. Reunion in a Trailer Camp. 2. Grade Card Day (a dialog). 3. The Tattle Tale. 4. On a Friend Lost Through Misunderstanding. 5. Breaking the News of a Football Defeat to the Team Member Who Couldn't Play. 6. Homecoming Day at School. 7. On a Classmate Who Has not Lived Up to One's Ideal of Him. 8. An Appeal for the Community Chest. 9. Coming Home after College or a Long Trip. 10. An Old Fairy Tale or Myth Told in Ballad Form. 11. The Class Prom. 12. The Wreck of Our Championship Hopes. 13. A Diverting Trip in Old Tin Lizzie. 14. You Are Young, Son William. 15. The Tale of a School Activity That Did (or Did Not) Succeed. 16. Turn one of the stories in the short story unit into a ballad.

IV

The Metrical Tale

OLDER than even the ballad is the metrical tale, or story in verse, which is found in the literature of the Romans, Greeks, and ancient oriental peoples, as well as in medieval Europe. Such tales were also composed by scops, bards, minstrels and troubadours. They were not sung but chanted rhythmically to chords struck upon a lute or harp. The story of a metrical tale is more amplified than that of a ballad, the whole series of incidents being included, and setting and characters being fully described.

In addition to the points of interest listed for the prose tale, the appropriateness and charm of the rhythm and its contribution to the mood of the tale is worthy of note. In the metrical tale, likewise, word pictures of great interest and beauty are likely to abound. The metrical tale is also interesting as revealing the ideals of manhood, manners, customs, and beliefs characteristic of earlier periods in history. Modern writers, too, have used this form.

ORPHEUS AND EURYDICE

Ovid (Rome)

Translated by William Congreve

At the wedding of the Grecian maiden, Eurydice, to the famous musician, Orpheus, unfavorable omens appeared during the sacrifice to Hymen, god of marriage.

❋   ❋   ❋

Thence, in his saffron robe, for distant Thrace
Hymen departs, through air's unmeasur'd space;
By Orpheus call'd, the nuptial pow'r attends,
But with ill-omen'd augury descends:

Nor cheerful look'd the god, nor prosp'rous spoke,
Nor blaz'd his torch, but wept in hissing smoke.
In vain they whirl it round, in vain they shake,
No rapid motion can its flames awake.

With dread these inauspicious signs were view'd,
And soon a more disastrous end ensu'd;　　　　　　　10
For as the bride, amid the Naiad train,
Ran joyful sporting o'er the flow'ry plain,
A venom'd viper bit her as she pass'd;
Instant she fell, and sudden breath'd her last.

When long his loss the Thracian had deplor'd,　　15
Not by superior pow'rs to be restor'd;
Inflam'd by love, and urg'd by deep despair,
He leaves the realms of light, and upper air;
Daring to tread the dark Tenarian road,
And tempt the shades in their obscure abode;　　20
Through gliding specters of th' interr'd to go,
And phantom people of the world below;
Persephone he seeks, and him who reigns
O'er ghosts, and Hell's uncomfortable plains.
Arriv'd, he, tuning to his voice his strings,　　　25
Thus to the king and queen of shadows sings.

"Ye pow'rs, who under Earth your realms extend,
To whom all mortals must one day descend;
If here 'tis granted sacred truth to tell,
I come not curious to explore your Hell;　　　　30
Nor come to boast (by vain ambition fir'd)
How Cerberus at my approach retir'd.
My wife alone I seek; for her lov'd sake
These terrors I support, this journey take.
She, luckless wand'ring, or by fate misled,　　　35
Chanc'd on a lurking viper's crest to tread;
The vengeful beast, inflam'd with fury, starts,
And through her heel his deathful venom darts.
Thus was she snatch'd untimely to her tomb;

11. *Naiad:* nymph.　19 *Tenarian road:* ghostly or spirit road.　23. *Persephone:*
queen of the dead.　32. *Cerberus:* three-headed watch dog of land of the dead.

Her growing years cut short, and springing bloom.   40
Long I my loss endeavor'd to sustain,
And strongly strove, but strove, alas! in vain:
At length I yielded, won by mighty Love;
Well known is that omnipotence above!
But here, I doubt, his unfelt influence fails;   45
And yet a hope within my heart prevails,
That here, ev'n here, he has been known of old;
At least if truth be by tradition told;
If fame of former tales belief may find,
You both by love, and love alone were join'd.   50
Now by the horrors which these realms surround;
By the vast chaos of these depths profound;
By the sad silence which eternal reigns
O'er all the waste of these wide-stretching plains,
Let me again Eurydice receive,   55
Let Fate her quick-spun thread of life reweave.
All our possessions are but loans from you,
And soon, or late, you must be paid your due;
Hither we haste to human-kind's last seat,
Your endless empire, and our sure retreat.   60
She too, when ripen'd years she shall attain,
Must, of avoidless right, be yours again:
I but the transient use of that require,
Which soon, too soon, I must resign entire.
But if the destinies refuse my vow,   65
And no remission of her doom allow;
Know, I'm determin'd to return no more;
So both retain, or both to life restore."

Thus, while the bard melodiously complains,
And to his lyre accords his vocal strains,
The very bloodless shades attention keep,   70
And silent, seem compassionate to weep;
Ev'n Tantalus his flood unthirsty views,
Nor flies the stream, nor he the stream pursues;
Ixion's wond'ring wheel its whirl suspends,
And the voracious vulture, charm'd, attends;   75
No more the Belides their toil bemoan,
And Sisyphus, reclin'd, sits list'ning on his stone.

73-78. Famous criminals who were enduring punishment in the after world.

Then first ('tis said) by sacred verse subdu'd,
The Furies felt their cheeks with tears bedew'd.   80
Nor could the rigid king or queen of Hell,
Th' impulse of pity in their hearts repel.

Now, from a troop of shades that last arriv'd
Eurydice was call'd, and stood reviv'd:
Slow she advanc'd, and halting seem'd to feel   85
The fatal wound, yet painful in her heel.
Thus he obtains the suit so much desir'd,
On strict observance of the terms requir'd:
For if, before he reach the realms of air,
He backward cast his eyes to view the fair,   90
The forfeit grant, that instant, void is made,
And she for ever left a lifeless shade.

Now through the noiseless throng their way they bend,
And both with pain the rugged road ascend;
Dark was the path, and difficult, and steep,   95
And thick with vapors from the smoky deep.
They well-nigh now had pass'd the bounds of night,
And just approach'd the margin of the light,
When he, mistrusting lest her steps might stray,
And gladsome of the glimpse of dawning day,   100
His longing eyes, impatient, backward cast,
To catch a lover's look, but look'd his last;
For, instant dying, she again descends,
While he to empty air his arm extends.
Again she died, nor yet her lord reprov'd;   105
What could she say, but that too well he lov'd?
One last farewell she spoke, which scarce he heard;
So soon she dropt, so sudden disappear'd.

All stunn'd he stood, when thus his wife he view'd
By second fate and double death subdu'd: 110
Not more amazement by that wretch was shown,
Whom Cerberus beholding turn'd to stone;

Now to repass the Styx in vain he tries:
Charon averse, his pressing suit denies.

---

80. *Furies:* demons who punish the wicked. 113. *Styx:* the river separating the land of the living from the land of the dead. 114. *Charon:* the ferryman who carries the dead across the Styx.

Sev'n days entire, along th' infernal shores,   115
Disconsolate, the bard Eurydice deplores;
Defil'd with filth his robe, with tears his cheeks,
No sustenance but grief and cares, he seeks:
Of rigid fate incessant he complains,
And Hell's inexorable gods arraigns.   120
This ended, to high Rhodope he hastes,
And Haemus' mountain, bleak with northern blasts.

And now his yearly race the circling Sun
Had thrice complete through wat'ry Pisces run,
Since Orpheus fled the face of womankind,   125
And all soft union with the sex declin'd.
Whether his ill success this change had bred,
Or binding vows made to his former bed;
Whate'er the cause, in vain the nymphs contest,
With rival eyes to warm his frozen breast: 130
For ev'ry nymph with love his lays inspir'd,
But ev'ry nymph repuls'd, with grief retir'd.

THE RIDE ROUND THE PARAPET

FRIEDRICH RUECKERT (GERMANY)

Translated by James Clarence Mangan

The following tale in verse, like *Gunga Din* by Kipling (on page
234) has the song-like quality of a ballad, even to the repeated line
or refrain, and the chorus. But as neither of these poems is modelled
on the ballad stanza, they are included with the tales. This shows how
narrow a line sometimes separates two literary types.

❋　　❋　　❋

She said, "I was not born to mope at home in loneliness,"—
　　　The Lady Eleanora von Alleyne,
She said, "I was not born to mope at home in loneliness.
When the heart is throbbing sorest there is balsam in the forest,
　　　There is balsam in the forest for its pain,"   5
　　　　Said the Lady Eleanora,
　　　Said the Lady Eleanora von Alleyne.

124. *Pisces:* The fishes—a sign in the Zodiac.

She doffed her silks and pearls, and donned instead her hunting-gear,
    The Lady Eleanora von Alleyne.
She doffed her silks and pearls, and donned instead her hunting-gear,
And, till summertime was over, as a huntress and a rover   11
        Did she couch upon the mountain and the plain,
           She, the Lady Eleanora,
        Noble Lady Eleanora von Alleyne.

Returning home again, she viewed with scorn the tournaments— 15
    The Lady Eleanora von Alleyne.
Returning home again, she viewed with scorn the tournaments;
She saw the morions cloven and the crowning chaplets woven,
        And the sight awakened only the disdain
           Of the Lady Eleanora,   20
        Of the Lady Eleanora von Alleyne.

"My feeling towards Man is one of utter scornfulness,"
    Said Lady Eleanora von Alleyne.
"My feeling towards Man is one of utter scornfulness,
And he that would o'ercome it, let him ride around the summit 25
        Of my battlemented castle by the Maine,"
           Said the Lady Eleanora,
        Said the Lady Eleanora von Alleyne.

So came a knight anon to ride around the parapet,
    For Lady Eleanora von Alleyne.   30
So came a knight anon to ride around the parapet,
Man and horse were hurled together o'er the crags that beetled
    nether.
        Said the Lady, "There, I fancy, they'll remain!"
           Said the Lady Eleanora,
        Queenly Lady Eleanora von Alleyne!   35

Came other knights anon to ride around the parapet,
    For Lady Eleanora von Alleyne.
Came other knights anon to ride around the parapet,
Till six and thirty corpses of both mangled men and horses
        Had been sacrificed as victims at the fane   40
           Of the Lady Eleanora,
        Stately Lady Eleanora von Alleyne!

That woeful year was by, and Ritter none came afterwards
      To Lady Eleanora von Alleyne.
That woeful year was by, and Ritter none came afterwards;   ₄₅
The Castle's lonely basscourt looked a wild o'ergrown-with-grass
    court.
      'Twas abandoned by the Ritters and their train
        To the Lady Eleanora,
    Haughty Lady Eleanora von Alleyne!

She clomb the silent wall, she gazed around her sovranlike,   ₅₀
      The Lady Eleanora von Alleyne!
She clomb the silent wall, she gazed around her sovranlike;
"And wherefore have departed all the brave, the lion-hearted,
      Who have left me here to play the Castellain?"
        Said the Lady Eleanora,   ₅₅
    Said the Lady Eleanora von Alleyne.

"And is it fled for aye, the palmy time of Chivalry?"
      Cried Lady Eleanora von Alleyne.
"And is it fled for aye, the palmy time of Chivalry?
Shame light upon the cravens! May their corpses gorge the ravens,
      Since they tremble thus to wear a woman's chain!"   ₆₁
        Said the Lady Eleanora,
    Said the Lady Eleanora von Alleyne.

The story reached at Gratz the gallant Margrave Gondibert
      Of Lady Eleanora von Alleyne.   ₆₅
The story reached at Gratz the gallant Margrave Gondibert.
Quoth he, "I trow the woman must be more or less than human;
      She is worth a little peaceable campaign,
        Is the Lady Eleanora,
    Is the Lady Eleanora von Alleyne!"   ₇₀

He trained a horse to pace round narrow stones laid merlonwise,
      For Lady Eleanora von Alleyne.
He trained a horse to pace round narrow stones laid merlonwise,
"Good Gray! do thou thy duty, and this rocky-bosomed beauty
      Shall be taught that all the vauntings are in vain   ₇₅
        Of the Lady Eleanora,
    Of the Lady Eleanora von Alleyne!"

43. *Ritter:* Knight, literally rider.   64. *Margrave:* a title of nobility.
71. *merlonwise:* like a battlement.

He left his castle-halls, he came to Lady Eleanora's,
  The Lady Eleanora von Alleyne.
He left his castle-halls, he came to Lady Eleanora's.   80
"O, lady, best and fairest, here am I,—and, if thou carest,
  I will gallop round the parapet amain,
   Noble Lady Eleanora,
  Noble Lady Eleanora von Alleyne!"

She saw him spring to horse, that gallant Margrave Gondibert,   85
  The Lady Eleanora von Alleyne.
She saw him spring to horse, that gallant Margrave Gondibert.
"O, bitter, bitter sorrow! I shall weep for this to-morrow!
  It were better that in battle he were slain,"
   Said the Lady Eleanora,   90
  Said the Lady Eleanora von Alleyne.

Then rode he round and round the battlemented parapet,
  For Lady Eleanora von Alleyne.
Then rode he round and round the battlemented parapet:
The Lady wept and trembled, and her paly face resembled,   95
  As she looked away, a lily wet with rain;
   Hapless Lady Eleanora!
  Hapless Lady Eleanora von Alleyne!

So rode he round and round the battlemented parapet,
  For Lady Eleanora von Alleyne!   100
So rode he round and round the battlemented parapet;
"Accurst be my ambition! He but rideth to perdition,
  He but rideth to perdition without rein!"
   Wept the Lady Eleanora,
  Wept the Lady Eleanora von Alleyne.   105

Then rode he round and off the battlemented parapet
  To Lady Eleanora von Alleyne.
Then rode he round and off the battlemented parapet.
"Now blest be God for ever! This is marvelous! I never
  Cherished hope of laying eyes on thee agayne,"   110
   Cried the Lady Eleanora,
  Joyous Lady Eleanora von Alleyne!

"The Man of Men thou art, for thou hast fairly conquered me,
  The Lady Eleanora von Alleyne!
The Man of Men thou art, for thou hast fairly conquered me. 115
I greet thee as my lover, and, ere many days be over,
  Thou shalt wed me and be Lord of my domain,"
   Said the Lady Eleanora,
  Said the Lady Eleanora von Alleyne.

Then bowed the graceful knight, the gallant Margrave Gondibert, 120
  To Lady Eleanora von Alleyne.
Then bowed that graceful knight, the gallant Margrave Gondibert,
And thus he answered coldly, "There be many who as boldly
  Will adventure an achievement they disdain,
   For the Lady Eleanora, 125
  For the Lady Eleanora von Alleyne.

"Mayest bide until they come, O stately Lady Eleanora!
  O Lady Eleanora von Alleyne!
Mayest bide until they come, O stately Lady Eleanora!
And thou and they may marry, but, for me, I must not tarry, 13●
  I have won a wife already out of Spain,
   Virgin Lady Eleanora,
  Virgin Lady Eleanora von Alleyne!"

Thereon he rode away, the gallant Margrave Gondibert,
  From Lady Eleanora von Alleyne.
Thereon he rode away, the gallant Margrave Gondibert. 135
And long in shame and anguish did that haughty Lady languish,
  Did she languish without pity for her pain,
   She the Lady Eleanora,
  She the Lady Eleanora von Alleyne. 140

And year went after year, and still in barren maidenhood
  Lived Lady Eleanora von Alleyne.
And wrinkled Eld crept on, and still her lot was maidenhood,
And woe! her end was tragic; she was changed, at length, by magic,
  To an ugly wooden image, they maintain; 145
   She, the Lady Eleanora,
  She, the Lady Eleanora von Alleyne!

And now, before the gate, in sight of all, transmogrified,
    Stands Lady Eleanora von Alleyne.
Before her castle-gate, in sight of all, transmogrified,   150
And he that won't salute her must be fined in foaming pewter,
    If a boor—but, if a burgher, in champagne,
      For the Lady Eleanora,
    Wooden Lady Eleanora von Alleyne!

MICHAEL

William Wordsworth (England)

Upon the forest-side in Grasmere Vale
There dwelt a shepherd, Michael was his name;
An old man, stout of heart and strong of limb.
His bodily frame had been from youth to age
Of an unusual strength: his mind was keen,   5
Intense, and frugal, apt for all affairs,
And in his shepherd's calling he was prompt
And watchful more than ordinary men.
Hence had he learned the meaning of all winds,
Of blasts of every tone; and, oftentimes,   10
When others heeded not, he heard the South
Make subterraneous music, like the noise
Of bagpipers on distant Highland hills.
The shepherd, at such warning, of his flock
Bethought him, and he to himself would say,   15
"The winds are now devising work for me!"
And, truly, at all times the storm, that drives
The traveler to a shelter, summoned him
Up to the mountains: he had been alone
Amid the heart of many thousand mists,   20
That came to him, and left him, on the heights.
So lived he till his eightieth year was past.
And grossly that man errs who should suppose
That the green valleys, and the streams and rocks,
Were things indifferent to the shepherd's thoughts.   25
Fields, where with cheerful spirits he had breathed
The common air; hills, which with vigorous step
He had so often climbed; which had impressed

148. *transmogrified:* changed for the worse.

So many incidents upon his mind
Of hardship, skill or courage, joy or fear; 30
Which, like a book, preserved the memory
Of the dumb animals, whom he had saved,
Had fed or sheltered, linking to such acts
The certainty of honorable gain;
Those fields, those hills—what could they less?—had laid 35
Strong hold on his affections, were to him
A pleasurable feeling of blind love,
The pleasure which there is in life itself.

His days had not been passed in singleness.
His helpmate was a comely matron, old— 40
Though younger than himself full twenty years.
She was a woman of a stirring life,
Whose heart was in her house: two wheels she had
Of antique form; this large, for spinning wool;
That small, for flax; and if one wheel had rest 45
It was because the other was at work.
The pair had but one inmate in their house,
An only child, who had been born to them
When Michael, telling o'er his years, began
To deem that he was old,—in shepherd's phrase, 50
With one foot in the grave. This only son,
With two brave sheep-dogs tried in many a storm,
The one of an inestimable worth,
Made all their household. I may truly say
That they were as a proverb in the vale 55
For endless industry. When day was gone,
And from their occupations out of doors
The son and father were come home, even then
Their labor did not cease.

Down from the ceiling, by the chimney's edge, 60
That in our ancient uncouth country style
With huge and black projection overbrowed
Large space beneath, as duly as the light
Of day grew dim the housewife hung a lamp.
This light was famous in its neighborhood, 65
That was a public symbol of the life
That thrifty pair had lived. For, as it chanced,
Their cottage on a plot of rising ground
Stood single, with large prospect, north and south,
High into Easedale, up to Dunmail-Raise, 70

And westward to the village near the lake;
And from this constant light, so regular
And so far seen, the house itself, by all
Who dwelt within the limits of the vale,
Both old and young, was named The Evening Star.   75

    Thus living on through such a length of years,
The shepherd, if he loved himself, must needs
Have loved his helpmate; but to Michael's heart
This son of his old age was yet more dear—
Less from instinctive tenderness, the same   80
Fond spirit that blindly works in the blood of all—
Than that a child, more than all other gifts
That earth can offer to declining man,
Brings hope with it, and forward-looking thoughts.
Exceeding was the love he bare to him,   85
His heart and his heart's joy! For oftentimes
Old Michael, while he was a babe in arms,
Had done him female service, not alone
For pastime and delight, as is the use
Of fathers, but with patient mind enforced   90
To acts of tenderness; and he had rocked
His cradle, as with a woman's gentle hand.

    And, in a later time, ere yet the boy
Had put on boys' attire, did Michael love,
Albeit of a stern unbending mind,   95
To have the young one in his sight, when he
Wrought in the field, or on his shepherd's stool
Sate with a fettered sheep before him stretched
Under the large old oak, that near his door
Stood single, and, from matchless depth of shade   100
Chosen for the shearer's covert from the sun,
Thence in our rustic dialect was called
The Clipping Tree, a name which yet it bears.
There, while they two were sitting in the shade,
With others round them, earnest all and blithe,   105
Would Michael exercise his heart with looks
Of fond correction and reproof bestowed
Upon the child, if he disturbed the sheep.

    And when by Heaven's good grace the boy grew up
A healthy lad, and carried in his cheek   110
Two steady roses that were five years old;
Then Michael from a winter coppice cut

With his own hand a sapling, which he hooped
With iron, making it throughout in all
Due requisites a perfect shepherd's staff, 115
And gave it to the boy; wherewith equipped
He as a watchman oftentimes was placed
At gate or gap, to stem or turn the flock.

But soon as Luke, full ten years old, could stand
Against the mountain blasts, and to the heights, 120
Not fearing toil, nor length of weary ways,
He with his father daily went, and they
Were as companions, why should I relate
That objects which the shepherd loved before
Were dearer now? that from the boy there came 125
Feelings and emanations—things which were
Light to the sun and music to the wind;
And that the old man's heart seemed born again?

Thus in his father's sight the boy grew up:
And now, when he had reached his eighteenth year, 130
He was his comfort and his daily hope.

While in this sort the simple household lived
From day to day, to Michael's ear there came
Distressful tidings. Long before the time
Of which I speak, the shepherd had been bound 135
In surety for his brother's son, a man
Of an industrious life, and ample means;
But unforeseen misfortunes suddenly
Had pressed upon him; and old Michael now
Was summoned to discharge the forfeiture, 140
A grievous penalty, but little less
Than half his substance. This unlooked-for claim,
At the first hearing, for a moment took
More hope out of his life than he supposed
That any old man ever could have lost. 145
As soon as he had armed himself with strength
To look his trouble in the face, it seemed
The shepherd's sole resource to sell at once
A portion of his patrimonial fields.
Such was his first resolve; he thought again, 150
And his heart failed him. "Isabel," said he,
Two evenings after he had heard the news,
"I have been toiling more than seventy years,

And in the open sunshine of God's love
Have we all lived; yet if these fields of ours   155
Should pass into a stranger's hand, I think
That I could not lie quiet in my grave.
Our Luke shall leave us, Isabel; the land
Shall not go from us, and it shall be free;
He shall possess it, free as is the wind   160
That passes over it. We have, thou know'st,
Another kinsman—he will be our friend
In this distress. He is a prosperous man,
Thriving in trade—and Luke to him shall go,
And with his kinsman's help and his own thrift   165
He quickly will repair this loss, and then
He may return to us. If here he stay,
What can be done? Where everyone is poor,
What can be gained?"

          At this the old man paused,
And Isabel was silent, for her mind   170
Was busy, looking back into past times.
"There's Richard Bateman," thought she to herself,
"He was a parish-boy—at the church-door
They made a gathering for him, shillings, pence,
And halfpennies, wherewith the neighbors bought   175
A basket, which they filled with pedlar's wares;
And, with this basket on his arm, the lad
Went up to London, found a master there,
Who, out of many, chose the trusty boy
To go and overlook his merchandise   180
Beyond the seas; where he grew wondrous rich,
And left estates and monies to the poor,
And at his birth-place built a chapel, floored
With marble which he sent from foreign lands."
These thoughts, and many others of like sort,   185
Passed quickly through the mind of Isabel,
And her face brightened. The old man was glad,
And thus resumed: "Well, Isabel! this scheme
These two days has been meat and drink to me.
Far more than we have lost is left us yet.   190
We have enough—I wish indeed that I
Were younger;—but this hope is a good hope.
Make ready Luke's best garments, of the best
Buy for him more, and let us send him forth

To-morrow, or the next day, or to-night:— 195
If he *could* go, the boy should go to-night."
   Here Michael ceased, and to the fields went forth
With a light heart. The housewife for five days
Was restless morn and night, and all day long
Wrought on with her best fingers to prepare 200
Things needful for the journey of her son.
At length
The expected letter from their kinsman came,
With kind assurances that he would do
His utmost for the welfare of the boy; 205
To which requests were added that forthwith
He might be sent to him. Ten times or more
The letter was read over; Isabel
Went forth to show it to the neighbors round;
Nor was there at that time on English land 210
A prouder heart than Luke's. When Isabel
Had to her house returned, the old man said,
"He shall depart to-morrow." To this word
The housewife answered, talking much of things
Which, if at such short notice he should go, 215
Would surely be forgotten. But at length
She gave consent, and Michael was at ease.

   Near the tumultuous brook of Greenhead Ghyll,
In that deep valley, Michael had designed
To build a sheepfold; and, before he heard 220
The tidings of his melancholy loss,
For this same purpose he had gathered up
A heap of stones, which by the streamlet's edge
Lay thrown together, ready for the work.
With Luke that evening thitherward he walked: 225
And soon as they had reached the place he stopped,
And thus the old man spake to him: "My son,
To-morrow thou wilt leave me: with full heart
I look upon thee, for thou art the same
That wert a promise to me ere thy birth, 230
And all thy life hast been my daily joy.
I will relate to thee some little part
Of our two histories: 'twill do thee good
When thou art from me, even if I should touch
On things thou canst not know of. After thou 235

First cam'st into the world—as oft befalls
To new-born infants—thou didst sleep away
Two days, and blessings from thy father's tongue
Then fell upon thee. Day by day passed on,
And still I loved thee with increasing love. 240
Never to living ear came sweeter sounds
Than when I heard thee by our own fireside
First uttering, without words, a natural tune;
While thou, a feeding babe, didst in thy joy
Sing at thy mother's breast. Month followed month, 245
And in the open fields my life was passed
And on the mountains; else I think that thou
Hadst been brought up upon thy father's knees.
But we were playmates, Luke; among these hills,
As well thou knowest, in us the old and young 250
Have played together, nor with me didst thou
Lack any pleasure which a boy can know."
Luke had a manly heart; but at these words
He sobbed aloud. The old man grasped his hand,
And said, "Nay, do not take it so—I see 255
That these are things of which I need not speak.
Even to the utmost I have been to thee
A kind and a good father; and herein
I but repay a gift which I myself
Received at others' hands; for, though now old 260
Beyond the common life of man, I still
Remember them who loved me in my youth.
Both of them sleep together: here they lived,
As all their forefathers had done; and when
At length their time was come, they were not loth 265
To give their bodies to the family mould.
I wished that thou shouldst live the life they lived:
But 'tis a long time to look back, my son,
And see so little gain from threescore years.
These fields were burdened when they came to me; 270
Till I was forty years of age, not more
Than half of my inheritance was mine.
I toiled and toiled; God blessed me in my work,
And till these three weeks past the land was free.
It looks as if it never could endure 275
Another master. Heaven forgive me, Luke,

270. *burdened:* mortgaged.

If I judge ill for thee, but it seems good
That thou shouldst go."
     At this the old man paused;
Then, pointing to the stones near which they stood,
Thus, after a short silence, he resumed: 280
"This was a work for us; and now, my son,
It is a work for me. But, lay one stone—
Here, lay it for me, Luke, with thine own hands.
Nay, boy, be of good hope;—we both may live
To see a better day. At eighty-four   285
I still am strong and hale;—do thou thy part;
I will do mine. I will begin again
With many tasks that were resigned to thee:
Up to the heights, and in among the storms,
Will I without thee go again, and do   290
All works which I was wont to do alone,
Before I knew thy face. Heaven bless thee, boy!
Thy heart these two weeks has been beating fast
With many hopes; it should be so—yes—yes—
I know that thou couldst never have a wish   295
To leave me, Luke: thou hast been bound to me
Only by links of love: when thou art gone,
What will be left to us!—But I forget
My purposes. Lay now the cornerstone,
As I requested; and hereafter, Luke,   300
When thou art gone away, should evil men
Be thy companions, think of me, my son,
And of this moment; hither turn thy thoughts,
And God will strengthen thee; amid all fear
And all temptation, Luke, I pray that thou   305
May'st bear in mind the life thy fathers lived,
Who, being innocent, did for that cause
Bestir them in good deeds. Now fare thee well—
When thou return'st, thou in this place wilt see
A work which is not here: a covenant   310
'Twill be between us; but, whatever fate
Befall thee, I shall love thee to the last,
And bear thy memory with me to the grave."

 The shepherd ended here; and Luke stooped down,
And, as his father had requested, laid   315
The first stone of the sheepfold. At the sight
The old man's grief broke from him; to his heart

He pressed his son, he kissèd him and wept;
And to the house together they returned.
—Hushed was that house in peace, or seeming peace, 320
Ere the night fell:—with morrow's dawn the boy
Began his journey, and when he had reached
The public way, he put on a bold face;
And all the neighbors, as he passed their doors,
Came forth with wishes and with farewell prayers, 325
That followed him till he was out of sight.

A good report did from their kinsman come,
Of Luke and his well-doing: and the boy
Wrote loving letters, full of wondrous news,
Which, as the housewife phrased it, were throughout 330
"The prettiest letters that were ever seen."
Both parents read them with rejoicing hearts.
So, many months passed on: and once again
The shepherd went about his daily work
With confident and cheerful thoughts; and now 335
Sometimes when he could find a leisure hour
He to that valley took his way, and there
Wrought at the sheepfold. Meantime Luke began
To slacken in his duty; and at length
He in the dissolute city gave himself 340
To evil courses: ignominy and shame
Fell on him, so that he was driven at last
To seek a hiding-place beyond the seas.
I have conversed with more than one who well
Remember the old man, and what he was 345
Years after he had heard this heavy news.
His bodily frame had been from youth to age
Of an unusual strength. Among the rocks
He went, and still looked up to sun and cloud,
And listened to the wind; and, as before, 350
Performed all kinds of labor for his sheep,
And for the land, his small inheritance.
And to that hollow dell from time to time
Did he repair, to build the fold of which
His flock had need. 'Tis not forgotten yet 355
The pity which was then in every heart
For the old man—and 'tis believed by all
That many and many a day he thither went,

And never lifted up a single stone.
    There, by the sheepfold, sometimes was he seen   360
Sitting alone, or with his faithful dog,
Then old beside him lying at his feet.
The length of full seven years, from time to time,
He at the building of this sheepfold wrought,
And left the work unfinished when he died.   365
Three years, or little more, did Isabel
Survive her husband. At her death the estate
Was sold, and went into a stranger's hand.
The cottage which was named The Evening Star
Is gone—the ploughshare has been through the ground   370
On which it stood; great changes have been wrought
In all the neighborhood:—yet the oak is left
That grew beside their door; and the remains
Of the unfinished sheepfold may be seen
Beside the boisterous brook of Greenhead Ghyll.   375

THE REVENGE

ALFRED TENNYSON (ENGLAND)

This tells of an actual encounter of an English ship with the Spanish
Armada in the days of Queen Elizabeth.

❋   ❋   ❋

At Flores in the Azores Sir Richard Grenville lay,
And a pinnace, like a fluttered bird, came flying from far away;
"Spanish ships of war at sea! we have sighted fifty-three!"
Then sware Lord Thomas Howard: " 'Fore God I am no coward;
But I cannot meet them here, for my ships are out of gear,   5
And the half my men are sick. I must fly, but follow quick.
We are six ships of the line; can we fight with fifty-three?"

Then spake Sir Richard Grenville: "I know you are no coward;
You fly them for a moment to fight with them again.
But I've ninety men and more that are lying sick ashore.   10
I should count myself the coward if I left them, my Lord Howard,
To these Inquisition dogs and the devildoms of Spain."

So Lord Howard passed away with five ships of war that day,
Till he melted like a cloud in the silent summer heaven;
But Sir Richard bore in hand all his sick men from the land   15
Very carefully and slow,
Men of Bideford in Devon,
And we laid them on the ballast down below:
For we brought them all aboard,
And they blessed him in their pain, that they were not left to Spain, 20
To the thumb-screw and the stake, for the glory of the Lord.

He had only a hundred seamen to work the ship and to fight
And he sailed away from Flores till the Spaniard came in sight,
With his huge sea-castles heaving upon the weather bow.
"Shall we fight or shall we fly?   25
Good Sir Richard, tell us now,
For to fight is but to die!
There'll be little of us left by the time this sun be set."
And Sir Richard said again: "We be all good English men.
Let us bang these dogs of Seville, the children of the devil,   30
For I never turned my back upon Don or devil yet."

Sir Richard spoke and he laughed, and we roared a hurrah, and so
The little *Revenge* ran on sheer into the heart of the foe,
With her hundred fighters on deck, and her ninety sick below;
For half of their fleet to the right and half to the left were seen, 35
And the little *Revenge* ran on thro' the long sea-lane between.

Thousands of their soldiers looked down from their decks and
    laughed,
Thousands of their seamen made mock at the mad little craft
Running on and on, till delayed
By their mountain-like *San Philip* that, of fifteen hundred tons 40
And up-shadowing high above us with her yawning tiers of guns,
Took the breath from our sails, and we stayed.

And while now the great *San Philip* hung above us like a cloud
Whence the thunderbolt will fall
Long and loud,   45
Four galleons drew away
From the Spanish fleet that day,
And two upon the larboard and two upon the starboard lay,
And the battle-thunder broke from them all.

But anon the great *San Philip,* she bethought herself and went, 50
Having that within her womb that had left her ill content;
And the rest they came aboard us, and they fought us hand to hand,
For a dozen times they came with their pikes and musqueteers,
And a dozen times we shook 'em off as a dog that shakes his ears
When he leaps from the water to the land. 55

And the sun went down, and the stars came out far over the summer
    sea,
But never a moment ceased the fight of the one and the fifty-three.
Ship after ship, the whole night long, their high-built galleons came,
Ship after ship, the whole night long, with her battle-thunder and
    flame:
Ship after ship, the whole night long, drew back with her dead and
    her shame. 60
For some were sunk and many were shattered, and so could fight us
    no more—
God of battles, was ever a battle like this in the world before?

For he said, "Fight on! fight on!"
Tho' his vessel was all but a wreck;
And it chanced that, when half of the short summer night was gone, 65
With a grisly wound to be dressed he had left the deck,
But a bullet struck him that was dressing it suddenly dead,
And himself he was wounded again in the side and the head,
And he said, "Fight on! fight on!"

And the night went down, and the sun smiled out far over the sum-
    mer sea, 70
And the Spanish fleet with broken sides lay round us all in a ring;
But they dared not touch us again, for they feared that we still could
    sting,
So they watched what the end would be.
And we had not fought them in vain,
But in perilous plight were we, 75
Seeing forty of our poor hundred were slain,
And half of the rest of us maimed for life
In the crash of the cannonades and the desperate strife:
And the sick men down in the hold were most of them stark and cold,
And the pikes were all broken or bent, and the powder was all of it
    spent; 80
And the masts and the rigging were lying over the side;
But Sir Richard cried in his English pride:

"We have fought such a fight for a day and a night
As may never be fought again!
We have won great glory, my men!   85
And a day less or more
At sea or ashore,
We die—does it matter when?
Sink me the ship, Master Gunner—sink her, split her in twain!
Fall into the hands of God, not into the hands of Spain!"   90

And the gunner said, "Ay, ay," but the sea-men made reply:
"We have children, we have wives,
And the Lord hath spared our lives.
We will make the Spaniard promise, if we yield, to let us go;
We shall live to fight again, to strike another blow."   95
And the lion there lay dying, and they yielded to the foe.

And the stately Spanish men to their flagship bore him then,
Where they laid him by the mast, old Sir Richard caught at last,
And they praised him to his face with their courtly foreign grace;
But he rose upon their decks, and he cried: 100
"I have fought for Queen and Faith like a valiant man and true;
I have only done my duty as a man is bound to do.
With a joyful spirit I, Sir Richard Grenville, die!"
And he fell upon their decks, and he died.

And they stared at the dead that had been so valiant and true, 105
And had holden the power and glory of Spain so cheap
That he dared her with one little ship and his English few;
Was he devil or man? He was devil for aught they knew,
But they sank his body with honor down into the deep.
And they manned the *Revenge* with a swarthier alien crew,   110
And away she sailed with her loss, and longed for her own;
When a wind from the lands they had ruined awoke from sleep,
And the water began to heave and the weather to moan,
And or ever that evening ended a great gale blew,
And a wave like the wave that is raised by an earthquake grew, 115
Till it smote on their hulls and their sails and their masts and their
        flags,
And the whole sea plunged and fell on the shot-shattered navy of
        Spain,
And the little *Revenge* herself went down by the island crags
To be lost evermore in the main.

PATTERNS

Amy Lowell (America)

This is the story of the betrothed of a soldier in the Duke of Marlborough's army, which was fighting to prevent France from setting a French prince on the Spanish throne. The date is the early eighteenth century.

❋　　❋　　❋

I walk down the garden paths,
And all the daffodils
Are blowing, and the bright blue squills.
I walk down the patterned garden-paths
In my stiff, brocaded gown.　　　　　　　　　　5
With my powdered hair and jewelled fan,
I too am a rare
Pattern as I wander down
The garden paths.

My dress is richly figured,　　　　　　　　　　10
And the train
Makes a pink and silver stain
On the gravel, and the thrift
Of the borders.
Just a plate of current fashion,　　　　　　　　15
Tripping by in high-heeled ribboned shoes.
Not a softness anywhere about me,
Only whalebone and brocade.
And I sink on a seat in the shade
Of a lime tree. For my passion　　　　　　　　20
Wars against the stiff brocade.
The daffodils and squills
Flutter in the breeze
As they please.
And I weep;　　　　　　　　　　　　　　　25
For the lime tree is in blossom
And one small flower has dropped upon my bosom.

And the plashing of waterdrops
In the marble fountain
Comes down the garden-paths.　　　　　　　　30
The dripping never stops.

Underneath my stiffened gown
Is the softness of a woman bathing in a marble basin,
A basin in the midst of hedges grown
So thick, she cannot see her lover hiding,   35
But she guesses he is near,
And the sliding of the water
Seems the stroking of a dear
Hand upon her.
What is Summer in a fine brocaded gown!   40
I should like to see it lying in a heap upon the ground,
All the pink and silver crumpled up on the ground.

I would be the pink and silver as I ran along the paths,
And he would stumble after,
Bewildered by my laughter.   45
I should see the sun flashing from his sword-hilt and the
    buckles on his shoes.
I would choose
To lead him in a maze along the patterned paths,
A bright and laughing maze for my heavy-booted lover.
Till he caught me in the shade,   50
And the buttons of his waistcoat bruised my body as he
    clasped me,
Aching, melting, unafraid.
With the shadows of the leaves and the sundrops,
And the plopping of the waterdrops,
All about us in the open afternoon—   55
I am very like to swoon
With the weight of this brocade,
For the sun sifts through the shade.

Underneath the fallen blossom
In my bosom,
Is a letter I have hid.   60
It was brought to me this morning by a rider from the
    Duke.
"Madam, we regret to inform you that Lord Hartwell
Died in action Thursday se'nnight."
As I read it in the white, morning sunlight,   65
The letters squirmed like snakes.
"Any answer, Madam," said my footman.
"No," I told him.
"See that the messenger takes some refreshment.
No, no answer."   70

And I walked into the garden,
Up and down the patterned paths,
In my stiff, correct brocade.
The blue and yellow flowers stood up proudly in the sun,
Each one ;   75
I stood upright too,
Held rigid to the pattern
By the stiffness of my gown.
Up and down I walked,
Up and down.   80

In a month he would have been my husband.
In a month, here, underneath this lime,
He would have broke the pattern ;
He for me, and I for him,
He as Colonel, I as Lady,   85
On this shady seat.
He had a whim
That sunlight carried blessing.
And I answered, "It shall be as you have said."
Now he is dead.   90

In Summer and in Winter I shall walk
Up and down
The patterned garden-paths
In my stiff, brocaded gown.
The squills and daffodils   95
Will give place to pillared roses, and to asters, and to
      snow.
I shall go
Up and down
In my gown,

Gorgeously arrayed,   100
Boned and stayed.
And the softness of my body will be guarded from
      embrace
By each button, hook, and lace.
For the man who should loose me is dead,
Fighting with the Duke in Flanders,   105
In a pattern called a war.
Christ ! What are patterns for ?

GUNGA DIN

RUDYARD KIPLING (ENGLAND)

In his *Barrack Room Ballads*, Kipling gives us the life and philosophy of the British common soldier. The "Tommy" is a shrewd, humorous fellow, and his reflections on the people and countries to which his army service takes him are always amusing. This is especially so since Kipling has kept faithfully to the cockney dialect spoken by the average soldier of his time. Tommy leaves out aitches where they belong and puts them in where they don't; calls ladies "lidies"; and does other strange things to English as spoken by the cultivated Britisher. In the following ballad, an old drill sergeant is telling a new recruit some things about India, particularly about the natives, who are represented in this poem by the *bhisti* or water carrier of his regiment.

❋   ❋   ❋

You may talk o' gin and beer
When you're quartered safe out 'ere
And you're sent to penny-fights an' Aldershot it;
But when it comes to slaughter
You will do your work on water,
An' you'll lick the bloomin' boots of 'im that's got it.   5
Now in Injia's sunny clime
Where I used to spend my time
A-servin' of 'Er Majesty the Queen,
Of all them black-faced crew
The finest man I knew   10
Was our regimental bhisti, Gunga Din.
　　　He was "Din! Din! Din!
　　　You limping lump o' brick-dust, Gunga Din!
　　　Hi! *slippy hitherao!*
　　　Water, get it! *Panee lao!*   15
　　　You squidgy-nosed old idol, Gunga Din!"

The uniform 'e wore
Was nothing much before,
And rather less than 'arf o' that be'ind,
For a twisty piece o' rag   20
An' a goatskin water bag
Was all the field-equipment 'e could find.

3. *Aldershot:* the training camp in England where new soldiers are drilled before being sent to foreign service. 16. *slippy hitherao—Panee lao:* come here quickly with water.

When the sweatin' troop train lay
On the sidin' through the day,
Where the 'eat would make your bloomin' eyebrows crawl,
We shouted "Harry By!"
Till our throats were bricky-dry,
Then we wopped 'im 'cause 'e couldn't serve us all.

   It was "Din! Din! Din!
   You 'eathen, where the mischief have you been?
   You put some *juldee* in it,
   Or I'll *marrow* you this minute
   If you don't fill up my helmet, Gunga Din!"

'E would dot and carry one
Till the longest day was done,
An' 'e didn't seem to know the use o' fear.
If we charged or broke or cut,
You could bet your bloomin' nut
'E'd be waitin' fifty paces right flank rear.
With his *mussick* on 'is back,
'E would skip with our attack,
An' watch us till the bugles made "Retire."
An' for all 'is dirty 'ide
'E was white, clear white inside
When he went to tend the wounded under fire!

   It was "Din! Din! Din!"
   With the bullets kickin' dust-spots on the green.
   When the cartridges ran out,
   You could hear the front-files shout:
   "Hi! Ammunition-mules an' Gunga Din!"

I sha'n't forgit the night
When I dropped behind the fight
With a bullet where my belt-plate should 'a' been.
I was chokin' mad with thirst,
An' the man that spied me first
Was our good old grinnin,' gruntin' Gunga Din.
'E lifted up my 'ead,
An' 'e plugged me where I bled,
An' 'e guv me 'arf-a-pint o' water green.

32. *juldee:* speed. 33. *marrow:* hit. 41. *mussick:* water bag.

It was crawlin' an' it stunk,
But of all the drinks I've drunk,
I'm gratefullest for one from Gunga Din.
      It was "Din! Din! Din!
      'Ere's a beggar with a bullet through 'is spleen;   65
      'E's chawin' up the ground an' 'e's kickin' all around;
      For Gawd's sake git the water, Gunga Din!"

'E carried me away
To where a *dooli* lay,
An a bullet came an' drilled the beggar clean.   70
'E put me safe inside,
An' just before 'e died:
"I 'ope you liked your drink," sez Gunga Din.
So I'll meet 'im later on
In the place where 'e is gone—   75
Where it's always double drill an' no canteen.
'E'll be squattin' on the coals
Givin' drink to pore damned souls,
An' I'll get a swig in Hell from Gunga Din!
      Din! Din! Din!   80
      You Lazarushian-leather Gunga din!
      Though I've belted you an' flayed you,
      By the livin' Gawd that made you,
      You're a better man than I am, Gunga Din.

READING PROBLEMS ON THE METRICAL TALE

1. *Orpheus and Eurydice:* What truth about life is expressed in the various incidents of this myth? How is the power of music revealed?

2. *The Ride Round the Parapet:* What has made Lady Eleanora von Alleyne despise men? Why does she require the test ride? Do you think she deserved the rebuke from the Margrave? Compare with the tale by Leigh Hunt called *The Glove and the Lions.* Does the repetition add to the effectiveness of this poem?

3. *Michael:* How is the love of the shepherd for his land explained? What did the son mean to this old couple? Of what did the father mean the projected sheepfold to be a symbol? How is the character of the old man revealed after the disgrace of his son? Explain line 359. Why does this little touch reveal his grief more keenly than could whole pages of description?

69. *dooli:* ambulance or litter.

4. *The Revenge:* Why did not Sir Richard wish his men to fall into Spanish hands? Was it necessary for him to fight the Spaniards? Why did he do it? Do you admire him for it? Explain how it was possible for *The Revenge* to damage the Armada so much. What is the attitude of the Spaniards toward Sir Richard? Read this poem aloud to yourself and see what the rhythm adds to the general effect. Select descriptive words and phrases that render the action vivid. Compare this poem with Sir Walter Raleigh's contemporary account of the actual battle.

5. *Patterns:* What is the significance of this title? How many "patterns" are mentioned in the poem? Why does the speaker keep emphasizing her stiff brocaded gown? Of what is it a symbol? Why is it peculiarly tragic that we see the lady in the midst of the beautiful garden? Is she really cold and unmoved? Point out examples of her great courage and self control. Explain the question in the last line. How is the view of war given in *Patterns* different from that in *The Revenge?*

6. *Gunga Din:* What phases of war not touched in the two other war poems are stressed by Kipling? What is the attitude of the Tommy toward the native? What does line 45 show as to his feeling toward the brown races? Is there any sense of superiority mixed in it? Does the sergeant expect he and Gunga will meet in Hell for the same reasons? Prove that Gunga deserves the sergeant's praise. What touches of humor do you find in the poem? Characterize the rhythm of the poem and tell what it adds to the effect.

FURTHER READINGS IN THE METRICAL TALE

SUGGESTIONS FOR ORIGINAL METRICAL TALES

1. Cupid and Psyche. 2. The Girl Who Demanded Expensive Entertainment from Her Dates. 3. The Daughter, Son or Mother Who Went to Work When Father Lost His Job. 4. The Football Game. 5. After the Accident. 6. The "Subs" and "Reserves" Who Helped Us Win the Game or Debate. 7. One of the Tales in the Unit on the Prose Tale.

V

Episodes from Novels

WE HAVE followed the short story back to the dawn of history. Now let us turn to the long story, or novel, which shares with the short story and motion picture the hearts of modern readers. The novel differs from the short story mainly in length. Instead of being built up around one episode, a novel goes on from episode to episode in a long and complicated series of events. Instead of one main character and a few minor characters, the novel is crowded with people. Instead of a single plot, there may be a main plot and one or more sub-plots (or secondary stories), each with its own cast of characters. These sub-plots cross the main plot at certain points, contributing something to its action and often illustrating the same idea as the main plot, but in a different fashion.

The young reader, accustomed to the few characters and simple plots of juvenile fiction, school stories, Western tales, and popular mystery stories, is often bewildered by the scores or even hundreds of characters and many sub-plots of a great novel, and has to learn to carry all these people and parallel stories in mind before he can enjoy such a novel.

But in spite of the difference in length and complexity between a short story and a novel, the novel like the short story is told in either the first or third person, and in either chronological or retrogressive order; and it presents us with the same centers of interest as we have already outlined for the short story; namely, plot, setting, character, theme, truth, and style.

EPISODIC AND PLOTTED NOVELS

The wider scope of the novel allows, however, for some features not found in the shorter forms of narrative. The action, as we have said, is more intricate. There are novels which, like tales, have no plots, but are a series of detached episodes arranged in chronological order and strung together by a connecting principal character. Such episodic novels are *Gösta Berling* and *The Three Musketeers*.

In novels with a plot, there is space to develop many interests of character, setting, and action which are impossible in the limited space of the short story.

DEVELOPING CHARACTERS

As the characters can be carried through a long period of time, their complex motives and reactions can be more fully analyzed. There is a chance, also, to show them changing and developing under the influence of events. The hero may first appear as a youth as in *The Count of Monte Cristo, David Copperfield,* or *Arrowsmith.* Or the main characters may even start as children as in *The Ordeal of Richard Feverel* or *The Mill on the Floss,* and their development may be traced into manhood and womanhood or even on into old age. Even when the novel covers a shorter period, crises in the lives of the characters may completely change their outlook and personality, as in *The Scarlet Letter* and *Anna Karenina.* On the other hand, some novelists keep their characters unchanged from start to finish.

As the number of characters in a novel is naturally much greater than in a short story, it is interesting to see which novelists present the largest number and widest variety of characters, and which specialize on the analysis of a few people of the same type. Some authors deal with all social classes; others with a single social level. Some mingle men, women, and children, young and old, good and bad, odd and ordinary, comic and tragic. Some authors portray men better than women · the old better than the young, or *vice versa.*

The personages in a novel are divided into main characters and minor characters. The main characters are those around whom the plot centers. The minor characters make possible the actions of the main characters and furnish a background for them. The minor characters furnish the cast for crowded scenes, they give the local or historical touches that help place the story, they sometimes add humor or pathos, or help to explain the main characters by contrast or by actual comment upon them. Sometimes an author uses a minor character to voice his own ideas, as Meredith uses Adrian in *The Ordeal of Richard Feverel.*

With the characterization more fully developed, it is easier to see whether the plot springs from the nature of the actors, from chance and coincidence, or from the setting in which the characters are placed. As the plot can include many incidents, it is interesting to ask which incidents reveal the setting, which display character, and which advance the action. Moreover, to sustain our interest, a long story must contain many minor crises, or points of conflict which arouse suspense, but are not necessarily the climax or turning point in the story. There are many methods of creating suspense such as foreshadowing, ending a chapter or section of the story at a high point of interest and then interpolating or turning to another plot and set of characters, withholding information from either the reader or the characters in the story (as in the case of disguise, where the reader may guess a person's identity but the other characters may be still in the dark), or introducing sudden surprises like the release of Rawdon Crawley from prison in *Vanity Fair* or the bishop's gift to Jean Valjean in *Les Misérables*.

SETTING

Setting can be much more fully depicted, and it is easy to see why a short story is less often historical than a full length novel, and why the effect of environment on character is more frequently studied in a novel like *The Scarlet Letter* or *Lord Jim* than in a short story.

THEME

As in a short story, the theme forms a major center of interest, but the novelist has more chances to develop the theme through plot, character, and setting than is possible within the cramped area of a short story. Some novels have a theme within a theme; for instance, a historical novel has not only the particular theme of the special story but the larger enveloping theme of picturing the spirit of its age.

TRUTH

The novel is naturally a severer test of the author's truth to life—both realistically and allegorically—than a brief narrative like a short story. Thousands can write a passable magazine story, but few can produce a full length novel that will absorb a reader throughout 500 to 1000 pages of incidents, dialog, characterization, problem presentation, and comment from author and characters.

STYLE

And the mere length of the novel demands a more subtle, various, and finished style if the words of the author are not to grow tedious. He must be able to describe everything well—people, places, things, animals, the weather, emotion. He must be able to create atmosphere, to excite a wide variety of emotions and not constantly harp on one string. He must diversify his style with humor, philosophy, figures of speech, imagination, poetic touches. He must be clear, sincere, and natural. To read a 1000 page novel is like living in the same home day by day with another person, and the author's literary manners must be not only above reproach but charming and varied!

TYPES OF NOVELS

The novel like the short story falls into certain types. There is the romantic novel which idealizes life, presenting it as the scene of colorful adventure, opportunity, goodness, and rosy happiness. Or the novel may be realistic—showing life as it is, full of commonplace incidents and characters whose motives are sadly mixed.

According to the major interest, purpose, or style of the writer, novels fall into the following classifications:

1. The character novel—stressing character study
2. The novel of adventure—stressing plot and action
3. The historical novel—picturing a period in history
4. The novel which presents a cross-section of society—giving dramatic contrasts and showing the inter-relation of social groups
5. The novel which studies a particular social group, as the society novel of manners, or the novel of low and criminal life
6. The novel which depicts a given locality (the novel of local color)
7. The problem novel or novel with a purpose
8. The fantastic or allegorical novel, disguising a philosophy of life in the garb of a symbolic story

A person's taste in fiction usually goes through a definite cycle of growth, which is perfectly right and natural. The child and youth love action and adventure. The child starts with Defoe's *Robinson Crusoe* and the youth goes on to the more romantic adventures of Dumas' *Three Musketeers,* watching entranced "the career of a gallant will meeting the unknown." For the maturing mind, character replaces action as the basis of interest, since character is the source of action. We read first character novels like those of Scott in which there is a balance between the two interests—in which characters are vividly portrayed and put into stirring action. Next we take up novels which show how character came to be what it is—which trace personality back to its sources in heredity, environment, training, and habit. At what point in this cycle are you?

To estimate the greatness of a good novel is a difficult task. But we may safely say that after a novel has passed such of the tests set forth on page 8 for the short story as are appropriate to the longer work, then its greatness may be judged by whether, as Professor Woodberry says, it "gives a full world, complete for the characters inhabiting it. There is no surer sign of greatness in a novel than this large grasp of general life, the crowded stage, the throng of affairs, the sense of a world of men." To make the world presented in a novel "complete for the characters inhabiting it" will demand a different range and number of characters, and a different breadth of social setting in different novels. But this sense of looking at characters from all sides and seeing their whole world is a supreme test of greatness.

Probably no literary type has contributed more to progress than the novel. It reveals human conditions, and diffuses not only facts but ideas. It widens our historical horizon. To quote Professor Woodberry again: "The reader of the modern historical novel has an intelligent knowledge of the development of the European world and its classic sources such as would have been impossible even to a scholar in a preceding age. No literary type has so expanded our knowledge and made the world so well known to itself in all its parts."

THE BISHOP'S CANDLESTICKS

Victor Hugo (France)

This extract from *Les Misérables* introduces us to the hero, Jean Valjean. As an orphan in his teens, this poor peasant lad had undertaken the support of a widowed sister with seven little children. In the midst of a bitter winter when work was scarce and the children starv-

ing, Jean broke a baker's window and stole a loaf of bread. For this
he was sentenced to the galleys [1] for five years. After four attempted
escapes, this term was lengthened to nineteen.

❅ ❅ ❅

I

An hour before sunset, on the evening of a day in the beginning
of October, 1815, a man travelling afoot entered the little town of
D——. The few persons who at this time were at their windows or
their doors, regarded this traveller with a sort of distrust. It would
have been hard to find a passer-by more wretched in appearance.
He was a man of middle height, stout and hardy, in the strength of
maturity; he might have been forty-six or seven. A slouched leather
cap half hid his face, bronzed by the sun and wind, and dripping
with sweat. His shaggy breast was seen through the coarse yellow
shirt which at the neck was fastened by a small silver anchor; he
wore a cravat twisted like a rope, coarse blue trousers, an old ragged
grey blouse patched on one side with a piece of green cloth sewed
with twine. Upon his back was a well-filled knapsack, strongly
buckled and quite new. In his hand he carried an enormous knotted
stick; his stockingless feet were in hobnailed shoes; his hair was
cropped and his beard long.

The sweat, the heat, his long walk, and the dust, added an indescribable meanness to his tattered appearance.

His hair was shorn, but bristly, for it had begun to grow a little,
and seemingly had not been cut for some time. Nobody knew him;
he was evidently a traveller. Whence had he come? From the south
—perhaps from the sea; for he was making his entrance into D——
by the same road by which, seven months before, the Emperor
Napoleon went from Cannes to Paris. This man must have walked
all day long; for he appeared very weary.

When he reached the corner of the Rue Poichevert, he turned to
the left and went toward the mayor's office. He went in, and a
quarter of an hour afterwards he came out. Without returning his
salutation, the gendarme [2] looked at him attentively, watched him
for some distance, and then went into the city hall.

The traveller turned his steps toward an inn, which was the best
in the place, and went at once into the kitchen, which opened out of
the street. All the ranges were fuming, and a great fire was burning

[1] *galleys:* prison ships.　　　　　　　　[2] *gendarme:* policeman.

briskly in the chimney-place. Mine host, who was at the same time head cook, was going from the fireplace to the sauce-pans, very busy superintending an excellent dinner for some wagoners who were laughing and talking noisily in the next room. A fat marmot, flanked by white partridges and goose, was turning on a long spit before the fire; upon the ranges were cooking two large carps from Lake Lauzet, and a trout from Lake Alloz.

The host, hearing the door open, and a newcomer enter, said without raising his eyes from his ranges—"What will monsieur have?"

"Something to eat and lodging."

"Nothing more easy," said mine host, but on turning his head and taking an observation of the traveller, he added, "for pay."

The man drew from his pocket a large leather purse, and answered, "I have money."

"Then," said mine host, "I am at your service."

The man put his purse back into his pocket, took off his knapsack and put it down hard by the door, and holding his stick in his hand, sat down on a low stool by the fire. D—— being in the mountains, the evenings of October are cold there.

However, as the host passed backwards and forwards, he kept a careful eye on the traveller.

"Is dinner almost ready?" said the man.

"Directly," said mine host.

While the newcomer was warming himself with his back turned, the worthy innkeeper took a pencil from his pocket, and then tore off the corner of an old paper which he pulled from a little table near the window. On the margin he wrote a line or two, folded it, and handed the scrap of paper to a child. The innkeeper whispered a word to the boy, and he ran off in the direction of the mayor's office.

The traveller saw nothing of this. He asked a second time: "Is dinner ready?"

"Yes: in a few moments," said the host.

The boy came back with a paper. The host unfolded it unhurriedly, as one who is expecting an answer. He seemed to read with attention, then throwing his head on one side, thought for a moment. Then he took a step towards the traveller, who seemed drowned in troublous thought.

"Monsieur," said he, "I cannot receive you."

The traveller half rose from his seat. "Why? Are you afraid I shall not pay you, or do you want me to pay in advance? I have money, I tell you."

"It is not that."

"What then?"

"You have money——"

"Yes," said the man.

"And I," said the host; "I have no room."

"Well, put me in the stable," quietly replied the man.

"I cannot."

"Why?"

"Because the horses take all the room."

"Well," responded the man, "a corner in the garret; a truss of straw: we will see about that after dinner."

"I cannot give you any dinner."

This declaration, made in a measured but firm tone, appeared serious to the traveller. He got up.

"Ah, bah! but I am dying with hunger. I have walked since sunrise; I have travelled twelve leagues. I will pay, and I want something to eat."

"I have nothing," said the host.

The man burst into a laugh, and turned towards the fireplace and the ranges. "Nothing! and all that?"

"All that is engaged."

"By whom?"

"By those persons, the wagoners."

"How many are there of them?"

"Twelve."

"There is enough there for twenty."

"They have engaged and paid for it all in advance."

The man sat down again and said, without raising his voice: "I am at an inn. I am hungry, and I shall stay."

The host bent down to his ear, and said in a voice which made him tremble: "Go away!"

At these words the traveller, who was bent over, poking some embers in the fire with the iron-shod end of his stick, turned suddenly around, and opened his mouth, as if to reply, when the host, looking steadily at him, added in the same low tone: "Stop, no more of that. Shall I tell you your name? Your name is Jean Valjean, now shall I tell you who you are? When I saw you enter, I suspected something. I sent to the mayor's office, and here is the reply. Can you read?" So saying he held towards him the open paper, which had just come from the mayor. The man cast a look upon it; the innkeeper, after a short silence, said: "It is my custom to be polite to all: Go!"

The man bowed his head, picked up his knapsack, and went out.

He took the principal street; he walked at random, slinking near the houses like a sad and humiliated man; he did not once turn around. If he had turned, he would have seen the innkeeper standing in his doorway with all his guests, and the passers-by gathered about him, speaking excitedly, and pointing him out; and from the looks of fear and distrust which were exchanged, he would have guessed that before long his arrival would be the talk of the whole town. He saw nothing of all this: people overwhelmed with trouble do not look behind; they know only too well that misfortune follows them.

He walked along in this way some time, going by chance down streets unknown to him, and forgetting fatigue, as is the case in sorrow. Suddenly he felt a pang of hunger; night was at hand, and he looked around to see if he could not discover a lodging.

The good inn was closed against him: he sought some humble tavern, some poor cellar. Just then a light shone at the end of the street; he saw a pine branch, hanging by an iron bracket, against the white sky of the twilight. He went thither.

The traveller stopped a moment and looked in at the little window upon the low hall of the tavern, lighted by a small lamp upon a table, and a great fire in the chimney place. Some men were drinking, and the host was warming himself; an iron pot hung over the fire seething in the blaze.

Two doors lead into this tavern, which was also a sort of eating-house—one from the street, the other from a small court full of rubbish. The traveller did not dare to enter by the street door; he slipped into the court, stopped again, then timidly raised the latch, and pushed open the door.

"Who is it?" said the host.

"One who wants supper and a bed."

"All right: here you can sup and sleep."

He went in, all the men who were drinking turned towards him; the lamp shining on one side of his face, the firelight on the other, they examined him for some time as he was taking off his knapsack.

The host said to him: "There is the fire; the supper is cooking in the pot; come and warm yourself, comrade."

He seated himself near the fireplace and stretched his feet out towards the fire, half dead with fatigue; an inviting odor came from the pot. All that could be seen of his face under his slouched cap assumed a vague appearance of comfort, which tempered the sorrowful aspect given him by long-continued suffering.

His profile was strong, energetic, and sad; a physiognomy

strangely marked: at first it appeared humble, but it soon became severe. His eye shone beneath his eyebrows like a fire beneath a thicket.

However, one of the men at the table was a fisherman who had put up his horse at the stable of the inn before entering the tavern. He beckoned to the tavern-keeper to come to him, which he did. They exchanged a few words in a low voice; the traveller had again relapsed into thought.

The tavern-keeper returned to the fire, and laying his hand roughly on his shoulder, said harshly: "You are going to clear out from here!"

The stranger turned round and said mildly, "Ah! Do you know?"

"Yes."

"They sent me away from the other inn."

"And we turn you out of this."

"Where would you have me go?"

"Somewhere else."

The man took up his stick and knapsack, and went off. As he went out, some children threw stones at him. He turned angrily and threatened them with his stick, and they scattered like a flock of birds.

He passed the prison: an iron chain hung from the door attached to a bell. He rang. The grating opened.

"Monsieur Turnkey," said he, taking off his cap respectfully, "will you open and let me stay here tonight?"

A voice answered: "A prison is not a tavern: get yourself arrested and we will open."

It was about eight o'clock in the evening: as he did not know the streets, he walked at hazard. On passing by the Cathedral square he shook his fist at the church. Exhausted with fatigue, and hoping for nothing better, he lay down on a stone bench.

Just then an old woman came out of the church. She saw the man lying there in the dark, and said: "What are you doing there, my friend?"

He replied harshly, and with anger in his tone: "You see, my good woman, I am going to sleep."

"Upon the bench?" said she.

"For nineteen years I have had a wooden mattress," said the man; "tonight I have a stone one."

"You have been a soldier?"

"Yes, my good woman, a soldier."

"Why don't you go to the inn?"

"Because I have no money."

"Alas!" said Madame de R——, "I have only four sous in my purse."

"Give them then." The man took the four sous, and Madame de R—— continued: "You cannot find lodging for so little in an inn. But have you tried? You cannot pass the night so. You must be cold and hungry. They should give you lodging for charity."

"I have knocked at every door."

"Well, what then?"

"Everybody has driven me away."

The good woman touched the man's arm and pointed out to him, on the other side of the square, a little low house beside the bishop's palace. "Have you knocked at that one there?"

"No."

"Knock there."

II

That evening, after his walk in the town, the Bishop of D—— remained quite late in his room. He was busy with his great work on Duty, which unfortunately is left incomplete. He carefully dissected all that the Fathers and Doctors have said on this serious topic. His book was divided into two parts: First, the duties of all: Secondly, the duties of each according to his position in life.

At eight o'clock he was still at work, writing with some inconvenience on little slips of paper, with a large book open on his knees, when Madame Magloire,[3] as usual, came in to take the silver from the panel near the bed. A moment after, the bishop, knowing that the table was laid, and that his sister was perhaps waiting, closed his book and went into the dining-room.

Madame Magloire had just finished placing the plates. While she was arranging the table, she was talking with Mademoiselle Baptistine.[4] The lamp was on the table, which was near the fireplace, where a good fire was burning.

Just as the bishop entered, Madame Magloire was speaking with some warmth. She was talking to Mademoiselle upon a familiar subject, and one to which the bishop was quite accustomed. It was a discussion on the means of fastening the front door.

It seems that while Madame Magloire was out making provision for supper, she had heard the news in sundry places. A suspicious

---

[3] Madame Magloire: the bishop's housekeeper.
[4] Mademoiselle Baptistine: his sister.

vagabond was lurking somewhere in the town, and every one ought to shut up, bolt, and bar his house properly, and secure his door thoroughly.

Madame Magloire dwelt upon these last words; but the bishop having come·from a cold room, seated himself before the fire and began to warm himself. He did not hear a word of what was let fall by Madame Magloire, and she repeated it.

Turning his chair half round, putting his hands on his knees, and raising towards the old servant his cordial and good-humored face, which the firelight shone upon, he said: "Well, well! what is the matter? Are we in any great danger?"

Then Madame Magloire began her story again, unconsciously exaggerating it a little. It appeared that a dangerous beggar was in the town. He had gone for lodging to Jacquin Labarre, who had refused to receive him; he had been seen to roam through the streets at dusk. A man with a knapsack and a rope, and a terrible-looking face.

"Indeed!" said the bishop.

This readiness to question her encouraged Madame Magliore; it seemed to indicate that the bishop was really well-nigh alarmed. She continued triumphantly: "Yes, Monseigneur; [5] it is true. There will something happen tonight in the town; everybody says so. And I say, Monseigneur, and Mademoiselle says also——

"Me?" interrupted the sister; "I say nothing. Whatever my brother does is well done."

Madame Magloire went on as if she had not heard this protestation: "We say that this house is not safe at all; and if Monseigneur will permit me, I will go and tell the locksmith to come and put the old bolts in the door again. I say we must have bolts, were it only for tonight; for I say that a door which opens by a latch on the outside to the first comer, nothing could be more horrible: and then Monseigneur has the habit of always saying 'Come in,' even at midnight. But, my goodness! there is no need even to ask leave——"

At this moment there was a violent knock on the door.

"Come in!" said the bishop.

III

The door opened. It opened quickly, quite wide, as if pushed by some one boldly and with energy. A man entered.

[5] *Monseigneur:* the title used for a bishop. Equivalent to "my lord."

That man we know already; it was the traveller we have seen wandering about in search of a lodging. He came in, took one step, and paused, leaving the door open behind him. He had his knapsack on his back, his stick in his hand, and a rough, hard, tired, and fierce look in his eyes, as seen by the firelight. He was hideous.

Madame Magloire had not even the strength to scream. She stood trembling with her mouth open. Mademoiselle Baptistine turned, saw the man enter, and started up half alarmed; then, slowly turning back again towards the fire, she looked at her brother, and her face resumed its usual calmness and serenity. The bishop looked upon the man with a tranquil eye.

As he was opening his mouth to speak, doubtless to ask the stranger what he wanted, the man, leaning with both hands on his club, glanced from one to another in turn, and without waiting for the bishop to speak, said in a loud voice: "See here! My name is Jean Valjean. I am a convict; I have been nineteen years in the galleys. Four days ago I was set free, and during those four days I have walked from Toulon. Today I have walked twelve leagues. When I reached this place this evening, I went to an inn, and they sent me away on account of my yellow passport,[6] which I had shown at the mayor's office, as was necessary. I went to another inn; they said: 'Get out!' It was the same with one as with another; nobody would have me. I went to the prison, and the turnkey would not let me in. There in the square I lay down upon a stone; a good woman showed me your house, and said: 'Knock there!' I have knocked. What is this place? Are you an inn? I have money; my savings, one hundred and nine francs and fifteen sous which I have earned in the galleys by my work for nineteen years.[7] I will pay. What do I care? I have money. I am very tired—twelve leagues on foot, and I am so hungry. Can I stay?"

"Madame Magloire," said the bishop, "put on another plate."

The man took three steps, and came near the lamp which stood on the table. "Stop," he exclaimed; as if he had not been understood, "not that; did you understand me? I am a galley-slave—a convict—I am just from the galleys." He drew from his pocket a large sheet of yellow paper, which he unfolded. "There is my passport, yellow as you see. That is enough to have me kicked out wherever I go. Will you read it? I know how to read, I do. I learned in the galleys. There is a school there for those who care for it.

[6] *yellow passport:* in Europe travellers have to show a passport for identification when they enter a strange town. The passport of an ex-convict was yellow.
[7] *one hundred and nine francs:* about twenty dollars.

See, here is what they have put in the passport: 'Jean Valjean, a liberated convict, native of ———,' you don't care for that, 'has been nineteen years in the galleys; five years for burglary; fourteen years for having attempted four times to escape. This man is very dangerous.' There you have it! Everybody has thrust me out; will you receive me? Is this an inn? Can you give me something to eat, and a place to sleep? Have you a stable?"

"Madame Magloire," said the bishop, "put some sheets on the bed in the alcove." Madame Magloire went out to fulfil her orders.

The bishop turned to the man: "Monsieur, sit down and warm yourself: we are going to take supper presently, and your bed will be made ready while you sup."

At last the man quite understood; his face, the expression of which till then had been gloomy and hard, now expressed stupefaction, doubt, and joy, and became absolutely wonderful. He began to stutter like a madman.

"True? What! You will keep me? you won't drive me away? a convict! You call me Monsieur and don't say 'Get out, dog!' as everybody else does. I thought that you would send me away, so I told first off who I am. Oh! the fine woman who sent me here! I shall have a supper! a bed like other people with mattress and sheets—a bed! It is nineteen years that I have not slept on a bed. You are really willing that I should stay? You are good people! Besides I have money: I will pay well. I beg your pardon, Monsieur Inn-keeper, what is your name? I will pay all you say. You are a fine man. You are an innkeeper, aren't you?"

"I am a priest who lives here," said the bishop.

While he was talking, the bishop shut the door, which he had left wide open. Madame Magloire brought in a plate and set it on the table.

"Madame Magloire," said the bishop, "put this plate as near the fire as you can." Then turning towards his guest, he added: "The night wind is raw in the Alps; you must be cold, Monsieur."

Every time he said this word monsieur, with his gently solemn, and heartily hospitable voice, the man's countenance lighted up. Monsieur to a convict is a glass of water to a man dying of thirst at sea. Ignominy thirsts for respect.

"The lamp," said the bishop, "gives a poor light."

Madame Magloire understood him, and going to his bed-chamber, took from the mantel the two silver candlesticks, lighted the candles, and placed them on the table.

Meantime she had served up supper; it consisted of soup made of water, oil, bread, and salt, a little pork, a scrap of mutton, a few figs, a cheese, and a large loaf of rye bread. She had, without asking, added to the usual dinner of the bishop a bottle of fine old Mauves wine.

The bishop's countenance was lighted up with the expression of pleasure peculiar to hospitable natures. "To supper!" he said briskly, as was his habit when he had a guest. He seated the man at his right. Mademoiselle Baptistine, perfectly quiet and natural, took her place at his left.

The bishop said the blessing, and then served the soup himself, according to his usual custom. The man fell to, eating greedily.

Suddenly the bishop said: "It seems to me something is lacking on the table."

The fact was that Madame Magliore had set out only the three plates which were necessary. Now it was the custom of the house, when the bishop had any one to supper, to set all six of the silver plates on the table, an innocent display. This graceful appearance of luxury was a sort of childlikeness which was full of charm in this gentle but austere household, which elevated poverty to dignity.[8]

Madame Magloire understood the remark; without a word she went out, and a moment afterwards the three plates for which the bishop had asked were shining on the cloth, symmetrically arranged before each of the three guests. During the meal there were few words spoken. The visitor was plainly weary and it was not long before they made ready for the night.

IV

After having said good-night to his sister, Monseigneur Bien-venu took one of the silver candlesticks from the table, handed the other to his guest, and said to him: "Monsieur, I will show you to your room."

The man followed him. The house was so arranged that one could reach the alcove only by passing through the bishop's room. Madame Magloire was putting up the silver in the cupboard at the head of the bed. It was the last thing she did every night before going to bed.

The bishop left his guest in the alcove before a clean white bed. The man set down the candlestick upon a small table.

[8] The Bishop had given his palace for a hospital and used his income for charity, living himself in a simple cottage. The only luxury he had kept was a silver table service.

"Come," said the bishop, "a good night's rest to you: tomorrow morning before you go, you shall have a cup of warm milk from our cows."

"Thank you, Monsieur l'Abbé," said the man.

Scarcely had he pronounced these words of peace, when he turned abruptly towards the old man, crossed his arms, and casting a wild look upon his host, exclaimed in a harsh voice: "Ah, now, indeed! You lodge me in your house, as near you as that!"

He checked himself, and added, with a laugh, in which there was something horrible: "Have you reflected upon it? Who tells you that I am not a murderer?"

The bishop responded: "God will take care of that."

Then with gravity, moving his lips like one praying or talking to himself, he raised two fingers of his right hand and blessed the man, who, however, did not bow; and without turning his head or looking behind him, went into his chamber.

As to the man, he was so completely exhausted that he did not even avail himself of the clean white sheets; he blew out the candle with his nostril, after the manner of convicts, and fell on the bed, dressed as he was, into a sound sleep.

V

As the cathedral clock struck two, Jean Valjean awoke. What awakened him was too good a bed. For nearly twenty years he had not slept in a bed, and although he had not undressed, the sensation was too novel not to disturb his sleep.

He had slept something more than four hours. His fatigue had passed away. He was not accustomed to give many hours to repose. He opened his eyes, and looked for a moment into the obscurity about him, then he closed them to go to sleep again. He could not get to sleep, and so he began to think.

He was in one of those moods in which the ideas we have in our minds are perturbed. There was a kind of vague ebb and flow in his brain. Many thoughts came to him, but there was one which continually presented itself, and which drove away all others. He had noticed the six silver plates and the large ladle that Madame Magloire had put on the table.

Those six silver plates took possession of him. There they were within a few steps. At the very moment that he passed through the middle room to reach the one he was now in, the old servant was placing them in a little cupboard at the head of the bishop's bed.

He had marked that cupboard well: on the right, coming from the dining-room. They were solid; and old silver. With the big ladle, they would bring at least two hundred francs, double what he had got for nineteen years' labor.

His mind wavered a whole hour, and a long one, in fluctuation and in struggle. The clock struck three. He opened his eyes, rose up hastily in bed, reached out his arm and felt his haversack, which he had put into the corner of the alcove, then he thrust out his legs and placed his feet on the ground, and found himself, he knew not how, seated on his bed.

He remained for some time lost in thought in that attitude, which would have had a rather ominous look, had any one seen him there in the dusk—he only awake in the slumbering house. All at once he stooped down, took off his shoes, and put them softly upon the mat in front of the bed, then he resumed his thinking posture, and was still again.

He continued in this situation, and would perhaps have remained there until daybreak, if the clock had not struck the quarter or the half-hour. The clock seemed to say to him: "Come along!"

He rose to his feet, hesitated for a moment longer, and listened; all was still in the house; he walked straight and cautiously towards the window, which he could discern. The night was not very dark; there was a full moon, across which large clouds were driving before the wind. On reaching the window, Jean Valjean examined it. It had no bars, opened into the garden, and was fastened, according to the fashion of the country, with a little wedge only. He opened it; but as the cold, keen air rushed into the room, he closed it again immediately. He looked into the garden with that absorbed look which studies rather than sees. The garden was enclosed with a white wall, quite low, and readily scaled. Beyond, against the sky, he distinguished the tops of trees at equal distances apart, which showed that this wall separated the garden from an avenue or a lane planted with trees.

When he had taken this observation, he turned like a man whose mind is made up, went to his alcove, took his haversack, opened it, fumbled in it, took out something which he laid upon the bed, put his shoes into one of his pockets, tied up his bundle, swung it upon his shoulders, put on his cap, and pulled the vizor down over his eyes, felt for his stick, and went and put it in the corner of the window, then returned to the bed, and resolutely took up the object which he had laid on it. It looked like a short iron bar, pointed at one end like a spear.

It would have been hard to distinguish in the darkness for what use this piece of iron had been made. Could it be a lever? Could it be a club? In the day-time, it would have been seen to be nothing but a miner's drill. At that time, the convicts were sometimes employed in quarrying stone on the high hills that surround Toulon, and they often had miners' tools in their possession.

He took the drill in his right hand, and holding his breath, with stealthy steps, he moved towards the door of the next room, which was the bishop's, as we know. On reaching the door, he found it unlatched. The bishop had not closed it.

VI

Jean Valjean listened. Not a sound.

He pushed the door.

He pushed it lightly with the end of his finger, with the stealthy and timorous carefulness of a cat. The door yielded to the pressure with a silent, imperceptible movement, which made the opening a little wider.

He waited a moment, and then pushed the door again more boldly.

It yielded gradually and silently. The opening was not wide enough for him to pass through; there was a small table near the door which barred the entrance.

Jean Valjean saw the obstacle. At all hazards the opening must be made still wider. He so determined, and pushed the door a third time, harder than before. This time a rusty hinge suddenly sent out into the darkness a harsh and prolonged creak.

Jean Valjean shivered. The noise of this hinge sounded in his ears as clear and terrible as the trumpet of the Judgment Day. In the fantastic exaggeration of the first moment, he almost imagined that this hinge had become animate and suddenly endowed with a terrible life; and that it was barking like a dog to warn everybody, and rouse the sleepers.

He stopped, shuddering and distracted, and dropped from his tip-toes to his feet. He felt the pulses of his temples beat like trip-hammers, and it appeared to him that his breath came from his chest with the roar of wind from a cavern. It seemed impossible that the horrible sound of this incensed hinge had not shaken the whole house with the shock of an earthquake: the door pushed by him had taken the alarm, and had called out; the old man would arise; the two old women would scream; help would come; in a quarter of an hour the town would be alive with it, and the gendarmes in pursuit. For a moment he thought he was lost.

He stood still, petrified, not daring to stir. Some minutes passed. The door was wide open; he ventured a look into the room. Nothing had moved. He listened. Nothing was stirring in the house. The noise of the rusty hinge had wakened nobody.

This first danger was over, but still he felt within him a frightful tumult. Nevertheless he did not flinch. Not even when he thought he was lost had he flinched. His only thought was to make an end of it quickly. He took one step and was in the room.

A deep calm filled the chamber. Here and there indistinct, confused forms could be distinguished; which by day, were papers scattered over a table, open folios, books piled on a stool, an armchair with clothes on it, a prie-dieu,[9] but now were only dark corners and whitish spots. Jean Valjean advanced, carefully avoiding the furniture. At the further end of the room, he could hear the equal and quiet breathing of the sleeping bishop.

Suddenly he stopped: he was near the bed, he had reached it sooner than he thought.

Nature sometimes joins her effects to our acts with a sort of serious and intelligent appropriateness, as if she would compel us to reflect. For nearly a half hour a great cloud had darkened the sky. At the moment when Jean Valjean paused before the bed, the cloud broke as if purposely, and a ray of moonlight crossing the high window suddenly lighted up the bishop's pale face. He slept tranquilly. His head had fallen on the pillow in the unstudied attitude of slumber; over the side of the bed hung his hand, ornamented with the pastoral ring, which had done so many good deeds, so many pious acts. His entire countenance was lit up with a vague expression of content, hope, and happiness. It was more than a smile and almost a radiance. On his forehead rested the indescribable reflection of an unseen light. The souls of the upright in sleep have vision of a mysterious heaven.

A reflection from this heaven shone upon the bishop. But it was also a luminous transparency, for this heaven was within him; this heaven was his conscience.

At the instant when the moonbeam overlay, so to speak, this inward radiance, the sleeping bishop appeared as if in a halo. The moon in the sky, nature drowsing, the garden without a pulse, the quiet house, the hour, the moment, the silence, added something

---

[9] *prie-dieu:* stool on which one kneeled for prayer, usually fitted with a rack to hold one's prayer book.

strangely solemn and unutterable to the venerable repose of this man, and enveloped his white locks and his closed eyes with a serene and majestic glory, this face where all was hope and confidence—this old man's head and infant's slumber.

There was something of divinity almost in this man, thus unconsciously august.

Jean Valjean was in the shadow with the iron drill in his hand, erect, motionless, terrified, at this radiant figure. He had never seen anything comparable to it. This confidence filled him with fear. The moral world has no greater spectacle than this: a troubled and restless conscience on the verge of committing an evil deed, contemplating the sleep of a good man.

He did not remove his eyes from the old man. The only thing which was plain from his attitude and his countenance was a strange indecision. You would have said he was hesitating between two realms, that of the doomed and that of the saved. He appeared ready either to cleave this skull, or to kiss this hand.

In a few minutes he raised his left hand slowly to his forehead and took off his hat; then, letting his hand fall with the same slowness, Jean Valjean resumed his contemplations, his cap in his left hand, his club in his right, and his hair bristling on his fierce-looking head.

Under this frightful gaze the bishop still slept in profoundest peace.

The crucifix above the mantelpiece was dimly visible in the moonlight, apparently extending its arms toward both, with a benediction for one and a pardon for the other.

Suddenly Jean Valjean put on his cap, then passed quickly, without looking at the bishop, along the bed, straight to the cupboard which he perceived near its head; he raised the drill to force the lock; the key was in it; he opened it; the first thing he saw was the basket of silver, he took it, crossed the room with hasty stride, careless of noise, reached the door, entered the alcove, took his stick, stepped out, put the silver in his knapsack, threw away the basket, ran across the garden, leaped over the wall like a tiger, and fled.

VII

The next day at sunrise, Monseigneur Bienvenu was walking in the garden. Madame Magloire ran towards him quite beside herself.

"Monseigneur, Monseigneur," cried she, "does your greatness know where the silver basket is?"

"Yes," said the bishop.

"God be praised!" said she, "I did not know what had become of it."

The bishop had just found the basket on a flower-bed. He gave it to Madame Magloire and said, "There it is."

"Yes," said she, "but there is nothing in it. The silver?"

"Ah!" said the bishop, "it is the silver then that troubles you. I do not know where that is."

"Good heavens! it is stolen. That man who came last night stole it."

While she was uttering this exclamation her eyes fell on an angle of the garden where a capstone of the wall had been thrown down.

"See, there is where he got out. The abominable fellow! he has stolen our silver!"

The bishop was silent for a moment, then raising his serious eyes, he said mildly to Madame Magloire: "Now first, did this silver belong to us?"

Madame Magloire did not answer; after a moment the bishop continued: "Madame Magloire, I have for a long time wrongfully withheld this silver; it belonged to the poor. Who was this man? A poor man evidently."

"Alas! alas!" returned Madame Magloire. "It is not on my account or Mademoiselle's; it is all the same to us. But it is on yours, monseigneur. What is monsieur going to eat from now?"

The bishop looked at her with amazement: "How so! have we no tin plates."

Madame Magloire made an expressive gesture. "Tin smells."

"Well," said the bishop, "then, wooden plates."

In a few minutes he was breakfasting at the same table at which Jean Valjean sat the night before. While breakfasting, Monseigneur Bienvenu pleasantly remarked to his sister who said nothing, and Madame Magloire who was grumbling to herself, that there was really no need even of a wooden spoon or fork to dip a piece of bread into a cup of milk.

"Was there ever such an idea?" said Madame Magloire to herself, as she went backwards and forwards: "to take in a man like that, and to give him a bed beside him; and yet what a blessing it was that he did nothing but steal! Oh, my stars! it makes the chills run over me when I think of it!"

Just as the brother and sister were rising from the table, there was a knock at the door.

"MY FRIEND, BEFORE YOU GO, HERE ARE YOUR CANDLESTICKS."

"Come in," said the bishop.

The door opened. A strange, fierce group appeared on the threshold. Three men were holding a fourth by the collar. The three men were gendarmes; the fourth Jean Valjean.

A brigadier of gendarmes, who appeared to head the group, was near the door. He advanced towards the bishop, giving a military salute.

"Monseigneur," said he——

At this word Jean Valjean, who was sullen and seemed entirely cast down, raised his head with a stupefied air. "Monseigneur!" he murmured, "then it is not the curé!"

"Silence!" said a gendarme, "it is Monseigneur, the bishop."

In the meantime Monsieur Bienvenu had approached as quickly as his great age permitted: "Ah, there you are!" said he, looking towards Jean Valjean, "I am glad to see you. But! I gave you the candlesticks also, which are silver like the rest, and would bring two hundred francs. Why did you not take them along with your plates?"

Jean Valjean opened his eyes and looked at the bishop with an expression which no human tongue could describe.

"Monseigneur," said the brigadier, "then what this man said was true? We met him. He was going like a man who was running away, and we arrested him in order to see. He had this silver."

"And he told you," interrupted the bishop, with a smile, "that it had been given him by a good old priest with whom he had passed the night. I see it all. And you brought him back here? It is all a mistake."

"If that is so," said the brigadier, "we can let him go."

"Certainly," replied the bishop.

The gendarmes released Jean Valean, who shrank back——

"My friend," said the bishop, "before you go away, here are your candlesticks; take them."

He went to the mantelpiece, took the two candlesticks, and brought them to Jean Valjean. The two women beheld the action without a word, or gesture, or look, that might disturb the bishop.

Jean Valjean was trembling in every limb. He took the two candlesticks mechanically, and with a wild appearance.

"Now," said the bishop, "go in peace. By the way, my friend, when you come again, you need not come through the garden. You can always come in and go out by the front door. It is closed only with a latch, day or night."

Then turning to the gendarmes, he said: "Messieurs, you can retire." The gendarmes withdrew.

Jean Valjean felt like a man who is just about to faint.

The bishop approached him, and said, in a low voice: "Forget not, never forget that you have promised me to use this silver to become an honest man."

Jean Valjean, who had no recollection of this promise, stood confounded. The bishop had laid much stress upon these words as he uttered them. He continued, solemnly: "Jean Valjean, my brother: you belong no longer to evil, but to good. It is your soul that I am buying for you. I withdraw it from dark thoughts and from the spirit of perdition, and I give it to God!"

MIGNON

Johann Wolfgang von Goethe (Germany)

Translated by Thomas Carlyle

Goethe is at once the greatest poet, dramatist and novelist of Germany—a combination of talents rarely found in one person. The following extract is from his most famous novel. *Wilhelm Meister* follows its hero through those early restless years when the youth is becoming the man, and making trial of diverse aims, companions, and loves before settling to his true mate and calling. At one time, Wilhelm is associated with a troupe of actors, and the critical comments on Shakespeare's *Hamlet* which occur in this part of the story form one of the most famous analyses of this dramatic masterpiece.

During this period of apprenticeship to life, Wilhelm rescues from a troupe of rope dancers a remarkable child of ten or twelve whom they had kidnapped in babyhood from a noble Italian family, and are now brutally abusing. For her care Wilhelm makes himself responsible—a difficult and exciting situation for so young a man.

❋ ❋ ❋

. . . Amused with this small adventure, he was going up-stairs to his chamber, when a young creature sprang against him, and attracted his attention. A short silk waistcoat with slashed Spanish sleeves, tight trousers with puffs, looked very pretty on the child. Its long black hair was curled, and wound in locks and plaits about the head. He looked at the figure with astonishment, and could not determine whether to take it for a boy or girl. However, he decided for the latter; and, as the child ran by, he took her up in his arms, bade her good day, and asked her to whom she belonged; though he easily perceived that she must be a member of the vaulting and dancing company lately arrived. She viewed him with a dark, sharp side-look, as she pushed herself out of his arms, and ran into the kitchen without making any answer. . . .

The child stood upon the threshold, as if she meant again to run off; laid her right hand on her breast, the left on her brow, and bowed deeply. "Fear nothing, my little dear," said Wilhelm, rising and going toward her. She viewed him with a doubting look, and came a few steps nearer.

"What is thy name?" he asked. "They call me Mignon." "How old art thou?" "No one has counted." "Who was thy father?" "The Great Devil[1] is dead."

They asked her a few more questions: she gave her answers in a kind of broken German, and with a strangely solemn manner; every time laying her hands on her breast and brow, and bowing deeply.

Wilhelm could not satisfy himself with looking at her. His eyes and his heart were irresistibly attracted by the mysterious condition of this being. He reckoned her about twelve or thirteen years of age: her body was well formed, only her limbs gave promise of a stronger growth, or else announced a stunted one. Her countenance was not regular, but striking; her brow full of mystery; her nose extremely beautiful; her mouth, although it seemed too closely shut for one of her age, and though she often threw it to a side, had yet an air of frankness, and was very lovely. Her brownish complexion could scarcely be discerned through the paint. This form stamped itself deeply in Wilhelm's soul: he kept looking at her earnestly, and forgot the present scene in the multitude of his reflections. . . .

In the meantime, Mignon's form, and manner of existence, were growing more attractive to him every day. In her whole system of proceedings there was something very singular. She never walked up or down the stairs, but jumped. She would spring along by the railing, and before you were aware would be sitting quietly above upon the landing. Wilhelm had observed, also, that she had a different sort of salutation for each individual. For himself, it had of late been with her arms crossed upon her breast. Often for the whole day she would be mute. At times she answered various questions more freely, yet always strangely; so that you could not determine whether it was caused by shrewd sense, or ignorance of the language; for she spoke in broken German interlaced with French and Italian. In Wilhelm's service she was indefatigable, and up before the sun. On the other hand, she vanished early in the evening, went to sleep in a little room upon the bare floor, and could not by any

---

[1] *Great Devil:* This was a nickname for the former head of the troupe of performers to which she belonged.

means be induced to take a bed or even a paillasse.[2] He often found her washing herself. Her clothes, too, were kept scrupulously clean; though nearly all about her was quilted two or three plies thick. Wilhelm was moreover told that she went every morning early to hear mass. He followed her on one occasion, and saw her kneeling down with a rosary in a corner of the church, and praying devoutly. She did not observe him; and he returned home, forming many a conjecture about this occurrence, yet unable to arrive at any probable conclusion. . . .

Mignon had been waiting for him: she lighted him upstairs. On setting down the light, she begged he would allow her, that evening, to compliment him with a piece of her art. He would rather have declined this, particularly as he knew not what it was; but he had not the heart to refuse anything this kind creature wished. After a little while she again came in. She carried below her arm a little carpet, which she then spread out upon the floor. Wilhelm said she might proceed. She thereupon brought four candles, and placed one upon each corner of the carpet. A little basket of eggs, which she next carried in, made her purpose clearer. Carefully measuring her steps, she then walked to and fro on the carpet, spreading out the eggs in certain figures and positions; which done, she called in a man that was waiting in the house, and could play on the violin. He retired with his instrument into a corner; she tied a band about her eyes, gave a signal; and, like a piece of wheel-work set a-going, she began moving the same instant as the music, accompanying her beats and the notes of the tune with the strokes of a pair of castanets.

Lightly, nimbly, quickly, and with hair's-breadth accuracy, she carried on the dance. She skipped so sharply and surely along between the eggs, and trod so closely down beside them, that you would have thought every instant she must trample one of them in pieces, or kick the rest away in her rapid turns. By no means! She touched no one of them, though winding herself through their mazes with all kinds of steps, wide and narrow, nay, even with leaps, and at last half kneeling.

Constant as the movement of a clock, she ran her course; and the strange music, at each repetition of the tune, gave a new impulse to the dance, recommencing and again rushing off as at first. Wilhelm was quite led away by this singular spectacle; he forgot his cares; he followed every movement of the dear little creature, and felt surprised to see how finely her character unfolded itself as she proceeded in the dance.

[2] *paillasse:* a pad on the floor.

Rigid, sharp, cold, vehement, and in soft postures, stately rather than attractive,—such was the light in which it showed her. At this moment he experienced at once all the emotions he had ever felt for Mignon. He longed to incorporate this forsaken being with his own heart, to take her in his arms, and with a father's love to awaken in her the joy of existence.

The dance being ended, she rolled the eggs together softly with her foot into a little heap, left none behind, harmed none; then placed herself beside it, taking the bandage from her eyes, and concluding her performance with a little bow.

Wilhelm thanked her for having executed, so prettily and unexpectedly, a dance he had long wished to see. He patted her; was sorry she had tired herself so much. He promised her a new suit of clothes; to which she vehemently replied, "Thy color!" This, too, he promised her, though not well knowing what she meant by it. She then lifted up the eggs, took the carpet under her arm, asked if he wanted anything further, and skipped out of the room.

The musician, being questioned, said that for some time she had taken much trouble in often singing over the tune of this dance, the well-known fandango, to him, and training him till he could play it accurately. For his labor she had likewise offered him some money; which, however, he would not accept. . . .

He threw himself into a chair; he felt greatly moved. Mignon came in, and asked whether she might help him. Her manner was still and shy: it had grieved her to the quick to be so abruptly dismissed by him before.

Nothing is more touching than the first disclosure of a love which has been nursed in silence, of a faith grown strong in secret, and which at last comes forth in the hour of need, and reveals itself to him who formerly has reckoned it of small account. The bud, which had been closed so long and firmly, was now ripe to burst its swathings; and Wilhelm's heart could never have been readier to welcome the impressions of affection.

She stood before him, and noticed his disquietude. "Master!" she cried, "if thou art unhappy, what will become of Mignon?" "Dear little creature," said he, taking her hands, "thou, too, art part of my anxieties. I must go hence." She looked at his eyes, glistening with restrained tears, and knelt down with vehemence before him. He kept her hands: she laid her head upon his knees, and remained quite still. He played with her hair, patted her, and spoke kindly to her. She continued motionless for a considerable time. At last he felt a sort of palpitating movement in her, which began very softly and then by degrees, with increasing violence, diffused itself over all her frame. "What ails thee, Mignon?" cried he: "What ails thee?" She raised her little head, looked at him, and all at once laid her hand upon her heart, with the countenance of one repressing the utterance of pain. He raised her up, and she fell upon his breast: he pressed her toward him, and kissed her. She replied not by any pressure of the hand, by any motion whatever. She held firmly against his heart, and all at once gave a cry, which was accompanied by spasmodic movements of the body. She started up, and immediately fell down before him, as if broken in every joint. It was an excruciating moment. "My child!" cried he, raising her up, and clasping her fast, "my child, what ails thee?" He held her faster and faster. "My child!" cried he, "my child! thou art indeed mine, if that word can comfort thee. Thou art mine! I will keep thee, I will never forsake thee!" Her tears continued flowing. At last she raised herself: a faint gladness shone upon her face. "My father!" cried she, "thou wilt not forsake me? Wilt be my father? I am thy child!"

Softly, at this moment, the harp began to sound before the door: the old man brought his most affecting songs as an evening offering to our friend, who, holding his child ever faster in his arms, enjoyed the most pure and undescribable felicity. . . .

Next morning, on looking for Mignon about the house, Wilhelm did not find her, but was informed that she had gone out early.

After the space of some hours, Wilhelm heard the sound of music before his door. At first he thought it was the harper come again to visit him; but he soon distinguished the tones of a cithern, and the voice which began to sing was Mignon's. Wilhelm opened the door: the child came in, and sang him the following song:

Know'st thou the land where the lemon-orchards bloom
And oranges glow like gold in the leafy gloom;
Where from an azure sky the soft wind blows,
The myrtles still, and high the laurel grows—
Know'st thou indeed? 'Tis there! 'tis there
I would with thee, O my belovéd, go!

Know'st thou the house, its porch with pillars tall,
Its shimmering rooms; its brightly glittering hall?
The marble statues stand and look at me.
What is't, poor child, that they have done to thee?
Know'st thou indeed? 'Tis there, 'tis there
I would with thee, O my protector, go!

Know'st thou the mount, whose path with clouds is fraught,
Where by the mule through mist the way is sought,
Where dwell in caves the dragon's ancient brood,
Where falls the rock, and over it the flood—
Know'st thou indeed? 'Tis there, 'tis there
Our road doth lie. O Father, let us go!

The music and general expression of it pleased our friend extremely, though he could not understand all the words. He made her once more repeat the stanzas, and explain them: he wrote them down, and translated them into his native language. But the originality of its turns he could imitate only from afar: its childlike innocence of expression vanished from it in the process of reducing its broken phraseology to uniformity, and combining its disjointed parts. The charm of the tune, moreover, was entirely incomparable.

She began every verse in a stately and solemn manner, as if she wished to draw attention toward something wonderful, as if she had something weighty to communicate. In the third line, her tones became deeper and gloomier; the words, "DOST KNOW?" were uttered with a show of mystery and eager circumspectness; in " 'TIS THERE! 'TIS THERE!" lay an irresistible longing; and her "LET US GO!" she modified at each repetition, so that now it appeared to entreat and implore, now to impel and persuade.

On finishing her song for the second time, she stood silent for a moment, looked keenly at Wilhelm, and asked him, "Know'st thou the land?" "It must mean Italy," said Wilhelm: "where did'st thou get the little song?" "Italy!" said Mignon, with an earnest air. "If thou go to Italy, take me along with thee; for I am too cold here." "Hast thou been there already, little dear?" said Wilhelm. But the child was silent, and nothing more could be got out of her.

PRISON MATES

ALEXANDRE DUMAS (FRANCE)

A young sea captain, Edmond Dantès, hero of the *Count of Monte Cristo,* is unjustly accused by a powerful enemy and confined in a prison overlooking the sea. In the extract given below, we see how after many years he finds a secret companion in solitude, an equally innocent, highly cultured, older prisoner, who educates young Dantès. When the old man dies, Dantès removes the corpse from its weighted burial sack, sews himself in, and is flung into the sea. After this dangerous and dramatic escape, he becomes enormously rich through discovering a treasure; and assuming the name of the Count of Monte Cristo, seeks vengeance on his betrayers.

✳ ✳ ✳

Dantès entreated to be allowed to walk about, to have books and instruments. Nothing was granted; no matter, he asked all the same. He accustomed himself to speak to his jailer, although he was, if possible, more taciturn than the former one; but still, to speak to a man, even though mute, was something. Dantès spoke for the sake of hearing his own voice; he had tried to speak when alone, but the sound of his voice terrified him. Often, before his captivity, Dantès's mind had revolted at the idea of those assemblages of prisoners, composed of thieves, vagabonds, and murderers. He now wished to be among them, in order to see some other face besides that of his jailer, who would not speak to him; he sighed for the galleys, with their infamous costume, their chain, and the brand on the shoulder. The galley-slaves breathed the fresh air of heaven, and saw each other. He besought the jailer one day to let him have a companion, were it even the mad abbé.[1]

The jailer, though rude and hardened by the constant sight of so much suffering, was yet a man. At the bottom of his heart he had often compassionated the unhappy young man who suffered thus; and he laid the request of No. 34 before the governor. But the latter imagined that Dantès wished to conspire or attempt an escape, and refused his request. Dantès had exhausted all human resources; he turned to God.

All the pious ideas that had been so long forgotten returned. He recollected the prayers his mother had taught him, and discovered a new meaning in every word; for in prosperity prayers seem but a mere assemblage of words, until the day when misfortune comes to explain for the unhappy sufferer the sublime language by which he invokes the pity of Heaven! He prayed aloud, no longer terrified at the sound of his voice, in a sort of ecstasy. He saw God listening to every word he uttered; he laid every action of his life before the Almighty, proposed tasks to accomplish, and at the end of every prayer introduced the entreaty oftener addressed to man than to God, "Forgive us our trespasses as we forgive them that trespass against us." In spite of his earnest prayers, Dantès remained a prisoner.

[1] abbé: priest.

Then a gloomy feeling took possession of him. He was simple and without education; he could not, therefore, in the solitude of his dungeon and of his thoughts, reconstruct the ages that had passed, reanimate the nations that had perished, and rebuild the ancient cities that imagination renders so vast and stupendous. He could not do this, he whose past life was so short, whose present so melancholy, and whose future so doubtful. Nineteen years of light to reflect upon in eternal darkness! No distraction could come to his aid; his energetic spirit, that would have exulted in thus revisiting the past, was imprisoned like an eagle in a cage. He clung to one idea,—that of his happiness, destroyed without apparent cause by an unheard-of fatality.

Rage succeeded to piety. Dantès uttered blasphemies that made his jailer recoil with horror, dashed himself furiously against the walls of his prison; he attacked everything around him, and especially himself, the least thing that annoyed him,—a grain of sand, a straw, or a breath of air. He said that it was the hatred of man, and not of Heaven, that had thus plunged him into the deepest misery. He devoted these unknown persecutors to the most horrible tortures he could imagine, and found them all insufficient, because after torture came death, and after death, if not repose, at least that insensibility that resembles it.

By dint of constantly dwelling on the idea that repose was death, and that in order to punish cruelly other tortures than death must be invented, he began to reflect on suicide. Unhappy he who on the brink of misfortune broods over such ideas! The idea of suicide is one of those dead seas that seem clear and smooth to the eye; but he who unwarily ventures within its embrace finds himself entangled in a quagmire that attracts and swallows him.

Edmond found some solace in this idea. All his sorrows, all his sufferings, with their train of gloomy spectres, fled from his cell when the angel of death seemed about to enter. Dantès reviewed with composure his past life, and looking forward with terror to his future, chose that middle line that seemed to afford him a refuge.

"Sometimes," said he, "in my voyages, when I was still a man, free and powerful, and commanded other men, I have seen the heavens become overcast, the sea rage and foam, the storm arise, and like a monstrous bird cover the sky with its wings. Then I felt that my vessel was a vain refuge, for like a feather in the hand of a giant, it trembled and shook before the tempest. Soon the fury of the waves and the sight of the sharp rocks announced the approach of death, and death then terrified me; and I used all my skill and intelligence as a man and a sailor. I did so because I was happy; because a return to life was a return to enjoyment. But now it is different. I have lost all that bound me to life; death smiles and invites me to repose. I die after my own manner, I die exhausted and broken-spirited, as I fall asleep after one of those evenings of despair and rage when I have paced three thousand times round my cell."

No sooner had this idea taken possession of him than he became more composed; he arranged his couch to the best of his power, ate and slept little, and found this existence almost supportable, because he felt he could throw it off at pleasure, like a worn-out garment. He had two means of dying,—one was to hang himself with his handkerchief to the stanchions[2] of the window; the other to refuse food and starve himself. But the former was repugnant to him. Dantès had always entertained a horror of pirates, who are hung up to the yardarm; he would not die by what seemed an infamous death. He resolved to adopt the second, and began that day to execute his resolve. Nearly four years had passed away; and he had lost track of time.

Dantès had said, "I wish to die," and had chosen the manner of his death; and fearful of changing his mind, he had taken an oath so to die. "When my morning and evening meals are brought," thought he, "I will cast them out of the window, and I shall be believed to have eaten them."

He kept his word; twice a day he cast out, by the barred aperture, the provisions his jailer brought him,—at first gaily, then with deliberation, and at last with regret. Nothing but the recollection of his oath gave him strength to proceed. Hunger rendered appetizing these viands, once so repugnant; sometimes he held the plate in his hand for an hour at a time, and gazed on the morsel of bad meat, of tainted fish, of black and moldy bread. The instinct of self-preservation strove within him, and occasionally vanquished his resolve; then his dungeon seemed less somber, his fate less desperate. He was young,—he was only four or five and twenty; he had nearly fifty years to live. In that vast space of time what unforeseen events might not open his prison door, and restore him to liberty? Then he raised to his lips the repast that, like a voluntary Tantalus[3] he had refused himself; but he thought of his oath, and he persisted, rigorous and pitiless. At last he had not sufficient force

[2] *stanchions:* bars.
[3] *Tantalus:* a character in a Greek myth who had food and drink forever before him but out of reach.

to cast his supper out of the loophole. The next morning he could not see or hear; the jailer feared he was dangerously ill. Edmond hoped he was dying.

The day passed away thus. Edmond felt a species of stupor creeping over him; the gnawing pain at his stomach had ceased; his thirst had abated; when he closed his eyes he saw myriads of lights dancing before them, like the meteors that play about the marshes. It was the twilight of that mysterious country called death!

Suddenly, about nine o'clock in the evening, Edmond heard a hollow sound in the wall against which he was lying.

So many loathsome animals inhabited the prison that their noise did not in general awake him; but now, whether abstinence had quickened his faculties, or whether the noise was really louder than usual, Edmond raised his head and listened. It was a continual scratching, as if made by a huge claw, a powerful tooth, or some iron instrument attacking the stones.

Although weakened, the young man's brain instantly recurred to the idea that haunts all prisoners,—liberty! It seemed to him that Heaven had at length taken pity on him, and had sent this noise to warn him on the very brink of the abyss. Perhaps one of those beloved ones he had so often thought of was thinking of him, and striving to diminish the distance that separated them.

No, no! doubtless he was deceived, and it was but one of those dreams that haunt the gate of death!

Edmond still heard the sound. It lasted nearly three hours; he then heard a noise of something falling, and all was silent.

Some hours afterwards it began nearer and more distinct; Edmond became already interested in that labor, which afforded him companionship. Suddenly the jailer entered.

While he was forming his resolution to die, and in the four days since he began to put his resolve into execution, Edmond had not spoken to this man, had not answered him when he inquired what was the matter with him, and had turned his face to the wall when he looked too curiously at him; but now the jailer might hear this noise, and might put an end to it, thus destroying a ray of something like hope that soothed his last moments.

The jailer brought him his breakfast. Dantès raised himself up, and began to speak on the bad quality of his food, on the coldness of his dungeon, grumbling and complaining in order to have an excuse for speaking louder, and wearying the patience of the jailer, who that very day had solicited some broth and white bread for his prisoner, and had brought it to him.

Fortunately the jailer fancied that Dantès was delirious; and placing his food on the rickety table, he withdrew. Free at last, Edmond again eagerly listened. The noise began again, and was now so distinct that he could hear it without effort.

There can be no doubt, thought he; it is some prisoner who is striving to obtain his freedom. Oh, if I were with him how I would help!

Suddenly a cloud darkened his mind, so used to misfortune that it could scarcely understand hope; the idea possessed him that the noise arose from workmen the governor had ordered to repair the neighboring dungeon.

It was easy to ascertain this; but how could he risk the question? It was easy to call his jailer's attention to the noise, and watch his countenance as he listened; but might he not by this means betray hopes far more precious than this short-lived satisfaction? Unfortunately, Edmond's brain was still so feeble that he could not bend his thoughts to anything in particular.

He saw but one means of restoring lucidity and clearness to his judgment. He turned his eyes towards the soup his jailer had brought him, rose, staggered towards it, raised the vessel to his lips, and drank off the contents with an indescribable sensation of comfort; then he had the courage to abstain. He had heard that shipwrecked persons had died through having eagerly devoured too much food. Edmond replaced on the table the bread he was about to devour, and returned to his couch; he no longer wished to die. He soon felt that his ideas became again collected; he could think, and strengthen his thoughts by reasoning. Then he said to himself, "I must put this to the test, but without compromising anybody. If it is a workman, I need but knock against the wall, and he will cease to work in order to find out who is knocking and why he does so; but as his occupation is sanctioned by the governor, he will soon resume it. If, on the contrary, it is a prisoner, the noise I make will alarm him; he will cease, and not resume until he thinks every one is asleep."

Edmond rose again, but this time his legs did not tremble, and his eyes were free from mists; he advanced to a corner of his dungeon, detached a stone loosened by the moisture, and with it knocked against the wall at the place where the sound came. He struck thrice! At the first blow the sound ceased, as if by magic.

Edmond listened intently. An hour passed, two hours passed, and no sound was heard from the wall,—all was silent there.

Full of hope Edmond swallowed a few mouthfuls of bread and

water, and thanks to the excellence of his constitution, found himself well-nigh recovered.

The day passed away in utter silence; night came without the noise having recommenced.

"It is a prisoner!" said Edmond, joyfully.

The night, too, passed in silence. Edmond did not close his eyes.

In the morning the jailer brought his rations—he had already devoured those of the previous day; he ate these, listening anxiously for the sound, walking round and round his cell shaking the iron bars of the loophole, restoring by exercise vigor and agility to his limbs, and preparing himself thus for what might lie ahead. At intervals he listened for the noise, and grew impatient at the prudence of the prisoner, who did not guess he had been disturbed by a captive as anxious for liberty as himself.

Three days passed,—seventy-two tedious hours, counted minute by minute!

At length, one evening just after the jailer's last visit, as for the hundredth time Dantès placed his ear against the wall, he fancied that he heard an almost imperceptible movement among the stones. Edmond recoiled, walked up and down his cell to collect his thoughts, and replaced his ear against the wall.

There could be no doubt that something was taking place on the other side; the prisoner had discovered the danger, and for greater security, had substituted the lever for the chisel.

Encouraged by this discovery, Edmond determined to assist the indefatigable laborer. He began by moving his bed, behind which it seemed to him the work of deliverance was going on, and sought with his eyes for something with which he might pierce the wall, penetrate the cement, and displace a stone.

He saw nothing; he had no knife or sharp instrument; the grating of his window alone was of iron, and he had too often assured himself of its solidity. All his furniture consisted of a bed, a chair, a table, a pail, and a jug. The bed had iron clamps; but they were screwed to the wood, and it would have required a screw-driver to take them off. The table and chair had nothing that would serve; the pail had had a handle, but that had been removed. Dantès had but one resource: to break the jug, and with one of the sharp fragments attack the wall. He let the jug fall on the floor, and it broke in pieces. He concealed two or three of the sharpest fragments in his bed, leaving the rest on the floor. The breaking of his jug was too natural an accident to excite suspicion. He had all the night to work in, but in the darkness he could not do much, and he soon perceived that his instrument was blunted against something hard; he pushed back his bed, and awaited the day. With hope, patience had returned to him.

All night he heard the subterranean workman, who continued to mine his way. The day came; the jailer entered. Dantès told him the jug had fallen from his hand in drinking, and the jailer went grumbling to fetch another, without giving himself the trouble to remove the fragments of the broken one. He returned speedily, recommended the prisoner to be more careful, and departed.

Dantès heard joyfully the key grate in the lock; he listened until the sound of steps died away, and then, hastily displacing his bed, saw by the faint light that penetrated into his cell that he had labored uselessly the previous evening in attacking the stone instead of removing the plaster that surrounded it. The damp had rendered it friable, and he saw joyfully the plaster detach itself,—in small morsels, it is true; but at the end of half an hour he had scraped off a handful.

A mathematician might have calculated that in two years, supposing that the rock was not encountered, a passage twenty feet long and two feet broad might be formed. The prisoner reproached himself with not having thus employed the hours which he had passed in prayers and despair. In the years of his imprisonment, what might he not have accomplished?

In three days Edmond had succeeded, with the utmost precaution, in removing the cement and exposing the stone. The wall was formed of rough stones, to give solidity to which blocks of hewn stone were imbedded at intervals. It was one of these he had uncovered, and which he must remove from its socket. He strove to do so with his nails, but they were too weak! The fragments of the jug broke, and after an hour of useless toil he paused. Was he to be thus stopped at the beginning, and was he to wait inactive until his neighbor, weary, perhaps, with toil, had accomplished everything? Suddenly an idea occurred to him; he smiled, and the perspiration dried on his forehead.

The jailer always brought Dantès's soup in an iron saucepan. The handle of this saucepan was of iron; Dantès would have given ten years of his life in exchange for it.

The jailer poured the contents of this saucepan into Dantès's plate, who, after eating his soup with a wooden spoon, washed the plate, which thus served for every day. In the evening Dantès placed his plate on the ground near the door; the jailer, as he entered, stepped on it and broke it. This time he could not blame

Dantès. He had done wrong in leaving it there, but the jailer was at fault in not noticing where he stepped.

The jailer therefore contented himself with grumbling. Then he looked about him for something to pour the soup into; Dantès's whole furniture consisted of one plate,—there was no alternative.

"Leave the saucepan," said Dantès; "you can take it away when you bring me my breakfast." This advice was to the jailer's taste, as it spared him the necessity of ascending, descending, and ascending again. He left the saucepan.

Dantès was beside himself with joy. He rapidly devoured his food, and after waiting an hour, lest the jailer should change his mind and return, he removed his bed, took the handle of the saucepan, inserted the point between the hewn stone and rough stones of the wall, and employed it as a lever. A slight oscillation showed Dantès that his plan was a good one. At the end of an hour the stone was extricated from the wall, leaving a cavity of a foot and a half in diameter.

Dantès carefully collected the plaster, carried it into the corners of his cell, and covered it with earth. Then, wishing to make the best use of this night, in which chance, or rather his own stratagem, had placed so precious an instrument in his hands, he continued to work without ceasing. At dawn he replaced the stone, pushed his bed against the wall, and lay down. The breakfast consisted of a piece of bread; the jailer entered and placed the bread on the table.

"Well, you do not bring me another plate," said Dantès.

"No," replied the turnkey, "you destroy everything. First you break your jug, then you make me break your plate; if all the prisoners followed your example the government would be ruined. I shall leave you the saucepan and pour your soup into that; perhaps then you will not break your dishes."

Dantès raised his eyes to heaven and clasped his hands beneath the coverlid and prayed. He felt more gratitude for the possession of this piece of iron than he had ever felt for anything. He had, however, remarked that the prisoner on the other side had ceased to labor. No matter, this was a greater reason for proceeding; if his neighbor would not come to him, he would go to him. All day he toiled on untiringly, and by the evening he had succeeded in extracting ten handfuls of plaster and fragments of stone. When the hour for his jailer's visit arrived, Dantès straightened the handle of the saucepan and put that receptacle in its accustomed place. The turnkey poured into it the customary ration of soup and meat, or rather of soup and fish, for it was a fast day; three times a week the prisoners were made to fast. This would have been a method of reckoning time, had not Dantès long ceased to do so. Having poured out the soup, the turnkey retired. Dantès wished to ascertain whether his neighbor had really ceased to work. He listened; all was silent, as it had been for the last three days. Dantès sighed; it was evident that his neighbor distrusted him. However, he toiled on all the night without being discouraged; but after two or three hours he encountered an obstacle. The iron made no impression, but glided on a smooth surface; Dantès touched it with his hands, and found it was a beam. This beam crossed, or rather blocked up, the hole Dantès had made; it was necessary, therefore, to dig above or under it. The unhappy young man had not thought of such an obstacle.

"Oh, my God! my God!" murmured he, "I have so earnestly prayed to thee that I hoped my prayers had been heard. After having deprived me of my liberty, after having denied to me the repose of death, after having recalled me to existence,—my God! have pity on me, and do not let me die in despair!"

"Who talks of God and despair at the same time?" said a voice that seemed to come from beneath the earth, and deadened by the distance, sounded hollow and sepulchral in the young man's ears. Edmond's hair stood on end, and he rose on his knees.

"Ah!" said he, "I hear a human voice." He had not heard any one speak save his jailer for four or five years; and to a prisoner the jailer is not a man,—he is a living door added to his door of oak, a barrier of flesh and blood added to his barriers of iron.

"In the name of Heaven," cried Dantès, "speak again, though the sound of your voice terrifies me; who are you?"

"Who are you?" said the voice.

"An unhappy prisoner," replied Dantès, who made no hesitation in answering.

"Of what country?"

"A Frenchman."

"Your name?"

"Edmond Dantès."

"Your profession?"

"A sailor."

"How long have you been here?"

"Since the 28th of February, 1815."

"Your crime?"

"I am innocent."

"But of what are you accused?"

"Of having conspired to aid the emperor's return."

"What! the emperor's return! The emperor is no longer on the throne, then?"

"He abdicated at Fontainebleau in 1814, and was sent to the island of Elba. But how long have you been here that you are ignorant of all this?"

"Since 1811."

Dantès shuddered; this man had been four years longer than himself in prison.

"Do not dig any more," said the voice; "only tell me how high up is your excavation?"

"On a level with the floor."

"How is it concealed?"

"Behind my bed."

"Has your bed been moved since you have been a prisoner?"

"No."

"What does your chamber open on?"

"A corridor."

"And the corridor?"

"On the court."

"Alas!" murmured the voice.

"Oh, what is the matter?" cried Dantès.

"I am deceived; and the imperfection of my plans has ruined all. An error of a line in the plan has been equivalent to fifteen feet in reality, and I took the wall you are mining for the wall of the fortress."

"But then you would be close to the sea?"

"That is what I hoped."

"And supposing you had succeeded?"

"I should have thrown myself into the sea, gained one of the islands near here,—the Isle de Daume or the Isle de Tiboulen,—and then I should have been safe."

"Could you have swum so far?"

"Heaven would have given me strength; but now all is lost!"

"All?"

"Yes; stop up your excavation carefully. Do not work any more; and wait until you hear from me."

"Tell me, at least, who you are."

"I am—I am No. 27."

"You mistrust me, then?" said Dantès. Edmond fancied he heard a bitter laugh proceed from the unknown.

"Oh, I am a Christian," cried Dantès, guessing instinctively that this man meant to abandon him. "I swear to you that I will let them kill me rather than utter a syllable of this to the jailer; but in the name of Heaven, do not deprive me of your voice, or I swear to you—for I have reached the end of my endurance—that I will dash my brains out against the wall, and you will have my death to reproach yourself with."

"How old are you? Your voice is that of a young man?"

"I do not know my age, for I have not counted the years I have been here. All I know is that I was just nineteen when I was arrested, the 28th of February, 1815."

"Not quite twenty-six!" murmured the voice; "at that age one cannot be a traitor."

"Oh, no, no!" cried Dantès. "I swear to you again, rather than betray you I will let them hew me to pieces!"

"You have done well to speak to me and entreat me, for I was about to form another plan, and leave you; but your age reassures me. I will come again. Expect me."

"When?"

"I must calculate our chances; I will give you the signal."

"But you will not leave me; you will come to me, or you will let me go to you. We will escape together, and if we cannot escape we will talk,—you of those whom you love, and I of those whom I love. You must love somebody?"

"No, I am alone in the world."

"Then you will love me. If you are young, I will be your comrade; if you are old, I will be your son. I have a father, who is seventy, if he yet lives; I love only him and a young girl called Mercédès. My father has not yet forgotten me, I am sure; but God alone knows if she loves me still. I shall love you as I loved my father."

"It is well," returned the voice; "tomorrow."

These few words were uttered with an accent that left no doubt of his sincerity. Dantès rose, hid the fragments with the same precaution as before, and pushed back his bed against the wall. He then gave himself up to his happiness. He would no longer be alone; he was perhaps about to regain his liberty. At the worst, if he remained a prisoner, he would have a companion; and captivity that is shared is but half captivity.

All day Dantès walked up and down his cell, his heart bounding with joy. From time to time his joy stifled him; he sat down on his bed, pressing his hand on his breast. At the slightest noise he bounded towards the door. Once or twice the fear crossed his mind that he might be separated from this unknown, whom he loved already. In that case resolution was formed; when his jailer moved his bed and stooped to examine the opening, he would kill him with the water-jug. He would be condemned to die, but he was already about to die of grief and despair when this miraculous noise recalled him to life.

The jailer came in the evening; Dantès was on his bed. It seemed to him that thus he better guarded the unfinished opening. Doubtless there was a strange expression in his eyes, for the jailer said, "Come, are you going mad again?"

Dantès did not answer; he feared that the emotion of his voice would betray him. The jailer retired, shaking his head. The night came; Dantès hoped that his neighbor would profit by the silence to address him, but he was mistaken. The next morning, however, just as he removed his bed from the wall, he heard three knocks; he threw himself on his knees.

"Is it you?" said he; "I am here."

"Is your jailer gone?"

"Yes," said Dantès; "he will not return until the evening; we have twelve hours."

"I can work, then?" said the voice.

"Oh, yes, yes; this instant, I entreat you!"

In an instant the portion of the floor on which Dantès (half-buried in the opening) was leaning his two hands, began to yield under him; he cast himself back, while a mass of stones and earth disappeared in a hole that opened beneath the aperture he himself had formed. Then from the bottom of this passage, the depth of which it was impossible to measure, he saw appear, first the head, then the shoulders, and lastly the body of a man, who sprang lightly into his cell.

BECKY SHARP UNMASKED

WILLIAM MAKEPEACE THACKERAY (ENGLAND)

Becky Sharp in *Vanity Fair* is the original gold digger and social climber of literature. Having worked her way into smart London society in the Napoleonic era by marriage with the scapegrace son of an impoverished noble family, she and her husband are living by their wits on his winnings at cards, and on the money which Becky, unknown to her husband, cajoles out of the wealthy Lord Steyne. Rawdon Crawley, her husband, is arrested for debt. Unexpectedly released, he returns home to face the following scene.

❈   ❈   ❈

It was nine o'clock at night. Rawdon ran across the streets, and the great squares of Vanity Fair,[1] and at length came up breathless opposite his own house. He started back and fell against the railings, trembling as he looked up. The drawing-room windows were blazing with light. She had said that she was in bed and ill. He stood there for some time, the light from the rooms on his pale face.

He took out his door-key and let himself into the house. He could hear laughter in the upper rooms. He was in the ball-dress in which he had been captured the night before. He went silently up the stairs; leaning against the banisters at the stair-head.—Nobody was stirring in the house besides—all the servants had been sent away. Rawdon heard laughter within—laughter and singing. Becky was singing a snatch of the song of the night before; a hoarse voice shouted "Brava! Brava!"—it was Lord Steyne's.

Rawdon opened the door and went in. A little table with a dinner was laid out, and wine and plate. Steyne was hanging over the sofa on which Becky sat. The wretched woman was in a brilliant full toilet, her arms and all her fingers sparkling with bracelets and rings: and the brilliants on her breast which Steyne had given her. He had her hand in his, and was bowing over it to kiss it, when Becky started up with a faint scream as she caught sight of Rawdon's white face. At the next instant she tried a smile, a horrid smile, as if to welcome her husband: and Steyne rose up, grinding his teeth, pale, and with fury in his looks.

He, too, attempted a laugh—and came forward holding out his hand. "What, come back! How d'ye do, Crawley?" he said, the nerves of his mouth twitching as he tried to grin at the intruder.

There was that in Rawdon's face which caused Becky to fling herself before him. "I am innocent, Rawdon," she said; "before God, I am innocent." She clung hold of his coat, of his hands; her own were all covered with serpents, and rings, and baubles. "I am innocent.—Say I am innocent," she said to Lord Steyne.

He thought a trap had been laid for him, and was as furious with

---

[1] *Vanity Fair:* fashionable districts of London.

the wife as with the husband. "You innocent! Damn you," he screamed out. "You innocent! Why, every trinket you have on your body is paid for by me. I have given you thousands of pounds which this fellow has spent, and for which he has sold you. Innocent, by—! You're as innocent as your mother, the ballet-girl, and your husband, the bully. Don't think to frighten me as you have done others. Make way, sir, and let me pass"; and Lord Steyne seized up his hat, and, with flame in his eyes, and looking his enemy fiercely in the face, marched upon him, never for a moment doubting that the other would give way.

But Rawdon Crawley, springing out, seized him by the neck-cloth, until Steyne, almost strangled, writhed, and bent under his arm. "You lie, you dog!" said Rawdon. "You lie, you coward and villain." And he struck the peer twice over the face with his open hand, and flung him bleeding to the ground. It was all done before Rebecca could interpose. She stood there trembling before him. She admired her husband, strong, brave, and victorious.

"Come here," he said.—She came up at once.

"Take off those things."—She began, trembling, pulling the jewels from her arms, and the rings from her shaking fingers, and held them all in a heap, quivering and looking up at him. "Throw them down," he said, and she dropped them. He tore the diamond ornament out of her breast, and flung it at Lord Steyne. It cut him on his bald forehead. Steyne wore the scar to his dying day.

"Come up stairs," Rawdon said to his wife. "Don't kill me, Rawdon," she said. He laughed savagely.—"I want to see if that man lies about the money as he has about me. Has he given you any?"

"No," said Rebecca, "that is——"

"Give me your keys," Rawdon answered, and they went out together. Rebecca gave him all the keys but one; and she was in hopes that he would not have remarked the absence of that. It belonged to the little desk which Amelia had given her in early days, and which she kept in a secret place. But Rawdon flung open boxes and wardrobes, throwing the multifarious trumpery of their contents here and there, and at last he found the desk. The woman was forced to open it. It contained papers, love-letters many years old—all sorts of small trinkets and woman's memoranda. And it contained a pocket-book with bank notes. Some of these were dated ten years back, too, and one was quite a fresh one—a note for a thousand pounds which Lord Steyne had given her.

"Did he give you this?" Rawdon said.

"Yes," Rebecca answered.

"I'll send it to him today," Rawdon said (for day had dawned again, and many hours had passed in this search), "and I will pay Briggs,[2] who was kind to the boy,[3] and some of the debts. You will let me know where I shall send the rest to you. You might have spared me a hundred pounds, Becky, out of all this—I have always shared with you."

"I am innocent," said Becky. And he left her without another word.

What were her thoughts when he left her? She remained for hours after he was gone, the sunshine pouring into the room, and Rebecca sitting alone on the bed's edge. The drawers were all opened and their contents scattered about,—dresses and feathers, scarfs and trinkets, a heap of tumbled vanities lying in a wreck. Her hair was falling over her shoulders; her gown was torn where Rawdon had wrenched the brilliants out of it. She heard him go downstairs a few minutes after he left her, and the door slamming and closing on him. She knew he would never come back. He was gone forever. Would he kill himself?—she thought—not until after he had met [4] Lord Steyne. She thought of her long past life, and all the dismal incidents of it. Ah, how dreary it seemed, how miserable, lonely, and profitless! Should she take laudanum, and end it, too—have done with all hopes, schemes, debts, and triumphs? The French maid found her in this position—sitting in the midst of her miserable ruins with clasped hands and dry eyes. The woman was her accomplice and in Steyne's pay. "Mon Dieu, madame, what has happened?" she asked.

What had happened? Was she guilty or not? She said not; but who could tell what was truth which came from those lips; or if that corrupt heart was in this case pure? All her lies and her schemes, all her selfishness and her wiles, all her wit and genius had come to this bankruptcy. The woman closed the curtains, and with some entreaty and show of kindness, persuaded her mistress to lie down on the bed. Then she went below and gathered up the trinkets which had been lying on the floor since Rebecca dropped them there at her husband's orders, and Lord Steyne went away.

---

[2] *Briggs:* a servant.   [3] *boy:* their son.   [4] *met:* in a duel.

I FALL INTO CAPTIVITY

CHARLES DICKENS (ENGLAND)

Young David Copperfield had just become a clerk in the office of Mr. Spenlow, a London lawyer, and had been invited to his employer's home for the week end to meet his daughter, newly returned from boarding school.

❋ ❋ ❋

"Where is Miss Dora?" said Mr. Spenlow to the servant. "Dora!" I thought. "What a beautiful name!"

We turned into a room near at hand and I heard a voice say, "Mr. Copperfield, my daughter Dora, and my daughter Dora's confidential friend!" It was, no doubt, Mr. Spenlow's voice, but I didn't know it, and I didn't care whose it was. All was over in a moment. I had fulfilled my destiny. I was a captive and a slave. I loved Dora Spenlow to distraction!

She was more than human to me. She was a Fairy, a Sylph, I don't know what she was—anything that no one ever saw, and everything that everybody ever wanted. I was swallowed up in an abyss of love in an instant. There was no pausing on the brink; no looking down, or looking back; I was gone, headlong, before I had sense to say a word to her.

"I," observed a well-remembered voice, when I had bowed and murmured something, "have seen Mr. Copperfield before."

The speaker was not Dora. No; the confidential friend, Miss Murdstone!

I don't think I was much astonished. To the best of my judgment, no capacity of astonishment was left in me. There was nothing worth mentioning in the material world, but Dora Spenlow, to be astonished about. I said, "How do you do, Miss Murdstone? I hope you are well." She answered, "Very well." I said, "How is Mr. Murdstone?" She replied, "My brother is robust, I am obliged to you."

Mr. Spenlow, who, I suppose, had been surprised to see us recognize each other, then put in his word.

"I am glad to find," he said, "Copperfield, that you and Miss Murdstone are already acquainted." [1]

"Mr. Copperfield and myself," said Miss Murdstone, with severe

---

[1] *acquainted:* Miss Murdstone was the sister of David's stepfather, and between them they had made his childhood extremely unhappy.

composure, "are connections. We were once slightly acquainted. It was in his childish days. Circumstances have separated us since. I should not have known him."

I replied that I should have known her, anywhere. Which was true enough.

"Miss Murdstone has had the goodness," said Mr. Spenlow to me, "to accept the office—if I may so describe it—of my daughter Dora's confidential friend. My daughter Dora having, unhappily, no mother, Miss Murdstone is obliging enough to become her companion and protector."

A passing thought occurred to me that Miss Murdstone was not so much designed for purposes of protection as of assault. But as I had none but passing thoughts for any subject save Dora, I glanced at her, directly afterwards, and was thinking that I saw, in her prettily pettish manner, that she was not very much inclined to be particularly confidential to her companion and protector, when a bell rang, which Mr. Spenlow said was the first dinner-bell, and so carried me off to dress.

The idea of dressing one's self, or doing anything in the way of action, in that state of love, was a little too ridiculous. I could only sit down before my fire, biting the key of my carpetbag, and thinking of the captivating, girlish, bright-eyed lovely Dora. What a form she had, what a face she had, what a graceful, variable, enchanting manner!

The bell rang again so soon that I made a mere scramble of my dressing, instead of the careful operation I could have wished under the circumstances, and went downstairs. There was some company; Dora was talking to an old gentleman with a gray head. Gray as he was—and a great-grandfather into the bargain, for he said so—I was madly jealous of him.

I don't remember who was there, except Dora. I have not the least idea what we had for dinner, besides Dora. My impression is, that I dined off Dora, entirely, and sent away half-a-dozen plates untouched. I sat next to her. I talked to her. She had the most delightful little voice, the gayest little laugh, the pleasantest and most fascinating little ways, that ever led a lost youth into hopeless slavery. She was rather diminutive altogether. So much the more precious, I thought.

All I know of the rest of the evening is, that I heard the empress of my heart sing enchanted ballads in the French language, generally to the effect that, whatever was the matter, we ought always to dance, Ta ra la, Ta ra la! accompanying herself on a glorified instrument, resembling a guitar. That I was lost in blissful delirium. That I refused refreshment. That my soul recoiled from punch particularly. That when Miss Murdstone took her into custody and led her away, she smiled and gave me her delicious hand. That I caught a view of myself in a mirror, looking perfectly imbecile and idiotic. That I retired to bed in a most maudlin state of mind, and got up in a crisis of feeble infatuation.

It was a fine morning, and early, and I thought I would go and take a stroll down one of those wire-arched garden walks, and indulge my passion by dwelling on her image. On my way through the hall, I encountered her little dog, who was called Jip—short for Gypsy. I approached him tenderly, for I loved even him; but he showed his whole set of teeth, got under a chair expressly to snarl, and wouldn't hear of the least familiarity.

The garden was cool and solitary. I walked about, wondering what my feelings of happiness would be, if I could ever become engaged to this dear wonder. To be allowed to call her "Dora," to write to her, to dote upon and worship her, to have reason to think that when she was with other people she was yet mindful of me, seemed to me the summit of human ambition—I am sure it was the summit of mine. There is no doubt whatever that I was a lackadaisical young spooney; but there was a purity of heart in all this still, that prevents my being quite contemptuous in recollection of it, let me laugh as I may.

I had not been walking long, when I turned a corner, and met her. I tingle again from head to foot as my recollection turns that corner, and my pen shakes in my hand.

"You—are—out early, Miss Spenlow," said I.

"It's so stupid at home," she replied, "and Miss Murdstone is so absurd! She talks such nonsense about its being necessary for the day to be aired, before I come out. Aired!" (She laughed here in the most melodious manner.) "On a Sunday morning, when I don't practice, I must do something. So I told papa last night I must come out. Besides, it's the brightest time of the whole day. Don't you think so?"

I hazarded a bold flight, and said (not without stammering) that it was very bright to me then, though it had been very dark to me a minute before.

"Do you mean a compliment," said Dora, "or that the weather has really changed?"

I stammered worse than before, in replying that I meant no compliment, but the plain truth; though I was not aware of any change having taken place in the weather. It was in the state of my own feelings, I added bashfully, to clench the explanation.

I never saw such curls—how could I, for there never were such curls!—as those she shook out to hide her blushes. As to the straw hat with blue ribbons which was on the top of the curls, if I could only have hung it up in my room in Buckingham Street, what a priceless possession it would have been!

"You have just come home from Paris," said I.

"Yes," said she. "Have you ever been there?"

"No."

"Oh! I hope you'll go soon. You would like it so much!"

Traces of deep-seated anguish appeared in my countenance. That she should hope I would go, that she should think it possible I could go, was insupportable. I depreciated Paris; I depreciated France. I said I wouldn't leave England, under existing circumstances, for any earthly consideration. Nothing should induce me. In short, she was shaking the curls again, when the little dog came running along the walk to our relief.

He was mortally jealous of me, and persisted in barking at me. She took him up in her arms—oh, my goodness!—and caressed him, but he insisted upon barking still. He wouldn't let me touch him, when I tried; and then she beat him. It increased my sufferings greatly to see the pats she gave him for punishment on the bridge of his blunt nose, while he winked his eyes, and licked her hand, and still growled within himself like a little double-bass. At length he was quiet—well he might be with her dimpled chin upon his head! —and we walked away to look at a greenhouse.

"You are not very intimate with Miss Murdstone, are you?" said Dora.—"My pet!"

(The two last words were to the dog. Oh, if they had only been to me!)

"No," I replied. "Not at all so."

"She is a tiresome creature," said Dora pouting. "I can't think what papa can have been about, when he chose such a vexatious thing to be my companion. Who wants a protector! I am sure I don't want a protector. Jip can protect me a great deal better than Miss Murdstone—can't you, Jip dear?"

He only winked lazily, when she kissed his ball of a head.

"Papa calls her my confidential friend, but I am sure she is no such thing—is she, Jip? We are not going to confide in any such cross people, Jip and I. We mean to bestow our confidence where we like, and to find out our own friends, instead of having them found out for us—don't we, Jip?"

Jip made a comfortable noise, in answer, a little like a teakettle when it sings. As for me, every word was a new heap of fetters, riveted above the last.

"It is very hard, because we have not a kind Mama, that we are to have, instead, a sulky, gloomy old thing like Miss Murdstone, always following us about—isn't it, Jip? Never mind, Jip. We won't be confidential, and we'll make ourselves as happy as we can in spite of her, and we'll tease her, and not please her—won't we, Jip?"

If it had lasted any longer, I think I must have gone down on my knees on the gravel, with the probability before me of grazing them, and of being presently ejected from the premises besides. But, by good fortune, the greenhouse was not far off, and these words brought us to it.

It contained quite a show of beautiful geraniums. We loitered along in front of them, and Dora often stopped to admire this one or that one, and I stopped to admire the same one, and Dora, laughing, held the dog up, childishly, to smell the flowers; and if we were not all three in Fairyland, certainly I was. The scent of a geranium leaf, at this day, strikes me with a half comical, half serious wonder as to what change has come over me in a moment; and then I see a straw hat and blue ribbons, and a quantity of curls, and a little black dog being held up, in two slender arms, against a bank of blossoms and bright leaves.

Miss Murdstone had been looking for us. She took Dora's arm in hers, and marched us in to breakfast as if it were a soldier's funeral.

How many cups of tea I drank, because Dora made it, I don't know. By-and-by we went to church. Miss Murdstone was between Dora and me in the pew; but I heard her sing, and the congregation vanished. A sermon was delivered—about Dora, of course—and I am afraid that is all I know of the service.

We had a quiet day. No company, a walk, a family dinner of four, and an evening of looking over books and pictures; Miss Murdstone with a homily before her and her eye upon us, keeping guard vigilantly.

We departed early in the morning, for we had a Salvage case coming on in the Admiralty Court. Dora was at the breakfast table to make the tea again, however; and I had the melancholy pleasure of taking off my hat to her in the phaeton, as she stood on the doorstep with Jip in her arms.

If the sleepy old Admiralty Court could rouse itself, and present in any visible form the daydreams I had in it about Dora, it would reveal my truth. I don't mean the dreams that I dreamed on that day alone, but day after day, from week to week, and term to term. I went there, not to attend to what was going on, but to think about Dora. If I ever bestowed a thought upon the cases, as they dragged their slow length before me, it was only to wonder, in the matrimonial cases (remembering Dora), how it was that married people could ever be otherwise than happy; and, in the Prerogative cases, to consider, if the money in question had been left to me, what were the foremost steps I should immediately have taken in regard to Dora. Within the first week of my passion, I bought four sumptuous waistcoats—not for myself; I had no pride in them; for Dora—and took to wearing straw-colored kid gloves in the streets, and laid the foundations of all the corns I ever had. If the boots I wore at that period could only be produced and compared with the natural size of my feet, they would show what the state of my heart was in a most affecting manner.

And yet, wretched cripple as I made myself by this act of homage to Dora, I walked miles upon miles daily in the hope of seeing her. Not only was I soon as well known on the Norwood Road as the postmen on that beat, but I pervaded London likewise. I walked about the streets where the best shops for ladies were, I haunted the Bazaar like an unquiet spirit, I fagged through the park again and again. Sometimes, at long intervals and on rare occasions, I saw her. Perhaps I saw her glove wave in a carriage window; perhaps I met her, walked with her and Miss Murdstone a little way, and spoke to her. In the latter case I was always very miserable afterwards, to think that I had said nothing to the purpose; or that she had no idea of the extent of my devotion, or that she cared nothing about me. I was always looking out, as may be supposed, for another invitation to Mr. Spenlow's house. I was always being disappointed, for I got none.

Mrs. Crupp [2] must have been a woman of penetration; for when this attachment was but a few weeks old, she found it out. She came up to me one evening, when I was very low. "Cheer up, sir," said Mrs. Crupp, "I can't bear to see you so, sir. I'm a mother myself."

I did not quite perceive the application of this fact to myself, but I smiled on Mrs. Crupp, as benignly as was in my power.

[2] *Mrs. Crupp:* David's landlady.

"Come, sir," said Mrs. Crupp. "Excuse me. I know what it is, sir. There's a young lady in the case."

"Mrs. Crupp?" I returned, reddening.

"Oh, bless you! Keep a good heart, sir!" said Mrs. Crupp, nodding encouragement. "Never say die, sir! If she don't smile upon you there's a many as will. You're a young gentleman to be smiled on, Mr. Copperfull, and you must learn your value, sir."

Mrs. Crupp always called me Mr. Copperfull: firstly, no doubt because it was not my name; and secondly, I am inclined to think, in some indistinct association with washing day.

"What makes you suppose there is any young lady in the case, Mrs. Crupp?" said I.

"Mr. Copperfull," said Mrs. Crupp, with feeling, "I'm a mother myself. When the present set were took for you by your dear aunt, my remark were, I had now found summun I could care for. 'Thank Ev'in!' were the expression, 'I have now found summum I can care for!' You don't eat enough, sir, nor yet drink."

"Is that what you found your supposition on, Mrs. Crupp?"

"Sir," said Mrs. Crupp, in a tone approaching to severity, "I've laundressed other young gentlemen besides yourself. A young gentleman may be over-careful of himself, or he may be under-careful of himself. He may brush his hair too regular, or too unregular. He may wear his boots much too large for him, or much too small. That is according as the young gentleman has his original character formed. But let him go to which extreme he may, sir, there's a young lady in both of 'em."

THE RACE

Leo Tolstoy (Russia)

Translated by Constance Garnett

See the introductory chapter for an account of *Anna Karenina,* the novel of aristocratic social life in Russia before the World War, from which this extract is drawn. It is a scene early in the book and pictures the diversions of the hero as a young cavalry officer. It is this professional life and its comradeship which Vronsky most misses when he takes Anna from her husband and they are forced to leave Saint Petersburg. It is Anna's emotion as she watches this race from the grandstand that reveals to her husband her love for Vronsky. As the reader of *Anna Karenina* lays down the finished volume, he will remember in a flash the incident of this race and see foreshadowed there the course of Vronsky's tragic destiny.

❊   ❊   ❊

The excitement of the approaching race gained upon Vronsky as he drove further and further, overtaking carriages driving up from the summer villas or out of Petersburg.

At his quarters no one was left at home; all were at the races, and his valet was looking out for him at the gate. While he was changing his clothes, his valet told him that the second race had begun already, that a lot of gentlemen had been to ask for him, and a boy had twice run up from the stables. Dressing without hurry (he never hurried himself, and never lost his self-possession), Vronsky drove to the sheds. From the sheds he could see a perfect sea of carriages, and people on foot, soldiers surrounding the race course, and pavilions swarming with people. The second race was apparently going on, for just as he went into the sheds he heard a bell ringing. Going toward the stable, he met the white-legged chestnut, Mahotin's Gladiator, being led to the race course in a blue forage horse cloth, with what looked like huge ears edged with blue.

"Where's Cord?" [1] he asked the stable boy.

"In the stable, putting on the saddle."

In the open horse box stood Frou-Frou, saddled ready. They were just going to lead her out.

Vronsky once more took in at one glance the exquisite lines of his favorite mare, who was quivering all over, and with an effort he tore himself from the sight of her, and went out of the stable. He went toward the pavilions at the most favorable moment for escaping attention. The mile-and-a-half race was just finishing, and all eyes were fixed on the horse guard in front and the light hussar behind, urging their horses on with a last effort close to the winning post. From the center and outside of the ring all were crowding to the winning post, and a group of soldiers and officers of the horse guards were shouting loudly their delight at the expected triumph of their officer and comrade. Vronsky moved into the middle of the crowd unnoticed, almost at the very moment when the bell rang at the finish of the race, and the tall, mud-spattered horse guard who came in first, bending over the saddle, let go the reins of his panting gray horse that looked dark with sweat.

The horse, stiffening out its legs, with an effort stopped its rapid

---

[1] *Cord:* the trainer for Vronsky's horse.

course, and the officer of the horse guards looked round him like a man waking up from a heavy sleep, and just managed to smile. A crowd of friends and outsiders pressed round him.

Vronsky intentionally avoided that select crowd of the upper world, which was moving and talking with discreet freedom before the pavilions. He knew that Madame Karenina was there, and Betsy, and his brother's wife, and he purposely did not go near them for fear of something distracting his attention. But he was continually met and stopped by acquaintances, who told him about the previous races, and kept asking him why he was so late. . . .

The horses which had run in the last race were being led home, steaming and exhausted, by the stable boys, and one after another the fresh horses for the coming race made their appearance, for the most part English racers, wearing horse cloths, and looking with their drawn-up bellies like strange, huge birds. On the right was led in Frou-Frou, lean and beautiful, lifting up her elastic, rather long pasterns, as though moved by springs. Not far from her they were taking the rug off the lop-eared Gladiator. The strong, exquisite, perfectly correct lines of the stallion, with his superb hind-quarters and excessively short pasterns almost over his hoofs, attracted Vronsky's attention in spite of himself. He would have gone up to his mare, but he was again detained by an acquaintance. . . .

Vronsky had not had time to look at the saddle, about which he had to give some direction, when the competitors were summoned to the pavilion to receive their numbers and places in the row at starting. Seventeen officers, looking serious and severe, many with pale faces, met together in the pavilion and drew the numbers. Vronsky drew the number seven. The cry was heard: "Mount!"

Feeling that with the others riding in the race, he was the center upon which all eyes were fastened, Vronsky walked up to his mare in that state of nervous tension in which he usually became deliberate and composed in his movements. Cord, in honor of the races, had put on his best clothes, a black coat buttoned up, a stiffly starched collar, which propped up his cheeks, a round black hat, and top-boots. He was calm and dignified as ever, and was with his own hands holding Frou-Frou by both reins, standing straight in front of her. Frou-Frou was still trembling as though in a fever. Her eye, full of fire, glanced sideways at Vronsky. Vronsky slipped his finger under the saddle-girth. The mare glanced aslant at him, drew up her lip, and twitched her ear. The Englishman puckered up his lips, intending to indicate a smile that any one should verify his saddling.

"Get up; you won't feel so excited."

Vronsky looked round for the last time at his rivals. He knew that he would not see them during the race. Two were already riding forward to the point from which they were to start. Galtsin, a friend of Vronsky's and one of his more formidable rivals, was moving round a bay horse that would not let him mount. A little light hussar in tight riding breeches rode off at a gallop, crouched up like a cat on the saddle, in imitation of English jockeys. Prince Kuzovlev sat with a white face on his thoroughbred mare from the Grabovsky stud, while an English groom led her by the bridle. Vronsky and all his comrades knew Kuzovlev and his peculiarity of "weak nerves" and terrible vanity. They knew that he was afraid of everything, afraid of riding a spirited horse. But now, just because it was terrible, because people broke their necks, and there was a doctor standing at each obstacle, and an ambulance with a cross on it, and a sister of mercy, he had made up his mind to take part in the race. Their eyes met, and Vronsky gave him a friendly and encouraging nod. Only one he did not see, his chief rival, Mahotin on Gladiator.

"Don't be in a hurry," said Cord to Vronsky, "and remember one thing: don't hold her in at the fences, and don't urge her on; let her go as she likes."

"All right, all right," said Vronsky, taking the reins.

"If you can, lead the race; but don't lose heart till the last minute, even if you're behind."

Before the mare had time to move, Vronsky stepped with an agile, vigorous movement into the steel-toothed stirrup, and lightly and firmly seated himself on the creaking leather of the saddle. Getting his right foot in the stirrup, he smoothed the double reins, as he always did, between his fingers, and Cord let go.

As though she did not know which foot to put first, Frou-Frou started, dragging at the reins with her long neck, and as though she were on springs, shaking her rider first on one side and then the other, pulled at the reins, and Vronsky tried in vain with voice and hand to soothe her.

They were just reaching the dammed-up stream on their way to the starting point. Several of the riders were in front and several behind, when suddenly Vronsky heard the sound of a horse galloping in the mud behind him, and he was overtaken by Mahotin on his white-legged, lop-eared Gladiator. Mahotin smiled, showing his long teeth, but Vronsky looked angrily at him. He did not like him, and regarded him now as his most formidable rival. He was angry with him for galloping past and exciting his mare. Frou-Frou started into a gallop, her left foot forward, made two bounds, and fretting at the tightened reins, passed into a jolting trot, bumping her rider up and down. . . .

There were seventeen officers in all riding in this race. The race course was a large three-mile ring of the form of an ellipse in front of the pavilion. On this course nine obstacles had been arranged: the stream, a big and solid barrier five feet high just before the pavilion, a dry ditch, a ditch full of water, a precipitous slope, an Irish barricade (one of the most difficult obstacles, consisting of a mound fenced with brushwood, beyond which was a ditch out of sight for the horses, so that the horse had to clear both obstacles or might be killed); then two more ditches filled with water, and one dry one; and the end of the race was just facing the pavilion. But the race began not in the ring, but two hundred yards away from it, and in that part of the course was the first obstacle, a dammed-up stream, seven feet in breadth, which the racers could leap or wade through as they preferred.

Three times they were ranged ready to start, but each time some horse thrust itself out of line, and they had to begin again. The umpire who was starting them, Colonel Sestrin, was beginning to lose his temper, when at last for the fourth time he shouted "Away!" and the racers started.

Every eye, every opera glass, was turned on the brightly colored group of riders at the moment they were in line to start.

"They're off! They're starting!" was heard on all sides after the hush of expectation.

The little groups and solitary figures among the public began running from place to place to get a better view. In the very first minute the close group of horsemen drew out, and it could be seen that they were approaching the stream in twos and threes and one behind another. To the spectators it seemed as though they had all started simultaneously, but to the racers there were seconds of difference that had great value to them.

Frou-Frou, excited and over-nervous, had lost the first moment, and several horses had started before her, but before reaching the stream, Vronsky, who was holding in the mare with all his force as she tugged at the bridle, easily overtook three, and there were left in front of him Mahotin's chestnut Gladiator, whose hind-quarters were moving lightly and rhythmically up and down exactly in front of Vronsky, and in front of all, the dainty mare Diana, bearing Kuzovlev more dead than alive.

For the first instant Vronsky was not master either of himself or his horse. Up to the first obstacle, the stream, he could not guide the motions of his mare.

Gladiator and Diana came up to it together and almost at the same instant; simultaneously they rose above the stream and flew across to the other side; Frou-Frou darted after them as if flying; but at the very moment when Vronsky felt himself in the air, he suddenly saw almost under his mare's hoofs Kuzovlev, who was floundering with Diana on the further side of the stream. (Kuzovlev had let go the reins as he took the leap, and the mare had sent him flying over her head.) Those details Vronsky learned later; at the moment all he saw was that just under him, where Frou-Frou must alight, Diana's legs or head might be in the way. But Frou-Frou drew up her legs and back in the very act of leaping, like a falling cat, and, clearing the other mare, alighted beyond her.

"Oh, the darling!" thought Vronsky.

After crossing the stream Vronsky had complete control of his mare, and began holding her in, intending to cross the great barrier behind Mahotin, and try to overtake him in the clear ground of about five hundred yards that followed it.

The great barrier stood just in front of the imperial pavilion. The Tsar and the whole court and crowds of people were all gazing at them—at him, and Mahotin a length ahead of him, as they drew near the "devil," as the solid barrier was called. Vronsky was aware of those eyes fastened upon him from all sides, but he saw nothing except the ears and neck of his own mare, the ground racing to meet him, and the back and white legs of Gladiator beating time swiftly before him, and keeping always the same distance ahead. Gladiator rose, with no sound of knocking against anything. With a wave of his short tail he disappeared from Vronsky's sight.

"Bravo!" cried a voice.

At the same instant, under Vronsky's eyes, right before him flashed the palings of the barrier. Without the slightest change in her action his mare flew over it; the palings vanished, and he heard only a crash behind him. The mare, excited by Gladiator's keeping ahead, had risen too soon before the barrier, and grazed it with her hind hoofs. But her pace never changed, and Vronsky, feeling a spatter of mud in his face, realized that he was once more the same distance from Gladiator. Once more he perceived in front of him the same back and short tail, and again the same swiftly moving white legs that got no further away.

At the very moment when Vronsky thought that now was the time to overtake Mahotin, Frou-Frou herself, understanding his thoughts, without any incitement on his part, gained ground considerably, and began getting alongside of Mahotin on the most favorable side, close to the inner cord. Mahotin would not let her pass that side. Vronsky had hardly formed the thought that he could perhaps pass on the outer side, when Frou-Frou shifted her pace and began overtaking him on the other side. Frou-Frou's shoulder, beginning by now to be dark with sweat, was even with Gladiator's back. For a few lengths they moved evenly. But before the obstacle they were approaching, Vronsky began working at the reins, anxious to avoid having to take the outer circle, and swiftly passed Mahotin just upon the declivity. He caught a glimpse of his mud-stained face as he flashed by. He even fancied that he smiled. Vronsky passed Mahotin, but he was immediately aware of him close upon him, and he never ceased hearing the even-thudding hoofs and the rapid and still quite fresh breathing of Gladiator.

The next two obstacles, the watercourse and the barrier, were easily crossed, but Vronsky began to hear the snorting and thud of Gladiator closer upon him. He urged on his mare, and to his delight felt that she easily quickened her pace, and the thud of Gladiator's hoofs was again heard at the same distance away.

Vronsky was at the head of the race, just as he wanted to be and as Cord had advised, and now he felt sure of being the winner. His excitement, his delight, and his tenderness for Frou-Frou grew keener, and keener. He longed to look round again, but he did not dare do this, and tried to be cool and not to urge on his mare, so as to keep the same reserve of force in her as he felt that Gladiator still kept. There remained only one obstacle, the most difficult; if he could cross it ahead of the others, he would come in first. He was flying toward the Irish barricade, Frou-Frou and he both together saw the barricade in the distance, and both the man and the mare had a moment's hesitation. He saw the uncertainty in the mare's ears and lifted the whip, but at the same time felt that his fears were groundless; the mare knew what was wanted. She quickened her pace and rose smoothly, just as he had fancied she would, and as she left the ground gave herself up to the force of her rush, which carried her far beyond the ditch; and with the same rhythm, without effort, with the same leg forward, Frou-Frou fell back into her pace again.

"Bravo, Vronsky!" he heard shouts from a knot of men—he knew they were his friends in the regiment—who were standing at the obstacle. He could not fail to recognize Yashvin's voice though he did not see him.

"O my sweet!" he said inwardly to Frou-Frou, as he listened for what was happening behind. "He's cleared it!" he thought, catching the thud of Gladiator's hoofs behind him. There remained only the last ditch, filled with water and five feet wide. Vronsky did not even look at it, but anxious to get in a long way first began sawing away at the reins, lifting the mare's head and letting it go in time with her paces. He felt that the mare was at her very last reserve of strength; not her neck and shoulders merely were wet, but the sweat was standing in drops on her mane, her head, her sharp ears, and her breath came in short, sharp gasps. But he knew that she had more than enough strength left for the remaining five hundred yards. It was only from feeling himself nearer the ground and from the peculiar smoothness of his motion that Vronsky knew how greatly the mare had quickened her pace.

She flew over the ditch as though not noticing it. She flew over it like a bird; but at the same instant Vronsky, to his horror, felt that he had failed to keep up with the mare's pace, that he had, he did not know how, made a fearful, unpardonable mistake, in recovering his seat in the saddle. All at once his position had shifted and he knew that something awful had happened. He could not yet make out what had happened, when the white legs of a chestnut horse flashed by close by him, and Mahotin passed at a swift gallop. Vronsky was touching the ground with one foot, and his mare was sinking on that foot. He just had time to free his leg when she fell on one side, gasping painfully, and, making vain efforts to rise with her delicate, soaking neck, she fluttered on the ground at his feet like a shot bird. The clumsy movement made by Vronsky had broken her back. But that he only knew much later. At the moment he knew only that Mahotin had flown swiftly by, while he stood staggering alone on the muddy, motionless ground, and Frou-Frou lay gasping before him, bending her head back and gazing at him with her exquisite eye. Still unable to realize what had happened, Vronsky tugged at his mare's reins. Again she struggled all over like a fish, and her shoulders setting the saddle heaving, she rose on her front legs, but unable to lift her back, she quivered all over and again fell on her side. . . . She did not stir, but thrusting her nose into the ground, she simply gazed at her master with her speaking eyes.

"A—a—a!" groaned Vronsky, clutching at his head. "Ah! what have I done!" he cried. "The race lost! And my fault! shameful, unpardonable! And the poor darling, ruined mare! Ah! what have I done!"

A crowd of men, a doctor and his assistant, the officers of his regiment, ran up to him. To his misery he felt that he was whole and unhurt. The mare had broken her back, and it was decided to shoot her. Vronsky could not answer questions, could not speak to any one. He turned, and without picking up his cap that had fallen off walked away from the race course, not knowing where he was going. He felt utterly wretched. For the first time in his life he knew the bitterest sort of misfortune, misfortune beyond remedy, and caused by his own fault. . . .

THE DETESTABLE MR. HYDE

ROBERT LOUIS STEVENSON (SCOTLAND)

The Strange Case of Dr. Jekyll and Mr. Hyde, Stevenson's great mystery story of dual personality, is likewise one of the world's most famous literary allegories. Into the brief chapters of this weird tale is packed more truth about the human heart than can be found in many a ponderous moralizing volume.

❋   ❋   ❋

THE STORY OF THE DOOR

Mr. Utterson, the lawyer, was a man of a rugged countenance, that was never lighted by a smile; cold, scanty, and embarrassed in discourse; backward in sentiment; lean, long, dusty, dreary, and yet somehow lovable. At friendly meetings, something eminently human beaconed from his eye; something indeed which never found its way into his talk, but which spoke not only in these silent symbols of the face, but more often and loudly in the acts of his life. He was austere with himself, but he had an approved tolerance for others; and in any extremity inclined to help rather than to reprove. In this character, it was frequently his fortune to be the last reputable acquaintance and the last good influence in the lives of down-going men. And to such as these, so long as they came about his chambers, he never marked a shade of change in his demeanor.

It chanced on a Sunday ramble with his cousin, Richard Enfield, that their way led them down a by-street in a busy quarter of London. The street was small and what is called quiet, but it drove a thriving trade on the week-days, and with its freshly painted shutters, well-polished brasses, and general cleanliness and gaiety of note, instantly caught and pleased the eye of the passenger.

Two doors from one corner, on the left hand going east, the line was broken by the entry of a court; and just at that point, a certain sinister block of building thrust forward its gable on the street. It was two stories high; showed no window, nothing but a door on the lower story and a blind forehead of discolored wall on the upper; and bore in every feature the marks of prolonged and sordid negligence. The door, which was equipped with neither bell nor knocker, was blistered and distained. Tramps slouched into the recess and struck matches on the panels; children kept shop upon the steps; the schoolboy had tried his knife on the moldings; and for close on a generation, no one had appeared to drive away these random visitors or to repair their ravages.

Mr. Enfield and the lawyer were on the other side of the by-street; but when they came abreast of the entry, the former lifted up his cane and pointed.

"Did you ever remark that door?" he asked; and when his companion had replied in the affirmative, "It is connected in my mind," added he, "with a very odd story."

"Indeed?" said Mr. Utterson, with a slight change of voice, "and what was that?"

"Well, it was this way," returned Mr. Enfield: "I was coming home from some place at the end of the world, about three o'clock of a black winter morning, and my way lay through a part of town where there was literally nothing to be seen but lamps. Street after street, and all the folks asleep—street after street, all lighted up as if for a procession and all as empty as a church—till at last I got into that state of mind when a man listens and listens and begins to long for the sight of a policeman. All at once, I saw two figures: one a little man who was stumping along eastward at a good walk, and the other a girl of maybe eight or ten who was running as hard as she was able down a cross street. Well, sir, the two ran into one another naturally enough at the corner; and then came the horrible part of the thing; for the man trampled calmly over the child's body and left her screaming on the ground. It sounds nothing to hear, but it was hellish to see. It wasn't like a man; it was like some damned Juggernaut.[1] I gave a view halloa, took to my heels, collared my gentleman, and brought him back to where there was already quite a group about the screaming child. He was perfectly cool and made no resistance, but gave me one look, so ugly that it brought out the sweat on me like running. The people who had

[1] *Juggernaut:* heavy car in which a Hindu god is dragged through the streets in a religious procession. Worshipers throw themselves under it and are crushed.

turned out were the girl's family; and pretty soon, the doctor, for whom she had been sent, put in his appearance. Well, the child was not much the worse, more frightened, according to the Sawbones; and there you might have supposed would be an end to it. But there was one curious circumstance. I had taken a loathing to my gentleman at first sight. So had the child's family, which was only natural. But the doctor's case was what struck me. He was the usual cut-and-dry apothecary, of no particular age and color, with a strong Edinburgh accent, and about as emotional as a bagpipe. Well, sir, he was like the rest of us; every time he looked at my prisoner, I saw that Sawbones turn sick and white with the desire to kill him. I knew what was in his mind, just as he knew what was in mine; and killing being out of the question, we did the next best. We told the man we could and would make such a scandal out of this, as should make his name stink from one end of London to the other. If he had any friends or any credit, we undertook that he should lose them. And all the time, as we were pitching it in red hot, we were keeping the women off him as best we could, for they were as wild as harpies. I never saw a circle of such hateful faces; and there was the man in the middle, with a kind of black, sneering coolness—frightened too, I could see that—but carrying it off, sir, really like Satan. 'If you choose to make capital out of this accident,' said he, 'I am naturally helpless. No gentleman but wishes to avoid a scene,' says he. 'Name your figure.' Well, we screwed him up to a hundred pounds for the child's family; he would have clearly liked to stick out; but there was something about the lot of us that meant mischief, and at last he struck. The next thing was to get the money; and where do you think he carried us but to that place with the door?—whipped out a key, went in, and presently came back with the matter of ten pounds in gold and a cheque for the balance on Coutts',[2] drawn payable to bearer and signed with a name that I can't mention, though it's one of the points of my story, but it was a name at least very well known and often printed. The figure was stiff; but the signature was good for more than that, if it was only genuine. I took the liberty of pointing out to my gentleman that the whole business looked apocryphal,[3] and that a man does not, in real life, walk into a cellar door at four in the morning and come out of it with another man's check for close upon a hundred pounds. But he was quite easy and sneering. 'Set your mind at rest,' says he, 'I will stay with you till the banks open and cash the check myself.' So we all set off, the doctor, and the child's father,

[2] *Coutts'*: a London bank.   [3] *apocryphal:* doubtful.

and our friend and myself, and passed the rest of the night in my chambers; and the next day, when we had breakfasted, went in a body to the bank. I gave in the check myself, and said I had every reason to believe it was a forgery. Not a bit of it. The check was genuine."

"Tut-tut," said Mr. Utterson.

"I see you feel as I do," said Mr. Enfield. "Yes, it's a bad story. For my man was a fellow that nobody could have to do with, a really damnable man; and the person that drew the check is the very pink of the proprieties, celebrated too; and (what makes it worse) one of your fellows who do what they call good. Blackmail, I suppose; an honest man paying through the nose for some of the capers of his youth. Blackmail House is what I call that place with the door, in consequence. Though even that, you know, is far from explaining all," he added, and with the words fell into a vein of musing.

From this he was recalled by Mr. Utterson asking rather suddenly: "And you don't know if the drawer of the check lives there?"

"A likely place, isn't it?" returned Mr. Enfield. "But I happen to have noticed his address; he lives in some square or other."

"And you never asked about the—place with the door?" said Mr. Utterson.

"No, sir: I had a delicacy," was the reply. "I feel very strongly about putting questions; it partakes too much of the style of the day of judgment. You start a question, and it's like starting a stone. You sit quietly on the top of a hill; and away the stone goes, starting others; and presently some bland old bird (the last you would have thought of) is knocked on the head in his own back garden and the family have to change their name. No, sir, I make it a rule of mine: the more it looks like Queer Street, the less I ask."

"A very good rule, too," said the lawyer.

"But I have studied the place for myself," continued Mr. Enfield. "It seems scarcely a house. There is no other door, and nobody goes in or out of that one but, once in a great while, the gentleman of my adventure. There are three windows looking on the court on the first floor; none below; the windows are always shut, but they're clean. And then there is a chimney which is generally smoking; so somebody must live there. And yet it's not so sure; for the buildings are so packed together about that court, that it's hard to say where one ends and another begins."

The pair walked on again for awhile in silence; and then "Enfield," said Mr. Utterson, "that's a good rule of yours."

"Yes, I think it is," returned Enfield.

"But for all that," continued the lawyer, "there's one point I want to ask: I want to ask the name of that man who walked over the child."

"Well," said Mr. Enfield, "I can't see what harm it would do. It was a man of the name of Hyde."

"H'm," said Mr. Utterson. "What sort of a man is he to see?"

"He is not easy to describe. There is something wrong with his appearance; something displeasing, something downright detestable. I never saw a man I so disliked, and yet I scarce know why. He must be deformed somewhere; he gives a strong feeling of deformity, although I couldn't specify the point. He's an extraordinary looking man, and yet I really can name nothing out of the way. No, sir; I can make no hand of it; I can't describe him. And it's not want of memory; for I declare I can see him this moment."

Mr. Utterson again walked some way in silence and obviously under a weight of consideration. "You are sure he used a key?" he inquired at last.

"My dear sir . . ." began Enfield, surprised out of himself.

"Yes, I know," said Utterson; "I know it must seem strange. The fact is, if I do not ask you the name of the other party, it is because I know it already. You see, Richard, your tale has gone home. If you have been inexact in any point, you had better correct it."

"I think you might have warned me," returned the other with a touch of sullenness. "But I have been pedantically exact, as you call it. The fellow had a key; and what is more, he has it still. I saw him use it, not a week ago."

Search for Mr. Hyde

That evening Mr. Utterson came home to his bachelor house in somber spirits and sat down to dinner without relish. It was his custom of a Sunday, when this meal was over, to sit close by the fire, a volume of some dry divinity on his reading-desk, until the clock of the neighboring church rang out the hour of twelve, when he would go soberly and gratefully to bed. On this night, however, as soon as the cloth was taken away, he took up a candle and went into his business room. There he opened his safe, took from the most private part of it a document endorsed on the envelope as Dr. Jekyll's Will, and sat down with a clouded brow to study its contents. Mr. Utterson, though he took charge of it now that it was made, had refused to lend the least assistance in the making of it; it provided not only that, in case of the decease of Henry Jekyll, M.D., D.C.L., LL.D., F.R.S.,[4] etc., all his possessions were to pass into the hands of his "friend and benefactor, Edward Hyde," but that in case of Dr. Jekyll's "disappearance or unexplained absence for any period exceeding three calendar months," the said Edward Hyde should step into the said Henry Jekyll's shoes without further delay and free from any burden or obligation, beyond the payment of a few small sums to the members of the doctor's household. This document had long been the lawyer's eyesore. It offended him both as a lawyer and as a lover of the sane and customary sides of life, to whom the fanciful was the immodest. And hitherto it was his ignorance of Mr. Hyde that had swelled his indignation; now, by a sudden turn, it was his knowledge. It was already bad enough when the name was but a name of which he could learn no more. It was worse when it began to be clothed with detestable attributes; and out of the shifting, insubstantial mists that had so long baffled his eye, there leaped up the sudden, definite presentment of a fiend.

"I thought it was madness," he said, as he replaced the obnoxious paper in the safe, "and now I begin to fear it is disgrace."

Six o'clock struck on the bells of the church that was so conveniently near to Mr. Utterson's dwelling, and still he was digging at the problem. Hitherto it had touched him on the intellectual side alone; but now his imagination also was engaged, or rather enslaved; and as he lay and tossed in the gross darkness of the night and the curtained room, Mr. Enfield's tale went by before his mind in a scroll of lighted pictures. He would be aware of the great field of lamps of a nocturnal city; then of the figure of a man walking swiftly; then of a child running from the doctor's; and then these met, and that human Juggernaut trod the child down and passed on regardless of her screams. Or else he would see a room in a rich house, where his friend lay asleep, dreaming and smiling at his dreams; and then the door of that room would be opened, the curtains of the bed plucked apart, the sleeper recalled, and lo! there would stand by his side a figure to whom power was given, and even at that dead hour, he must rise and do its bidding. The figure in these two phases haunted the lawyer all night; and if at any time he dozed over, it was but to see it glide more stealthily through sleeping houses, or move the more swiftly and still the more swiftly, even to dizziness, through wider labyrinths of lamp-lighted city,

---

[4] Most of these letters are medical and honorary degrees. F.R.S. means Fellow of the Royal Society, or member of the famous English scientific society.

and at every street corner crush a child and leave her screaming. And still the figure had no face by which he might know it; even in his dreams, it had no face, or one that baffled him and melted before his eyes; and thus it was that there sprang up and grew apace in the lawyer's mind a singularly strong, almost an inordinate, curiosity to behold the features of the real Mr. Hyde. If he could but once set eyes on him, he thought the mystery would lighten and perhaps roll altogether away, as was the habit of mysterious things when well examined. He might see a reason for his friend's strange preference or bondage (call it which you please) and even for the startling clause of the will. At least it would be a face worth seeing; the face of a man who was without mercy: a face which had but to show itself to raise up in the mind of the unimpressionable Enfield a spirit of enduring hatred.

From that time forward, Mr. Utterson began to haunt the door in the by-street of shops. In the morning before office hours, at noon when business was plenty, and time scarce, at night under the face of the fogged city moon, by all lights and at all hours of solitude or concourse, the lawyer was to be found on his chosen post.

"If he be Mr. Hyde," he had thought, "I shall be Mr. Seek."

And at last his patience was rewarded. It was a fine dry night; frost in the air; the streets as clean as a ballroom floor; the lamps, unshaken by any wind, drawing a regular pattern of light and shadow. By ten o'clock, when the shops were closed, the by-street was very solitary and, in spite of the low growl of London from all round, very silent. Small sounds carried far; domestic sounds out of the houses were clearly audible on either side of the roadway; and the rumor of the approach of any passenger preceded him by a long time. Mr. Utterson had been some minutes at his post, when he was aware of an odd, light footstep drawing near. In the course of his nightly patrols, he had long grown accustomed to the quaint effect with which the footfalls of a single person, while he is still a great way off, suddenly spring out distinct from the vast hum and clatter of the city. Yet his attention had never before been so sharply and decisively arrested; and it was with a strong, superstitious prevision of success that he withdrew into the entry of the court.

The steps drew swiftly nearer, and swelled out suddenly louder as they turned the end of the street. The lawyer, looking forth from the entry, could soon see what manner of man he had to deal with. He was small and very plainly dressed, and the look of him, even at that distance, went somehow strongly against the watcher's inclination. But he made straight for the door, crossing the roadway to save time; and as he came, he drew a key from his pocket like one approaching home.

Mr. Utterson stepped out and touched him on the shoulder as he passed. "Mr. Hyde, I think?"

Mr. Hyde shrank back with a hissing intake of the breath. But his fear was only momentary; and though he did not look the lawyer in the face, he answered coolly enough: "That is my name. What do you want?"

"I see you are going in," returned the lawyer. "I am an old friend of Dr. Jekyll's—Mr. Utterson of Gaunt Street—you must have heard my name; and meeting you so conveniently, I thought you might admit me."

"You will not find Dr. Jekyll; he is from home," replied Mr. Hyde, blowing in the key. And then suddenly, but still without looking up, "How did you know me?" he asked.

"On your side," said Mr. Utterson, "will you do me a favor?"

"With pleasure," replied the other. "What shall it be?"

"Will you let me see your face?" asked the lawyer.

Mr. Hyde appeared to hesitate, and then, as if upon some sudden reflection, fronted about with an air of defiance; and the pair stared at each other pretty fixedly for a few seconds. "Now I shall know you again," said Mr. Utterson. "It may be useful."

"Yes," returned Mr. Hyde, "it is as well we have met; and *à propos*, you should have my address." And he gave a number of a street in Soho.

"Good God!" thought Mr. Utterson, "can he, too, have been thinking of the will?" But he kept his feelings to himself and only grunted in acknowledgment of the address.

"And now," said the other, "how did you know me?"

"By description," was the reply.

"Whose description?"

"We have common friends," said Mr. Utterson.

"Common friends?" echoed Mr. Hyde, a little hoarsely. "Who are they?"

"Jekyll, for instance," said the lawyer.

"He never told you," cried Mr. Hyde, with a flush of anger. "I did not think you would have lied."

"Come," said Mr. Utterson, "that is not fitting language."

The other snarled aloud into a savage laugh; and the next moment, with extraordinary quickness, he had unlocked the door and disappeared into the house.

The lawyer stood awhile when Mr. Hyde had left him, the picture of disquietude. Then he began slowly to mount the street, pausing every step or two and putting his hand to his brow like a man in mental perplexity. The problem he was thus debating as he walked, was one of a class that is rarely solved. Mr. Hyde was pale and dwarfish, he gave an impression of deformity without any namable malformation, he had a displeasing smile, he had borne himself to the lawyer with a sort of murderous mixture of timidity and boldness, and he spoke with a husky, whispering and somewhat broken voice; all these were points against him, but not all of these together could explain the hitherto unknown disgust, loathing, and fear with which Mr. Utterson regarded him. "There must be something else," said the perplexed gentleman. "There is something more, if I could find a name for it. God bless me, the man seems hardly human! O my poor old Harry Jekyll, if ever I read Satan's signature upon a face, it is on that of your new friend."

Round the corner from the by-street, there was a square of ancient, handsome houses, now for the most part decayed from their high estate and let in flats and chambers to all sorts and conditions of men: map-engravers, architects, shady lawyers, and the agents of obscure enterprises. One house, however, second from the corner, was still occupied entire; and at the door of this, which wore a great air of wealth and comfort, though it was now plunged in darkness except for the fanlight, Mr. Utterson stopped and knocked. A well-dressed, elderly servant opened the door.

"Is Dr. Jekyll at home, Poole?" asked the lawyer.

"I will see, Mr. Utterson," said Poole, admitting the visitor, as he spoke, into a large, low-roofed, comfortable hall, paved with flags, warmed (after the fashion of a country house) by a bright, open fire, and furnished with costly cabinets of oak. "Will you wait here by the fire, sir? or shall I give you a light in the dining-room?"

"Here, thank you," said the lawyer, and he drew near and leaned on the tall fender. This hall, in which he was now left alone, was a pet fancy of his friend the doctor's; and Utterson himself was wont to speak of it as the pleasantest room in London. But tonight there was a shudder in his blood; the face of Hyde sat heavy on his memory; he felt (what was rare with him) a nausea and distaste of life; and in the gloom of his spirits, he seemed to read a menace in the flickering of the firelight on the polished cabinets and the uneasy starting of the shadow on the roof. He was ashamed of his relief, when Poole presently returned to announce that Dr. Jekyll was gone out.

"I saw Mr. Hyde go in by the old dissecting room door, Poole," he said. "Is that right, when Dr. Jekyll is from home?"

"Quite right, Mr. Utterson, sir," replied the servant. "Mr. Hyde has a key."

"Your master seems to repose a great deal of trust in that young man, Poole," resumed the other musingly.

"Yes, sir, he do indeed," said Poole. "We have all orders to obey him."

"I do not think I ever met Mr. Hyde?" asked Utterson.

"O, dear no, sir. He never dines here," replied the butler. "Indeed, we see very little of him on this side of the house; he mostly comes and goes by the laboratory."

"Well, good-night, Poole."

"Good-night, Mr. Utterson."

And the lawyer set out homeward with a very heavy heart. "Poor Harry Jekyll," he thought, "my mind misgives me he is in deep waters! He was wild when he was young; a long while ago to be sure; but in the law of God, there is no statute of limitations. Ay, it must be that; the ghost of some old sin, the cancer of some concealed disgrace: punishment coming years after memory has forgotten and self-love condoned the fault." And then he conceived a spark of hope. "This Master Hyde, if he were studied," thought he, "must have secrets of his own; black secrets, by the look of him; secrets compared to which poor Jekyll's worst would be like sunshine. Things cannot continue as they are. It turns me cold to think of this creature stealing like a thief to Harry's bedside; poor Harry, what a wakening! And the danger of it; for if this Hyde suspects the existence of the will, he may grow impatient to inherit. Ay, I must put my shoulder to the wheel—if Jekyll will but let me," he added, "if Jekyll will only let me." For once more he saw before his mind's eye, as clear as a transparency, the strange clauses of the will.

A WILD RIDE

Selma Lagerlöf (Sweden)

Translated by Pauline Bancroft Flack

The Story of Gösta Berling, Selma Lagerlöf's strange tale of the Swedish countryside, centers about an enigmatical figure, half beggar, half gentleman—Gösta Berling, "strongest and weakest of men, a poet who never wrote a line." Incapable of directing his own life, he touches the lives of others with a powerful influence.

On one occasion, a friend of his, whose family are in dire financial straits, discovers that his wealthy fiancée, a reckless and beautiful coquette, has in a moment of wilfulness betrothed herself to another. Gösta goes to a mid-winter ball to bring back Anna to his friend. In the struggle of wills between them, Gösta and Anna fall in love. Impetuously, he determines to elope with her, and they start in his open sleigh through the moonlit, snowy forest. The only house they will pass for six miles is Berga, the home of the friend he is about to betray.

❊   ❊   ❊

That was a wild drive through the night. Absorbed in their love, they let Don Juan [1] take his own pace. The noise of the runners was like the lamentations of those they had deceived. What did they care for that? She hung on his neck, and he leaned forward and whispered in her ear.

"Can any happiness be compared in sweetness to stolen pleasures?"

What did the banns matter? They had love. And the anger of men! Gösta Berling believed in fate; fate had mastered them: no one can resist fate.

If the stars had been the candles which had been lighted for her wedding, if Don Juan's bells had been the church chimes, calling the people to witness her marriage to old Dahlberg, still she must have fled with Gösta Berling. So powerful is fate.

They had passed the vicarage and Munkerud. They had three miles to Berga and three miles more to Ekeby. The road skirted the edge of the wood; on their right lay dark hills, on their left a long, white valley.

Tancred [2] came rushing. He ran so fast that he seemed to lie along the ground. Howling with fright, he sprang up in the sledge and crept under Anna's feet.

Don Juan shied and bolted.

"Wolves!" said Gösta Berling.

They saw a long, gray line running by the fence. There were at least a dozen of them.

Anna was not afraid. The day had been richly blessed with adventure, and the night promised to be equally so. It was life,—to speed over the sparkling snow, defying wild beasts and men.

---

[1] *Don Juan:* the horse.
[2] *Tancred:* Gösta's dog, which was following the sleigh.

Gösta uttered an oath, leaned forward, and struck Don Juan a heavy blow with the whip.

"Are you afraid?" he asked. "They mean to cut us off there, where the road turns."

Don Juan ran, racing with the wild beasts of the forest, and Tancred howled in rage and terror. They reached the turn of the road at the same time as the wolves, and Gösta drove back the foremost with the whip.

"Ah, Don Juan, my boy, how easily you could get away from twelve wolves, if you did not have us to drag."

They tied the green plaid behind them. The wolves were afraid of it, and fell back for a while. But when they had overcome their fright, one of them ran, panting, with hanging tongue and open mouth up to the sledge. Then Gösta took Madame de Stael's *Corinne* [3] and threw it into his mouth.

Once more they had breathing-space for a time, while the brutes tore their booty to pieces, and then again they felt the dragging as the wolves seized the green plaid, and heard their panting breath. They knew that they should not pass any human dwelling before Berga, but worse than death it seemed to Gösta to see those he had deceived. But he knew that the horse would tire, and what should become of them then?

They saw the house at Berga at the edge of the forest. Candles burned in the windows. Gösta knew too well for whose sake.

But now the wolves drew back, fearing the neighborhood of man, and Gösta drove past Berga. He came no farther than to the place where the road once again buried itself in the wood; there he saw a dark group before him,—the wolves were waiting for him.

"Let us turn back and say that we took a little pleasure trip in the starlight. We can't go on."

They turned, but in the next moment the sledge was surrounded by wolves. Gray forms brushed by them, their white teeth glittered in gaping mouths, and their glowing eyes shone. They howled with hunger and thirst for blood. The glittering teeth were ready to seize the soft human flesh. The wolves leaped up on Don Juan, and hung on the saddle-cloth. Anna sat and wondered if they would eat them entirely up, or if there would be something left, so that people the next morning would find their mangled limbs on the trampled, bloody snow.

"It's a question of our lives," she said, and leaned down and seized Tancred by the nape of the neck.

[3] *Corinne:* a novel which had just been given him.

THEN GÖSTA TOOK MADAME DE STAEL'S "CORINNE" AND
THREW IT INTO HIS MOUTH.

"Don't—that will not help! It is not for the dog's sake the wolves are out tonight."

Thereupon Gösta drove into the yard at Berga, but the wolves hunted him up to the very steps. He had to beat them off with the whip.

"Anna," he said, as they drew up, "God would not have it. Keep a good countenance; if you are the woman I take you for, keep a good countenance!"

They had heard the sleigh-bells in the house, and came out.

"He has her!" they cried. "He has her! Long live Gösta Berling!" and the newcomers were embraced by one after another.

Few questions were asked. The night was far advanced, the travelers were agitated by their terrible drive and needed rest. It was enough that Anna had come.

The whole house slept. But Gösta rose, dressed himself, and stole out. Unnoticed he led Don Juan out of the stable, harnessed him to the sledge, and meant to set out. But Anna came out from the house.

"I heard you go out," she said. "So I got up, too. I am ready to go with you."

He went up to her and took her hand.

"Don't you understand it yet? It cannot be. God does not wish it. Listen now and try to understand. I was here to dinner and saw their grief over your faithlessness. I went to Borg to bring you back to Ferdinand. But I have always been a good-for-nothing and will never be anything else. I betrayed him, and kept you for myself. There is an old woman here who believes that I shall become a man. I betrayed her. And another poor old thing will freeze and starve here for the sake of dying among friends, but I was ready to let the wicked Sintram [4] take her home. You were beautiful, and sin is sweet. It is so easy to tempt Gösta Berling. Oh, what a miserable wretch I am! I know how they love their home, all those in there, but I was ready just now to leave it to be pillaged. I forgot everything for your sake, you were so sweet in your love. But now, Anna, now since I have seen their joy, I will not keep you; no, I will not. Oh, my beloved! He there above mocks at our desires. We must bow under His chastising hand. Tell me that from this day you will take up your burden! All of them rely upon you. Say that you will stay with them and be their prop and help! If you love me, if

[4] *Sintram:* a cruel moneylender who holds a mortgage on Ferdinand's family home.

you will lighten my deep sorrow, promise me this! My beloved, is your heart so great that you can conquer yourself, and smile in doing it?"

She accepted the renunciation in a sort of ecstasy. "I shall do as you wish,—sacrifice myself and smile."

"And not hate my poor friends?"

She smiled sadly. "As long as I love you, I shall love them."

"Now for the first time I know what you are. It is hard to leave you."

"Farewell, Gösta! Go, and God be with you! My love shall not tempt you to sin."

Don Juan became impatient and set off. Gösta did not take the reins. He sat backwards and looked after her. Then he leaned against the seat and wept despairingly.

"I have possessed happiness and driven her from me; I myself drove her from me. Why did I not keep her?"

Ah, Gösta Berling, strongest and weakest of men!

UPON HIS HEAD

Joseph Conrad (Poland and England)

Lord Jim might well be called the *Les Misérables* of the sea and the jungle. The hero is a young sailor from a good English family who while first mate of a passenger ship plying in the Eastern seas, was tried by a naval court for abandoning his ship and its passengers after an accident. The other officers involved fled, leaving Jim to stand trial alone. As it turned out that the ship could have been saved had the officers stuck to it, the sailing certificates of all were cancelled. The loss of his chosen career was as nothing to Jim compared with his own loss of self-respect. The story followed him wherever he went, and to escape into a world where he could build a new life and a new personality, Jim went to a Malay village in the heart of the jungle as agent for a trading company. Single-handed, he brought peace and order out of plunder and chaos. To Doramin, the ablest native leader in the district, he had brought a silver ring which Doramin had given years before to Jim's employer as a pledge of gratitude and loyalty. Supported by Doramin, Jim became virtual dictator of the district and was worshipped with implicit trust by the natives, who called him Tuan Jim or Lord Jim. To them, his word was law, and they placed their lives confidently in his hands.

Years passed. Then a crew of white scoundrels in a stolen ship attempted a raid on Jim's village during his absence. The determined resistance of the village led by Doramin's son, Dain Waris—Jim's best friend—drove the invaders onto a hill where they nearly starved to death.

On Jim's return, to save further bloodshed, Jim offered them a clear road to the sea and their ship, if they would depart. They accepted. Jim, trusting in their good faith, persuaded the natives to let them go in safety, though the river bank was lined from the village to the sea with armed savages eager to annihilate the robbers. Jim promised his people that in this way, they themselves should all be safe. The departing marauders, however, enraged at the loss of the plunder of the village, surprised and wantonly butchered a company of guards placed near the mouth of the river under Dain Waris.

Tamb' Itam, Jim's loyal body servant, brought the first news of the disaster, as he had been sent by Jim with the silver ring as a token, to tell the river guard to let the white men go in peace.

When the news reached the village and it was discovered that Jim had failed them, Jim's new world fell to pieces. He found himself alone among a hostile people who did not understand his relation to these new white men, but knew only that Jim said they would be safe and that Dain Waris and his band were dead. Jim's wife closed his stockade gates and urged him to fight and escape.

❊　　❊　　❊

Then Jim understood. He had retreated from one world, and now the other, the work of his own hands, had fallen in ruins upon his head. It was not safe for his servant to go out amongst his own people! I believe that in that very moment he had decided to defy the disaster in the only way it occurred to him such a disaster could be defied; but all I know is that without a word he came out of his room and sat before the long table, at the head of which he was accustomed to regulate the affairs of his world, proclaiming daily the truth that surely lived in his heart. The dark powers should not rob him twice of his peace. He sat like a stone figure.

What thoughts passed through his head—what memories? Who can tell? Everything was gone, and he who had been once unfaithful to his trust had lost again all men's confidence. Loneliness was closing on him. People had trusted him with their lives—only for that; and they could never be made to understand. Those without did not hear him make a sound. Later, toward the evening, he came out into the courtyard. "Open the gates," he ordered. Afterwards, turning to those of his men who were inside, he gave them leave to depart to their homes.

"For how long, Tuan?" asked one of them timidly.

"For all life," he said, in a sombre tone.

A hush had fallen upon the town after the outburst of wailing and lamentation that had swept over the river like a gust of wind from the opened abode of sorrow. But rumors flew in whispers, filling the hearts with consternation and horrible doubts. Perhaps the robbers were coming back, bringing many others with them, in a great ship, and there would be no refuge in the land for any one. A sense of utter insecurity, as during an earthquake, pervaded the minds of men who whispered their suspicions, looking at each other as if in the presence of some awful portent.

The sun was sinking toward the forest when Dain Waris's body was brought into Doramin's campong.[1] They laid him at Doramin's feet, and the old man sat still for a long time, one hand on each knee, looking down. The fronds of palms swayed gently and the foliage of fruit trees stirred above his head. Every single man of his people was there, fully armed, when the old nakhoda [2] at last raised his eyes. He moved them slowly over the crowd, as if seeking for a missing face. Again his chin sank on his breast. The whispers of many men mingled with the slight rustling of the leaves.

When Dain Waris's body was uncovered at a sign of Doramin's, he whom they often called the white lord's friend was disclosed lying unchanged with his eyelids a little open as if about to wake. Doramin's eyes searched the body from its feet to its head, for the wound, maybe. It was in the forehead, and small; and there was no word spoken while one of the bystanders, stooping over the body, took off the silver ring from the cold, stiff hand. In silence he held it up before Doramin. A murmur of dismay and horror ran through the crowd at the sight of that familiar token. The old nakhoda stared at it, and suddenly let out one great fierce cry, deep from the chest, a roar of pain and fury, as mighty as the bellow of a wounded bull, bringing fear into men's hearts by the magnitude of his anger and his sorrow that could be plainly discerned without words. There was a great stillness afterwards for a space, while the body was being borne aside by four men. They laid it down under a tree, and on the instant, with one long shriek, all the women of the household began to wail together; they mourned with shrill cries; the sun was setting, and in the intervals of screamed lamentations, the high sing-song voices of two old men intoning the Koran chanted alone.

[1] *campong:* the space enclosed by a stockade in which were the dwellings of Doramin and his household.
[2] *nakhoda:* leader.

About this time Jim, leaning on a gun-carriage, looked at the river, and turned his back on the house; and the Girl, in the doorway, panting as if she had run herself to a standstill, was looking at him across the yard. Tamb' Itam stood not far from his master, waiting patiently for what might happen. All at once, Jim, who seemed to be lost in quiet thought, turned to him and said, "Time to finish this."

"Tuan?" said Tamb' Itam, with alacrity. He did not know what his master meant, but as soon as Jim made a movement, the Girl started too and walked down into the open space. She tottered slightly, and about halfway down called out to Jim, who had apparently resumed his peaceful contemplation of the river. He turned round, setting his back against the gun. "Will you fly?" she cried. "There is no escape," he said, stopping short, and she stood still also, silent, devouring him with her eyes. "And you shall go?" she said slowly. He bent his head. "Ah!" she exclaimed, peering at him, as it were, "you are mad or false. Do you remember the night you said you would never leave me? I asked for no promise. You promised unasked—remember." "Enough, poor girl," he said. "I should not be worth having."

Tamb' Itam saw her lean forward where she stood, open her arms, and run at him swiftly. She flung herself upon his breast and clasped him round the neck. "Ah! but I shall hold thee thus," she cried. "Thou art mine!" She sobbed violently.

The sky over Patusan was blood-red, immense, streaming like an open vein. An enormous sun nestled crimson amongst the tree-tops, and the forest below had a black and forbidding face.

Suddenly Tamb' Itam saw Jim catch her arms, trying to unclasp her hands. She hung on them with her head fallen back; her hair touched the ground. "Come here!" his master called, and Tamb' Itam helped to ease her down. It was difficult to separate her fingers. Jim, bending over her, looked long at her face and all at once ran to the landing-stage. Tamb' Itam followed him, but turning his head, he saw that she had struggled to her knees. "Tuan! Tuan!" called Tamb' Itam. "Look back"; but Jim was already in a canoe, standing up, paddle in hand. He did not look back. Tamb' Itam had just time to scramble in after him when the canoe floated clear. The Girl on her knees, with clasped hands, at the water-gate. "You are false!" she screamed out after Jim. "Forgive me," he cried. "Never! Never!" she called back.

Tamb' Itam took the paddle from Jim's hands, it being unseemly that he should sit while his lord paddled. When they reached the other shore, his master forbade him to come any farther; but Tamb' Itam did follow him at a distance, walking up the slope to Doramin's campong.

It was beginning to grow dark. Torches twinkled here and there. Those they met stood aside hastily to let Jim pass. The wailing of women came from above. The courtyard was full of armed Bugis with their followers, and of Patusan people.

Doramin, alone, immense and desolate, sat in his armchair with the pair of flintlock pistols on his knees, faced by an armed throng. When Jim appeared, at somebody's exclamation all the heads turned round together, and then the mass opened right and left, and he walked up a lane of averted glances. Whispers followed him; murmurs: "He has worked all the evil." "He hath a charm.". . . He heard them—perhaps!

When he came up into the light of torches, the wailing of the women ceased suddenly. Doramin did not lift his head, and Jim stood silent before him for a time. Then he looked to the left, and moved in that direction with measured steps. Dain Waris's mother crouched at the head of the body, and the gray dishevelled hair concealed her face. Jim came up slowly, looked at his dead friend, lifting the sheet, then dropped it without a word. Slowly he walked back.

"He came! He came," was running from lip to lip, making a murmur to which he moved. "He hath taken it upon his own head," a voice said aloud.

He heard this and turned to the crowd. "Yes. Upon my head." A few people recoiled. Jim waited a while before Doramin, and then said gently, "I am come in sorrow." He waited again. "I am come, ready and unarmed," he repeated.

The unwieldy old man, lowering his big forehead like an ox under a yoke, made an effort to rise, clutching at the flintlock pistols on his knees. From his throat came gurgling, choking, inhuman sounds, and his two attendants helped him from behind. People remarked that the ring which he had dropped on his lap fell and rolled against the foot of the white man, and that poor Jim glanced down at the talisman that had opened for him the door of fame, love, and success within the wall of forests fringed with white foam, within the coast that under the western sun looks like the very stronghold of the night. Doramin, struggling to keep his feet, made with his two supporters a swaying, tottering group; his little eyes stared with an expression of mad pain, of rage, with a ferocious glitter, and then, while Jim stood—stiffened and with bared head in the light of torches, looking him straight in the face—he clung heavily with his left arm round the neck of a bowed youth, and lifting deliberately his right, shot his son's friend through the chest.

The crowd, which had fallen apart behind Jim as soon as Doramin had raised his hand, rushed tumultuously forward after the shot. They say that the white man sent right and left at all those faces a proud and unflinching glance. Then, with his hand over his lips, he fell forward, dead.

He passed away under a cloud, inscrutable, unforgiven, and excessively romantic—tearing himself from a living woman to celebrate his pitiless wedding with a shadowy ideal of conduct. Is he satisfied—quite, now, I wonder?

THE ESSAY CONTEST

James M. Barrie (Scotland)

Sentimental Tommy is the story of an unaccountable, exasperating, clever, imaginative boy in a small Scottish town. Tommy develops a knack for writing and supplants the professional letter writer of the community because of his gift for thinking himself into the place of the supposed correspondent and sharing and expressing his clients' thoughts and feelings.

Tommy enters an essay contest, whose prize will mean a college education. There are two schools in the village—taught by Mr. Ogilvy and Mr. Cathro. The former's pupils have won the contest for seven years. Tommy is Mr. Cathro's pupil. If he loses this chance, he will be sent to work as a sheepherder.

❋　❋　❋

The subject of the essay was changed yearly. This time "A Day in Church" was announced, and immediately Lauchlan McLauchlan, who had not missed a service since his scarlet fever year (and too few then), smote his red head in agony, while Tommy, who had missed as many as possible, looked calmly confident. For two hours the competitors were put into a small room communicating with the larger one, and Tommy began at once with a confident smirk that presently gave way to a most holy expression; while Lauchlan gaped at him and at last got started also, but had to pause occasionally to rub his face on his sleeve, for, like Corp, he was one of the kind who cannot think without perspiring. In the large room the ministers gossiped about eternal punishment, and of the two dominies [1] one sat at his ease, like a passenger who knows that the coach will reach the goal without any exertion on his part, while the other paced the floor, with many a despondent glance through the open door whence the scraping proceeded; and the one was pleasantly cool; and the other in a plot of heat; and the one made genial remarks about everyday matters, and the answers of the other stood on their heads. It was a familiar comedy to Mr. Ogilvy, hardly a variation on what had happened five times in six for many years: the same scene, the same scraping in the little room, the same background of ministers, the same dominies; everything was as it had so often been, except that he and Cathro had changed places; it was Cathro who sat smiling now and Mr. Ogilvy who dolefully paced the floor.

Mr. Ogilvy's many triumphs in this competition had not dulled his appetite for more, and depressed he was at the prospect of a reverse. That it was coming now he could not doubt. McLauchlan, who was to be Rev., had a flow of words (which would prevent his perspiring much in the pulpit), but he could no more describe a familiar scene with the pen than a milkmaid can draw a cow. The Thrums representatives were sometimes as little gifted, it is true, and never were they so well exercised, but this Tommy had the knack of it, as Mr. Ogilvy could not doubt, for the story of his letter-writing had been through the glens.

"Keep up your spirits," Mr. Lorrimer had said to him as they walked together to the fray, "Cathro's loon may compose the better of the two, but, as I understand, the first years of his life were spent in London, and so he may bogle [2] at the Scotch."

But the dominie replied, "Don't buoy me up on a soap bubble. If there's as much in him as I fear, that should be a help to him instead of a hindrance, for it will have set him a-thinking about the words he uses."

And the satisfaction on Tommy's face when the subject of the essay was given out, with the business-like way in which he set to work, had added to the Dominie's misgivings; if anything was required to dishearten him utterly it was provided by Cathro's confident smile. The two Thrums ministers were naturally desirous that Tommy should win, but the younger of them was very fond of Mr. Ogilvy, and noticing his unhappy peeps through the door dividing the rooms, proposed that it should be closed. He shut it him-

---

[1] *dominies:* teachers.   [2] *bogle:* have difficulty, come to grief.

self, and as he did so he observed that Tommy was biting his pen
and frowning, while McLauchlan, having ceased to think, was getting on nicely. But it did not strike Mr. Dishart that this was worth
commenting on. Mr. Ogilvy still hovered about the door of com-
munication, and his face fell more and more, making Mr. Dishart
quite unhappy.

"I'm an old fool," the dominie admitted, "but I can't help being
cast down. The fact is that— I have only heard the scrape of one
pen for nearly an hour."

"Poor Lauchlan!" exclaimed Mr. Cathro, rubbing his hands gleefully, and indeed it was such a shameless exhibition that the minister said reproachfully, "You forget yourself, Mr. Cathro, let us
not be unseemly exalted in the hour of our triumph."

Then Mr. Cathro sat upon his hands as the best way of keeping
them apart, but the moment Mr. Dishart's back presented itself, he
winked at Mr. Ogilvy.

He winked a good deal more presently.

For after all—how to tell it! Tommy was ignominiously beaten,
making such a beggarly show that the judges thought it unnecessary
to take the essays home with them for leisurely consideration before
pronouncing Mr. Lauchlan McLauchlan winner. There was quite
a commotion in the schoolroom. At the end of the allotted time, the
two competitors had been told to hand in their essays, and how Mr.
McLaughlan was sniggering is not worth recording, so dumb-
founded, confused and raging was Tommy. He clung to his papers,
crying fiercely that the two hours could not be up yet, and Lauchlan
having tried to keep the laugh in too long, it exploded in his mouth,
whereupon, said he, with a guffaw, "He hasna written a word for
near an hour!"

"What! It was you I heard!" cried Mr. Ogilvy gleaming, while
the unhappy Cathro tore the essay from Tommy's hands. Essay!
It was no more an essay than a twig is a tree, for the gowk had stuck
in the middle of his second page. Yes, stuck is the right expression,
as his chagrined teacher had to admit when the boy was cross-
examined.

He had brought himself to public scorn for lack of a word. What
word? they asked testily, but even now he could not tell. He had
wanted a Scotch word that would signify how many people were in
church, and it was on the tip of his tongue but would come no
farther. Puckle was nearly the word, but it did not mean so many
people as he meant. The hour had gone by just like winking; he
had forgotten all about time while searching his mind for the word.

When Mr. Ogilvy heard this he seemed to be much impressed,[3] repeatedly he nodded his head as some beat time to music, and he muttered to himself, "The right word—yes, that's everything," and " 'the time went by like winking'—exactly, precisely," and he would have liked to examine Tommy's bumps, but did not, nor said a word aloud, for was he not there in McLaughlan's interest?

The other five were furious; even Mr. Lorrimer, though his man had won, could not smile in face of such imbecility. "You little tattie doolie," Cathro roared, "were there not a dozen words to wile [4] from if you had an ill-will to puckle? What ailed you at manzy, or——"

"I thought of manzy," replied Tommy woefully, for he was ashamed of himself, "but—but a manzy's a swarm. It would mean that the folk in the kirk were buzzing thegither like bees, instead of sitting still."

"Even if it does mean that," said Mr. Duthie, with impatience, "what was the need of being so particular? Surely the art of essay-writing consists in using the first word that comes and hurrying on."

"That's how I did," said the proud McLauchlan, who is now leader of a party in the church, and a figure in Edinburgh during the month of May.

"I see," interposed Mr. Gloag, "that McLauchlan speaks of there being a mask of people in the church. Mask is a fine Scotch word."

"Admirable," assented Mr. Dishart.

"I thought of mask," whimpered Tommy, "but that would mean the kirk was crammed, and I just meant it to be middling full."

"Flow would have done," suggested Mr. Lorrimer.

"Flow's but a handful," said Tommy.

"Curran, then, you jackanapes!"

"Curran's no enough."

Mr. Lorrimer flung up his hands in despair.

"I wanted something between curran and mask," said Tommy, dogged, yet almost at the crying.

Mr. Ogilvy, who had been hiding his admiration with difficulty, spread a net for him. "You said you wanted a word that meant middling full. Well, why did you not say middling full or fell mask?"

"Yes, why not?" demanded the ministers, unconsciously caught in the net.

"I wanted one word," replied Tommy, unconsciously avoiding it.

[3] Mr. Ogilvy had dreamed of himself being an author and had done some secret writing. [4] *wile:* choose.

"You jewel!" muttered Mr. Ogilvy under his breath, but Mr. Cathro would have banged the boy's head had not the ministers interfered.

"It is so easy, too, to find the right word," said Mr. Gloag.

"It's no; it's as difficult as to hit a squirrel," cried Tommy and again Mr. Ogilvy nodded approval.

But the ministers were only pained.

"The lad is merely a numskull," said Mr. Dishart, kindly.

"And no teacher could have turned him into anything else," said Mr. Duthie.

"And so, Cathro, you need not feel sore over your defeat," added Mr. Gloag; but nevertheless Cathro took Tommy by the neck and ran him out of the parish school of Thrums. When he returned to the others, he found the ministers congratulating McLauchlan, whose nose was in the air, and complimenting Mr. Ogilvy, who listened to their formal phrases solemnly and accepted their handshakes with a dry chuckle.

"Ay, grin away, sir," the mortified dominie of Thrums said to him sourly, "the joke is on your side."

"You are right, sir," replied Mr. Ogilvy mysteriously. "The joke is on my side, and the best of it is that not one of you knows what the joke is!"

And then an odd thing happened. As they were preparing to leave the school, the door opened a little and there appeared in the aperture the face of Tommy, tear-stained but excited. "I ken the word now," he cried, "it came to me a' at once; it is hantle!"

The door closed with a victorious bang, just in time to prevent Cathro——

"Oh, the sumph!" exclaimed Mr. Lauchlan McLauchlan, "as if it mattered what the word is now!"

And said Mr. Dishart, "Cathro, you had better tell Aaron Latta that the sooner he sends this nincompoop to the herding the better."

But Mr. Ogilvy, giving his Lauchlan a push that nearly sent him sprawling, said in an ecstasy to himself, "He had to think of it till he got it—and he got it. The laddie is a genius!" They were about to tear up Tommy's essay, but he snatched it from them and put it in his outer pocket. "I am a collector of curiosities," he explained, "and this paper may be worth money yet."

"Well," said Cathro savagely, "I have one satisfaction, I ran him out of my school."

"Who knows," replied Mr. Ogilvy, "but what you may be proud to dust a chair for him when he comes back?"

THE FAREWELL ADDRESS

Sinclair Lewis (America)

Arrowsmith is a study of the medical profession in all its branches, including the medical school of Winnemac University. On the crowded canvas of this story, Lewis has drawn some unforgettable satirical portraits of minor characters. One of these, Dr. Roscoe Geake, professor of otolaryngology,[1] is especially detested by the hero, Martin Arrowsmith, who even as a raw young student already displays a keen intellectual interest in the science of medicine and a flair for medical research. Needless to say, in this portrait of a self-seeking doctor, Lewis is not satirizing doctors in general or nose-and-throat specialists in particular, but only a certain type of objectionable individual who might be found in any specialty or any profession.

❊   ❊   ❊

Roscoe Geake was a peddler. He would have done well with oil stock. As an otolaryngologist he believed that tonsils had been placed in the human organism for the purpose of providing specialists with closed motor cars. A physician who left the tonsils in any patient was, he felt, foully and ignorantly overlooking his future health and comfort—the physician's future health and comfort. His earnest feeling regarding the nasal septum was that it never hurt any patient to have part of it removed, and if the most hopeful examination could find nothing the matter with the patient's nose and throat except that he was smoking too much, still, in any case, the enforced rest after an operation was good for him. Geake denounced this cant[2] about Letting Nature Alone. Why, the average well-to-do man appreciated attention! He really didn't think much of his specialists unless he was operated on now and then—just a little and not very painfully. Geake had one classic annual address in which, winging far above otolaryngology, he evaluated all medicine, and explained to grateful healers like Irving Watters the method of getting suitable fees:

"Knowledge is the greatest thing in the medical world but it's no good whatever unless you can sell it, and to do this you must first impress your personality on the people who have the dollars. Whether a patient is a new or an old friend, you must always use salesmanship on him. Explain to him, also to his stricken and anxious family, the hard work and thought you are giving his case,

[1] *otolaryngology:* the treatment of the nose and throat.
[2] *cant:* foolish pretence.

and so make him feel that the good you have done him, or intend to do him, is even greater than the fee you plan to charge. Then, when he gets your bill, he will not misunderstand or kick."

It was announced in the *Winnemac Daily News* that Dr. Geake had been called from the chair of otolaryngology to the vice-presidency of the puissant New Ideal Medical Instrument and Furniture Company of Jersey City. In celebration he gave a final address to the entire medical school on "The Art and Science of Furnishing the Doctor's Office."

He was a neatly finished person, Geake, eye-glassed and enthusiastic and fond of people. He beamed on his loving students and cried:

"Gentlemen, the trouble with too many doctors, even those splendid old pioneer war-horses who through mud and storm, through winter's chill blast and August's untempered heat, go bringing cheer and surcease from pain to the world's humblest, yet even these old Nestors not so infrequently settle down in a rut and never shake themselves loose. Now that I am leaving this field where I have labored so long and happily, I want to ask every man jack of you to read, before you begin to practise medicine, not merely your Rosenau and Howell and Gray,[3] but also, as a preparation for being that which all good citizens must be, namely, practical men, a most valuable little manual of modern psychology, *How to Put Pep in Salesmanship*, by Grosvenor A. Bibby. For don't forget, gentlemen, and this is my last message to you, the man worth while is not merely the man who takes things with a smile but also the man who's trained in philosophy, practical philosophy, so that instead of daydreaming and spending all his time talking about 'ethics,' splendid though they are, and 'charity,' glorious virtue though that be, yet he never forgets that unfortunately the world judges a man by the amount of good hard cash he can lay away. The graduates of the University of Hard Knocks judge a physician as they judge a business man, not merely by his alleged 'high ideals' but by the horsepower he puts into carrying them out—and making them pay! And from a scientific standpoint, don't overlook the fact that the impression of properly remunerated competence which you make on a patient is of just as much importance, in these days of the new psychology, as the drugs you get into him or the operations he lets you get away with. The minute he begins to see that other folks appreciate and reward your skill, that minute he must begin to feel your power and so to get well.

[3] Great authorities on medical science.

"Nothing is more important in inspiring him than to have such an office that as soon as he steps into it, you have begun to sell him the idea of being properly cured. I don't care whether a doctor has studied in Germany, Munich, Baltimore, and Rochester. I don't care whether he has all science at his finger tips, whether he can instantly diagnose with a considerable degree of accuracy, the most obscure ailment, whether he has the surgical technique of a Mayo, a Crile, a Blake, an Ochsner, a Cushing.[4] If he has a dirty old office, with hand-me-down chairs and a lot of secondhand magazines, then the patient isn't going to have confidence in him; he is going to resist the treatment—and the doctor is going to have difficulty in putting over and collecting an adequate fee.

"To go far below the surface of this matter into the fundamental philosophy and esthetics of office furnishings for the doctor, there are today two warring schools, the Tapestry School and the Aseptic [5] School, if I may venture to so denominate and conveniently distinguish them. Both of them have their merits. The Tapestry School claims that luxurious chairs for waiting patients, handsome hand-painted pictures, a bookcase jammed with the world's best literature in expensively bound sets, together with cut-glass vases and potted palms, produce an impression of that opulence which can come only from sheer ability and knowledge. The Aseptic School, on the other hand, maintains that what the patient wants is that appearace of scrupulous hygiene which can be produced only by furnishing the outer waiting room as well as the inner offices in white-painted chairs and tables, with merely a Japanese print against a gray wall.

"But, gentlemen, it seems obvious to me, so obvious that I wonder it has not been brought out before, that the ideal reception room is a combination of these two schools! Have your potted palms and handsome pictures—to the practical physician they are as necessary a part of his working equipment as a sterilizer or a Baumanometer.[6] But so far as possible have everything in sanitary-looking white—and think of the color schemes you can evolve, or the good wife for you, if she be one blessed with artistic tastes! Rich golden or red cushions, in a Morris chair enameled the purest white! A floor covering of white enamel, with just a border of delicate rose! Recent and unspotted numbers of expensive magazines, with art covers, lying on a white table! Gentlemen, there is the idea of imaginative salesmanship which I wish to leave with you; there is the gospel which I hope to spread in my fresh field of en-

---

[4] The most famous modern surgeons.   [5] *Aseptic:* germ proof.
[6] Medical apparatus.

deavor, the New Ideal Instrument Company of Jersey City, where at any time I shall be glad to see and shake by the hand any and all of you."

READING PROBLEMS ON EPISODES FROM NOVELS

1. *The Bishop's Candlesticks:* Two forces are struggling for the soul of Jean Valjean. Can you classify the characters and incidents in this extract as forces that drive him toward evil and forces that drive him toward good? Pick out any details of description or action that show the fundamental traits of Jean's own character. How many times does Hugo use contrast—of character, of action, of scene—in this extract, and for what purpose are these contrasts used? How many times and how does Hugo create surprise? What is the effect in each case? About what does this episode leave you in suspense?

2. *Mignon:* How does Goethe create an air of mystery about Mignon? Select details of face, action, or speech which reveal the child's character. Does she change throughout this extract? How does Mignon's song express the longing of the northerner for a southern land—in particular, for Italy? Do you think the hero will fall in love with her?

3. *Prison Mates:* How is the tragedy of solitary confinement emphasized in this story? How are the superior mind and character of Dantès and the other prisoner demonstrated? What minor crisis in the story occurs in this extract? How is suspense created? About what points in the story preceding and following this episode are you curious?

4. *Becky Sharp Unmasked:* Remembering that Becky has left Rawdon in jail for twenty-four hours without any help but a note saying she was ill and in bed, point out each detail in the scene which convinces Rawdon that she is false to him. Do you think she was? What does Lord Steyne think Becky and Rawdon are trying to do? All three of the people who appear in this scene are in one way or another dishonest. Which of them is the worst and which the best? Who dominates this scene? How? Rawdon has appeared up to this point in the story mainly as a stupid tool of Becky's and a card sharper. How does this scene enlarge the reader's impression of him? Select small details in the action which add reality and vividness to the scene or which throw a sudden light on the character and motives of the participants. Three-fourths of the book precedes this scene and one-fourth follows it. What do you think happens before and after it?

5. *I Fall Into Captivity:* What does it add to this episode to have it told in the first person? What cause is given for David's sudden infatuation? Analyze the description, conversation, and behavior of Dora to see if you can account for her charm. Compare her with the Baby-Talk Girl in Tarkington's *Seventeen.* Which is the cleverer of the two? In the scene of Willie Baxter's first meeting with the visiting girl, what has Tarkington taken from this scene in *David Copperfield* and what has he changed? How does David betray his infatuation? In spite of the fact that this is a humorous

chapter, find in it touches of beauty and sentiment. David's landlady, Mrs. Crupp, is typical of Dickens' minor characters. She has come to David's room for two purposes. One appears in the extract given here. The other is to get a glass of brandy, to which she is addicted, alas! Picture Mrs. Crupp and point out how Dickens has indicated the various elements of shrewdness, sympathy, and comicality which make up her character. Guess whether David's marriage to Dora will be successful.

6. *The Race:* Students who are familiar with horses should note lifelike details in the behavior of the various mounts. Athletes who have taken part in games and meets should point out whether Vronsky's emotions during and after the race are accurately portrayed. How is the background for and excitement of the races indicated? How is Vronsky wise in handling Frou Frou and what mistake does he make? What makes the outcome of the race so hard for him to bear?

7. *The Detestable Mr. Hyde:* How does the setting of the opening scene create a sense of mystery? Does the appearance or behavior of Mr. Hyde entirely account for the detestation he arouses in all beholders? How many mysterious points do you notice in the actions of Mr. Hyde? What arouses your curiosity in the questions of Mr. Utterson? in the provisions of Dr. Jekyll's will? What interpretation does Mr. Utterson give to the will? List all the questions that these chapters raise in your mind. Then list every fact told in these chapters that you think may offer a clue to the answers. Finish the story to see how many clues you detected.

8. *Upon His Head:* Why does Jim decide to face Doramin unarmed instead of to fight or fly? What does he mean by "the dark powers should not rob him twice of his peace" (page 313) and "I should not be worth having" (page 315)? Do you think he has any hope of saving his life? Why does he not look back at the girl? How has Conrad given the atmosphere of a jungle village? Could the story have occurred elsewhere? Explain the last line of the story. If you read the entire story, compare Jim's feelings during his trial and during this final episode.

9. *A Wild Ride:* Account for the calmness of Anna in the midst of danger. Why does Gösta say, "God would not have it"? Explain the words "strongest and weakest of men." Would Gösta and Anna have been happy together? What will be the real test of Anna's sacrifice?

10. *The Essay Contest:* Which of the two boys really had the writing gift? Is Tommy right about its not being easy to find the right word? Find an English equivalent for the Scotch word he wanted. What is Mr. Ogilvy's private opinion about the result of the contest? Why is it important to know that Ogilvy had himself tried to write? Why does he save Tommy's essay? Do you think Tommy will remain a sheepherder?

11. *The Farewell Address:* What type of patient is Dr. Geake interested in? How does he regard medical work? What is his test of success? What purpose does he think should guide a doctor in furnishing his office? What message would you expect a professor of medicine to leave with his students in a farewell lecture? Is Dr. Geake's leaving his professorship to become a

super-salesman symbolic? If you read *Arrowsmith*, contrast **Dr. Geake** with the hero's favorite professor, **Dr. Gottlieb**.

FURTHER READINGS IN THE NOVEL

FRANCE
  Dumas: *The Three Musketeers*
  Hugo: *The Hunchback of Notre Dame*
  Balzac: *Eugénie Grandet*
  Gaboriau: *File Number 113*
  Verne: *The Mysterious Island*
  Expery: *Night Flight*

GERMANY
  Sudermann: *Dame Care*
  Freytag: *Debit and Credit*

HOLLAND
  Couperus: *Majesty*

NORWAY
  Hamsun: *Growth of the Soil*
  Bojer: *Hunger*

RUSSIA
  Dostoievski: *Crime and Punishment*
  Gogol: *Taras Bulba*

POLAND
  Sienkiewicz: *Quo Vadis?*

SPAIN
  Ibanez: *The Cabin*

GREAT BRITAIN
  Scott: *Ivanhoe*
  Austen: *Pride and Prejudice*
  Brontë: *Jane Eyre*
  Eliot: *Mill on the Floss*
  Thackeray: *Henry Esmond*
  Dickens: *Tale of Two Cities*
    Oliver Twist
  Blackmore: *Lorna Doone*

Stevenson: *Saint Ives*
    The Master of Ballantrae
Meredith: *The Ordeal of Richard Feverel*
Hardy: *Tess of the D'Urbervilles*
Galsworthy: *The Forsyte Saga*
Bennett: *The Old Wives' Tale*
Barrie: *Tommy and Grizel*
Conrad: *Typhoon*
    Heart of Darkness
Hudson: *Green Mansions*
De Morgan: *Alice for Short*
Olliphant: *Bob Son of Battle*
Kipling: *The Light that Failed*
Wells: *The Time Machine*
Hope: *The Prisoner of Zenda*

AMERICA
Cooper: *The Last of the Mohicans*
Melville: *Moby Dick*
Hawthorne: *The Scarlet Letter*
Twain: *Huckleberry Finn*
Stowe: *Uncle Tom's Cabin*
James: *The Portrait of a Lady*
Wharton: *Ethan Frome*
Cather: *My Antonia*
    The Professor's House
Tarkington: *The Turmoil*
Wister: *The Virginian*
London: *The Call of the Wild*
Lewis: *Main Street*
Westcott: *David Harum*
Buck: *The Good Earth*

SUGGESTIONS FOR ORIGINAL EPISODES

1. Why Jack Came Back to School. 2. The Student No One Understood. 3. The Lonely New-comer Finds a Friend. 4. How I Accidentally Discovered Someone's True Character (Good or Bad). 5. The Football Hero Captivates the Girls. 6. My Feelings Before and During an Athletic Event. 7. A Mysterious Family Moves into Our Neighborhood. 8. Paying the Price of Cheating. 9. Driving Ahead of a Storm. 10. The Debate that Was Decided Wrongly. 11. An Occupational Misfit. 12. The Farewell Speech of a Class President.

VI

The Romance

WE CAN no more imagine life without novels than life without telephones, automobiles, and electric lights. But the novel we know with its closely knit plot is scarcely two hundred years old. Before that, the reader's hunger for long stories was satisfied by the romance, which was really nothing but a series of tales about the same main characters, arranged in chronological order and following the hero and heroine through a long series of adventures. There was, perhaps, some motive for the adventures, but it was so much less important than the adventures themselves and so much in the background during most of the story, that it would be stretching a point to claim that any of the old romances had a plot.

The motive for the adventures in a romance is not necessarily love, and a romance is not always a love story. Anything strange, colorful and out of the ordinary is romantic. The Greek scientist, philosopher, and literary critic, Aristotle wrote long ago that a good writer always dealt with what was possible. But, said Aristotle, there are two kinds of possibility: the probable possible and the improbable possible. The improbable possible makes the most exciting stories, thought Aristotle, and it is the improbable possible of which romances are made.

These old romances were sometimes in prose, sometimes in verse, and sometimes in both. The European romances which flourished during the Middle Ages and the Renaissance, and from which our modern novel developed were of four types: romances of chivalry, religious romances, pastoral romances, and picaresque romances. The romances of chivalry told of the adventures of knights and ladies and often followed their heroes to the Crusades or on pilgrimages and travels into the Orient—the point of the story being to unite the hero and heroine after their separate wanderings. Pastoral romances took their principal characters into the country, where they played at being shepherds and shepherdesses. The picaresque romance was named from the Spanish word *picaro* or rogue, and related a long series of escapades of some clever rascal who was always getting into trouble and escaping by his quick wit. Typical of religious romances were those gathered together in the legend of the Holy Grail and in the Golden Legend—the world's most famous collection of pious stories.

These romances were first inspired by works of the Greek and Roman writers. The pastoral romances imitate the rural stories of Virgil and Ovid. Rascal tales were popular on the Roman stage. And in the period of Greek decadence after the Roman conquest —when the center of the Greek world was at Alexandria in Egypt, when Greek and Asiatic were fused, and a rich trading class developed on the ruins of the old aristocracy—countless prose romances were written in Greek to satisfy the craving of this new social group to see themselves depicted in literature. The hero and heroine of one Greek romance travel all over northern Europe and even explore the North Pole—alternately separated and reunited. Another Greek hero and heroine reach final happiness in Ethiopia! These Greek romances abound in kidnappings, magic, murders, and suicides, and could give pointers to the most lurid writer for the current wood-pulp magazines. As in every true romance, however, vice is punished, virtue rewarded, and the hero and heroine live happily ever after.

The Orient, too, had its quota of romances, those of China coming nearest to the style and method of our modern novels. The American reader is struck by the fact that in a Chinese romance, love begins in mutual respect for character and attainment, and the tenderer passion comes after the hero and heroine are married!

All the tests of excellence which we apply to a novel cannot be used in judging these old romances. However, no romantic adventure story, whether of long ago or of today—and there are a great many of this type among our best-selling works of fiction and in our popular magazines—can be worth reading unless:

(1) The incidents are natural and possible
(2) The details of action and feeling are true to life
(3) The local color in all scenes is accurate
(4) The characters are clearly drawn, individualized, and interesting or important enough to keep us anxious about their fate
(5) The moral tone is sound and true
(6) The style has variety and charm

AUCASSIN AND NICOLETE

Anonymous (France)

Translated by Andrew Lang

The medieval romance of *Aucassin and Nicolete* was composed partly in prose and partly in verse by a captive troubadour in Picardy in the days when the Crusades and pilgrimages to the Holy Land had aroused a romantic interest in the Saracens. The hero of the story is a young French count, but the heroine is a lovely captive pagan maid who has been brought back as a slave from the Orient by a captain in the holy wars.

❋   ❋   ❋

Who would list to the good lay
Gladness of the captive grey?
'Tis how two young lovers met,
Aucassin and Nicolete,
Of the pains the lover bore   5
And the sorrows he outwore,
For the goodness and the grace,
Of his love, so fair of face.

Sweet the song, the story sweet,
There is no man hearkens it,   10
No man living neath the sun,
So outwearied, so foredone,
Sick and woeful, worn and sad,
But is healed, but is glad
    'Tis so sweet.   15

So say they, speak they, tell they the Tale:

How the Count Bougars de Valence made war on Count Garin de Biaucaire, war so great, and so marvellous, and so mortal that never a day dawned but always he was there, by the gates and walls, and barriers of the town with a hundred knights, and ten thousand men at arms, horsemen and footmen: so burned he the Count's land, and spoiled his country, and slew his men. Now the Count Garin de Biaucaire was old and frail, and his good days were gone over. No heir had he, neither son nor daughter, save one young man only; such an one as I shall tell you. Aucassin was the name of the damoiseau: fair was he, goodly, and great, and featly [1] fashioned of

---

[1] *featly*: well.

his body, and limbs. His hair was yellow, in little curls, his eyes blue and laughing, his face beautiful and shapely, his nose high and well set, and so richly seen was he in all things good, that in him was none evil at all. But so suddenly overtaken was he of Love, who is a great master, that he would not, of his will, be dubbed knight, nor take arms, nor follow tourneys, nor do whatsoever him beseemed. Therefore his father and mother said to him:

"Son, go take thine arms, mount thy horse, and hold thy land, and help thy men, for if they see thee among them, more stoutly will they keep in battle their lives, and lands, and thine, and mine."

"Father," said Aucassin, "I marvel that you will be speaking. Never may God give me aught of my desire if I be made knight, or mount my horse, or face stour and battle wherein knights smite and are smitten again, unless thou give me Nicolete, my true love, that I love so well."

"Son," said the father, "this may not be. Let Nicolete go, a slave girl she is, out of a strange land, and the captain of this town bought her of the Saracens, and carried her hither, and hath reared her and let christen the maid, and took her for his daughter in God, and one day will find a young man for her, to win her bread honorably. Herein hast thou nought to make or mend, but if a wife thou wilt have, I will give thee the daughter of a King, or a Count. There is no man so rich in France, but if thou desire his daughter, thou shalt have her."

"Faith! my father," said Aucassin, "tell me where is the place so high in all the world, that Nicolete, my sweet lady and love, would not grace it well? If she were Empress of Constantinople or of Germany, or Queen of France or England, it were little enough for her; so gentle is she and courteous, and debonaire, and compact of all good qualities."

Here singeth one:

Aucassin was of Biaucaire
Of a goodly castle there,
But from Nicolete the fair
None might win his heart away
Though his father, many a day,   5
And his mother said him nay.
"Ha! fond child, what wouldest thou?
Nicolete is glad enow!
Was from Carthage cast away,
Paynims sold her on a day!"   10

Wouldst thou win a lady fair
Choose a maid of high degree
Such an one is meet for thee."
"Nay of these I have no care,
Nicolete is debonaire,   15
Her body sweet and the face of her
Take my heart as in a snare.
Loyal love is but her share
          That is so sweet."

Then speak they, say they, tell they the Tale:

When the Count Garin de Biaucaire knew that he would avail
not to withdraw Aucassin his son from the love of Nicolete, he went
to the Captain of the city, who was his man, and spake to him
saying:

"Sir Count; away with Nicolete thy daughter in God; cursed be
the land whence she was brought into this country, for by reason
of her do I lose Aucassin, that will neither be dubbed knight, nor
do aught of the things that fall to him to be done. And wit ye well,"
he said, "that if I might have her at my will, I would burn her in a
fire, and yourself might well be sore adread."

"Sir," said the Captain, "sith it is thy will and thy pleasure, I
will send her into that land and that country where never will he
see her with his eyes."

So parted they from each other. Now the Captain was a right rich
man: so had he a rich palace with a garden in face of it; in an upper
chamber thereof he let place Nicolete with one old woman to keep
her company, and in that chamber put bread and meat and wine
and such things as were needful. Then he let seal the door, that none
might come in or go forth, save that there was one window, over
against the garden, and strait enough, where through came to them
a little air.

Here singeth one:

Nicolete as ye heard tell
Prisoned is within a cell
That is painted wondrously
With colors of a fair countrie,
And the window of marble wrought.
There the maiden stood in thought,
With straight brows and yellow hair
Never saw ye fairer fair!

On the wood she gazed below,
And she saw the roses blow,   10
Heard the birds sing loud and low,
Therefore spoke she woefully:
"Ah me, wherefore do I lie
Here in prison wrongfully?
Aucassin, my love, my knight,   15
Am I not thy heart's delight,
Thou that lovest me aright!
'Tis for thee that I must dwell
In the vaulted chamber cell,
Hard beset and all alone!   20
By our Lady Mary's Son
Here no longer will I wonne,
    If I may flee!

Then speak they, say they, tell they the Tale:

(It is noised abroad that Nicolete has been sent into a distant land.
Aucassin bitterly upbraids the Captain, who tells him he shall never
see her more.)

Here singeth one:

Aucassin did so depart
Much in dole and heavy at heart
For his love so bright and dear,
None might bring him any cheer,
None might give good words to hear.   5
To the palace doth he fare
Climbeth up the palace-stair,
Passeth to a chamber there,
Thus great sorrow doth he bear,
For his lady and love so fair.   10
"Nicolete how fair art thou,
Sweet thy foot-fall, sweet thine eyes,
Sweet the mirth of thy replies,
Sweet thy laughter, sweet thy face,
Sweet thy lips and sweet thy brow,   15
And the touch of thine embrace,
All for thee I sorrow now,
Captive in an evil place,
Whence I ne'er may go my ways,
    Sister, sweet friend!"   20

22. *wonne:* dwell.

(As Aucassin sorrows in his chamber, his father's castle is assailed and almost taken by Count Bougars. Aucassin's father begs his son to help repel the attack, which Aucassin agrees to do on condition that he may see Nicolete, have three words from her, and one kiss.

Here one singeth:

Of the kiss heard Aucassin
That returning he shall win.
None so glad would he have been
Of a myriad marks of gold
Of a hundred thousand told.   5
Called for raiment brave of steel,
Then they clad him, head to heel,
Twyfold hauberk doth he don,
Firmly braced the helmet on.
Girt the sword with hilt of gold,   10
Horse doth mount, and lance doth wield,
Looks to stirrups and to shield,
Wondrous brave he rode to field.
Dreaming of his lady dear
Setteth spurs to the destrere,   15
Rideth forward without a fear,
Through the gate and forth away
        To the fray.

So speak they, say they, tell they the Tale:

(However, when Aucassin has saved the day, captured Count Bougars, and delivered him to his father, his father refuses to fulfill his promise concerning Nicolete. Aucassin at once frees Count Bougars after obtaining the Count's pledge never to cease warring upon his father.)

Here one singeth:

When the Count Garin doth know
That his child would ne'er forego
Love of her that loved him so,
Nicolete, the bright of brow,
In a dungeon deep below   5
Childe Aucassin did he throw.

15. *destrere:* steed.

Even there the Childe must dwell
In a dun-walled marble cell.
There he waileth in his woe
Crying thus as ye shall know.   10

"Nicolete, thou lily white,
My sweet lady, bright of brow,
Sweeter than the grape art thou,
Sweeter than sack posset good
In a cup of maple wood!   15
Was it not but yesterday
That a palmer came this way,
Out of Limousin came he,
And at ease he might not be,
For a passion him possessed   20
That upon his bed he lay,
Lay, and tossed, and knew not rest
In his pain discomforted.
But thou camest by the bed,
Where he tossed amid his pain,   25
Holding high thy sweeping train,
And thy kirtle of ermine,
And thy smock of linen fine,
Then these fair white limbs of thine,
Did he look on, and it fell   30
That the palmer straight was well,
Straight was hale—and comforted,
And he rose up from his bed,
And went back to his own place,
Sound and strong, and full of face! 35
My sweet lady, lily white,
Sweet thy footfall, sweet thine eyes,
And the mirth of thy replies.
Sweet thy laughter, sweet thy face,
Sweet thy lips and sweet thy brow,   40
And the touch of thine embrace.
Who but doth in thee delight?
I for love of thee am bound
In this dungeon underground,
All for loving thee must lie   45
Here where loud on thee I cry,
Here for loving thee must die
    For thee, my love."

Then say they, speak they, tell they the Tale:

Aucassin was cast into prison as ye have heard tell, and Nicolete, of her part, was in the chamber. Now it was summer time, the month of May, when days are warm, and long, and clear, and the night still and serene. Nicolete lay one night on her bed, and saw the moon shine clear through a window, yea, and heard the nightingale sing in the garden, so she minded her of Aucassin her lover whom she loved so well. Then fell she to thoughts of Count Garin de Biaucaire, that hated her to the death; therefore deemed she that there she would no longer abide, for that, if she were told of, and the Count knew whereas she lay, an ill death would he make her die. Now she knew that the old woman slept who held her company. Then she arose, and clad her in a mantle of silk she had by her, very goodly, and took napkins, and sheets of the bed, and knotted one to the other, and made therewith a cord as long as she might, so knitted it to a pillar in the window, and let herself slip down into the garden, then caught up her raiment in both hands, behind and before, and kilted up her kirtle, because of dew that she saw lying deep on the grass, and so went her way down the garden. Her locks were yellow and curled, her eyes blue and smiling, her face featly fashioned, the nose high and fairly set, the lips more red than cherry or rose in time of summer, her teeth white and small; her breasts so firm that they bore up the folds of her bodice as they had been two apples; so slim she was in the waist that your two hands might have clipped her, and the daisy flowers that brake beneath her as she went tip-toe, and that bent above her instep, seemed black against her feet, so white was the maiden. She came to the postern gate, and unbarred it, and went out through the streets of Biaucaire, keeping always on the shadowy side, for the moon was shining right clear, and so wandered she till she came to the tower where her lover lay. The tower was flanked with buttresses, and she cowered under one of them, wrapped in her mantle. Then thrust she her head through a crevice of the tower that was old and worn, and so heard she Aucassin wailing within, and making dole and lament for the sweet lady he loved so well. And when she had listened to him she began to say:

Here one singeth:

"Gentle knight withouten fear,
Little good befalleth thee,
Little help of sigh or tear,
Ne'er shalt thou have joy of me.

Never shalt thou win me; still   5
Am I held in evil will
Of thy father and thy kin,
Therefore must I cross the sea,
And another land must win."
Then she cut her curls of gold,   10
Cast them in the dungeon hold,
Aucassin doth clasp them there,
Kissed the curls that were so fair,
Them doth in his bosom bear,
Then he wept, even as of old,   15
    All for his love!

(When Aucassin hears that she is fleeing the country, he bitterly complains that she cannot love him as he loves her.)

Now while Aucassin and Nicolete held this parley together, the town's guards came down a street, with swords drawn beneath their cloaks, for the Count Garin had charged them that if they could take her they should slay her. But the sentinel that was on the tower saw them coming, and heard them speaking of Nicolete as they went, and threatening to slay her.

"God!" quoth he, "this were great pity to slay so fair a maid! Right great charity it were if I could say aught to her, and they perceive it not, and she should be on her guard against them, for if they slay her, then were Aucassin, my damoiseau, dead, and that were great pity."

Here one singeth:

Valiant was the sentinel,
Courteous, kind, and practiced well,
So a song did sing and tell
Of the peril that befell.
"Maiden fair that lingerest here,   5
Gentle maid of merry cheer,
Hair of gold, and eyes as clear
As the water in a mere,
Thou, meseems, hast spoken word
To thy lover and thy lord,
That would die for thee, his dear;   10

Now beware the ill accord,
Of the cloaked men of the sword,
These have sworn and keep their word
They will put thee to the sword   15
    Save thou take heed!"

Then speak they, say they, tell they the Tale:

So Nicolete shrank under her mantle into the shadow of the pillar till they had passed by, and then took she farewell of Aucassin, and so fared till she came unto the castle wall. Now that wall was wasted and broken, and some deal mended, so she clomb thereon till she came between wall and fosse,[1] and so looked down, and saw that the fosse was deep and steep, whereat she was sore adread.

"Ah, God," saith she, "sweet Savior! If I let myself fall hence, I shall break my neck, and if here I abide, tomorrow they will take me and burn me in a fire. Yet liefer would I perish here than that tomorrow the folk should stare on me for a gazing-stock."

Then she crossed herself, and so let herself slip into the fosse, and when she had come to the bottom, her fair feet, and fair hands that had not custom thereof, were bruised and frayed, and the blood springing from a dozen places, yet felt she no pain nor hurt, by reason of the great dread wherein she went. But if she were in cumber to win there, in worse was she to win out. But she deemed that there to abide was of none avail, and she found a pike sharpened, that they of the city had thrown out to keep the cold. Therewith made she one stepping place after another, till, with much travail, she climbed the wall. Now the forest lay within two crossbow shots, and the forest was of thirty leagues this way and that. Therein also were wild beasts, and beasts serpentine, and she feared that if she entered there they would slay her. But anon she deemed that if men found her here they would hale her back into the town to burn her.

Then commended she herself to God, and anon fared till she came unto the forest. But to go deep in it she dared not, by reason of the wild beasts, and beasts serpentine. Anon crept she into a little thicket, where sleep came upon her, and she slept till prime next day, when the shepherds issued forth from the town and drove their beasts between wood and water. Anon came they all into one place by a fair fountain which was on the fringe of the forest, thereby spread they a mantle, and thereon set bread. So while they

[1] *fosse:* the deep ditch between the castle and town wall.

were eating, Nicolete wakened, with the sound of the singing birds and the shepherds, and she went unto them, saying, "Fair boys, our Lord keep you!"

"God bless thee," quoth he that had more words to his tongue than the rest.

"Fair boys," quoth she, "know ye Aucassin, the son of Count Garin de Biaucaire?"

"Yea, well we know him."

"So may God help you, fair boys," quoth she, "tell him there is a beast in this forest, and bid him come chase it, and if he can take it, he would not give one limb thereof for a hundred marks of gold, nay, nor for five hundred, nor for any ransom."

Then looked they on her, and saw her so fair that they were all astonished.

"Will I tell him thereof?" quoth he that had more words to his tongue than the rest. "These are but visions ye tell of, for there is no beast so great in this forest, stag, nor lion, nor boar. Foul fall him that believes your word, and him that telleth Aucassin. Ye be a Fairy, and we have none liking for your company, nay, hold on your road."

"Nay, fair boys," quoth she, "nay, ye will do my bidding. And lo! I have five sols in my purse, take them, and tell him: for within three days must he come hunting it hither, and if within three days he find it not, never will he be healed of his torment."

"My faith," quoth he, "the money will we take, and if he come hither we will tell him, but seek him we will not."

"In God's name," quoth she; and so took farewell of the shepherds, and went her way.

Here one singeth:

> Nicolete the bright of brow
> From the shepherds doth she pass
> All below the blossomed bough
> Where an ancient way there was,
> Overgrown and choked with grass,   5
> Till she found the cross-roads where
> Seven paths do all way fare.
> Then she deemeth she will try,
> Should her lover pass thereby,
> If he love her loyally.   10

So she gathered white lilies,
Oak-leaf, that in green wood is,
Leaves of many a branch I wis,
Therewith built a lodge of green,
Goodlier was never seen,   15
Swore by God who may not lie,
"If my love the lodge should spy,
He will rest awhile thereby
If he love me loyally."
Thus his faith she deemed to try,   20
"Or I love him not, not I,
Nor he loves me!"

Then speak they, say they, tell they the Tale:

(Nicolete being gone, Aucassin is released from prison. So sunk is
he in grief, however, that a friend suggests that he divert himself by
riding in the forest. Here he is given Nicolete's message by the
shepherds.)

Here singeth one:

Aucassin when he had heard,
Sore within his heart was stirred,
Left the shepherds on that word,
Far into the forest spurred
Rode into the wood; and fleet   5
Fled his horse through paths of it,
Three words spake he of his sweet,
"Nicolete the fair, the dear,
'Tis for thee I follow here
Track of boar, nor slot of deer,   10
But thy sweet body and eyes so clear,
All thy mirth and merry cheer,
That my very heart have slain.
So please God to me maintain
I shall see my love again,   15
Sweet sister, friend!"

Then speak they, say they, tell they the Tale:

Aucassin fared through the forest from path to path after Nicolete, and his horse bare him furiously. Think ye not that the thorns

him spared, nor the briars, nay, not so, but tare his raiment, that scarce a knot might be tied with the soundest part thereof, and the blood sprang from his arms, and flanks, and legs, in forty places, or thirty, so that men might follow on the track of his blood in the grass. But so much he went in thoughts of Nicolete, his lady sweet, that he felt no pain nor torment, and all the day hurled through the forest in this fashion nor heard no word of her. Through the night, Aucassin rode on: the night was fair and still, and so long he went that he came to the lodge of boughs, that Nicolete had builded and woven within and without, over and under, with flowers, and it was the fairest lodge that might be seen. When Aucassin was ware of it, he stopped suddenly, and the light of the moon fell therein.

"God!" quoth Aucassin, "here was Nicolete, my sweet lady, and this lodge builded she with her fair hands. For the sweetness of it, and for love of her, will I alight, and rest here this night long."

And he looked through a gap in the lodge and saw the stars in heaven, and one that was brighter than the rest; so began he to say:

Here one singeth:

"Star, that I from far behold,
    Star, the Moon calls to her fold,
    Nicolete with thee doth dwell,
    My sweet love with locks of gold,
    God would have her dwell afar,   5
    Dwell with him for evening star,
    Would to God, whate'er befell,
    Would that with her I might dwell.
    I would clip her close and strait,
    Nay, were I of much estate,   10
    Some king's son desirable,
    Worthy she to be my mate,
    Me to kiss and clip me well,
        Sister, sweet friend!"

So speak they, say they, tell they the Tale:

When Nicolete heard Aucassin, right so came she unto him, for she was not far away. She passed within the lodge, and threw her arms about his neck, and clipped and kissed him.

"Fair sweet friend, welcome be thou."

9. *clip:* hug.

"And thou, fair sweet love, be thou welcome."

So either kissed and clipped the other, and fair joy was them between.

"Aucassin," saith she, "fair sweet love, take counsel what thou wilt do. If thy father let search this forest tomorrow, and men find me here, they will slay me, come to thee what will."

"Certes, fair sweet love, therefore should I sorrow heavily, but, an if I may, never shall they take thee."

Anon gat he on his horse, and his lady before him, and so rode they at adventure.

Here one singeth:

Aucassin the frank, the fair,
Aucassin of the yellow hair,
Gentle knight, and true lover,
From the forest doth he fare,
Holds his love before him there,   5
Kissing cheek, and chin, and eyes.
But she spake in sober wise,
"Aucassin, true love and fair,
To what land do we repair?"
"Sweet my love, I take no care,   10
Thou art with me everywhere!"
So they pass the woods and downs,
Pass the villages and towns,
Hills and dales and open land,
Came at dawn to the sea sand,   15
Lighted down upon the strand,
    Beside the sea.

(A ship takes the lovers to the comical country of Torelore, where war is only a game fought with fresh cheeses and baked apples for weapons and where no one is ever killed in battle. Here they live happily, till pirates seize them and carry them away on separate ships to different countries. Aucassin escapes to his own land. Finding his father dead, he becomes Count of Biaucaire.)

Here singeth one:

Lo ye, Aucassin hath gone
To Biaucaire that is his own,
Dwelleth there in joy and ease
And the kingdom is at peace.

Swears he by the Majesty 5
Of our Lord that is most high,
Rather would he they should die
All his kin and parentry,
So that Nicolete were nigh.
"Ah sweet love, and fair of brow, 10
I know not where to seek thee now,
God made never that countrie,
Not by land, and not by sea,
Where I would not search for thee,
    If that might be!" 15

Then speak they, say they, tell they the Tale:

(By great good luck, the pirates carry Nicolete to Carthage. Now she was really Princess of Carthage, having been stolen from the palace as a child and carried into captivity. She is received with joy and the king her father would have married her to another great pagan ruler, but she dreams day and night only of how she can rejoin Aucassin.)

So she stole forth by night, and came to the seaport, and dwelt with a poor woman thereby. Then took she a certain herb, and therewith smeared her head and her face, till she was all brown and stained. And she let make coat, and mantle, and smock, and hose, and attired herself as if she had been a harper. So took she the viol and went to a mariner, and so wrought on him that he took her aboard his vessel. Then hoisted they sail, and fared on the high seas even till they came to the land of Provence. And Nicolete went forth and took the viol, and went playing through all that country, even till she came to the castle of Biaucaire, where Aucassin lay.

Here one singeth:

At Biaucaire below the tower
Sat Aucassin, on an hour,
Heard the bird, and watched the flower,
With his barons him beside,
Then came on him in that tide, 5
The sweet influence of love
And the memory thereof;
Thought of Nicolete the fair,
And the dainty face of her
He had loved so many years, 10
Then was he in dule and tears!

Even then came Nicolete,
On the stair a foot she set,
And she drew the viol bow
Through the strings and chanted so; 15
"Listen, lords and knights, to me,
Lords of high or low degree,
To my story list will ye
All of Aucassin and her
That was Nicolete the fair? 20
And their love was long to tell.
Deep woods through he sought her well,
Paynims took them on a day
In Torelore and bound they lay.
Of Aucassin naught know we, 25
But fair Nicolete the free
Now in Carthage doth she dwell,
There her father loves her well,
Who is king of that countrie.
Her a husband hath he found, 30
Paynim lord that serves Mahound!
Ne'er with him the maid will go,
For she loves a damoiseau,
Aucassin, that ye may know,
Swears to God that never mo 35
With a lover she will go
Save with him she loveth so
In long desire."

So speak they, say they, tell they the Tale:

(Aucassin eagerly questions the supposed harper as to how he can find his beloved Nicolete. Convinced of his fidelity, Nicolete promises to bring his love to him herself in a short space of time.)

When Aucassin heard that, he was right glad thereof. And she departed from him, and went into the city to the house of the Captain's wife, for the Captain her father in God was dead. So she dwelt there, and told all her tale; and the Captain's wife knew her, and knew well that she was Nicolete that she herself had nourished. Then she let wash and bathe her, and there rested she eight full days. Then took she an herb that was named *Eyebright* and anointed herself therewith, and was as fair as ever she had been all the days of her life. Then she clothed herself in rich robes of silk whereof the lady had great store, and then sat herself in the chamber on a silken coverlet, and called the lady and bade her go and bring Aucassin her love, and she did even so. And when she came to the Palace she found Aucassin weeping, and making lament for Nicolete his love, for that she delayed so long. And the lady spake unto him and said:

"Aucassin, sorrow no more, but come thou on with me, and I will shew thee the thing in the world that thou lovest best; even Nicolete thy dear love, who from far lands hath come to seek of thee." And Aucassin was right glad.

Here singeth one:

When Aucassin heareth now
That his lady bright of brow
Dwelleth in his own countrie,
Never man was glad as he.
To her castle doth he hie   5
With the lady speedily,
Passeth to the chamber high,
Findeth Nicolete thereby.
Of her true love found again
Never maid was half so fain.   10
Straight she leaped upon her feet;
When this love he saw at last,
Arms about her did he cast,
Kissed her often, kissed her sweet,
Kissed her lips and brows and eyes.   15
Thus all night do they devise,
Even till the morning white.
Then Aucassin wedded her,
Made her Lady of Biaucaire.
Many years abode they there,   20
Many years in shade or sun,
In great gladness and delight.
Ne'er hath Aucassin regret
Nor his lady Nicolete.
Now my story all is done,   25
     Said and sung!

THE WINDMILLS

MIGUEL DE CERVANTES (SPAIN)

Translated by George Santayana

In *Don Quixote,* Cervantes writes a parody on the romances of chivalry, showing the extravagances of such tales when contrasted with life's realities. Don Quixote was a poor gentleman whose imagination was so excited by reading old romances of knights wandering the world performing noble deeds and succoring ladies in distress that he started out to search for such adventures. The era of chivalry had long since passed, but he interpreted every ordinary occurrence in terms of these old tales. He persuaded a country fellow named Sancho Panza to accompany him as his squire. Though Sancho half believed Don Quixote, he was a practical sort of fellow who proved very useful to his imaginative master.

❊　❊　❊

Meanwhile Don Quixote worked upon a farm laborer, a neighbor of his, an honest man (if indeed that title can be given to him who is poor), but with very little wit in his pate. In a word, he so talked him over, and with such persuasions and promises, that the poor clown made up his mind to sally forth with him and serve him as esquire. Don Quixote, among other things, told him he ought to be ready to go with him gladly, because at any moment an adventure might occur; he might win an island in the twinkling of an eye and leave him governor of it.

On these and the like promises Sancho Panza (for so the laborer was called) left wife and children, and engaged himself as esquire to his neighbor. Don Quixote next set about getting some money; and selling one thing and pawning another, and making a bad bargain in every case, he got together a fair sum. He provided himself with a buckler, which he begged as a loan from a friend, and restoring his battered helmet as best he could, he warned his squire Sancho of the day and hour he meant to set out, that he might provide himself with what he thought most needful. Above all, he charged him to take a wallet with him. The other said he would, and that he meant to take also a very good ass he had, as he was not much given to going on foot. About the ass, Don Quixote hesitated a little, trying whether he could call to mind any knight-errant taking with him an esquire mounted on ass-back, but no instance occurred to his memory. For all that, however, he determined to take him; intending to furnish him with a more honorable mount when a chance of it presented itself, by appropriating the horse of the first discourteous knight he encountered. Himself he provided with shirts and such other things as he could, according to the advice the host had given him; all which being settled and done, without taking leave, Sancho Panza of his wife and children, or Don Quixote of his housekeeper and niece, they sallied forth unseen by anybody from the village one night, and made such good way in the course of it that by daylight they held themselves safe from discovery, even should search be made for them.

Sancho rode on his ass like a patriarch, with his wallet and leathern bottle and longing to see himself soon governor of the island his master had promised him. Don Quixote decided upon taking the same route and road he had taken on his first journey, that over the Campo de Montiel, which he traveled with less discomfort than on the last occasion; for as it was early morning and the rays of the sun fell on them obliquely, the heat did not distress them.

And now said Sancho Panza to his master, "Your Worship will take care, Señor Knight-Errant, not to forget about the island you have promised me, for be it ever so big I'll be equal to governing it."

To which Don Quixote replied: "Thou must know, friend Sancho Panza, that it was a practice very much in vogue with the knights-errant of old to make their squires governors of the islands or kingdoms they won, and I am determined that there shall be no failure on my part in so liberal a custom; on the contrary, I mean to improve upon it, for they sometimes, and perhaps most frequently, waited until their squires were old, and then when they had had enough of service and hard days and worse nights, they gave them some title or other, of count, or at the most marquis, of some valley or province more or less; but if thou livest and I live, it may well be that before six days are over I may have won some kingdom that has others dependent upon it, which will be just the thing to enable thee to be crowned king of one of them. Nor needst thou count this wonderful, for things and chances fall to the lot of such knights in ways so unexampled and unexpected that I might easily give thee even more than I promise thee."

"In that case," said Sancho Panza, "if I should become a king by one of those miracles your Worship speaks of, even Juana Gutierrez, my old woman, would come to be queen and my children infantas."

"Well, who doubts it?" said Don Quixote.

"I doubt it," replied Sancho Panza, "because for my part I am persuaded that though God should shower down kingdoms upon earth, not one of them would fit the head of Mari Gutierrez. Let me tell you, señor, she is not worth two maravedis for a queen; countess will fit her better, and that only with God's help."

"Leave it to God, Sancho," returned Don Quixote, "for he will give her what suits her best; but do not undervalue thyself so much as to come to be content with anything less than being governor of a province."

"I will not, señor," answered Sancho, "especially as I have a man of such quality for master in your Worship, who will be able to give me all that will be suitable for me and that I can bear."

At this point they came in sight of thirty or forty windmills that there are on that plain, and as soon as Don Quixote saw them he said to his squire, "Fortune is arranging matters for us better than we could have shaped our desires ourselves; for look there, friend Sancho Panza, where thirty or more monstrous giants present themselves, all of whom I mean to engage in battle and slay, and with whose spoils we shall begin to make our fortunes; for this is righteous warfare, and it is God's good service to sweep so evil a breed from off the face of the earth."

"What giants?" said Sancho Panza.

"Those thou seest there," answered his master, "with the long arms; and some have them nearly two leagues long."

"Look, your Worship," said Sancho, "what we see there are not giants but windmills, and what seem to be their arms are the sails that turned by the wind make the millstones go."

"It is easy to see," replied Don Quixote, "that thou art not used to this business of adventures; those are giants; and if thou art afraid, away with thee out of this and betake thyself to prayer, while I engage them in fierce and unequal combat."

So saying, he gave the spur to his steed Rosinante, heedless of the cries his squire Sancho sent after him, warning him that most certainly they were windmills and not giants he was going to attack. He however was so positive that they were giants that he neither heard the cries of Sancho, nor perceived, near as he was, what they were; but made at them, shouting, "Fly not, cowards and vile beings, for it is a single knight that attacks you!"

A slight breeze at this moment sprang up, and the great sails began to move; seeing which, Don Quixote exclaimed, "Though ye flourish more arms that the giant Briareus, ye have to reckon with me."

So saying, and commending himself with all his heart to his lady Dulcinea, imploring her to support him in such a peril, with lance

AS HE DROVE HIS LANCE-POINT INTO THE SAIL IT SHIVERED THE
LANCE TO PIECES, SWEEPING WITH IT HORSE AND RIDER.

in rest and covered by his buckler, he charged at Rosinante's fullest gallop and fell upon the first mill that stood in front of him; but as he drove his lance-point into the sail the wind whirled it round with such force that it shivered the lance to pieces, sweeping with it horse and rider, who went rolling over on the plain in a sorry condition. Sancho hastened to his assistance as fast as his ass could go, and when he came up found him unable to move, with such a shock had Rosinante fallen with him.

"God bless me!" said Sancho, "did I not tell your Worship to mind what you were about, for they were only windmills? and no one could have made any mistake about it but one had something of the same kind in his head."

"Hush, friend Sancho," replied Don Quixote, "the fortunes of war more than any other are liable to frequent fluctuations; and moreover I think, and it is the truth, that that same sage Friston who carried off my study and books has turned these giants into mills in order to rob me of the glory of vanquishing them,—such is the enmity he bears me; but in the end his wicked arts will avail but little against my good sword."

"God order it as he may," said Sancho Panza; and helping him to rise, got him up again on Rosinante, whose shoulder was half out; and then, discussing the late adventure, they followed the road to Puerto Lapice, for there, said Don Quixote, they could not fail to find adventures in abundance and variety, as it was a great thoroughfare.

HE WHO MARRIED A DUMB WIFE

FRANÇOIS RABELAIS (FRANCE)

Translated by Urquhart and Le Motteux

Into *Gargantua and Pantagruel* Rabelais poured all his satire of the devouring greed of the old French royalty, who are personified by two jovial giants, Gargantua and his son Pantagruel, who can eat, drink, and wear enough to feed and clothe a nation. The book is a series of amusing adventures illustrating their eat, drink and be merry philosophy. In it are embedded many a humorous tale and anecdote, such as the following.

❋ ❋ ❋

A good honest man who had married a dumb wife was very earnestly urgent to have the fillet of her tongue untied, and would needs have her speak by all means: At his desire some pains were taken on her, and partly by the industry of the physician, other part by the expertness of the surgeon, the encyliglotte,[1] which she had under her tongue, being cut, she spoke and spoke again; yea, within few hours she spoke so loud, so much, so fiercely, and so long, that her poor husband returned to the same physician for a recipe to make her hold her peace: "There are," quoth the physician, "many proper remedies in our art, to make dumb women speak, but there are none, that ever I could learn therein, to make them silent. The only cure which I have found out, is their husband's deafness." The wretch became within few weeks thereafter, by virtue of some drugs, charms or enchantments, which the physician had prescribed unto him, so deaf, that he could not have heard the thundering of nineteen hundred cannons at a salvo. His wife, perceiving that indeed he was as deaf as a door-nail, and that her scolding was but in vain, sith that he heard her not, she grew stark mad. Some time after, the doctor asked for his fee of the husband; who answered, That truly he was deaf, and so was not able to understand what the tenure of his demand might be. Whereupon the leech bedusted him with a little, I know not what, sort of powder; which rendered him a fool immediately: so great was the stiltificating virtue of that strange kind of pulverized dose. Then did this fool of a husband and his mad wife join together, falling on the doctor and the surgeon, did so scratch, bethwack, and bang them, that they were left half dead upon the place, so furious were the blows which they received.

READING PROBLEMS ON THE ROMANCE

1. *Aucassin and Nicolete:* Point out incidents or details in this story that are highly improbable. How does the plot of this story follow the pattern of a romance of chivalry as described in the introduction? How is the charm of Nicolete indicated? Select passages of unusual freshness and beauty in either the songs or the prose passages. Find examples of exaggerated feeling. The story is not without touches of humor. Find them. Is the story true to the spirit of youthful romance?

2. *The Windmills:* How are the respective characters of the two men made clear in the opening conversation? As this is a parody, the adventures will all be ludicrous. Nevertheless they must be made to seem possible by a stretch of the imagination. How is the windmill episode rendered plausible? How does Don Quixote explain the outcome? Is this story more than a take-off of old romances? Does it burlesque certain familiar types of character?

[1] *encycliglotte:* tendon that was too tight.

3. *He Who Married a Dumb Wife:* Is the humor of this tale due to character or situation? Would developing the characters more fully add interest? Read Anatole France's farce, *A Man Who Married a Dumb Wife* (suggested by this tale in Rabelais), to settle the preceding question. Is the ending of the tale a logical result of the beginning or is it only another joke added for full measure?

FURTHER READINGS IN THE ROMANCE

Malory: *Le Morte D'Arthur*
Anonymous: *Huon of Bordeaux*
Marie de France: *Lays*
Anonymous: *Gawain and the Green Knight*
Tristan and Isolt

Defoe: *Robinson Crusoe*
Swift: *Gulliver's Travels*
Borrow: *Lavengro*
Undset: *Kristin Lavransdatter*
Allen: *Anthony Adverse*

SUGGESTIONS FOR EPISODES FROM ORIGINAL ROMANCES

1. Imaginary episodes from the lives of explorers and heroes of the frontier (Ponce de Leon, Pierre Marquette, Jim Bridger, Daniel Boone, Lewis and Clarke, etc.) or from the early careers of industrial magnates (Carnegie, Rockefeller, Ford). 2. Adventures of a Trailer Family or Traveling Salesman. 3. An Allegory of the Perpetual Relief Taker.

VII

The Epic

THE novel of the ancient world was the epic.[1] It was a long story in verse celebrating the exploits of a hero whose life summed up the life of his people. In primitive society, the leader was of the utmost importance, as his courage, strength, generosity, and gift of command made possible the defense and preservation of his tribe or nation. Therefore the epic hero is always a king, chieftain or noble; the early epic invariably has an aristocratic tone; and the characters speak and act and the author himself talks in an elevated, grand style suitable to the lofty scene of the story. The hero is represented as well-nigh superhuman. He often has supernatural powers, and supernatural forces play a considerable part in the story. None the less, the epic always has a legendary basis; behind it lies a kernel of historic truth. There really was a King Arthur: there really were a Troy and a Trojan war. But these characters, places, and events had grown into legend long before the epic poet fixed them in his tale; and seeing them through the misty haze of distance, he idealized them and drew all the details larger and finer than life, just as the Western frontier is now romanticized in Western stories and on the screen. The names of many heroes were forgotten, and the favorite hero appropriated to himself the exploits of a dozen lesser men; the favorite heroine acquired the suitors, the heartaches, and the joys of a dozen lovely ladies of yesteryear!

Because the epic dealt with familiar legends, the poet who told the story did not need to begin with full explanation of the characters and events leading up to the special adventure he wished to recount. He could and usually did jump immediately into the middle of his story, going back afterward to pick up any necessary threads of antecedent action. As the epic, like the metrical tale, was usually chanted aloud in the hall of chief or king after the evening's meal, each installment had to be complete in itself and

[1] See pages 27–29 in Weeks, Lyman and Hill: *English Literature*.

354

stand alone—as the same audience might not be present another night to hear the continuation of the story. Thus an epic reads like a series of tales.

Before the days of the printed book, the magazine, the motion picture, and easy travel, audiences who listened to the bard or minstrel chant a chapter from a hero epic, pictured with difficulty the scenes and personages in the legendary tale. Hence the poet illustrated his story with word pictures, worked out in minute detail —pictures which stop the flow of the story as we might today stop to examine a lovely colored illustration by Maxfield Parrish or Edmond Dulac or Arthur Wrackham in a *de luxe* edition of a modern book.

Every nation in the world has produced epic hero tales of the folk heroes of its primitive period—written not in primitive days but in the period of settled culture that immediately followed. Greece had its *Iliad* and *Odyssey,* put into final form by a poet named Homer who worked over the many tales told of the Trojan War by his predecessors and gave his compilation of them a unified style. India had its *Ramayana;* France its *Song of Roland;* Spain its story of the Cid; Germany its *Niebelungenlied* or tale of Siegfried; and England its story of King Arthur. These were all based on legends and composed one or two hundred years after the supposed date of the story.

At later periods in the history of certain peoples, artificial epics have been written entirely by one poet in imitation of the genuine folk epics, which were the cumulative efforts of generations of bards and minstrels. There are four famous artificial epics. *The Aeneid* was written in imitation of Homer by the Roman Virgil and narrates a fictitious story of the founding of the Roman race. *The Divine Comedy* by the Italian poet, Dante, is a real summary of the religious faith of the Middle Ages, but is entirely the creation of Dante's own mind. Milton's *Paradise Lost* similarly pictures the faith of the English Puritan world. Longfellow's *Hiawatha* is a compilation of American Indian legends.

The world's great epics are not merely fascinating stories composed for the most part in magnificent poetry. They are also the most reliable, indeed, the only reliable records of the ideals of manhood, manners, customs, and beliefs of the ancient world. In describing Greek civilization before the dawn of history, the modern historian does little more than systematize the information as to methods of warfare, social life, and government scattered through the *Iliad* and *Odyssey*. Studying the epic is using the great source books on which much of history is based. The reader of the epic drinks from the original spring of knowledge, and hears the life he is studying described by the men who lived it and had the genius to see and picture its color and charm.

The thorough student will, then, seek illustrations in the epics he reads of the following distinguishing characteristics of the epic style:

1. The legendary basis
2. The plunge into the midst of the story
3. The completeness of the separate episodes
4. The aristocratic tone of the narrative
5. The elevated style
6. The well-nigh superhuman heroism
7. The supernatural element
8. The frequent pictures in words

He will likewise study with interest the ideals of manhood embodied in the heroic epic characters and compare what primitive man demanded of his heroes with what we ask of heroic characters today. Peculiarly interesting will be the share of women in the epic stories and the traits then admired in heroines of fiction. The student will further seek for details revealing the manners, customs, ideals and beliefs of the ancient world, and by comparing the epics of different races ask himself if he can see there in the germ those racial differences in thought, feeling, and philosophy which still distinguish the Occidental from the Oriental and the Germanic from the Latin races.

THE CRAWL

John Neihardt (America)

The history of the West during the first half of the nineteenth century is the story of the trappers and fur traders who explored the unknown lands west of the Missouri River. In 1823, Major Andrew Henry led such a band of trappers to the Big Horn mountains. Attached to the group was a famous hunter, Hugh Glass, whose job was to provide the party with food. Neihardt tells in *The Song of Hugh Glass* how during an Indian raid Hugh saved the life of a golden-haired youngster named Jamie. The grizzled old scout and the happy-go-lucky lad became fast friends, and Hugh centered upon the boy all the love of a generous lonely heart. Separated from the party for a few days' scouting, Glass was attacked at a spring by a bear. His leg was broken, his body mangled, and when the group discovered him, he was unconscious and apparently at the point of death. As the party must move on, Jamie and another soldier were detailed to stay with Hugh till his death and bury his body to save it from the wolves. Hugh, without regaining consciousness, lingered for four days. As Indians were known to be on the warpath, the two men prepared everything for a quick departure. They dug the grave; stripped Hugh of his knife, flints, rifle, powder and shot; and packed the horses. Then, frightened at each other's stories of Indian massacres, they decamped, leaving the old man unburied but, as they supposed, breathing his last. However, his hardy constitution conquered death. He lived. He woke. He saw the remains of the camp—the open grave. He felt for his knife and rifle. They were gone. He knew what had happened. Jamie had abandoned him. Hate flared in his heart. He was empty-handed in the desert. His broken leg dragged useless. He was 100 miles from the nearest outpost of the white man. But the desire for revenge supported him, and he started to crawl toward the horizon.

* * *

The trailing leg was like a galling chain,
And bound him to a doubt that would not pass.
Defiant clumps of thirst-embittered grass
That bit parched earth with bared and fang-like roots;
Dwarf thickets, jealous for their stunted fruits,   5
Harsh-tempered by their disinheritance—
These symbolized the enmity of Chance
For him who, with his fate unreconciled,
Equipped for travel as a weanling child,
Essayed the journey of a mighty man.   10

Like agitated oil the heat-waves ran
And made the scabrous gulch appear to shake
As some reflected landscape in a lake
Where laggard breezes move. A taunting reek
Rose from the grudging seepage of the creek,   15
Whereof Hugh drank and drank, and still would drink.
And where the mottled shadow dripped as ink
From scanty thickets on the yellow glare,
The crawler faltered with no heart to dare
Again the torture of that toil, until   20
The master-thought of vengeance woke the will

7. *enmity:* hatred. 12. *scabrous:* scurfy, rough.

To goad him forth. And when the sun quiesced
Amid ironic heavens in the West—
The region of false friends—Hugh gained a rise
Whence to the fading cincture of the skies
A purpling panorama swept away.   25

Scarce far⁺her than a shout might carry, lay
The place of his betrayal. He could see
The yellow blotch of earth where treachery
Had digged his grave. O futile wrath and toil!
Tucked in beneath yon coverlet of soil,   30
Turned back for him, how soundly had he slept!
Fool, fool! to struggle when he might have crept
So short a space, yet farther than the flight
Of swiftest dreaming through the longest night,
Into the quiet house of no false friend. . . .   35

Ere noon the crawler chanced upon a feast
Of bread-root sunning in a favored draw.
A sentry gopher from his stronghold saw
Some three-legged beast, bear-like, yet not a bear, 40
With quite misguided fury digging where
No hapless brother gopher might be found.
And while, with stripèd nose above his mound,
The sentinel chirped shrilly to his clan
Scare-tales of that anomaly, the man
Devoured the chance-flung manna of the plains   45
That some vague reminiscence of old rains
Kept succulent, despite the burning drouth.

So with new vigor Hugh assailed the South,
His pockets laden with the precious roots   50
Against the coming traverse, where no fruits
Of herb or vine or shrub might brave the land
Spread rooflike 'twixt the Moreau and the Grand.
The coulee deepened; yellow walls flung high,
Sheer to the ragged strip of blinding sky,   55
Dazzled and sweltered in the glare of day.
Capricious draughts that woke and died away

25. *cincture:* circle. 45. *anomaly:* something unusual. 48. *succulent:* juicy.
53. *Moreau and Grand:* two rivers of the Nebraska, Wyoming, Dakota area.
54. *coulee:* deep water channel, usually dry.

Into the heavy drowse, were breatht as flame.
And midway down the afternoon, Hugh came
Upon a little patch of spongy ground. 60
His thirst became a rage. He gazed around,
Seeking a spring; but all about was dry
As strewn bones bleaching to a desert sky;
Nor did a clawed hole, bought with needed strength,
Return a grateful ooze. And when at length 65
Hugh sucked the mud, he spat it in disgust.
It had the acrid tang of broken trust,
The sweetish, tepid taste of feigning love!

Still hopeful of a spring somewhere above,
He crawled the faster for his taunted thirst. 70
More damp spots, no less grudging than the first,
Occurred with growing frequence on the way,
Until amid the purple wane of day
The crawler came upon a little pool!
Clear as a friend's heart, 'twas, and seeming cool— 75
A crystal bowl whence skyey deeps looked up.
So might a god set down his drinking cup
Charged with a distillation of haut skies.
As famished horses, thrusting to the eyes
Parched muzzles, take a long-sought water-hole, 80
Hugh plunged his head into the brimming bowl
As though to share the joy with every sense.
And lo, the tang of that wide insolence
Of sky and plain was acrid in the draught!
How ripplingly the lying water laughed! 85
How like fine sentiment the mirrored sky
Won credence for a sink of alkali!
So with false friends. And yet, as may accrue
From specious love some profit of the true,
One gift of kindness had the tainted sink. 90
Stripped of his clothes, Hugh let his body drink
At every thirsting pore. Through trunk and limb
The elemental blessing solaced him;
Nor did he rise till, vague with stellar light,
The lone gulch, buttressing an arch of night, 95
Was like a temple to the Holy Ghost.
Like priests in slow procession with the Host,

78. *haut*: haughty.

A gusty breeze intoned—now low, now loud.
Aloft along the dusky architrave
The wander-tale of drifting stars evolved;　　100
And Hugh lay gazing till the whole resolved
Into a haze.
　　　　　　It seemed that Little Jim
Had come to share a merry fire with him,
And there had been no trouble 'twixt the two.
And Jamie listened eagerly while Hugh　　105
Essayed a tangled tale of bears and men,
Bread-root and stars. But ever now and then
The shifting smoke-cloud dimmed the golden hair,
The leal blue eyes; until with sudden flare
The flame effaced them utterly—and lo,　　110
The gulch bank-full with morning!
　　　　　　　　　　　Loath to go,
Hugh lay beside the pool and pondered fate.
He saw his age-long pilgrimage of hate
Stretch out—a fool's trail; and it made him cringe;
But when the sun, a tilted cauldron set　　115
Upon the gulch rim, poured a blaze of day,
He rose and bathed again, and went his way,
Sustaining wrath returning with the toil.

At noon the gulch walls, hewn in lighter soil,
Fell back; and coulees dense with shrub and vine　　120
Climbed zigzag to the sharp horizon line,
Whence one might choose the pilotage of crows.
He labored upward through the noonday doze
Of breathless shade, where plums were turning red
In tangled bowers, and grapevines overhead　　125
Purpled with fruit to taunt the crawler's thirst.
With little effort Hugh attained the first;
The latter bargained sharply ere they sold
Their luscious clusters for the hoarded gold
Of strength that had so very much to buy.　　130
Now, having feasted, it was sweet to lie
Beneath a sun-proof canopy; and sleep
Came swiftly. . . .

99. *architrave*: vault.

Now when the night wore on in middle swoon,
The crawler, roused from stupor, was aware
Of some strange alteration in the air.   135
To breathe became an act of conscious will.
The starry waste was ominously still.
The far-off kiote's yelp came sharp and clear
As through a tunnel in the atmosphere—
A ponderable, resonating mass.   140
The limp leg dragging on the sun-dried grass
Produced a sound unnaturally loud.

Crouched, panting, Hugh looked up but saw no cloud.
An oily film seemed spread upon the sky
Now duly staring as the open eye   145
Of one in fever. Gasping, choked with thirst,
A childish rage assailed Hugh, and he cursed:
And briefly space seemed crowded with the voice.

To wait and die, to move and die—what choice?
Hugh chose not, yet he crawled; though more and more   150
He felt the futile strife was nearly o'er.
And as he went, a muffled rumbling grew,
More felt than heard; for long it puzzled Hugh.
Then suddenly a mountain peak of sound
Came toppling to a heaven-jolting fall!   155
The prairie shuddered, and a raucous drawl
Ran far and perished in the outer deep.

Then—once—twice—thrice—a blade of blinding light
Ripped up the heavens, and the deluge came—
A burst of wind and water, noise and flame   160
That hurled the watcher flat upon the ground.
A moment past Hugh famished; now, half drowned,
He gasped for breath amid the hurtling drench.

Prone to the roaring flaw and ceaseless flare,
The man drank deeply with the drinking grass;   165
Until it seemed the storm would never pass.
Flame, flood, wind, noise and darkness were a river
Tearing a cosmic channel to no sea.

137. *ominously*: threateningly.

The tortured night wore on; then suddenly
Peace fell. Remotely the retreating Wrath　　170
Trailed dull, reluctant thunders in its path,
And up along a broken stair of cloud
The Dawn came creeping whitely. Like a shroud
Gray vapors clung along the sodden plain.
Up rose the sun to wipe the final stain　　175
Of fury from the sky and drink the mist.
Against a flawless arch of amethyst
The butte soared, like a soul serene and white
Because of the katharsis of the night.

All day Hugh fought with sleep and struggled on　　180
Southeastward; for the heavy heat was gone
Despite the naked sun. The blank Northwest
Breathed coolly; the crawler thought it best
To move while yet each little break and hollow
And shallow basin of the bison-wallow　　185
Begrudged the earth and air its dwindling store.
But now that thirst was conquered, more and more
He felt the gnaw of hunger like a rage.
And once, from dozing in a clump of sage,
A lone jackrabbit bounded. As a flame　　190
Hope flared in Hugh, until the memory came
Of him who robbed a sleeping friend and fled.
Then hate and hunger merged; the man saw red,
And momently the hare and Little Jim
Were one blurred mark for murder unto him—　　195
Elusive, taunting, sweet to clutch and tear.
The rabbit paused to scan the crippled bear
That ground its teeth as though it chewed a root.
But when, in witless rage, Hugh drew his boot
And hurled it with a curse, the hare loped off,　　200
Its critic ears turned back, as though to scoff
At silly brutes that threw their legs away.
To southward with a painful pace and slow
He went stiff-jointed; and a gnawing ache
In that hip-wound he had for Jamie's sake
Oft made him groan—nor wrought a tender mood:　　205
The rankling weapon of ingratitude
Was turned again with every puckering twinge.

178. *butte:* a turret-shaped hill, usually isolated.　179. *katharsis:* purging, purification.

Far down the vale a narrow winding fringe
Of wilted green betokened how a spring
There sent a little rill meandering;   210
And Hugh was greatly heartened, for he knew
What fruits and herbs might flourish in the slough,
And thirst, henceforth, should torture not again.

So day on day, despite the crawler's pain
All in the windless, golden autumn weather,   215
These two, as comrades, struggled south together—
The homeless graybeard and the homing rill:
And one was sullen with the lust to kill,
And one went crooning of the moon-wooed vast;
For each the many-fathomed peace at last,   220
But oh the boon of singing on the way!
So came these in the golden fall of day
Unto a sudden turn in the ravine,
Wherefrom Hugh saw a flat of cluttered green
Beneath the further bluffs of the Moreau.   225

With sinking heart he paused and gazed below
Upon the goal of so much toil and pain.
Yon green had seemed a paradise to gain
The while he thirsted where the lonely butte
Looked far and saw no toothsome herb or fruit   230
In all that yellow barren dim with heat.
But now the wasting body cried for meat,
And sickness was upon him. Game would pass,
Nor deign to fear the mighty hunter Glass,
But curiously sniffing, pause to stare.   235

(Suddenly Hugh heard the thunder of a herd of buffalo. They
filled the wooded gully below him, stripping its thickets of leaves and
fruit. He tried to roll a boulder on one of the animals but in vain.)

Yet hope and courage mounted with the sun.
Surely, Hugh thought, some ill-begotten one
Of all that striving mass had lost the strife
And perished in the headlong stream of life—
A feast to fill the bellies of the strong,   240
That still the weak might perish. All day long

He struggled down the stricken vale, nor saw
What thing he sought. But when the twilight awe
Was creeping in, beyond a bend arose
A din as though the kiotes and the crows
Fought there with shrill and raucous battle cries. 245

Small need had Hugh to ponder and surmise
What guerdon beak and fang contended for.
Within himself the oldest cause of war
Brought forth upon the instant fang and beak. 250
He too would fight! Nor had he far to seek
Amid the driftwood strewn about the sand
For weapons suited to a brawny hand
With such a purpose. Armed with club and stone
He forged ahead into the battle zone, 255
And from a screening thicket spied his foes.

He saw a bison carcass black with crows,
And over it a welter of black wings,
And round about, a press of tawny rings
That, like a muddy current churned to foam 260
Upon a snag, flashed whitely in the gloam
With naked teeth; while close about the prize
Red beaks and muzzles bloody to the eyes
Betrayed how worth a struggle was the feast.

Then came on Hugh the fury of the beast— 265
To eat or to be eaten! Better so
To die contending with a living foe,
Than fight the yielding distance and the lack.
Masked by the brush he opened the attack,
And ever where a stone or club fell true, 270
About the stricken one an uproar grew
And brute tore brute, forgetful of the prey,
Until the whole pack tumbled in the fray
With bleeding flanks and lacerated throats.
Then, as the leader of a host who notes 275
The cannon-wrought confusion of the foe,
Hugh seized the moment for a daring blow.
The wolf's a coward, who, in goodly packs,
May counterfeit the courage that he lacks

And with a craven's fury crush the bold.   280
But when the disunited mass that rolled
In suicidal strife, became aware
How some great beast that shambled like a bear
Bore down with roaring challenge, fell a hush
Upon the pack, some slinking to the brush   285
With tails a-droop; while some that whined in pain
Writhed off on reddened trails. With bristled mane
Before the flying stones a bolder few
Snarled menace at the foe as they withdrew
To fill the outer dusk with clamorings.   290
Aloft upon a moaning wind of wings
The crows with harsh, vituperative cries
Now saw a gray wolf of prodigious size
Devouring with the frenzy of the starved.
Thus fell to Hugh a bison killed and carved. . . . 295
But with the facing of the afterglow
The routed wolves found courage to return:
Amid the brush Hugh saw their eye-balls burn;
And well he knew how futile stick and stone
Should prove by night to keep them from their own. 300
Better is less with safety, than enough
With ruin. He retreated to a bluff,
And scarce had reached it when the pack swooped in
Upon the carcass.
           All night long, the din
Of wrangling wolves assailed the starry air,   305
While high above them in a brushy lair
Hugh dreamed of gnawing at the bloody feast.

Along about the blanching of the east,
. . . as light in smoke,
Upon the jumble of Hugh's dreaming broke
A buzz of human voices.
              But when again the sound   310
Grew up, and seemed to come from under ground,
He cast the drowse, and peering down the slope,
Beheld what set at grapple fear and hope—
Three Indian horsemen riding at a jog!
Their ponies, wading belly-deep in fog,   315
That clung along the valley, seemed to swim,
And through a thinner vapor moving dim,

The men were ghost-like.
                          Could they be the Sioux?
Almost the wish became belief in Hugh.
Or were they Rees? As readily the doubt   320
Withheld him from the hazard of a shout.
And while he followed them with baffled gaze,
Grown large and vague, dissolving in the haze,
They vanished westward.

(Shortly the whole tribe of the Rees driven northward by hunger
on the trail of the buffalo passed through the valley below Hugh. He
feared the ranging dogs would smell him out, and huddled closer in his
covered nook. After all had passed, he waited till sundown to move
on.)

Scarce had he crossed the open flat, and won   325
The half-way fringe of willows, when he saw,
Slow plodding up the trail, a tottering squaw
Whose years made big the little pack she bore.
Crouched in the brush Hugh watched her. More and more
The little burden tempted him. Why not?   330
A thin cry throttled in that lonely spot
Could bring no succor. None should ever know,
Save him, the feasted kiote and the crow,
Why one poor crone found not the midnight fire.
Nor would the vanguard, quick with young desire,   335
Devouring distance westward like a flame,
Regret this ash dropped rearward.

                              On she came,
Slow-footed, staring blankly on the sand—
So close now that it needed but a hand
Out-thrust to overthrow her; aye, to win   340
That priceless spoil, a little tent of skin,
A flint and steel, a kettle and a knife!
What did the dying with the means of life,
That thus the fit-to-live should suffer lack?

Poised for the lunge, what whimsy held him back?   345
Why did he gaze upon the passing prize,
Nor seize it? Did some gust of ghostly cries

318. *Sioux:* friendly Indians. 320. *Rees:* hostile Indians.

Awaken round her—whisperings of Eld,
Wraith-voices of the babies she had held—
To plead for pity on her graveward days? 350
Far down a moment's cleavage in the haze
Of backward years Hugh saw her now—nor saw
The little burden and the feeble squaw,
But someone sitting haloed like a saint
Beside a hearth long cold. The dream grew faint; 355
And when he looked again, the crone was gone
Beyond a clump of willow.
                              Crawling on,
He reached the river. Leaning to a pool
Calm in its cup of sand, he saw—a fool.
A wild, wry mask of mirth, a-grin, yet grim, 360
Rose there to claim identity with him
And ridicule his folly. Pity? Faugh!
Who pitied this, that it should spare a squaw
Spent in the spawning of a scorpion brood?

(Creeping on through the twilight, Hugh smelled wood smoke,
and came on the day-old camp ground of the Indians where a fire was
still smouldering.)

Glad-hearted now, Hugh gained the vale below, 365
Keen to possess once more the ancient gift.
Nearing the glow, he saw vague shadows lift
Out of the painted gloom of smouldering logs—
Distorted bulks that bristled, and were dogs
Snarling at this invasion of their lair. 370
Hugh charged upon them, growling like a bear,
And sent them whining.
                          Now again to view
The burgeoning of scarlet, gold and blue,
The immemorial miracle of fire!
From heaped-up twigs a tenuous smoky spire 375
Arose, and made an altar of the place.
The spark-glow, faint upon the grizzled face,
Transformed the kneeling outcast to a priest;
And, native of the light-begetting East,
The Wind, became a chanting acolyte. 380
These two, entempled in the vaulted night,

348. *Eld:* old. 380. *acolyte:* a priest.

Breathed conjuries of interwoven breath.
Then, hark!—the snapping of the chains of Death!
From dead wood, lo!—the epiphanic god!

Light-heartedly he fed the singing flame   385
And took its blessing: till a soft sleep came
With dreaming that was like a pleasant tale.

The far white dawn was peering up the vale
When he awoke to indolent content.
A few shorn stars in pale astonishment   390
Were huddled westward; and the fire was low.
Three scrawny camp-curs, mustered in a row
Beyond the heap of embers, heads askew,
Ears pricked to question what the man might do.
Sat wistfully regardant. He arose;   395
And they, grown canny in a school of blows
Skulked to a safer distance, there to raise
A dolorous chanting of the evil days,
Their gray breath like the body of a prayer.
Hugh nursed the sullen embers to a flare,   400
He knew that he could finish in the race.
The staring impassivity of space
No longer mocked; the dreadful skyward climb,
Where distance seemed identical with time,
Was past now; and that mystic something, luck,   405
Without which worth may flounder in the ruck,
Had turned to him again.
                         So flamelike soared
Rekindled hope in him as he explored
Among the ash-heaps; and the lean dogs ran
And barked about him, for the love of man   410
Wistful, yet fearing. Surely he could find
Some trifle in the hurry left behind—
Or haply hidden in the trampled sand—
That to the cunning of a needy hand
Should prove the master-key of circumstance: 415
For 'tis the little gifts of grudging Chance,
Well husbanded, make victors.
                              Long he sought
Without avail; and, crawling back, he thought

384. *epiphanic:* revealed, manifested.

Of how the dogs were growing less afraid,
And how one might be skinned without a blade.   420
A flake of flint might do it: he would try.
And then he saw—or did the servile eye
Trick out a mental image like the real?
He saw a glimmering of whetted steel
Beside a heap now washed with morning light!   425

Scarce more of marvel and the sense of might
Moved Arthur when he reached a hand to take
The fay-wrought brand emerging from the lake,
Whereby a kingdom should be lopped of strife,
Than Hugh now, pouncing on a trader's knife   430
Worn hollow in the use of bounteous days!

'Twixt urging hunger and restraining fear
The gaunt dogs, hovered round the man; while he
Cajoled them in the language of the Ree
And simulated feeding them with sand,   435
Until the boldest dared to sniff his hand,
Bare-fanged and with conciliative whine.
Through bristled mane the quick blade bit the spine
Below the skull; and as a flame-struck thing
The body humped and shuddered, withering;   440
The lank limbs huddled, wilted.

                            Now to skin
The carcass, dig a hole, arrange therein
And fix the pelt with stakes, the flesh-side up.
This done, he shaped the bladder to a cup
On willow witches, and filled the rawhide pot   445
With water from the river—made it hot
With roasted stones, and set the meat a-boil.
Those days of famine and prodigious toil
Had wrought bulimic cravings in the man,
And scarce the cooking of the flesh outran   450
The eating of it. As a fed flame towers
According to the fuel it devours,
His hunger with indulgence grew, nor ceased
Until the kettle, empty of the feast,
Went dim, the sky and valley, merging, swirled   455
In subtle smoke that smothered out the world.
Hugh slept.

426–429. The reference is to King Arthur's taking his sword from the fairy
Lady of the Lake. 449. *bulimic:* voracious, devouring.

(While he slept, the fire died out. Not a spark was left in the ashes when he waked. However, Hugh struck a spark from a flake of flint with his steel knife and rekindled the flame. Then he carved a pair of crutches and, upright at last, rapidly forged ahead.)

So day on day he toiled; and when, afloat
Above the sunset like a stygian boat,
The new moon bore the spectre of the old,   460
He saw—a dwindling strip of blue outrolled—
The valley of the tortuous Cheyenne.
And ere the half moon sailed the night again,
Those far lone leagues had sloughed their garb of blue,
And dwindled, dwindled, dwindled after Hugh,   465
Until he saw that Titan of the plains,
The sinewy Missouri. Dearth of rains
Had made the Giant gaunt as he who saw.
This loud Chain-Smasher of a late March thaw
Seemed never to have bellowed at his banks;   470
And yet, with staring ribs and hollow flanks,
The urge of an indomitable will
Proclaimed him of the breed of giants still;
And where the current ran a boiling track,
'Twas like the muscles of a mighty back   475
Grown Atlantean in the wrestler's craft.

Hugh set to work and built a little raft,
Of driftwood bound with grapevines. So it fell
That one with an amazing tale to tell
Came drifting to the gates of Kiowa.   480

(For the first of the story and for the dramatic ending, we must refer you to the poem itself.)

SOHRAB AND RUSTUM

From the Shah Nameh (Persia)

Translated very freely by Matthew Arnold

The *Shah Nameh* is an ancient book of Persian hero tales from the feudal era of the Orient. In it we read how, when the hostile armies of

459. *stygian boat:* boat in which the dead crossed the River Styx to the after world. 476. *Atlantean:* powerful as those of the giant Atlas, who was fabled to support the sky on his shoulders.

the Tartars and the Persians were drawn up for battle, the Tartars challenged the Persians to choose a champion to meet their champion, Sohrab, in single combat. Young Sohrab had sought far and wide for his famous Persian father, the mighty Rustum, whom he had never seen. He thought that if he won this combat, his fame would reach Rustum's ears. Sohrab was unaware that Rustum never knew he had a son but supposed the baby born to Sohrab's mother was a girl, and so had never returned to claim it. The Persian chiefs, who knew they had no champion to match Sohrab, hold a hasty council. News was brought that Rustum, who long ago quarreled with the Persian king and withdrew from the army, had arrived in camp during the night. Rustum at first refused to accept the challenge, but stung by the taunt that people would say he feared to risk his fame against a younger man, he agreed to fight—but unknown and in plain arms.

❊ ❊ ❊

But Rustum strode to his tent-door, and called
His followers in, and bade them bring his arms,
And clad himself in steel; the arms he chose
Were plain, and on his shield was no device,
Only his helm was rich, inlaid with gold,   5
And, from the fluted spine atop, a plume
Of horsehair waved, a scarlet horsehair plume.
So armed, he issued forth; and Ruksh, his horse,
Followed him like a faithful hound, at heel,
Ruksh, whose renown was noised through all the earth—   10
The horse whom Rustum on a foray once
Did in Bokhara by the river find
A colt beneath its dam, and drove him home,
And reared him—a bright bay, with lofty crest,
Dight with a saddlecloth of broidered green   15
Crusted with gold, and on the ground were worked
All beasts of chase, all beasts which hunters know.
So followed, Rustum left his tents, and crossed
The camp, and to the Persian host appeared.
And all the Persians knew him, and with shouts   20
Hailed; but the Tartars knew not who he was.
And dear as the wet diver to the eyes
Of his pale wife who waits and weeps on shore,
By sandy Bahrein, in the Persian Gulf,
Plunging all day in the blue waves, at night,   25

15. *Dight:* adorned. 24. *Bahrein:* islands noted for pearl fisheries.

Having made up his tale of precious pearls,
Rejoins her in their hut upon the sands—
So dear, to the pale Persians Rustum came.

And Rustum to the Persian front advanced,
And Sohrab armed in Haman's tent, and came.   30
And as afield the reapers cut a swath
Down through the middle of a rich man's corn,
And on each side are squares of standing corn,
And in the midst a stubble, short and bare—
So on each side were squares of men, with spears   35
Bristling, and in the midst, the open sand.
And Rustum came upon the sand, and cast
His eyes toward the Tartar tents, and saw
Sohrab come forth, and eyed him as he came.

As some rich woman, on a winter's morn,   40
Eyes through her silken curtains the poor drudge
Who with numb blackened fingers makes her fire
At cockcrow, on a starlit winter's morn,
When the frost flowers the whitened windowpanes,
And wonders how she lives, and what the thoughts   45
Of that poor drudge may be—so Rustum eyed
The unknown, adventurous youth, who from afar
Came seeking Rustum, and defying forth
All the most valiant chiefs. Long he perused
His spirited air, and wondered who he was;   50
For very young he seemed, tenderly reared;
Like some young cypress, tall, and dark, and straight,
Which in a queen's secluded garden throws
Its slight dark shadow on the moonlit turf,
By midnight, to a bubbling fountain's sound—   55
So slender Sohrab seemed, so softly reared.
And a deep pity entered Rustum's soul
As he beheld him coming; and he stood,
And beckoned to him with his hand, and said:

"O thou young man, the air of heaven is soft,   60
And warm, and pleasant; but the grave is cold!
Heaven's air is better than the cold, dead grave.

26. *tale:* quota.

Behold me; I am vast, and clad in iron,
And tried; and I have stood on many a field
Of blood, and I have fought with many a foe—   65
Never was that field lost, or that foe saved.
O Sohrab, wherefore wilt thou rush on death?
Be governed! quit the Tartar host, and come
To Iran, and be as my son to me,
And fight beneath my banner till I die!   70
There are no youths in Iran brave as thou."

So he spake, mildly; Sohrab heard his voice,
The mighty voice of Rustum, and he saw
His giant figure planted on the sand,
Sole, like some single tower, which a chief   75
Hath builded on the waste in former years
Against the robbers; and he saw that head,
Streaked with its first gray hairs; hope filled his soul,
And he ran forward and embraced his knees,
And clasped his hand within his own, and said: 80

"Oh, by thy father's head! by thine own soul!
Art thou not Rustum? Speak! art thou not he?"

But Rustum eyed askance the kneeling youth,
And turned away, and spake to his own soul:

"Ah me, I muse what this young fox may mean!   85
False, wily, boastful, are these Tartar boys.
For if I now confess this thing he asks,
And hide it not, but say: 'Rustum is here!'
He will not yield indeed, nor quit our foes
But he will find some pretext not to fight,   90
And praise my fame, and proffer courteous gifts,
A belt or sword, perhaps, and go his way.
And on a feast day, in Afrasiab's hall,
In Samarcand, he will arise and cry,
'I challenged once, when the two armies camped   95
Beside the Oxus, all the Persian lords
To cope with me in single fight; but they
Shrank, only Rustum dared; then he and I
Changed gifts, and went on equal terms away.'
So will he speak, perhaps, while men applaud.   100
Then were the chiefs of Iran shamed through me."

And then he turned, and sternly spake aloud:
"Rise! wherefore dost thou vainly question thus
Of Rustum? I am here, whom thou hast called
By challenge forth; make good thy vaunt, or yield! 105
Is it with Rustum only thou wouldst fight?
Rash boy, men look on Rustum's face and flee!
For well I know, that did great Rustum stand
Before thy face this day, and were revealed,
There would be then no talk of fighting more. 110
But being what I am, I tell thee this—
Do thou record it in thine inmost soul—
Either thou shalt renounce thy vaunt and yield,
Or else thy bones shall strew this sand, till winds
Bleach them, or Oxus with his summer-floods, 115
Oxus in summer, wash them all away."

He spoke; and Sohrab answered, on his feet:
"Art thou so fierce? Thou wilt not fright me so!
I am no girl, to be made pale by words.
Yet this thou hast said well, did Rustum stand 120
Here on this field, there were no fighting then.
But Rustum is far hence, and we stand here.
Begin! thou art more vast, more dread than I,
And thou art proved, I know, and I am young.
But yet success sways with the breath of Heaven; 125
And though thou thinkest that thou knowest sure
Thy victory, yet thou canst not surely know;
For we are all, like swimmers in the sea,
Poised on the top of a huge wave of fate,
Which hangs, uncertain to which side to fall, 130
And whether it will heave us up to land,
Or whether it will roll us out to sea,
Back out to sea, to the deep waves of death,
We know not, and no search will make us know;
Only the event will teach us, in its hour." 135

He spoke, and Rustum answered not, but hurled
His spear. Down from the shoulder, down it came,
As on some partridge in the corn a hawk,
That long has towered in the airy clouds,
Drops like a plummet. Sohrab saw it come, 140
And sprang aside, quick as a flash; the spear

Hissed, and went quivering down into the sand,
Which it sent flying wide; then Sohrab threw
In turn, and full struck, Rustum's shield sharp rang,
The iron plates rang sharp, but turned the spear. 145
And Rustum seized his club, which none but he
Could wield; an unlopped trunk it was, and huge,
Still rough—like those which men in treeless plains,
To build them boats, fish from the flooded rivers,
Hyphasis or Hydaspes, when, high up 150
By their dark springs, the wind in wintertime
Hath made in Himalayan forests wrack,
And strewn the channels with torn boughs; so huge
The club which Rustum lifted now, and struck
One stroke. But again Sohrab sprang aside, 155
Lithe as the glancing snake, and the club came
Thundering to earth, and leaped from Rustum's hand.
And Rustum followed his own blow, and fell
To his knees, and with his fingers clutched the sand;
And now might Sohrab have unsheathed his sword, 160
And pierced the mighty Rustum while he lay
Dizzy, and on his knees, and choked with sand;
But he looked on, and smiled, nor bared his sword,
But courteously drew back, and spoke, and said:

"Thou strik'st too hard! that club of thine will float 195
Upon the summer-floods, and not my bones.
But rise, and be not wroth! not wroth am I;
No, when I see thee, wrath forsakes my soul.
Thou say'st thou art not Rustum; be it so!
Who art thou then, that canst so touch my soul? 170
Boy as I am, I have seen battles too,
Have waded foremost in their bloody waves,
And heard their hollow roar of dying men,
But never was my heart thus touched before.
Are they from Heaven, these softenings of the heart? 175
O thou old warrior, let us yield to Heaven!
Come, plant we here in earth our angry spears,
And make a truce, and sit upon this sand,
And pledge each other in red wine, like friends;
And thou shalt talk to me of Rustum's deeds. 180
There are enough foes in the Persian host,

150. *Hyphasis, Hydaspes:* rivers in northern India. 152. *wrack:* destruction.

Whom I may meet, and strike, and feel no pang;
Champions enough Afrasiab has, whom thou
Mayst fight; fight *them,* when they confront thy spear!
But oh, let there be peace 'twixt thee and me!"   185

He ceased, but while he spake, Rustum had risen
And stood erect, trembling with rage; his club
He left to lie, but had regained his spear,
Whose fiery point now in his mailed right hand
Blazed bright and baleful, like that autumn-star,   190
The baleful sign of fevers; dust had soiled
His stately crest and dimmed his glittering arms.
His breast heaved, his lips foamed, and twice his voice
Was choked with rage; at last these words broke way:

"Girl! nimble with thy feet, not with thy hands!   195
Curled minion, dancer, coiner of sweet words!
Fight! let me hear thy hateful voice no more.
Thou art not in Afrasiab's gardens now
With Tartar girls, with whom thou art wont to dance,
But on the Oxus sands, and in the dance   200
Of battle, and with me, who make no play
Of war; I fight it out, and hand to hand.
Speak not to me of truce, and pledge, and wine!
Remember all thy valor; try thy feints
And cunning! All the pity I had is gone,   205
Because thou hast shamed me before both the hosts
With thy light, skipping tricks, and thy girl's wiles."

He spoke; and Sohrab kindled at his taunts,
And he too drew his sword. At once they rushed
Together, as two eagles on one prey   210
Come rushing down together from the clouds,
One from the east, one from the west. Their shields
Dashed with a clang together, and a din
Rose, such as that the sinewy woodcutters
Make often in the forest's heart at morn,   215
Of hewing axes, crashing trees—such blows
Rustum and Sohrab on each other hailed.
And you would say that sun and stars took part
In that unnatural conflict; for a cloud

190. *autumn-star:* Sirius, the Dog Star.

Grew suddenly in heaven, and darked the sun 220
Over the fighters' heads; and a wind rose
Under their feet, and moaning swept the plain,
And in a sandy whirlwind wrapped the pair.
In gloom they twain were wrapped, and they alone;
For both the on-looking hosts on either hand 225
Stood in broad daylight, and the sky was pure,
And the sun sparkled on the Oxus stream.
But in the gloom they fought, with bloodshot eyes
And laboring breath. First Rustum struck the shield
Which Sohrab held stiff out; the steel-piked spear 230
Rent the tough plates, but failed to reach the skin,
And Rustum plucked it back with angry groan.
Then Sohrab with his sword smote Rustum's helm,
Nor clove its steel quite through; but all the crest
He shore away, and that proud horsehair plume, 235
Never till now defiled, sank to the dust;
And Rustum bowed his head; but then the gloom
Grew blacker, thunder rumbled in the air,
And lightnings rent the cloud; and Ruksh, the horse,
Who stood at hand, uttered a dreadful cry— 240
No horse's cry was that, most like the roar
Of some pained desert lion, who all day
Hath trailed the hunter's javelin in his side,
And comes, at night, to die upon the sand.
The two hosts heard that cry, and quaked for fear, 245
And Oxus curdled as it crossed his stream.
But Sohrab heard, and quailed not, but rushed on,
And struck again; and again Rustum bowed
His head; but this time all the blade, like glass,
Sprang in a thousand shivers on the helm, 250
And in the hand the hilt remained alone.
Then Rustum raised his head; his dreadful eyes
Glared, and he shook on high his menacing spear,
And shouted, *"Rustum!"*—Sohrab heard that shout,
And shrank amazed; back he recoiled one step, 255
And scanned with blinking eyes the advancing form;
And then he stood bewildered; and he dropped
His covering shield, and the spear pierced his side.
He reeled, and staggering back, sank to the ground;
And then the gloom dispersed, and the wind fell, 260
And the bright sun broke forth, and melted all

The cloud; and the two armies saw the pair,
Saw Rustum standing, safe upon his feet,
And Sohrab, wounded, on the bloody sand.

Then, with a bitter smile, Rustum began: 265
"Sohrab, thou thoughtest in thy mind to kill
A Persian lord this day, and strip his corpse,
And bear thy trophies to Afrasiab's tent,
Or else that the great Rustum would come down
Himself to fight, and that thy wiles would move 270
His heart to take a gift, and let thee go.
And then that all the Tartar host would praise
Thy courage or thy craft, and spread thy fame,
To glad thy father in his weak old age.
Fool, thou art slain, and by an unknown man! 275
Dearer to the red jackals shalt thou be
Than to thy friends, and to thy father old."

And, with a fearless mien, Sohrab replied:
"Unknown thou art; yet thy fierce vaunt is vain.
Thou dost not slay me, proud and boastful man! 280
No! Rustum slays me, and this filial heart.
For were I matched with ten such men as thee,
And I were that which till today I was,
They should be lying here, I standing there.
But that belovèd name unnerved my arm, 285
That name, and something, I confess, in thee,
Which troubles all my heart, and made my shield
Fall; and thy spear transfixed an unarmed foe.
And now thou boastest, and insult'st my fate.
But hear thou this, fierce man, tremble to hear: 290
The mighty Rustum shall avenge my death,
My father, whom I seek through all the world!
He shall avenge my death, and punish thee."

As when some hunter in the spring hath found
A breeding eagle sitting on her nest, 295
Upon the craggy isle of a hill-lake,
And pierced her with an arrow as she rose,
And followed her to find her where she fell
Far off—anon her mate comes winging back
From hunting, and a great way off descries 300

His huddling young left sole; at that, he checks
His pinion, and with short, uneasy sweeps
Circles above his aerie, with loud screams
Chiding his mate back to her nest; but she
Lies dying, with the arrow in her side,   305
In some far, stony gorge out of his ken,
A heap of fluttering feathers. Never more
Shall the lake glass her, flying over it;
Never the black and dripping precipices
Echo her stormy scream as she sails by.   310
As that poor bird flies home, nor knows his loss,
So Rustum knew not his own loss, but stood
Over his dying son, and knew him not.

But with a cold incredulous voice, he said:
"What prate is this of fathers and revenge?   315
The mighty Rustum never had a son."
And, with a failing voice, Sohrab replied:
"Ah, yes, he had; and that lost son am I.
Surely the news will one day reach his ear,
Reach Rustum, where he sits, and tarries long,   320
Somewhere, I know not where, but far from here,
And pierce him like a stab, and make him leap
To arms, and cry for vengeance upon thee,
Fierce man, bethink thee! for an only son.
What will that grief, what will that vengeance be?   325
Oh, could I live till I that grief had seen!
Yet him I pity not so much, but her,
My mother, who in Ader-baijan dwells
With that old King, her father, who grows gray
With age, and rules over the valiant Koords.   330
Her most I pity, who no more will see
Sohrab returning from the Tartar camp,
With spoils and honor, when the war is done.
But a dark rumor will be bruited up,
From tribe to tribe, until it reach her ear;   335
And then will that defenseless woman learn
That Sohrab will rejoice her sight no more,
But that in battle with a nameless foe.
By the far-distant Oxus, he is slain."

306. *ken:* beyond his knowledge. 308. *glass:* mirror. 330. *Koords:* tribes in
Central Asia. 334. *bruited up:* noised about.

He spoke; and as he ceased, he wept aloud,   340
Thinking of her he left, and his own death.
He spoke; but Rustum listened, plunged in thought,
Nor did he yet believe it was his son
Who spoke, although he called back names he knew;
For he had had sure tidings that the babe,   345
Which was in Ader-baijan born to him,
Had been a puny girl, no boy at all—
So that sad mother sent him word, for fear
Rustum should seek the boy, to train in arms.
And so he deemed that either Sohrab took,   350
By a false boast, the style of Rustum's son,
Or that men gave it him, to swell his fame.
So deemed he; yet he listened, plunged in thought.
And his soul set to grief, as the vast tide
Of the bright rocking ocean sets to shore   355
At the full moon; tears gathered in his eyes,
For he remembered his own early youth,
And all its bounding rapture; as, at dawn,
The shepherd from his mountain-lodge descries
A far, bright city, smitten by the sun,   360
Through many rolling clouds—so Rustum saw
His youth; saw Sohrab's mother, in her bloom;
And that old King, her father, who loved well
His wandering guest, and gave him his fair child
With joy; and all the pleasant life they led,   365
They three, in that long-distant summer time;
The castle, and the dewy woods, and hunt
And hound, and morn on those delightful hills
In Ader-baijan. And he saw that youth,
Of age and looks to be his own dear son,   370
Piteous and lovely, lying on the sand,
Like some rich hyacinth which by the scythe
Of an unskillful gardener has been cut,
Mowing the garden grassplots near its bed,
And lies, a fragrant tower of purple bloom,   375
On the mown, dying grass; so Sohrab lay,
Lovely in death, upon the common sand.
And Rustum gazed on him with grief, and said:

"O Sohrab, thou indeed art such a son
Whom Rustum, wert thou his, might well have loved.   380

Yet here thou errest, Sohrab, or else men
Have told thee false; thou art not Rustum's son,
For Rustum had no son; one child he had,
But one, a girl who with her mother now
Plies some light female task, nor dreams of us;   385
Of us she dreams not, nor of wounds, nor war."

But Sohrab answered him in wrath; for now
The anguish of the deep-fixed spear grew fierce,
And he desirèd to draw forth the steel,
And let the blood flow free, and so to die;   390
But first he would convince his stubborn foe.
And, rising sternly on one arm, he said:

"Man, who art thou who dost deny my words?
Truth sits upon the lips of dying men;
And falsehood, while I lived, was far from mine.   395
I tell thee, pricked upon this arm I bear
That seal which Rustum to my mother gave,
That she might prick it on the babe she bore."

He spoke; and all the blood left Rustum's cheeks.
And his knees tottered, and he smote his hand   400
Against his breast, his heavy-mailèd hand,
That the hard iron corselet clanked aloud;
And to his heart he pressed the other hand,
And in a hollow voice he spake, and said:

"Sohrab, that were a proof which could not lie!   405
If thou show this, then art thou Rustum's son."

Then, with weak, hasty fingers, Sohrab loosed
His belt, and near the shoulder bared his arm,
And showed a sign in faint vermilion points
Pricked. As a cunning workman, in Pekin,   410
Pricks with vermilion some clear porcelain vase,
An emperor's gift; at early morn he paints,
And all day long; and, when night comes, the lamp
Lights up his studious forehead and thin hands—
So delicately pricked the sign appeared   415
On Sohrab's arm, the sign of Rustum's seal.
It was that griffin, which of old reared Zal,

Rustum's great father, whom they left to die,
A helpless babe, among the mountain-rocks;
Him that kind creature found, and reared, and loved.   420
Then Rustum took it for his glorious sign.
And Sohrab bared that image on his arm,
And himself scanned it long with mournful eyes,
And then he touched it with his hand, and said:

"How say'st thou? Is that sign the proper sign   425
Of Rustum's son, or of some other man's?"

He spoke; but Rustum gazed, and gazed, and stood
Speechless; and then he uttered one sharp cry:
"O boy—thy father!" and his voice choked there.
And then a dark cloud passed before his eyes,   430
And his head swam, and he sank down to earth.
But Sohrab crawled to where he lay, and cast
His arms about his neck, and kissed his lips,
And with fond, faltering fingers stroked his cheeks,
Trying to call him back to life; and life   435
Came back to Rustum; and he oped his eyes,
And they stood wide with horror; and he seized
In both his hands the dust which lay around,
And threw it on his head, and smirched his hair,
His hair, and face, and beard, and glittering arms;   440
And strong, convulsive groanings shook his breast,
And his sobs choked him; and he clutched his sword,
To draw it, and forever let life out.
But Sohrab saw his thought, and held his hands,
And with a soothing voice he spake, and said: 445

"Father, forbear! for I but meet today
The doom which at my birth was written down
In Heaven; and thou art Heaven's unconscious hand.
Surely my heart cried out that it was thou,
When first I saw thee; and thy heart spoke too,   450
I know it; but fate trod those promptings down
Under its iron heel; fate, fate engaged
The strife, and hurled me on my father's spear.
But let us speak no more of this. I find
My father; let me feel that I have found!   455

Come, sit beside me on this sand, and take
My head betwixt thy hands, and kiss my cheeks,
And wash them with thy tears, and say, '*My son!*'
Quick! quick! for numbered are my sands of life,
And swift; for like the lightning to this field
I came, and like the wind I go away— 460
Sudden, and swift, and like a passing wind.
But it was writ in Heaven that this should be."

So said he, and his voice released the heart
Of Rustum, and his tears broke forth; he cast 465
His arms round his son's neck, and wept aloud,
And kissed him. And awe fell on both the hosts,
When they saw Rustum's grief; and Ruksh, the horse,
With his head bowing to the ground, and mane
Sweeping the dust, came near, and in mute woe 470
First to the one, then to the other, moved
His head, as if inquiring what their grief
Might mean; and from his dark, compassionate eyes,
The big warm tears rolled down, and caked the sand.
But Rustum chid him with stern voice, and said: 475

"Ruksh, now thou grievest; but, O Ruksh, thy feet
Should first have rotted on their nimble joints,
Or e'er they brought thy master to this field!"

But Sohrab looked upon the horse and said:
"Is this, then, Ruksh? How often, in past days, 480
My mother told me of thee, thou brave steed,
My terrible father's terrible horse! and said
That I should one day find thy lord and thee.
Come, let me lay my hand upon thy mane!
O Ruksh, thou art more fortunate than I; 485
For thou hast gone where I shall never go,
And snuffed the breezes of my father's home.
And thou hast trod the sands of Seïstan,
And seen the River of Helmund, and the Lake
Of Zirrah; and the aged Zal himself 490
Has often stroked thy neck, and given thee food,
Corn in a golden platter, soaked with wine,
And said, '*O Ruksh, bear Rustum well!*'—but I
Have never known my grandsire's furrowed face,

Nor seen his lofty house in Seïstan,   495
Nor slaked my thirst at the clear Helmund stream;
But lodged among my fathers' foes, and seen
Afrasiab's cities only—Samarcand,
Bokhara, and lone Khiva in the waste,
And the black Toorkmun tents; and only drunk   500
The desert rivers—Moorghab and Tejend,
Kohik, and where the Kalmuks feed their sheep,
The northern Sir; and this great Oxus stream,
The yellow Oxus, by whose brink I die."

And, with a heavy groan, Rustum bewailed: 505
"Oh, that its waves were flowing over me!
Oh, that I saw its grains of yellow silt
Roll tumbling in the current o'er my head!"

But, with a grave, mild voice, Sohrab replied:
"Desire not that, my father! thou must live;   510
For some are born to do great deeds, and live,
As some are born to be obscured, and die.
Do thou the deeds I die too young to do,
And reap a second glory in thine age—
Thou art my father, and thy gain is mine.   515
But come; thou seest this great host of men
Which follow me; I pray thee, slay not these!
Let me entreat for them! What have they done?
They followed me, my hope, my fame, my star.
Let them all cross the Oxus back in peace.   520
But me thou must bear hence, not send with them,
But carry me with thee to Seïstan,
And place me on a bed, and mourn for me;
Thou, and the snow-haired Zal, and all thy friends.
And thou must lay me in that lovely earth,   525
And heap a stately mound above my bones,
And plant a far-seen pillar over all,
That so the passing horseman on the waste
May see my tomb a great way off, and cry:
'Sohrab, the mighty Rustum's son, lies there,   530
Whom his great father did in ignorance kill!'
And I be not forgotten in my grave."

501-3. Rivers of Turkestan.

And, with a mournful voice, Rustum replied:
"Fear not! as thou hast said, Sohrab, my son,
So shall it be; for I will burn my tents, 535
And quit the host, and bear thee hence with me,
And carry thee away to Seïstan,
And place thee on a bed, and mourn for thee,
With the snow-headed Zal, and all my friends.
And I will lay thee in that lovely earth, 540
And heap a stately mound above thy bones,
And plant a far-seen pillar over all,
And men shall not forget thee in thy grave.
And I will spare thy host; yea, let them go;
Let them all cross the Oxus back in peace. 545
What should I do with slaying any more?
For would that all that I have ever slain
Might be once more alive—my bitterest foes,
And they who were called champions in their time,
And through whose death I won that fame I have— 550
And I were nothing but a common man,
A poor, mean soldier, and without renown,
So thou mightest live, too, my son, my son!
Or rather would that I, even I myself,
Might now be lying on this bloody sand, 555
Near death, and by an ignorant stroke of thine,
Not thou of mine! and I might die, not thou,
And I, not thou, be borne to Seïstan;
And Zal might weep above my grave, not thine,
And say, 'O son, I weep thee not too sore, 560
For willingly, I know, thou met'st thine end!'
But now in blood and battles was my youth,
And full of blood and battles is my age;
And I shall never end this life of blood."

Then, at the point of death, Sohrab replied: 565
"A life of blood indeed, thou dreadful man!
But thou shalt yet have peace; only not now,
Not yet; but thou shalt have it on that day,
When thou shalt sail in a high-masted ship,
Thou and the other peers of Kai Khosroo, 570
Returning home over the salt blue sea,
From laying thy dear master in his grave."

And Rustum gazed in Sohrab's face, and said:
"Soon be that day, my son, and deep that sea!
Till then, if fate so wills, let me endure."   575
He spoke; and Sohrab smiled on him, and took
The spear, and drew it from his side, and eased
His wound's imperious anguish; but the blood
Came welling from the open gash, and life
Flowed with the stream; all down his cold, white side   580
The crimson torrent ran, dim now and soiled,
Like the soiled tissue of white violets
Left, freshly gathered, on their native bank,
By children whom their nurses call with haste
Indoors from the sun's eye; his head drooped low,   585
His limbs grew slack; motionless, white, he lay,
White, with eyes closed; only when heavy gasps,
Deep, heavy gasps, quivering through all his frame,
Convulsed him back to life, he opened them,
And fixed them feebly on his father's face;   590
Till now all strength was ebbed; and from his limbs
Unwillingly the spirit fled away,
Regretting the warm mansion which it left,
And youth, and bloom, and this delightful world.

So, on the bloody sand, Sohrab lay dead.   595
And the great Rustum drew his horseman's cloak
Down o'er his face, and sat by his dead son.
As those black granite pillars, once high-reared
By Jemshid in Persepolis, to bear
His house, now mid their broken flights of steps   600
Lie prone, enormous, down the mountain side—
So, in the sand, lay Rustum by his son.

And night came down over the solemn waste,
And the two gazing hosts, and that sole pair,
And darkened all; and a cold fog, with night,   605
Crept from the Oxus. Soon a hum arose,
As of a great assembly loosed, and fires
Began to twinkle through the fog; for now
Both armies moved to camp, and took their meal.
The Persians took it on the open sands   610
Southward, the Tartars by the river marge;
And Rustum and his son were left alone.

599. *Jemshid:* a legendary Persian king. *Persepolis:* a capital of ancient Persia.

But the majestic river floated on,
Out of the mist and hum of that low land,
Into the frosty starlight, and there moved, 615
Rejoicing, through the hushed Chorasmian waste,
Under the solitary moon ; he flowed
Right for the polar star, past Orgunjè,
Brimming, and bright, and large ; then sands begin
To hem his watery march, and dam his streams, 620
And split his currents, that for many a league
The shorn and parceled Oxus strains along
Through beds of sand and matted, rushy isles ;
Oxus, forgetting the bright speed he had
In his high mountain-cradle in Pamere, 625
A foiled, circuitous wanderer ; till at last
The longed-for dash of waves is heard, and wide
His luminous home of waters opens, bright
And tranquil, from whose floor the new-bathed stars
Emerge, and shine upon the Aral Sea. 630

ILMARINEN'S WOOING

FROM THE KALEVALA (FINLAND)

Translated by John Martin Crawford

The Kalevala, or Praise of Heroes, is of enormous antiquity, probably originating 1000 years before Christ. Scholars assume this great age from the fact that it contains no references to Russians, Germans, or Scandinavians. The episodes in the poem are called runes. These runes are ballad-like in style, though not in rhythm. It is from the four beat lines of *The Kalevala* that Longfellow borrowed the rhythm of *Hiawatha.*

❋   ❋   ❋

Ilmarinen, hero-blacksmith,
The eternal metalworker,
Hastens forward to the court-room
Of the hostess of Pohyola,
Of the master of the Northland, 5
Hastens through the open portals
Into Louhi's home and presence.

616. *Chorasmian waste:* a region in Turkestan. 628. *luminous home:* the Oxus
empties into the Aral Sea.

Servants come with silver pitchers,
Filled with Northland's richest brewing;
Honey-drink is brought and offered   10
To the blacksmith of Wainola,
Ilmarinen thus replying:
"I shall not in all my lifetime
Taste the drink that thou has brought me,
Till I see the Maid of Beauty,   15
Fairy Maiden of the Rainbow;
I will drink with her in gladness,
For whose hand I journey hither."

Spake the hostess of Pohyola: . . .
"Only canst thou woo my daughter,   20
Only canst thou win the maiden,
When thou hast by aid of magic
Plowed the serpent-field of Hisi,
Plowed the field of hissing vipers,
Touching neither beam nor handles. . . ."   25

Ilmarinen of Wainola
Straightway hastens to the chamber
Of the Maiden of the Rainbow,
Speaks these words in hesitation:
"Thou of Night and Dawn the daughter,   30
Tell me, dost thou not remember
When for thee I forged the Sampo,
Hammered thee the lid in colors?
Thou didst swear by oath the strongest, . . .
Thou wouldst follow me hereafter,   35
Be my bride, my life-companion,
Be my honored wife forever.
Now thy mother is exacting,
Will not give to me her daughter,
Till by means of magic only,   40
I have plowed the field of serpents,
Plowed the hissing soil of Hisi."

The affianced Bride of Beauty
Gives this answer to the suitor:
"O, thou blacksmith, Ilmarinen,   45

32. *Sampo:* a magic mill out of which she could grind anything she wished.

The eternal wonder-forger,
Forge thyself a golden plowshare,
Forge the beam of shining silver,
And of copper forge the handles;
Then with ease, by aid of magic,   50
Thou canst plow the field of serpents,
Plow the hissing soil of Hisi."

    Ilmarinen, welcome suitor,
Straightway builds a forge and smithy,
Places gold within the furnace,   55
In the forge he lays the silver,
Forges then a golden plowshare,
Forges, too, a beam of silver,
Forges handles out of copper,
Forges boots and gloves of iron,   60
Forges him a mail of metal,
For his limbs a safe protection,
Safe protection for his body.
Then a horse of fire selecting,
Harnesses the flaming stallion,   65
Goes to plow the field of serpents,
Plow the viper-lands of Hisi.

    In the field were countless vipers,
Serpents there of every species,
Crawling, writhing, hissing, stinging,   70
Harmless all against the hero,
Thus he stills the snakes of Lempo:
"Vipers, ye by God created, . . .
Get ye hence before my plowing,
Writhe ye through the grass and stubble,   75
Crawl ye to the nearest thicket,
Keep your heads beneath the heather,
Hunt your holes to Mana's kingdom.
If your poison-heads be lifted,
Then will mighty Ukko smite them   80
With his iron-pointed arrows,
With the lightning of his anger."
Thus the blacksmith, Ilmarinen,

78. *Mana's kingdom:* Mana or Tuoni was god of the dead. 80. *Ukko:* god of the skies.

Safely plows the field of serpents,
Lifts the vipers in his plowing,
Buries them beneath the furrow,   85
Harmless all against his magic.

When the task had been completed,
Ilmarinen, quick returning,
Thus addressed Pohyola's hostess:
"I have plowed the field of Hisi,   90
Plowed the field of hissing serpents,
Stilled and banished all the vipers;
Give me, ancient dame, thy daughter,
Fairest maiden of the Northland."   95

Spake the hostess of Pohyola:
"Shall not grant to thee my daughter, . . .
Till Tuoni's bear is muzzled,
Till Manala's wolf is conquered,
In the forests of the Death-land,
In the boundaries of Mana.   100
Hundreds have been sent to hunt him,
No one yet has been successful,
All have perished in Manala."

Thereupon young Ilmarinen   105
To the maiden's chamber hastens,
Thus addresses his affianced:
"Still another test demanded,
I must go to Tuonela,
Bridle there the bear of Mana,
Bring him from the Death-land forests,   110
From Tuoni's grove and empire!"

This advice the maiden gives him:
"O thou artist, Ilmarinen,
The eternal metal-worker,
Forge of steel a magic bridle, . . .   115
Make the straps of steel and copper,
Bridle then the bear of Mana,
Lead him from Tuoni's forests."

109. *Tuonela:* the land of the dead.

Then the blacksmith, Ilmarinen, 120
Forged of steel a magic bridle, . . .
Made the straps of steel and copper,
Straightway went the bear to muzzle,
In the forests of the Death-land,
Spake these words in supplication: 125
"Terhenetar, ether-maiden,
Daughter of the fog and snowflake,
Sift the fog, and let it settle
O'er the hills and lowland thickets,
Where the wild bear feeds and lingers, 130
That he may not see my coming,
May not hear my stealthy footsteps!"

Terhenetar hears his praying,
Makes the fog and snowflake settle
On the coverts of the wild-beasts; 135
Thus the bear he safely bridles,
Fetters him in chains of magic,
In the forests of Tuoni,
In the blue groves of Manala.

When this task had been completed, 140
Ilmarinen, quick returning,
Thus addressed the ancient Louhi:
"Give me, worthy dame, thy daughter,
Give me now my bride affianced,
I have brought the bear of Mana 145
From Tuoni's fields and forests.". . .

Spake the hostess of Pohyola:
"I will give to thee my daughter,
Will prepare my snow-white virgin,
For the suitor, Ilmarinen; 150
Thou hast won the Maid of Beauty,
Bride is she of thine hereafter,
Fit companion of thy fireside,
Help and joy of all thy lifetime."

THE FAREWELL OF HECTOR AND ANDROMACHE

HOMER (GREECE)

Translated by Lang, Leaf, and Myers

The Iliad tells a legend of the Trojan war, which was fought by the Greeks to recover Helen, the wife of the Spartan king, from a Trojan prince named Paris, who had eloped with her after a visit to her husband. Before Helen's betrothal, her father had exacted from her many suitors an oath to assist her husband Agamemnon in case this world-famed beauty should be stolen from him. Therefore Agamemnon, Ulysses, Achilles and many other Greek heroes come to Menelaus' aid and besiege Troy for ten years before the city is taken by a stratagem suggested by the wily Ulysses. Chief defender of Troy is Hector, son of the aged Trojan king, Priam. It is only after Hector is slain by Achilles, that the Greeks can triumph.

The story of how the Greeks returned to their homes after the sack of Troy is told in *The Odyssey*—especially the adventures of Ulysses during the ten years of storm-tossed wandering which elapse before he can reach his little island kingdom of Ithaca, where his faithful wife Penelope and the manly son whom he left a babe in arms, await his coming.

These legends of the Trojan War, which had been sung by Grecian bards for nearly two centuries, were put into final form in the *Iliad* and *Odyssey* by Homer about 1000 B.C. Recently, archaeologists have unearthed on the coast of Asia Minor an ancient buried city closely corresponding to Troy as Homer pictures it. But how much is legend and how much is fiction in this famous tale we shall never know.

Many poetical translations of the Homeric epics have been made but none catch so well the beautiful simplicity of the poems as the prose translation from which we quote.

In the following extract from *The Iliad* we see Hector parting from his wife and baby before the battle which ended in his death and sealed the doom of Troy.

❅　❅　❅

So spake the housedame, and Hector hastened from his house back by the same way down the well-builded streets. When he had passed through the great city and was come to the Skaian gates, whereby he was minded to issue upon the plain, then came his dear-won wife, running to meet him, even Andromache, daughter of great-hearted Eëtion, Eëtion that dwelt beneath wooded Plakos, in

Thebe under Plakos, and was king of the men of Kilikia; for his daughter was wife to bronze-harnessed Hector. So she met him now, and with her went the handmaid bearing in her bosom the tender boy, the little child, Hector's loved son, like unto a beautiful star. So now he smiled and gazed at his boy silently, and Andromache stood by his side weeping, and clasped her hand in his, and spake and called upon his name. "Dear my lord, this thy hardihood will undo thee, neither hast thou any pity for thine infant boy, nor for me forlorn that soon shall be thy widow; for soon will the Greeks all set upon thee and slay thee. But it were better for me to go down to the grave if I lose thee; for never more will any comfort be mine, when once thou, even thou, hast met thy fate, but only sorrow. Moreover I have no father nor lady mother: my father was slain by goodly Achilles, for he wasted the populous city of the Kilikians, even high-gated Thebe, and slew Eëtion; yet he despoiled him not, for his soul had shame of that, but he burnt him in his inlaid armour and raised a barrow over him; and all about were elm-trees planted by the mountain nymphs, daughters of aegis-bearing Zeus.[1] And the seven brothers that were mine within our halls, all these on the selfsame day went within the house of Hades;[2] for fleet-footed goodly Achilles slew them all amid their kine of trailing gait and white-fleeced sheep. And my mother, that was queen beneath wooded Plakos, her brought he hither with the other spoils, but afterward took a ransom untold to set her free; but in her father's halls was she smitten by the Archer Artemis.[3] Nay, Hector, thou art to me father and lady mother, yea and brother, even as thou art my goodly husband. Come now, have pity and abide here upon the tower, lest thou make thy child an orphan and thy wife a widow. And stay thy folk beside the fig-tree, where best the city may be scaled and the wall is assailable. Thrice came thither the most valiant that are with the two Aiantes and famed Idomeneus and the sons of Atreus and Tydeus' valiant son, and essayed to enter; whether one skilled in soothsaying revealed it to them, or whether their own spirit urgeth and biddeth them on."

Then great Hector of the glancing helm answered her: "Surely I take thought for all these things, my wife; but I should have very sore shame before the Trojans and Trojan dames with trailing robes, if like a coward I shrank away from battle. Moreover mine own soul forbiddeth me, seeing I have learnt ever to be valiant and fight in the forefront of the Trojans, winning my father's great

---

[1] *aegis-bearing Zeus:* king of the gods. The ægis was his shield. [2] *Hades:* land of the dead. [3] *Artemis:* Diana or goddess of the hunt.

glory and mine own. Yea of a surety I know this in heart and soul ; the day shall come for holy Troy to be laid low, and Priam and the folk of Priam of the good ashen spear. Yet doth the anguish of the Trojans hereafter not so much trouble me, neither Hecuba's own, neither king Priam's, neither my brethren's, the many and brave that shall fall in the dust before their foemen, as doth thine anguish in the day when some mailclad Greek shall lead thee weeping and rob thee of the light of freedom. So shalt thou abide in Argos and ply the loom at another woman's bidding, and bear water from the fount of Messeis or Hypereia,[4] being grievously entreated, and sore constraint shall be laid upon thee. And then shall one say that beholdeth thee weep : 'This is the wife of Hector, that was foremost in battle of the horse-taming Trojans when men fought about Ilios.'[5] Thus shall one say hereafter, and fresh grief will be thine for lack of such an husband as thou hadst to ward off the day of thraldom. But me in death may the heaped-up earth be covering, ere I hear thy crying and thy carrying into captivity."

So spake glorious Hector, and stretched out his arms to his boy. But the child shrunk crying to the bosom of his fair-girdled nurse, dismayed at his dear father's aspect, and in dread at the bronze and horsehair crest that he beheld nodding fiercely from the helmet's top. Then his dear father laughed aloud, and his lady mother ; forthwith glorious Hector took the helmet from his head, and laid it, all gleaming, upon the earth ; then kissed he his dear son and dandled him in his arms, and spake in prayer to Zeus and all the gods, "O Zeus and all ye gods, vouchsafe ye that this my son may likewise prove even as I, pre-eminent amid the Trojans, and as valiant in might, and be a great king of Troy. Then may men say of him, 'Far greater is he than his father' as he returneth home from battle ; and may he bring with him blood-stained spoils from the foeman he hath slain, and may his mother's heart be glad."

So spake he, and laid his son in his dear wife's arms ; and she took him to her fragrant bosom, smiling tearfully. And her husband had pity to see her, and caressed her with his hand, and spake and called upon her name : "Dear one, I pray thee be not of oversorrowful heart ; no man against my fate shall hurl me to Hades ; only destiny, I ween, no man hath escaped, be he coward or be he valiant, when once he hath been born. But go thou to thine house and see to thine own tasks, the loom and distaff, and bid thine handmaidens

[4] *Hypereia:* the Muses (or deities of poetry, music and arts) were said to drink of this spring.
[5] *Ilios:* Troy.

ply their work; but for war shall men provide and I in chief of all men that dwell in Troy."

So spake glorious Hector, and took up his horsehair crested helmet; and his dear wife departed to her home oft looking back and letting fall big tears.

DIDO AND AENEAS

VIRGIL (ROME)

Translated by John Covington

Virgil's *Aeneid* was not, like Homer's *Iliad* and *Odyssey,* a retelling of genuine legends, but a fictitious epic composed by the poet himself. He wrote it at the height of Rome's imperial grandeur under Augustus Caesar in order to arouse patriotic faith in the great destiny of Rome by a heroic tale of the founding of the nation at the command of Jupiter by a Trojan prince fleeing from the sack of Troy. *The Aeneid* is in many respects an imitation of Homer's *Odyssey,* and Aeneas, the hero, like Ulysses, is blown hither and thither by tempests and experiences similar adventures. But the most appealing episode is one of Virgil's own invention and tells of the love of Aeneas and Dido, Queen of Carthage, who succored Aeneas when his storm-scattered fleet was shipwrecked on her shores. Like Homer, Virgil has been translated more successfully into prose than into verse.

❊ ❊ ❊

Arms and the man I sing, who at the first from Troy's shores, the exile of destiny, won his way to Italy and her Latian coast—a man much buffeted on land and on the deep by violence from above, to sate the unforgetting wrath of Juno [1] the cruel—much scourged too in war, as he struggled to build him a city, and find his gods a home in Latium—himself the father of the Latian people, and the chiefs of Alba's [2] houses, and the walls of high towering Rome.

Bring to my mind, O Muse,[3] the causes—for what treason against her godhead, or what pain received, the queen of heaven [4] drove a man of piety so signal to turn the wheel of so many calamities, to bear the brunt of so many hardships! Can heavenly natures hate so fiercely and so long?

Of old there was a city, its people emigrants from Tyre, Car-

---

[1] *Juno:* queen of the gods. [2] *Alba:* another name for Rome. [3] *Muse:* goddess of poetry. [4] *queen of heaven:* Juno.

thage,[5] over against Italy and Tiber's mouths, yet far removed—rich and mighty, and formed to all roughness by war's iron trade—a spot where Juno, it was said, loved to dwell more than in all the world beside, Samos holding but the second place. Here was her armor, here her chariot—here to fix by her royal act the empire of the nations, could Fate be brought to assent, was even then her aim, her cherished scheme. But she had heard that the blood of Troy was sowing the seed of a race to overturn one day those Tyrian towers—from that seed a nation, monarch of broad realms and glorious in war, was to bring ruin on Libya [6]—such the turning of Fate's wheel.

With such thoughts sweeping through the solitude of her enkindled breast, the goddess comes to the storm-cloud's birthplace, the teeming womb of fierce southern blasts, Aeolia. Here, in a vast cavern, King Aeolus is bowing to his sway struggling winds and howling tempests, and bridling them with bond and prison. They, in their passion, are raving at the closed doors, while the huge rock roars responsive: Aeolus is sitting aloft in his fortress, his scepter in his hand, soothing their moods and allaying their rage; were he to fail in this, sea and land, and the deep of heaven, would all be forced along by their blast, and swept through the air. But the almighty sire has buried them in caverns dark and deep, with this fear before his eyes, and placed over them giant bulk and tall mountains, and given them a king who, by the terms of his compact, should know how to tighten or slacken the reins at his patron's will.

(Juno begs Aeolus to release the storm winds so that Aeneas, whose fleet is merrily sailing across the Mediterranean from Troy to Italy, may be shipwrecked and prevented from founding the Roman race which is some day to destroy her beloved Carthage.)

So soon as this is said, he turns his spear, and pushes the hollow mountain on its side, and the winds, as though in column formed, rush forth where they see an outlet, and sweep over the earth in hurricane. Heavily they fall on the sea, and from its very bottom crash down the whole expanse—one and all, east and south, and south-west with his storms thronging at his back—and roll huge billows shoreward. Hark to the shrieks of the crew, and the creaking of the cables! In an instant the clouds snatch sky and

---

[5] *Carthage:* a city in northern Africa opposite Italy.
[6] *Libya:* the district in Africa where Carthage was situated. Rome did conquer Carthage, her great commercial rival; destroyed the city; and sowed the site with salt so that grass should never grow on the spot again.

daylight from the Trojans' eyes—night lies on the deep, black and heavy—pole thunders to pole; heaven flashes thick with fires, and all nature brandishes instant death in the seaman's face. At once Aeneas' limbs are unstrung and chilled—he groans aloud, and, stretching his clasped hands to the stars, fetches from his breast words like these:—"O happy, thrice and again, those whose lot it was, in their fathers' sight, under Troy's high walls to meet death! O thou, the bravest of the Danaan [7] race, Tydeus' son, why was it not thine to lay me low on Ilion's [8] plains, and yield this fated life to thy right hand? Aye, there it is that Hector, stern as in life, lies stretched by the spear of Achilles—there lies Sarpedon's giant bulk—there it is that Simois [9] seizes and sweeps down her channel these many shields and helms, and bodies of the brave."

Such words as he flings wildly forth, a blast roaring from the north strikes his sail full in front and lifts the billows to the stars. Shattered are the oars; then the prow turns and presents the ship's side to the waves; down crashes in a heap a craggy mountain of water. Look! some of the crew are hanging on the surge's crest—to others the yawning deep is giving a glimpse of land down among the billows; surf and sand are raving together. Three ships the south wind catches, and flings upon hidden rocks. Three the east drives from the main on to the shallows, a piteous sight, and dashes them on shoals, and embanks them in mounds of sand. One in which the Lycians were sailing, and true Orontes, a mighty sea strikes from on high on the stem before Aeneas' very eyes; down goes the helmsman, washed from his post, and topples on his head, while the ship is thrice whirled round by the billow in the spot where she lay, and swallowed at once by the greedy gulf. You might see them here and there swimming in that vast abyss—heroes' arms, and planks, and Troy's treasures glimmering through the water. Already Ilioneus' stout ship, already brave Achates', and that in which Abas sailed, and that which carried old Aletes, are worsted by the storm; their side-jointings loosened, one and all give entrance to the watery foe, and part failingly asunder.

(Aeneas parted by the wreck from all but his faithful friend, Achates, makes his way to Carthage. This city is being founded by Dido, an able and adventurous Tyrian queen, who has also fled from persecution in her own land to found a new nation. In a temple to Juno, still under construction, the amazed Trojans see their own sad story frescoed upon the walls and feel hopeful of aid since: "Here,

[7] *Danaan:* Grecian. [8] *Ilion's:* Troy's. [9] *Simois:* the river of Troy.

too, there are tears for human fortune and hearts are touched by mortality." When the gracious Dido welcomes the Trojans, Aeneas cries out to her in gratitude):

"May the gods—if there are powers that regard the pious, if justice and conscious rectitude count for aught anywhere on earth —may they give you the reward you merit! What age had the happiness to bring you forth? what godlike parents gave such nobleness to the world? While the rivers run into the sea, while the shadows sweep along the mountain-sides, while the stars draw life from the sky, your glory and your name and your praise shall still endure, whatever the land whose call I must obey."

(For a year Aeneas remains in Carthage, captivated by the love of Dido, who in turn neglects her realm, absorbed in her passion for him. Then a messenger comes to Aeneas from the gods warning him that his destiny lies elsewhere; that he must not forget in love the founding of Rome. Aeneas, fearing the grief of the impassioned queen, secretly begins his preparations.)

But the queen (who can cheat a lover's sense?) scented the plot, and caught the first sound of the coming stir, alive to fear in the midst of safety. At length she thus bespeaks Aeneas, unaddressed by him: "To hide, yes, hide your enormous crime, perfidious wretch, did you hope that might be done—to steal away in silence from my realm? Has our love no power to keep you? has our troth, once plighted, none, nor she whom you doom to a cruel death, your Dido? Nay, are you fitting out your fleet with winter's sky overhead, and hastening to cross the deep in the face of all the northern winds, hard-hearted as you are? Why, suppose you were not seeking a strange clime and a home you know not—suppose old Troy were still standing—would even Troy draw you to seek her across a billowy sea? Flying, and from me! By the tears I shed, and by your plighted hand—by our union—if I have ever deserved well of you, or aught of mine ever gave you pleasure—have pity on a falling house, and strip off, I conjure you, if prayer be not too late, the mind that clothes you. To whom are you abandoning a dying woman, my guest?—since the name of husband has dwindled to that. Why do I live any longer?—to give my brother Pygmalion time to batter down my walls, or Iarbas the Moor to carry me away captive? Had I but borne any offspring of you before your flight, were there some tiny Aeneas to play in my hall, and remind me of you, though but in look, I should not then feel captive and forlorn."

But good Aeneas, though yearning to solace and soothe her agonized spirit, and by his words to check the onset of sorrow, with many a groan, his whole soul upheaved by the force of love, goes nevertheless about the commands of Heaven, and repairs to his fleet. The Trojans redouble their efforts, and along the whole range of the shore drag their tall ships down. The keels are careened and floated. They carry oars with their leaves still on, and timber unfashioned as it stood in the woods, so strong is their eagerness to fly. You may see them all in motion, streaming from every part of the city. Even as ants when they are sacking a huge heap of wheat, provident of winter days, and laying up the plunder in their stores; a black column is seen moving through the plain, and they convey their booty along the grass in a narrow path; some are putting their shoulders to the big grains, and pushing them along; others are rallying the force and punishing the stragglers; the whole track is in a glow of work. What were your feelings then, poor Dido, at a sight like this! How deep the groans you heaved, when you looked out from your lofty tower on a beach all seething and swarming, and saw the whole sea before you deafened with that hubbub of voices! Tyrant love! what force dost thou not put on human hearts?

"What am I about? Am I to make fresh proof of my former suitors, with scorn before me? Must I stoop to court Nomad bridegrooms, whose offered hand I have spurned so often? Well, then, shall I follow the fleet of Ilion,[10] and be at the beck and call of Trojan masters? Do they think with pleasure on the succor once rendered them? Does gratitude for past kindness yet live in their memory? But even if I wished it, who will give me leave, or admit the unwelcome guest to his haughty ships? Are you so ignorant, poor wretch? Do you not yet understand the perjury of the race of Laomedon?[11] What then? Shall I fly alone, and swell the triumph of their crews? or shall I put to sea, with the Tyrians and the whole force of my people at my back, dragging those whom it was so hard to uproot from their Sidonian[12] home again into the deep, and bidding them spread sail to the winds? No!—die the death you have merited, and let the sword put your sorrow to flight. Why could I not forswear wedlock, and live an unblamed life in savage freedom, nor meddle with troubles like these? Why did I not keep the faith I vowed to the ashes of Sychaeus?"[13] Such were the reproaches that broke from that bursting heart.

[10] *Ilion:* Troy. [11] *race of Laomedon:* the Trojans. [12] *Sidonian:* Tyrian. [13] *Sychaeus:* her first husband, now deceased.

(On a rocky headland overlooking the sea, Dido builds a lofty funeral pyre, on which she places all her relics of Aeneas and their love. When morning dawns and she sees that Aeneas has stolen away without farewell, and that the Trojan ships have cleared the harbor, Dido mounts the funeral pyre. She unsheaths Aeneas' sword.)

Then, after surveying the Trojan garments and the bed, too well known, and pausing a while to weep and think, she pressed her bosom to the couch, and uttered her last words: "Relics, once darlings of mine, while Fate and Heaven gave leave, receive this my soul, and release me from these my sorrows. I have lived my life—the course assigned me by Fortune is run, and now the august phantom of Dido shall pass underground. I have built a splendid city. I have seen my walls completed. In vengeance for a husband, I have punished a brother that hated me—blest, ah! blest beyond human bliss, if only Trojan ships had never touched our coasts!" Then kissing the the couch, "Is it to be death without revenge? But be it death," she cries, "this, this is the road by which I love to pass to the shades. Let the heartless Trojan's eyes drink in this flame from the deep, and let him carry with him the presage of my death."

She spoke, and even while she was yet speaking, her attendants see her fallen on the sword.

Aeneas, meantime, was well on his road, holding with set purpose on the watery way, and cutting through billows gloomed by the north wind, with eyes ever and anon turned back to the city, which poor Dido's funeral flame now began to illumine. What cause has lit up a blaze so mighty they cannot tell; but as they think of the cruel pangs which follow outrage on great love, and of what a frantic woman can attempt, the Trojan hearts are filled with sad foreboding.

(Long afterwards Aeneas, by permission of the gods, descends into the afterworld to speak again with his beloved father, whom he had carried on his back from the flames of Troy but who had died on the journey in search of a new home. As Aeneas passes through the various regions in the under-world—Tartarus, where the evil are punished for their sins, and the Elysian fields where the good and happy dead live a life of shadowy ease—he comes to the Mourning Fields.)

Here dwell those whom cruel Love's consuming tooth has eaten to the heart, in the privacy of hidden walks and an enshrouding myrtle wood: their tender sorrows quit them not even in death. Among these was Phoenicia's daughter, Dido, fresh from her death-wound, wandering in that mighty wood. Soon as the Trojan hero stood at her side, and knew her, looming dimly through the dusk— as a man sees or thinks he sees through the clouds, when the month is young, the rising moon—his tears broke forth, and he addressed her tenderly and lovingly. "Unhappy Dido!—and was it then a true messenger that reached me with the tale that you were dead: that the sword had done its worst? Was it, alas, to a grave that I brought you? By the stars of heaven I swear, by the powers above, by all that is most sacred here underground, against my will, fair queen, I quitted your coast. No; it was the command of the gods; the same stern force which compels me now to pass through this realm of shade, this wilderness of squalor and abysmal night; it was that which drove me by its uttered will: nor could I have thought that my departure would bring on you such violence of grief. Stay your step and withdraw not from the look I bend on you. Whom would you shun? The last word which fate suffers me to address you is this." With words like these, Aeneas kept soothing the soul that blazed forth through those gloomy eyes, and moving himself to tears. She stood with averted head and eyes on the ground, her features as little moved by the speech he essayed as if she held the station of a stubborn flint, or a crag of Marpessa. At length she flung herself away, and, unforgiving still, fled into the shadow of the wood.

PAOLA AND FRANCESCA

DANTE ALIGHIERI (ITALY)

Translated by Henry Francis Cary

The grand epic poem which summarizes human destiny as pictured by the medieval world is Dante's *Divine Comedy*. Dante in a dream meets the Roman poet, Virgil, who guides him through the three regions of the afterworld. In the Inferno he sees the spirits of the damned suffering everlasting punishment. In Purgatory ordinary mortals are being prepared for Paradise by purging them of lesser sins. Purgatory is a mountain up which they climb ledge by ledge—

being cleansed on each ledge from a different defect. When a soul has reached the summit and soars up to Paradise, the whole mountain trembles with joy. In Paradise, Dante sees the souls of the blessed saints ringed about the throne of God in glory, like the petals of a great glowing rose of light.

When the *Divine Comedy* first appeared, it had a lively current interest due to the fact that Dante peopled the hereafter with real personages, not only from history, but from contemporary life. People were naturally curious to see to what position in the hereafter they and their friends and enemies were consigned. Moreover, the stories of the departed spirits are told with vivid, unsparing detail and brilliant analysis—etched forever against that weird background by the master hand of genius. One can imagine the contemporary Italian turning with fear, curiosity, and rage to pages that still grip the modern reader by their eternal reality.

The following episode takes place in the Inferno, in that circle where guilty lovers are blown forever before a fiery tempest. Semiramis, Cleopatra, Helen, and Dido are seen amid the throng. Then Dante notes Paola and Francesca da Rimini, who had been married by her father to the deformed Duke of Rimini, a man considerably her elder. Having fallen in love with his handsome younger brother, Paola, Francesca was slain with her lover by her enraged husband.

❊   ❊   ❊

When I had heard my sage instructor name
Those dames and knights of antique days, o'erpower'd
By pity, well-nigh in amaze my mind
Was lost; and I began: "Bard! willingly
I would address those two together coming,   5
Which seem so light before the wind." He thus:
"Note thou, when nearer they to us approach.
Then by that love which carries them along,
Entreat; and they will come." Soon as the wind
Sway'd them towards us, thus I framed my speech: 10
"O wearied spirits! come, and hold discourse
With us, if by none else restrain'd." As doves
By fond desire invited, on wide wings
And firm, to their sweet nest returning home,
Cleave the air, wafted by their will along;   15
Thus issued, from the troop where Dido ranks,
They, through the ill air speeding: with such force
My cry prevail'd, by strong affection urged.
    "O gracious creature and benign! who go'st

Visiting, through this element obscure, 20
Us, who the world with bloody stain imbrued;
If, for a friend, the King of all, we own'd,
Our prayer to him should for thy peace arise,
Since thou hast pity on our evil plight.
Of whatsoe'er to hear or to discourse 25
It pleases thee, that will we hear, of that
Freely with thee discourse, while e'er the wind,
As now, is mute. The land, that gave me birth,
Is situate on the coast, where Po descends
To rest in ocean with his sequent streams. 30
    "Love, that in gentle heart is quickly learnt,
Entangled him by that fair form, from me
Ta'en in such cruel sort, as grieves me still:
Love, that denial takes from none beloved,
Caught me with pleasing him so passing well, 35
That, as thou seest, he yet deserts me not.
Love brought us to one death: Caina waits
The soul, who spilt our life." Such were their words;
At hearing which, downward I bent my looks,
And held them there so long, that the bard cried: 40
"What art thou pondering?" I in answer thus:
"Alas! by what sweet thoughts, what fond desire
Must they at length to that ill pass have reach'd!"
    Then turning, I to them my speech address'd,
And thus began: "Francesca! your sad fate 45
Even to tears my grief and pity moves.
But tell me; in the time of your sweet sighs,
By what and how Love granted that ye knew
Your yet uncertain wishes?" She replied:
"No greater grief than to remember days 50
Of joy, when misery is at hand. That kens
Thy learn'd instructor. Yet so eagerly
If thou art bent to know the primal root,
From whence our love gat being, I will do
As one who weeps and tells his tale. One day, 55
For our delight we read of Lancelot,
How him love thrall'd. Alone we were, and no
Suspicion near us. Oft-times by that reading

29. Rimini is in north Italy near Florence on the River Po. 37. *Caina:* a part of
Hell where murderers were punished. 56. *Lancelot:* a knight of the Round Table
who fell in love with Guinevere, wife of his best friend, King Arthur.

Our eyes were drawn together, and the hue
Fled from our alter'd cheek. But at one point   60
Alone we fell. When of that smile we read,
The wished smile so rapturously kiss'd
By one so deep in love, then he, who ne'er
From me shall separate, at once my lips
All trembling kiss'd. The book and writer both   65
Were love's purveyors. In its leaves that day
We read no more." While thus one spirit spake,
The other wail'd so sorely, that heart-struck
I, through compassion fainting, seem'd not far
From death, and like a corse fell to the ground.   70

GARETH AND LYNETTE

Alfred Tennyson (England)

Tennyson has retold in his *Idylls of the King* the story of King Arthur, legendary Christian king of Britain at the time when the pagan Saxons were invading England and dispossessing the ancient Celts.[1] Arthur was the last Celtic king to offer real resistance to the invader. His story has been told and retold, first by the Welsh bards of his own region, then later by the Norman French troubadours, who pictured Arthur as a feudal king of their own days of knighthood and chivalry. In the fifteenth century it was put into final medieval form by Sir Thomas Malory in his *Le Morte D'Arthur*. Tennyson has based his *Idylls* on Malory. Each idyll [2] tells a different episode in the story of Arthur and his knights. Tennyson has presented Arthur as an idealist striving to raise his kingdom from savagery to civilization and overcome the animal nature of man by the spiritual. The twelve stories Tennyson retells are drawn from different periods in Arthur's reign. *Gareth and Lynette* pictures the early years when all his knights were full of youthful hope and enthusiasm and struggled to live up to Arthur's ideals. Gareth—a young squire winning the spurs of knighthood—typifies this idealism of youth. Alas that Arthur's knights could not have held ever true to his dream!

✳   ✳   ✳

The last tall son of Lot and Bellicent,
And tallest, Gareth, in a showerful spring
Stared at the spate. A slender-shafted pine
Lost footing, fell, and so was whirled away.

[1] The Welsh were defeated for the last time by the Saxons in A.D. 597. This is supposed to be the date of Arthur's overthrow.
[2] *idyll:* a tale.
[3] *spate:* river in spring flood.

"How he went down," said Gareth, "as a false
    knight   5
Or evil king before my lance, if lance
Were mine to use—O senseless cataract,
Bearing all down in thy precipitancy—
And yet thou art but swollen with cold snows
And mine is living blood: thou dost His will,   10
The Maker's, and not knowest, and I that know,
Have strength and wit, in my good mother's hall
Linger with vacillating obedience,
Prisoned, and kept and coaxed and whistled to—
Since the good mother holds me still a child!   15
Good mother is bad mother unto me!
A worse were better; yet no worse would I.
Heaven yield her for it, but in me put force
To weary her ears with one continuous prayer,
Until she let me fly discaged to sweep   20
In ever-highering eagle-circles up
To the great Sun of Glory, and thence swoop
Down upon all things base, and dash them dead,
A knight of Arthur, working out his will,
To cleanse the world. Why, Gawain, when he came   25
With Modred hither in the summertime,
Asked me to tilt with him, the proven knight.
Modred, for want of worthier, was the judge.
Then I so shook him in the saddle, he said,
'Thou hast half prevail'd against me,' said so—he—   30
Tho' Modred biting his thin lips was mute,
For he is always sullen: what care I?"

And Gareth went, and hovering round her chair
Asked, "Mother, tho' ye count me still the child,
Sweet mother, do ye love the child?" She laughed,   35
"Thou art but a wild-goose to question it."
"Then, mother, an ye love the child," he said,
"Being a goose and rather tame than wild,
Hear the child's story." "Yea, my well-beloved,
An 'twere but of the goose and golden eggs."   40

And Gareth answered her with kindling eyes,
"Nay, nay, good mother, but this egg of mine
Was finer gold than any goose can lay;

18. *yield:* reward.   26. Gawain and Modred were brothers of Gareth.   37. *an:* if.

For this an Eagle, a royal Eagle, laid
Almost beyond eye-reach, on such a palm   45
As glitters gilded in thy Book of Hours.
And there was ever haunting round the palm
A lusty youth, but poor, who often saw
The splendor sparkling from aloft, and thought
'An I could climb and lay my hand upon it,   50
Then were I wealthier than a leash of kings.'
But ever when he reached a hand to climb,
One, that had loved him from his childhood, caught
And stayed him, 'Climb not lest thou break thy neck,
I charge thee by my love,' and so the boy,   55
Sweet mother, neither clomb, nor brake his neck,
But brake his very heart in pining for it,
And passed away."

                    To whom the mother said,
"True love, sweet son, had risked himself and
     climbed,
And handed down the golden treasure to him."   60

And Gareth answered her with kindling eyes,
"Gold? said I gold?—ay then, why he, or she,
Or whosoe'er it was, or half the world
Had ventured—*had* the thing I spake of been
Mere gold—but this was all of that true steel,   65
Whereof they forged the brand Excalibur,
And lightnings played about it in the storm,
And all the little fowl were flurried at it,
And there were cries and clashings in the nest,
That sent him from his senses:—let me go."   70

Then Bellicent bemoaned herself and said,
"Hast thou no pity upon my loneliness?
Lo, where thy father Lot beside the hearth
Lies like a log, and all but smouldered out!
For ever since when traitor to the King   75
He fought against him in the Barons' war,
And Arthur gave him back his territory,

46. *Book of Hours:* a prayer-book (often beautifully illuminated). 51. *leash of:* three (from a "leash of hounds"). 66. *brand:* sword.

His age hath slowly drooped, and now lies there
A yet-warm corpse, and yet unburiable,
No more; nor sees, nor hears, nor speaks, nor knows. 80
And both thy brethren are in Arthur's hall,
Albeit neither loved with that full love
I feel for thee, nor worthy such a love:
Stay therefore thou; red berries charm the bird,
And thee, mine innocent, the jousts, the wars,
Who never knewest finger-ache, nor pang
Of wrenched or broken limb—an often chance
In those brain-stunning shocks, and tourney-falls,
Frights to my heart; but stay: follow the deer
By these tall firs and our fast-falling burns; 90
So make thy manhood mightier day by day;
Sweet is the chase: and I will seek thee out
Some comfortable bride and fair, to grace
Thy climbing life, and cherish my prone year,
Till falling into Lot's forgetfulness 95
I know not thee, myself, nor anything.
Stay, my best son! ye are yet more boy than man."

Then Gareth, "An ye hold me yet for child,
Hear yet once more the story of the child.
For, mother, there was once a King, like ours. 100
The prince his heir, when tall and marriageable,
Asked for a bride; and thereupon the King
Set two before him. One was fair, strong, armed—
But to be won by force—and many men
Desired her; one, good lack, no man desired. 105
And these were the conditions of the King:
That save he won the first by force, he needs
Must wed that other, whom no man desired,
A red-faced bride who knew herself so vile,
That evermore she longed to hide herself, 110
Nor fronted man or woman, eye to eye—
Yea—some she cleaved to, but they died of her.
And one—they called her Fame—and one—O Mother,
How can ye keep me tethered to you—Shame.
Man am I grown, a man's work must I do. 115
Follow the deer? follow the Christ, the King,
Live pure, speak true, right wrong, follow the King—
Else, wherefore born?"

90. *burns:* brooks. 94. *prone:* fallen.

To whom the mother said,
"Sweet son, for there be many who deem him not,
Or will not deem him, wholly proven King—   120
Albeit in mine own heart I knew him King,
When I was frequent with him in my youth,
And heard him Kingly speak, and doubted him
No more than he, himself; but felt him mine,
Of closest kin to me: yet—wilt thou leave   125
Thine easeful biding here, and risk thine all,
Life, limbs, for one that is not proven King?
Stay, till the cloud that settles round his birth
Hath lifted but a little. Stay, sweet son."

   And Gareth answered quickly, "Not an hour,   130
So that ye yield me—I will walk thro' fire,
Mother, to gain it—your full leave to go.
Not proven, who swept the dust of ruined Rome
From off the threshold of the realm, and crushed
The Idolaters, and made the people free?   135
Who should be King save him who makes us free?"

   So when the Queen, who long had sought in vain
To break him from the intent to which he grew,
Found her son's will unwaveringly one,
She answered craftily, "Will ye walk thro' fire?   140
Who walks thro' fire will hardly heed the smoke.
Ay, go then, an ye must: only one proof,
Before thou ask the King to make thee knight,
Of thine obedience and thy love to me,
Thy mother,—I demand."

                         And Gareth cried,   145
"A hard one, or a hundred, so I go.
Nay—quick! the proof to prove me to the quick!"

   But slowly spake the mother, looking at him,
"Prince, thou shalt go disguised to Arthur's hall,
And hire thyself to serve for meats and drinks   150
Among the scullions and the kitchen-knaves,
And those that hand the dish across the bar.
Nor shalt thou tell thy name to any one.
And thou shalt serve a twelvemonth and a day."

152. *bar:* serving shelf in the butler's pantry.

For so the Queen believed that when her son   155
Beheld his only way to glory lead
Low down thro' villain kitchen-vassalage,
Her own true Gareth was too princely-proud
To pass thereby; so should he rest with her,
Closed in her castle from the sound of arms.   160

Silent awhile was Gareth, then replied,
"The thrall in person may be free in soul.
And I shall see the jousts. Thy son am I,
And since thou art my mother, must obey.
I therefore yield me freely to thy will;   165
For hence will I, disguised, and hire myself
To serve with scullions and with kitchen-knaves;
Nor tell my name to any—no, not the King."

Gareth awhile lingered. The mother's eye,
Full of the wistful fear that he would go,   170
And turning toward him whereso'er he turned,
Perplexed his outward purpose, till an hour,
When, wakened by the wind which with full voice
Swept bellowing thro' the darkness on to dawn,
He rose, and out of slumber calling two   175
That still had tended on him from his birth,
Before the wakeful mother heard him, went.

(Dressed like a peasant Gareth arrived at)

Camelot, a city of shadowy palaces
And stately, rich in emblem and the work
Of ancient kings who did their days in stone;   180
Which Merlin's hand, the Mage at Arthur's court,
Knowing all arts, had touched, and everywhere
At Arthur's ordinance, tipped with lessening peak
And pinnacle, and had made it spire to heaven.
And ever and anon a knight would pass   185
Outward, or inward to the hall: his arms
Clashed; and the sound was good to Gareth's ear.
And out of bower and casement shyly glanced
Eyes of pure women, wholesome stars of love;
And all about a healthful people stepped   190
As in the presence of a gracious king.

157. *villain*: lowly. 176. *still*: always.

Then into hall Gareth ascending heard
A voice, the voice of Arthur, and beheld
Far over heads in that long-vaulted hall
The splendor of the presence of the King   195
Throned, and delivering doom—and looked no more—
But felt his young heart hammering in his ears,
And thought: "For this half-shadow of a lie
The truthful King will doom me when I speak."
Yet pressing on, tho' all in fear to find   200
Sir Gawain or Sir Modred, saw nor one
Nor other, but in all the listening eyes
Of those tall knights, that ranged about the throne,
Clear honor shining like the dewy star
Of dawn, and faith in their great King, with pure   205
Affection, and the light of victory,
And glory gained, and evermore to gain.

Then came a widow crying to the King,
"A boon, Sir King! Thy father, Uther, reft
From my dead lord a field with violence: 210
For howsoe'er at first he proffered gold,
Yet, for the field was pleasant in our eyes,
We yielded not; and then he reft us of it
Perforce, and left us neither gold nor field."

Said Arthur, "Whether would ye? gold or field?"   215
To whom the woman weeping, "Nay, my lord,
The field was pleasant in my husband's eye."

And Arthur: "Have thy pleasant field again,
And thrice the gold for Uther's use thereof,
According to the years. No boon is here,   220
But justice, so thy say be proven true.
Accursed, who from the wrongs his father did
Would shape himself a right!"

                                And while she passed,
Came yet another widow crying to him,
"A boon, Sir King! Thine enemy, King, am I.   225
With thine own hand thou slewest my dear lord,
A knight of Uther in the Barons' war,

196. *doom:* judgment. 215. *Whether:* Which.

When Lot and many another rose and fought
Against thee, saying thou wert basely born.
I held with these, and loathe to ask thee aught.   230
Yet lo! my husband's brother had my son
Thralled in his castle, and hath starved him dead;
And standeth seized of that inheritance
Which thou that slewest the sire hast left the son.
So tho' I scarce can ask it thee for hate,   235
Grant me some knight to do the battle for me,
Kill the foul thief, and wreak me for my son."

Then strode a good knight forward, crying to him,
"A boon, Sir King! I am her kinsman, I.
Give me to right her wrong, and slay the man."   240

Then came Sir Kay, the seneschal, and cried,
"A boon, Sir King! even that thou grant her none,
This railer, that hath mocked thee in full hall—
None; or the wholesome boon of gyve and gag."

But Arthur, "We sit King, to help the wronged   245
Thro' all our realm. The woman loves her lord.
Peace to thee, woman, with thy loves and hates!
The kings of old had doomed thee to the flames,
Aurelius Emrys would have scourged thee dead,
And Uther slit thy tongue: but get thee hence—   250
Lest that rough humor of the kings of old
Return upon me! Thou that art her kin,
Go likewise; lay him low and slay him not,
But bring him here, that I may judge the right,
According to the justice of the King: 255
Then, be he guilty, by that deathless King
Who lived and died for men, the man shall die."

And many another suppliant crying came
With noise of ravage wrought by beast and man,
And evermore a knight would ride away.   260

Last, Gareth, leaning both hands heavily
Down on the shoulders of the twain, his men,
Approached between them toward the King, and asked,

233. *seized of:* in possession of. 237. *wreak:* avenge.

"A boon, Sir King" (his voice was all ashamed),
"For see ye not how weak and hunger-worn 265
I seem—leaning on these? grant me to serve
For meat and drink among thy kitchen-knaves
A twelvemonth and a day, nor seek my name.
Hereafter I will fight."

                To him the King,
"A goodly youth and worth a goodlier boon! 270
But so thou wilt no goodlier, then must Kay,
The master of the meats and drinks, be thine."

He rose and passed; then Kay, a man of mien
Wan-sallow as the plant that feels itself
Root-bitten by white lichen,

                   "Lo ye now! 275
This fellow hath broken from some Abbey, where,
God wot, he had not beef and brewis enow,
However that might chance! but an he work,
Like any pigeon will I cram his crop,
And sleeker shall he shine than any hog." 280

Then Lancelot standing near, "Sir Seneschal,
Sleuth-hound thou knowest, and gray, and all the
     hounds;
A horse thou knowest, a man thou dost not know:
Broad brows and fair, a fluent hair and fine,
High nose, a nostril large and fine, and hands 285
Large, fair and fine!—Some young lad's mystery—
But, or from sheepcot or king's hall, the boy
Is noble-natured. Treat him with all grace,
Lest he should come to shame thy judging of him."

Then Kay, "What murmurest thou of mystery? 290
Think ye this fellow will poison the King's dish?
Nay, for he spake too fool-like: mystery!
Tut, an the lad were noble, he had asked
For horse and armor: fair and fine, forsooth!
Sir Fine-face, Sir Fair-hands? but see thou to it 295
That thine own fineness, Lancelot, some fine day
Undo thee not—and leave my man to me."

277. *brewis*: broth.

So Gareth all for glory underwent
The sooty yoke of kitchen-vassalage;
Ate with young lads his portion by the door, 300
And couched at night with grimy kitchen-knaves.
And Lancelot ever spake him pleasantly,
But Kay the seneschal, who loved him not,
Would hustle and harry him, and labor him
Beyond his comrade of the hearth, and set 305
To turn the broach, draw water, or hew wood,
Or grosser tasks; and Gareth bowed himself
With all obedience to the King, and wrought
All kinds of service with a noble ease
That graced the lowliest act in doing it. 310
And when the thralls had talk among themselves,
And one would praise the love that linked the King
And Lancelot—how the King had saved his life
In battle twice, and Lancelot once the King's—
For Lancelot was the first in Tournament, 315
But Arthur mightiest on the battle-field—
Gareth was glad. Or if some other told,
How once the wandering forester at dawn,
Far over the blue tarns and hazy seas,
On Caer-Eryri's highest found the King, 320
A naked babe, of whom the Prophet spake,
"He passes to the Isle Avilion,
He passes and is healed and cannot die"—
Gareth was glad. But if their talk were foul,
Then would he whistle rapid as any lark, 325
Or carol some old roundelay, and so loud
That first they mocked, but, after, reverenced him.
Or Gareth, telling some prodigious tale
Of knights who sliced a red life-bubbling way
Thro' twenty folds of twisted dragon, held 330
All in a gap-mouthed circle his good mates
Lying or sitting round him, idle hands,
Charmed; till Sir Kay, the seneschal, would come
Blustering upon them, like a sudden wind
Among dead leaves, and drive them all apart. 335
Or when the thralls had sport among themselves,
So there were any trial of mastery,

304. *harry:* drive. 306. *broach:* roasting spit. 319. *tarns:* lakes. 320. *Caer-Eryri:* Mount Snowdon.

He, by two yards in casting bar or stone
Was counted best; and if there chanced a joust,
So that Sir Kay nodded him leave to go,   340
Would hurry thither, and when he saw the knights
Clash like the coming and retiring wave,
And the spear spring, and good horse reel, the boy
Was half beyond himself for ecstasy.

So for a month he wrought among the thralls;   345
But in the weeks that followed, the good Queen,
Repentant of the word she made him swear,
And saddening in her childless castle, sent,
Between the in-crescent and de-crescent moon,
Arms for her son, and loosed him from his vow.   350

This, Gareth hearing from a squire of Lot
With whom he used to play at tourney once,
When both were children, and in lonely haunts
Would scratch a ragged oval on the sand,
And each at either dash from either end—   355
Shame never made girl redder than Gareth joy.
He laughed; he sprang. "Out of the smoke, at once
I leap from Satan's foot to Peter's knee—
These news be mine, none other's—nay, the King's—
Descend into the city": whereon he sought   360
The King alone, and found, and told him all.

"I have staggered thy strong Gawain in a tilt
For pastime; yea, he said it: joust can I.
Make me thy knight—in secret! let my name
Be hidden, and give me the first quest, I spring   365
Like flame from ashes."

                              Here the King's calm eye
Fell on, and checked, and made him flush, and bow
Lowly, to kiss his hand, who answered him,
"Son, the good mother let me know thee here,
And sent her wish that I would yield thee thine.   370
Make thee my knight? my knights are sworn to vows
Of utter hardihood, utter gentleness,
And, loving, utter faithfulness in love,
And uttermost obedience to the King."

Then Gareth, lightly springing from his knees,   375
"My King, for hardihood I can promise thee.
For uttermost obedience make demand
Of whom ye gave me to, the Seneschal,
No mellow master of the meats and drinks!
And as for love, God wot, I love not yet,   380
But love I shall, God willing."

         And the King—
"Make thee my knight in secret? yea, but he,
Our noblest brother, and our truest man,
And one with me in all, he needs must know."

    "Let Lancelot know, my King, let Lancelot know,   385
Thy noblest and thy truest!"

         And the King—
"But wherefore would ye men should wonder at you?
Nay, rather for the sake of me, their King,
And the deed's sake my knighthood do the deed,
Than to be noised of."

        Merrily Gareth asked,   390
"Have I not earned my cake in baking of it?
Let be my name until I make my name!
My deeds will speak: it is but for a day."
So with a kindly hand on Gareth's arm
Smiled the great King, and half-unwillingly,   395
Loving his lusty youthhood, yielded to him.
Then, after summoning Lancelot privily,
"I have given him the first quest: he is not proven.
Look therefore, when he calls for this in hall,
Thou get to horse and follow him far away.   400
Cover the lions on thy shield, and see
Far as thou mayest, he be nor ta'en nor slain."

Then that same day there passed into the hall
A damsel of high lineage, and a brow
May-blossom, and a cheek of apple-blossom,   405
Hawk-eyes; and lightly was her slender nose
Tip-tilted like the petal of a flower;
She into hall passed with her page and cried,

"O King, for thou hast driven the foe without
See to the foe within! bridge, ford, beset   410
By bandits, every one that owns a tower
The lord for half a league. Why sit ye there?
Rest would I not, Sir King, an I were king,
Till ev'n the lonest hold were all as free
From cursèd bloodshed, as thine altarcloth   415
From that best blood it is a sin to spill."

"Comfort thyself," said Arthur, "I nor mine
Rest: so my knighthood keep the vows they swore,
The wastest moorland of our realm shall be
Safe, damsel, as the center of this hall.   420
What is thy name? thy need?"

                 "My name?" she said—
"Lynette my name; noble; my need, a knight
To combat for my sister, Lyonors,
A lady of high lineage, of great lands,
And comely, yea, and comelier than myself.   425
She lives in Castle Perilous: a river
Runs in three loops about her living-place;
And o'er it are three passings, and three knights
Defend the passings, brethren, and a fourth
And of that four the mightiest, holds her stayed   430
In her own castle, and so besieges her
To break her will, and make her wed with him:
And but delays his purport till thou send
To do the battle with him, thy chief man,
Sir Lancelot, whom he trusts to overthrow,   435
Then wed, with glory: but she will not wed
Save whom she loveth, or a holy life.
Now, therefore, have I come for Lancelot."

Then Arthur, mindful of Sir Gareth, asked,
"Damsel, ye know this Order lives to crush   440
All wrongers of the Realm. But say, these four,
Who be they? What the fashion of the men?"

"They be of foolish fashion, O Sir King,
The fashion of that old knight-errantry
Who ride abroad, and do but what they will;   445

Courteous or bestial from the moment, such
As have nor law nor king; and three of these
Proud in their fantasy call themselves the Day,
Morning-Star, and Noon-Sun, and Evening-Star,
Being strong fools; and never a whit more wise   450
The fourth, who alway rideth armed in black,
A huge man-beast of boundless savagery.
He names himself the Night and oftener Death,
And wears a helmet mounted with a skull,
And bears a skeleton figured on his arms,   455
To show that who may slay or scape the three,
Slain by himself, shall enter endless night.
And all these four be fools, but mighty men,
And therefore am I come for Lancelot."

      Hereat Sir Gareth called from where he rose,   460
A head with kindling eyes above the throng,
"A boon, Sir King—this quest!" then—for he marked
Kay near him groaning like a wounded bull—
"Yea, King, thou knowest thy kitchen-knave am I,
And mighty thro' thy meats and drinks am I,   465
And I can topple over a hundred such.
Thy promise, King," and Arthur, glancing at him,
Brought down a momentary brow. "Rough, sudden,
And pardonable, worthy to be knight—
Go therefore," and all hearers were amazed.   470

      But on the damsel's forehead shame, pride, wrath
Slew the May-white: she lifted either arm,
"Fie on thee, King! I asked for thy chief knight,
And thou hast given me but a kitchen-knave."
Then ere a man in hall could stay her, turned,   475
Fled down the lane of access to the King,
Took horse, descended the slope street, and passed
The weird white gate, and paused without, beside
The field of tourney, murmuring "kitchen-knave."

      Now two great entries opened from the hall,   480
At one end one, that gave upon a range
Of level pavement where the King would pace
At sunrise, gazing over plain and wood;

And down from this a lordly stairway sloped
Till lost in blowing trees and tops of towers; 485
And out by this main doorway passed the King.
But one was counter to the hearth, and rose
High that the highest-crested helm could ride
Therethro' nor graze; and by this entry fled
The damsel in her wrath, and on to this 490
Sir Gareth strode, and saw without the door
King Arthur's gift, the worth of half a town,
A warhorse of the best, and near it stood
The two that out of north had followed him:
This bare a maiden shield, a casque; that held 495
The horse, the spear; whereat Sir Gareth loosed
A cloak that dropped from collar-bone to heel,
A cloth of roughest web, and cast it down,
And from it, like a fuel-smothered fire,
That looked half-dead, brake bright, and flashed
      as those 500
Dull-coated things, that making slide apart
Their dusk wing-cases, all beneath there burns
A jeweled harness, ere they pass and fly.
So Gareth, ere he parted, flashed in arms.
Then as he donned the helm, and took the shield, 505
And mounted horse and grasped a spear, of grain
Storm-strengthened on a windy site, and tipped
With trenchant steel, around him slowly pressed
The people, while from out of kitchen came
The thralls in throng, and seeing who had worked 510
Lustier than any, and whom they could but love,
Mounted in arms, threw up their caps and cried,
"God bless the King, and all his fellowship!"
And on thro' lanes of shouting Gareth rode
Down the slope street, and passed without the gate. 515

But by the field of tourney lingering yet
Muttered the damsel, "Wherefore did the King
Scorn me? for, were Sir Lancelot lacked, at least
He might have yielded to me one of those
Who tilt for lady's love and glory here, 520
Rather than—O sweet heaven! O fie upon him!—
His kitchen-knave."

To whom Sir Gareth drew
(And there were none but few goodlier than he)
Shining in arms, "Damsel, the quest is mine.
Lead, and I follow." She thereat, as one   525
That smells a foul-fleshed agaric in the holt,
And deems it carrion of some woodland thing,
Or shrew, or weasel, nipped her slender nose
With petulant thumb and finger, shrilling, "Hence!
Avoid, thou smellest all of kitchen-grease."   530

"Damsel," Sir Gareth answered gently, "say
Whate'er ye will, but whatsoe'er ye say,
I leave not till I finish this fair quest,
Or die therefor."

          "Ay, wilt thou finish it?
Sweet lord, how like a noble knight he talks!   535
The listening rogue hath caught the manner of it.
But, knave, anon thou shalt be met with, knave,
And then by such a one that thou for all
The kitchen brewis that was ever supped
Shalt not once dare to look him in the face."   540

"I shall assay," said Gareth with a smile
That maddened her, and away she flashed again
Down the long avenues of a boundless wood,
And Gareth following was again be-knaved.

"Sir Kitchen-knave, I have missed the only way   545
Where Arthur's men are set along the wood;
The wood is nigh as full of thieves as leaves:
If both be slain, I am rid of thee: but yet,
Sir Scullion, canst thou use that spit of thine?
Fight, and thou canst: I have missed the only way."   550

So till the dusk that followed evensong
Rode on the two, reviler and reviled;
Then after one long slope was mounted, saw,
Bowl-shaped, thro' tops of many thousand pines
A gloomy-gladed hollow slowly sink   555
To westward—in the deeps whereof a mere,

526. *agaric—holt:* fungus—woods. 541. *assay:* try. 556. *mere:* lake.

Round as the red eye of an Eagle-owl,
Under the half-dead sunset glared; and shouts
Ascended, and there brake a servingman
Flying from out of the black wood, and crying,   560
"They have bound my lord to cast him in the mere."
Then Gareth, "Bound am I to right the wronged,
But straitlier bound am I to bide with thee."
And when the damsel spake contemptuously,
"Lead, and I follow," Gareth cried again,   565
"Follow, I lead!" so down among the pines
He plunged; and there, blackshadowed nigh the mere,
And mid-thigh-deep in bulrushes and reed,
Saw six tall men haling a seventh along,
A stone about his neck to drown him in it.   570
Three with good blows he quieted, but three
Fled thro' the pines; and Gareth loosed the stone
From off his neck, then in the mere beside
Tumbled it; oilily bubbled up the mere.
Last, Gareth loosed his bonds and on free feet   575
Set him, a stalwart Baron, Arthur's friend.

"Well that ye came, or else these caitiff rogues
Had wreaked themselves on me; good cause is theirs
To hate me, for my wont hath ever been
To catch my thief, and then like vermin here   580
Drown him, and with a stone about his neck;
And under this wan water many of them
Lie rotting, but at night let go the stone,
And rise, and flickering in a grimly light
Dance on the mere. Good now, ye have saved a life   585
Worth somewhat as the cleanser of this wood.
And fain would I reward thee worshipfully.
What guerdon will ye?"

                    Gareth sharply spake;
"None! for the deed's sake have I done the deed,
In uttermost obedience to the King.   590
But wilt thou yield this damsel harborage?"

Whereat the Baron saying, "I well believe
You be of Arthur's Table," a light laugh
Broke from Lynette, "Ay, truly of a truth,

582. *wan:* glimmering.   587. *worshipfully:* honorably.

And in a sort, being Arthur's kitchen-knave!— 595
But deem not I accept thee aught the more,
Scullion, for running sharply with thy spit
Down on a rout of craven foresters.
A thresher with his flail had scattered them.
Nay—for thou smellest of the kitchen still. 600
But an this lord will yield us harborage,
Well."

    So she spake. A league beyond the wood,
All in a full-fair manor and a rich,
His towers, where that day a feast had been
Held in high hall, and many a viand left, 605
And many a costly cate, received the three.
And there they placed a peacock in his pride
Before the damsel, and the Baron set
Gareth beside her, but at once she rose.

    "Meseems, that here is much discourtesy, 610
Setting this knave, Lord Baron, at my side.
Hear me—this morn I stood in Arthur's hall,
And prayed the King would grant me Lancelot
To fight the brotherhood of Day and Night—
The last a monster unsubduable 615
Of any save òf him for whom I called—
Suddenly bawls this frontless kitchen-knave,
'The quest is mine; thy kitchen-knave am I,
And mighty thro' thy meats and drinks am I.'
Then Arthur, all at once gone mad, replies, 620
'Go therefore,' and so gives the quest to him—
Him—here—a villain fitter to stick swine
Than ride abroad redressing women's wrong,
Or sit beside a noble gentlewoman."

    Then half-ashamed and part-amazed, the lord 625
Now looked at one and now at other, left
The damsel by the peacock in his pride,
And, seating Gareth at another board,
Sat down beside him, ate and then began.

599. *had:* would have. 606. *cate:* dainty. 617. *frontless:* shameless.

"Friend, whether thou be kitchen-knave, or not,　630
Or whether it be the maiden's fantasy,
And whether she be mad, or else the King,
Or both or neither, or thyself be mad,
I ask not: but thou strikest a strong stroke,
For strong thou art and goodly therewithal,　635
And saver of my life; and therefore now,
For here be mighty men to joust with, weigh
Whether thou wilt not with thy damsel back
To crave again Sir Lancelot of the King.
Thy pardon; I but speak for thine avail,　640
The saver of my life."

　　　　　　　　And Gareth said,
"Full pardon, but I follow up the quest,
Despite of Day and Night and Death and Hell."

So when, next morn, the lord whose life he saved
Had, some brief space, conveyed them on their way　645
And left them with God-speed, Sir Gareth spake,
"Lead, and I follow." Haughtily she replied,

"I fly no more: I allow thee for an hour.
Lion and stoat have isled together, knave,
In time of flood. Nay, furthermore, methinks　650
Some ruth is mine for thee. Back wilt thou, fool?
For hard by here is one will overthrow
And slay thee: then will I to court again,
And shame the King for only yielding me
My champion from the ashes of his hearth."　655

To whom Sir Gareth answered courteously,
"Say thou thy say, and I will do my deed.
Allow me for mine hour, and thou wilt find
My fortunes all as fair as hers who lay
Among the ashes and wedded the King's son."　660

Then to the shore of one of those long loops
Wherethro' the serpent river coiled, they came.
Rough-thicketed were the banks and steep; the stream

637. *weigh:* think. 649. *isled:* fled to an island. 651. *ruth:* pity.

Full, narrow; this a bridge of single arc
Took at a leap; and on the further side   665
Arose a silk pavilion, gay with gold
In streaks and rays, and all Lent-lily in hue,
Save that the dome was purple, and above,
Crimson, a slender banneret fluttering.
And therebefore the lawless warrior paced   670
Unarmed, and calling, "Damsel, is this he,
The champion thou hast brought from Arthur's hall
For whom we let thee pass?" "Nay, nay," she said,
"Sir Morning-Star. The King in utter scorn
Of thee and thy much folly hath sent thee here   675
His kitchen-knave: and look thou to thyself:
See that he fall not on thee suddenly,
And slay thee unarmed: he is not knight but knave."

Then at his call, "O daughters of the Dawn,
And servants of the Morning-Star, approach,   680
Arm me," from out the silken curtainfolds
Bare-footed and bare-headed three fair girls
In gilt and rosy raiment came: their feet
In dewy grasses glistened; and the hair
All over glanced with dewdrop or with gem   685
Like sparkles in the stone Avanturine.
These armed him in blue arms, and gave a shield
Blue also, and thereon the morning star.
And Gareth silent gazed upon the knight,
Who stood a moment, ere his horse was brought,   690
Glorying; and in the stream beneath him, shone
Immingled with Heaven's azure waveringly,
The gay pavilion and the naked feet,
His arms, the rosy raiment, and the star.

Then she that watched him, "Wherefore stare ye so?
Thou shakest in thy fear: there yet is time: 696
Flee down the valley before he get to horse.
Who will cry shame? Thou art not knight but knave."

Said Gareth, "Damsel, whether knave or knight,
Far liefer had I fight a score of times   700
Than hear thee so missay me and revile.

667. *Lent-lily*: daffodil. 686. *Avanturine*: quartz.

Fair words were best for him who fights for thee;
But truly foul are better, for they send
That strength of anger thro' mine arms, I know
That I shall overthrow him."

      And he that bore 705
The star, when mounted, cried from o'er the bridge,
"A kitchen-knave, and sent in scorn of me!
Such fight not I, but answer scorn with scorn.
For this were shame to do him further wrong
Than set him on his feet, and take his horse 710
And arms, and so return him to the King.
Come, therefore, leave thy lady lightly, knave.
Avoid: for it beseemeth not a knave
To ride with such a lady."

      "Dog, thou liest!
I spring from loftier lineage than thine own." 715
He spake; and all at fiery speed the two
Shocked on the central bridge, and either spear
Bent but not brake, and either knight at once,
Hurled as a stone from out of a catapult
Beyond his horse's crupper and the bridge, 720
Fell, as if dead; but quickly rose and drew,
And Gareth lashed so fiercely with his brand
He drave his enemy backward down the bridge,
The damsel crying, "Well-stricken, kitchen-knave!"
Till Gareth's shield was cloven; but one stroke 725
Laid him that clove it grovelling on the ground.

Then cried the fall'n, "Take not my life: I yield."
And Gareth, "So this damsel ask it of me,
Good—I accord it easily as a grace."
She reddening, "Insolent scullion: I of thee? 730
I bound to thee for my favor asked!"
"Then shall he die." And Gareth there unlaced
His helmet as to slay him, but she shrieked,
"Be not so hardy, scullion, as to slay
One nobler than thyself." "Damsel, thy charge 735
Is an abounding pleasure to me. Knight,
Thy life is thine at her command. Arise

. . . AND ALL AT FIERY SPEED THE TWO
SHOCKED ON THE CENTRAL BRIDGE. . . .

And quickly pass to Arthur's hall, and say
His kitchen-knave hath sent thee. See thou crave
His pardon for thy breaking of his laws.   740
Myself, when I return, will plead for thee.
Thy shield is mine—farewell; and, damsel, thou,
Lead, and I follow."

                 And fast away she fled.
Then when he came upon her, spake, "Methought,
Knave, when I watched thee striking on the bridge   745
The savor of thy kitchen came upon me
A little faintlier; but the wind hath changed;
I scent it twenty-fold." And then she sang,
" 'O morning star' (not that tall felon there
Whom thou by sorcery or unhappiness   750
Or some device, hast foully overthrown),
O morning star that smilest in the blue,
O star, my morning dream hath proven true,
Smile sweetly, thou! my love hath smiled on me.'

    "But thou begone, take counsel, and away,   755
For hard by here is one that guards a ford—
The second brother in their fools' parable—
Will pay thee all thy wages, and to boot.
Care not for shame: thou art not knight but knave."

    To whom Sir Gareth answered laughingly,   760
"Parables? Hear a parable of the knave.
When I was kitchen-knave among the rest
Fierce was the hearth, and one of my co-mates
Owned a rough dog, to whom he cast his coat,—
'Guard it,' and there was none to meddle with it.   765
And such a coat art thou, and thee the King
Gave me to guard, and such a dog am I,
To worry, and not to flee—and—knight or knave—
The knave that doth thee service as full knight
Is all as good, meseems, as any knight   770
Toward thy sister's freeing."

                   "Ay, Sir Knave!
Ay, knave, because thou strikest as a knight,
Being but knave, I hate thee all the more."

"Fair damsel, you should worship me the more,
That, being but knave, I throw thine enemies."   775

"Ay, ay," she said, "but thou shalt meet thy match."

So when they touched the second riverloop,
Huge on a huge red horse, and all in mail
Burnished to blinding, shone the Noonday Sun
Beyond a raging shallow. As if the flower,   780
That blows a globe of after arrowlets,
Ten thousand-fold had grown, flashed the fierce shield,
All sun; and Gareth's eyes had flying blots
Before them when he turned from watching him.
He from beyond the roaring shallow roared,   785
"What doest thou, brother, in my marches here?"
And she athwart the shallow shrilled again,
"Here is a kitchen-knave from Arthur's hall
Hath overthrown thy brother, and hath his arms."
"Ugh!" cried the Sun, and vizoring up a red   790
And cipher face of rounded foolishness,
Pushed horse across the foamings of the ford,
Whom Gareth met mid-stream: no room was there
For lance or tourney-skill: four strokes they struck
With sword, and these were mighty; the new knight   795
Had fear he might be shamed; but as the Sun
Heaved up a ponderous arm to strike the fifth,
The hoof of his horse slipped in the stream, the stream
Descended, and the Sun was washed away.

Then Gareth laid his lance athwart the ford;   800
So drew him home; but he that fought no more,
As being all bone-battered on the rock,
Yielded; and Gareth sent him to the King.
"Myself when I return will plead for thee"—
"Lead, and I follow." Quietly she led.   805
"Hath not the good wind, damsel, changed again?"
"Nay, not a point: nor art thou victor here.
There lies a ridge of slate across the ford;
His horse thereon stumbled—ay, for I saw it.

774. *worship:* respect. 781. the dandelion. 786. *marches:* territory.

" 'O Sun' (not this strong fool whom thou, Sir Knave,
Hast overthrown thro' mere unhappiness),   811
'O Sun, that wakenest all to bliss or pain,
O moon, that layest all to sleep again,
Shine sweetly : twice my love hath smiled on me.'

"What knowest thou of lovesong or of love?   815
Nay, nay, God wot, so thou wert nobly born,
Thou hast a pleasant presence. Yea, perchance,—

" 'O dewy flowers that open to the sun,
O dewy flowers that close when day is done,
Blow sweetly : twice my love hath smiled on me.'   820

"What knowest thou of flowers, except, belike,
To garnish meats with ? hath not our good King
Who lent me thee, the flower of kitchendom,
A foolish love for flowers ? what stick ye round
The pasty ? wherewithal deck the boar's head ?   825
Flowers ? nay, the boar hath rosemaries and bay.

" 'O birds, that warble to the morning sky,
O birds that warble as the day goes by,
Sing sweetly : twice my love hath smiled on me.'

"What knowest thou of birds, lark, mavis, merle,   830
Linnet ? what dream ye when they utter forth
May-music growing with the growing light,
Their sweet sun-worship ? these be for the snare
(So runs thy fancy), these be for the spit,
Larding and basting. See thou have not now   835
Larded thy last, except thou turn and fly.
There stands the third fool of their allegory."

For there beyond the bridge of treble bow,
All in a rose-red from the west, and all
Naked it seemed, and glowing in the broad   840
Deep-dimpled current underneath, the knight,
That named himself the Star of Evening, stood.

811. *unhappiness*: accident. 838. *treble bow*: triple arch.

And Gareth, "Wherefore waits the madman there
Naked in open dayshine?" "Nay," she cried,
"Not naked, only wrapt in hardened skins
That fit him like his own; and so ye cleave
His armor off him, these will turn the blade."

845

Then the third brother shouted o'er the bridge,
"O brother-star, why shine ye here so low?
Thy ward is higher up: but have ye slain
The damsel's champion?" and the damsel cried,

850

"No star of thine, but shot from Arthur's heaven
With all disaster unto thine and thee!
For both thy younger brethren have gone down
Before this youth; and so wilt thou, Sir Star;
Art thou not old?"

855

"Old, damsel, old and hard,
Old, with the might and breath of twenty boys."
Said Gareth, "Old, and over-bold in brag!
But that same strength which threw the Morning Star
Can throw the Evening."

Then that other blew
A hard and deadly note upon the horn.
"Approach and arm me!" With slow steps from out
An old storm-beaten, russet, many-stained
Pavilion, forth a grizzled damsel came,
And armed him in old arms, and brought a helm
With but a drying evergreen for crest,
And gave a shield whereon the Star of Even
Half-tarnished and half-bright, his emblem, shone.
But when it glittered o'er the saddle-bow,
They madly hurled together on the bridge;
And Gareth overthrew him, lighted, drew,
There met him drawn, and overthrew him again;
But up like fire he started: and as oft
As Gareth brought him grovelling on his knees,
So many a time he vaulted up again;
Till Gareth panted hard, and his great heart,
Foredooming all his trouble was in vain,

860

865

870

875

850. *ward:* post.

Labored within him, for he seemed as one
That all in later, sadder age begins
To war against ill uses of a life,   880
But these from all his life arise, and cry,
"Thou hast made us lords, and canst not put us down!"
He half despairs; so Gareth seemed to strike
Vainly, the damsel clamoring all the while,
"Well done, knave-knight, well stricken,   885
    O good knight-knave—
O knave, as noble as any of all the knights—
Shame me not, shame me not. I have prophesied—
Strike, thou art worthy of the Table Round—
His arms are old, he trusts the hardened skin—   890
Strike—strike—the wind will never change again."
And Gareth, hearing, ever stronglier smote,
And hewed great pieces of his armor off him,
But lashed in vain against the hardened skin,
And could not wholly bring him under, more   895
Than loud Southwesterns, rolling ridge on ridge,
The buoy that rides at sea, and dips and springs
For ever; till at length Sir Gareth's brand
Clashed his, and brake it utterly to the hilt.
"I have thee now;" but forth that other sprang,   900
And, all unknightlike, writhed his wiry arms
Around him, till he felt, despite his mail,
Strangled, but straining ev'n his uttermost
Cast, and so hurled him headlong o'er the bridge
Down to the river, sink or swim, and cried,   905
"Lead, and I follow."

                        But the damsel said,
"I lead no longer; ride thou at my side;
Thou art the kingliest of all kitchen-knaves.

    " 'O trefoil, sparkling on the rainy plain,
O rainbow with three colors after rain,   910
Shine sweetly; thrice my love hath smiled on me.'

    "Sir,—and, good faith, I fain had added Knight,
But that I heard thee call thyself a knave,—
Shamed am I that I so rebuked, reviled,

909. *trefoil:* clover.

Missaid thee; noble I am; and thought the King　915
Scorned me and mine; and now thy pardon, friend,
For thou hast ever answered courteously,
And wholly bold thou art, and meek withal
As any of Arthur's best, but, being knave,
Hast mazed my wit: I marvel what thou art."　920

"Damsel," he said, "you be not all to blame,
Saving that you mistrusted our good King
Would handle scorn, or yield you, asking, one
Not fit to cope your quest. You said your say;
Mine answer was my deed. Good sooth! I hold　925
He scarce is knight, yea but half-man, nor meet
To fight for gentle damsel, he, who lets
His heart be stirred with any foolish heat
At any gentle damsel's waywardness.
Shamed? care not! thy foul sayings fought for me:　930
And seeing now thy words are fair, methinks
There rides no knight, not Lancelot, his great self,
Hath force to quell me."

　　　　　　　　　　　Nigh upon that hour
When the lone hern forgets his melancholy,
Lets down his other leg, and stretching, dreams　935
Of goodly supper in the distant pool,
Then turned the noble damsel smiling at him,
And told him of a cavern hard at hand,
Where bread and baken meats and good red wine
Of Southland, which the Lady Lyonors　940
Had sent her coming champion, waited him.

Anon they passed a narrow comb wherein
Were slabs of rock with figures, knights on horse
Sculptured, and decked in slowly-waning hues.
"Sir Knave, my knight, a hermit once was here,　945
Whose holy hand hath fashioned on the rock
The war of Time against the soul of man.
And yon four fools have sucked their allegory
From these damp walls, and taken but the form.
Know ye not these?" and Gareth looked and read—　950
In letters like to those the vexillary

934. *hern:* heron. 951. *vexillary:* A Roman standard-bearer carved an inscription which still can be seen on the cliff about the River Gelt.

Hath left crag-carven o'er the streaming Gelt—
"Phosphorus," then "Meridies,"—"Hesperus"—
"NOX"—"MORS," beneath five figures, armèd men,
Slab after slab, their faces forward all,   955
And running down the Soul, a Shape that fled
With broken wings, torn raiment and loose hair,
For help and shelter to the hermit's cave.
"Follow the faces, and we find it.—Look,
Who comes behind?"

                         For one—delayed at first—   960
Sir Lancelot, having swum the riverloops—
His blue shield-lions covered—softly drew
Behind the twain, and when he saw the star
Gleam, on Sir Gareth's turning to him, cried,
"Stay, felon knight, I avenge me for my friend."   965
And Gareth crying pricked against the cry;
But when they closed—in a moment—at one touch
Of that skilled spear, the wonder of the world—
Went sliding down so easily, and fell,
That when he found the grass within his hands   970
He laughed.

          The laughter, jarred upon Lynette:
Harshly she asked him, "Shamed and overthrown,
And tumbled back into the kitchen-knave,
Why laugh ye? that ye blew your boast in vain?"
"Nay, noble damsel, but that I, the son   975
Of old King Lot and good Queen Bellicent,
And victor of the bridges and the ford,
And knight of Arthur, here lie thrown by whom
I know not, all thro' mere unhappiness—
Device and sorcery and unhappiness—   980
Out, sword; we are thrown!" And Lancelot an-
      swered, "Prince,
O Gareth—thro' the mere unhappiness
Of one who came to help thee, not to harm,
Lancelot, and all as glad to find thee whole,
As on the day when Arthur knighted him."   985

953. Dawn, Noon, Evening. 954. *Nox, Mors*: Night, Death.

Then Gareth, "Thou—Lancelot!—thine the hand
That threw me? An some chance to mar the boast
Thy brethren of thee make—which could not chance—
Had sent thee down before a lesser spear,
Shamed had I been, and sad—O Lancelot—thou!"   990

Whereat the maiden, petulant: "Lancelot,
Why came ye not, when called? and wherefore now
Come ye, not called? I gloried in my knave,
Who being still rebuked, would answer still
Courteous as any knight—but now, if knight,   995
The marvel dies, and leaves me fooled and tricked,
And only wondering wherefore played upon:
And doubtful whether I and mine be scorned.
Where should be truth if not in Arthur's hall,   999
In Arthur's presence? Knight, knave, prince and fool,
I hate thee and for ever."

                         And Lancelot said,
"Blessed be thou, Sir Gareth! knight art thou
To the King's best wish. O damsel, be you wise
To call him shamed, who is but overthrown?
Thrown have I been, nor once, but many a time.   1005
Victor from vanquished issues at the last,
And overthrower from being overthrown.
With sword we have not striven; and thy good horse
And thou are weary; yet not less I felt
Thy manhood thro' that wearied lance of thine.   1010
Well hast thou done; for all the stream is freed,
And thou hast wreaked his justice on his foes,
And when reviled, hast answered graciously,
And makest merry when overthrown. Prince, Knight,
Hail, Knight and Prince, and of our Table Round!"   1015

And then when turning to Lynette he told
The tale of Gareth, petulantly she said,
"Ay well—ay well—for worse than being fooled
Of others, is to fool one's self. A cave,
Sir Lancelot, is hard by, with meats and drinks   1020
And forage for the horse, and flint for fire.
But all about it flies a honeysuckle.

Seek, till we find." And when they sought and found,
Sir Gareth drank and ate, and all his life
Passed into sleep ; on whom the maiden gazed.   1025
"Sound sleep be thine! sound cause to sleep hast
   thou.
Wake lusty! Seem I not as tender to him
As any mother? Ay, but such a one
As all day long hath rated at her child,
And vexed his day, but blesses him asleep—   1030
Good Lord, how sweetly smells the honeysuckle
In the hushed night, as if the world were one
Of utter peace, and love, and gentleness!
O Lancelot, Lancelot,"—and she clapped her hands—
"Full merry am I to find my goodly knave   1035
Is knight and noble. See now, sworn have I—
Else yon black felon had not let me pass—
To bring thee back to do the battle with him.
Thus an thou goest, he will fight thee first ;
Who doubts thee victor? so will my knight-knave   1040
Miss the full flower of this accomplishment."

   Said Lancelot : "Peradventure, he you name
May know my shield. Let Gareth, an he will,
Change his for mine, and take my charger, fresh,
Not to be spurred, loving the battle as well   1045
As he that rides him." "Lancelot-like," she said,
"Courteous in this, Lord Lancelot, as in all."

   And Gareth, wakening, fiercely clutched the shield ;
"Ramp, ye lance-splintering lions, on whom all spears
Are rotten sticks! ye seem agape to roar!   1050
Yea, ramp and roar at leaving of your lord!—
Care not, good beasts, so well I care for you.
O noble Lancelot, from my hold on these
Streams virtue—fire—thro' one that will not shame
Even the shadow of Lancelot under shield.   1055
Hence: let us go."

                    Silent the silent field
They traversed. Arthur's Harp, tho' summer-wan,
In counter motion to the clouds, allured
The glance of Gareth dreaming on his liege.

1029. *rated:* scolded. 1057. *Arthur's harp:* the constellation Lyra. 1062. *liege:*
king.

A star shot : "Lo," said Gareth, "the foe falls !"   1060
An owl whooped : "Hark the victor pealing there !"
Suddenly she that rode upon his left
Clung to the shield that Lancelot lent him, crying,
"Yield, yield him this again : 'tis he must fight :
I curse the tongue that all thro' yesterday   1065
Reviled thee, and hath wrought on Lancelot now
To lend thee horse and shield : wonders ye have done ;
Miracles ye cannot : here is glory enow
In having flung the three : I see thee maimed,
Mangled : I swear thou canst not fling the fourth."   1070

"And wherefore, damsel ? tell me all ye know.
You cannot scare me ; nor rough face, or voice,
Brute bulk of limb, or boundless savagery
Appal me from the quest."

                              "Nay, Prince," she cried,
"God wot, I never looked upon the face,   1075
Seeing he never rides abroad by day,
But watched him have I like a phantom pass
Chilling the night : nor have I heard the voice.
Always he made his mouthpiece of a page
Who came and went, and still reported him   1080
As closing in himself the strength of ten,
And when his anger tare him, massacring
Man, woman, lad and girl—yea, the soft babe !
Some hold that he hath swallowed infant flesh,
Monster ! O Prince, I went for Lancelot first,   1085
The quest is Lancelot's : give him back the shield."

Said Gareth laughing, "And he fight for this,
Belike he wins it as the better man :
Thus—and not else !"

                              But Lancelot on him urged
All the devisings of their chivalry   1090
When one might meet a mightier than himself ;
How best to manage horse, lance, sword and shield,
And so fill up the gap where force might fail
With skill and fineness. Instant were his words.

1094. *instant :* urgent.

Then Gareth, "Here be rules. I know but one— 1095
To dash against mine enemy and to win.
Yet have I watched thee victor in the joust,
And seen thy way." "Heaven help thee!" sighed
 Lynette.

Then for a space, and under cloud that grew
To thunder-gloom palling all stars, they rode 1100
In converse till she made her palfrey halt,
Lifted an arm, and softly whispered, "There."
And all the three were silent, seeing, pitched
Beside the Castle Perilous on flat field,
A huge pavilion like a mountain peak 1105
Sunder the glooming crimson on the marge,
Black, with black banner, and a long black horn
Beside it hanging; which Sir Gareth grasped,
And so, before the two could hinder him,
Sent all his heart and breath thro' all the horn. 1110
Echoed the walls, a light twinkled; anon
Came lights and lights, and once again he blew;
Whereon were hollow tramplings up and down
And muffled voices heard, and shadows passed;
Till high above him, circled with her maids, 1115
The Lady Lyonors at a window stood,
Beautiful among lights, and waving to him
White hands, and courtesy; but when the Prince
Three times had blown—after long hush—at last—
The huge pavilion slowly yielded up, 1120
Thro' those black foldings, that which housed
 therein.
High on a nightblack horse, in nightblack arms,
With white breast-bone, and barren ribs of Death,
And crowned with fleshless laughter—some ten steps—
In the half-light—thro' the dim dawn—advanced 1125
The monster, and then paused, and spake no word.

But Gareth spake and all indignantly,
"Fool, for thou hast, men say, the strength of ten,
Canst thou not trust the limbs thy God hath given,
But must, to make the terror of thee more, 1130

1106. *marge:* horizon.

Trick thyself out in ghastly imageries
Of that which Life hath done with, and the clod,
Less dull than thou, will hide with mantling flowers
As if for pity?" But he spake no word;
Which set the horror higher: a maiden swooned;   1135
The Lady Lyonors wrung her hands and wept,
As doomed to be the bride of Night and Death;
Sir Gareth's head prickled beneath his helm;
And even Sir Lancelot thro' his warm blood felt
Ice strike, and all that marked him were aghast.   1140

    At once Sir Lancelot's charger fiercely neighed,
And Death's dark war-horse bounded forward with him.
Then those that did not blink the terror, saw
That Death was cast to ground, and slowly rose.
But with one stroke Sir Gareth split the skull.   1145
Half fell to right and half to left and lay.
Then with a stronger buffet he clove the helm
As throughly as the skull; and out from this
Issued the bright face of a blooming boy
Fresh as a flower new-born, and crying, "Knight,   1150
Slay me not: my three brethren bade me do it,
To make a horror all about the house,
And stay the world from Lady Lyonors.
They never dreamed the passes would be passed."
Answered Sir Gareth graciously to one   1155
Not many a moon his younger, "My fair child,
What madness made thee challenge the chief knight
Of Arthur's hall?" "Fair Sir, they bade me do it.
They hate the King, and Lancelot, the King's friend,
They hoped to slay him somewhere on the stream;
They never dreamed the passes could be passed."   1161

    Then sprang the happier day from underground;
And Lady Lyonors and her house, with dance
And revel and song, made merry over Death,
As being, after all their foolish fears   1165
And horrors, only proven a blooming boy.
So large mirth lived, and Gareth won the quest.

    And he that told the tale in older times
Says that Sir Gareth wedded Lyonors,
But he, that told it later, says Lynette.   1170

1148. *throughly*: clear through.

READING PROBLEMS ON THE EPIC

1. *The Crawl:* Why is the hero of this frontier epic not a king or noble? Is he, however, painted as superhuman? Does the supernatural play any part in this epic? Why? Show in what way Hugh is a glorified composite of the frontier scout and trapper. Find examples of detailed word pictures. What do these add to the effect of the narrative? Why is it appropriate for Neihardt to treat of such commonplace things as eating, drinking, cooking, in so serious and elevated a style?

2. *Sohrab and Rustum:* Why had Rustum never seen his son? Why has Sohrab's mother sent word that the baby is a girl? Why has Sohrab joined the Tartar army? Why does he suggest the single combat? Why did Rustum decide to fight, and in plain armor? How many times might the combat have ceased? Why does Rustum refuse peace? Is Sohrab really beaten? Prove. How is Sohrab's identity proved? What does the presence of the horse add to the story? Why does Arnold open and close the story with the river? What does it symbolize?

3. *Ilmarinen's Wooing:* In the legends of many Slavic and Teutonic peoples the hero is a skillful smith. Why should this be true? Why should such a test as plowing a field of vipers be set for the hero? What apparently gives the hero power to vanquish the serpents? Why? Compare this story with that of the wooing of Medea by Jason in Greek mythology. Prove from this extract the great age of the *Kalevala*. Show how this episode in the *Kalevala* is complete in itself.

4. *Farewell of Hector and Andromache:* See the introductory chapter for a discussion of this extract. What details would need to be changed to make this a scene during the World War? Point out thoughts and feelings of the wife and husband that would be the same in any age. What little touches give such a human and natural quality to the scene with the baby? This whole extract relates a simple incident simply. What is there about the style that gives it so grand and elevated a tone? Find examples of Greek fatalism in this incident. Does this philosophy reduce the bravery of Hector? Why?

5. *Dido and Aeneas:* What part do supernatural forces play in this story? Does this succeed in making Aeneas appear to you blameless at the end? Tennyson has called Virgil "lord of language, wielder of the stateliest measure moulded by the lips of man." Find phrases in the description of the cave of the winds and the storm at sea which even in translation give you this impression. What makes the storm scene so clear and vivid? Contrast Aeneas' opening speech to Dido with his behavior at the end. What gives Dido dignity even when abandoned, despairing, and in anguish? Is Virgil a good psychologist? Why does he introduce the final meeting of the lovers in the land of the dead? Compare the women so far met in the epics as to their character, position, and share in the story. Compare the literary style, interest and ideals of the different races whose epics you have read.

6. *Paola and Francesca:* Are Paola and Francesca unhappy in the midst of their torment? Prove. Why instead of telling their whole story does the

author center upon a single incident in it? Is this the significant incident? Select several phrases from the extract which prove Dante's skill at suggesting without narrating. Which character do you seem to know best—Paola or Francesca? Is this as it should be?

7. *Gareth and Lynette:* Why does Tennyson place this story in the spring? How is Gareth's relation to his mother typical of all youth passing into manhood? How is Gareth's character revealed by his acceptance of the position of kitchen knave? What impression do we receive of Arthur from our glimpse of him dispensing justice? Lynette and Gareth are both typical of youth. What defects and virtues of youth does each represent? This poem is full of allegory. Explain what is meant by (1) the four knights —Morning Star, Day, Night, and Death; (2) Lynette's songs. Why has Lancelot followed Gareth? How is Gareth's character shown by his behavior to Lynette and to Lancelot? Select word pictures of great descriptive beauty from this poem. How does this idyll illustrate the completeness of the single episodes in an epic? the plunge into the middle of the story? the aristocratic tone? the elevated style? Does Gareth strike you as more or less of a superman than the other heroes we have met? Why? Compare Lynette to other heroines of epics.

FURTHER READINGS IN THE EPIC

Guerber: *Book of the Epic*
Rabb: *National Epics*
Anonymous (Morris' Translation): *Sigurd the Volsung*
Benét: *John Brown's Body*
Gregory: *Archulain and Muirthemne*
Homer (Palmer's Translation): *The Odyssey*
Longfellow: *Hiawatha*

Milton: *Paradise Lost,* Books I and II
Neihardt: *Song of Three Friends Songs of the Indian Wars*
Tennyson: *The Coming of Arthur Lancelot and Elaine The Passing of Arthur*
Valmicki (Dutt Translation): *Ramayana*

SUGGESTIONS FOR ORIGINAL EPIC EPISODES

1. The Building of the Acropolis. 2. The Barbarian Invaders Are Awed by the Roman Senators Sitting Silent in their Places. 3. The Maid of the Mist: An Indian Legend of Niagara. 4. An Episode in the Life of Daniel Boone or of Buffalo Bill, or the Story of a Pioneer Mother. 5. Building the Panama Canal, the Cascade Tunnel, or the Woolworth Building. 6. Lindbergh Spans the Atlantic, or Byrd Flies Over the Pole. 7. The Forest Rangers Combat a Fire. 8. G-Men Break Up a Criminal Gang. 9. Edison Invents the Incandescent Lamp, the Dynamo, the Phonograph, or the Motion Picture. 10. Marconi Invents the Radio.

VIII

The Drama

THE spontaneous play of a child is almost entirely composed of dramatizing the life of his elders or his story-book heroes and heroines. A favorite recreation of high-school students and adults is attending the theater and seeing plays on the stage or screen. It is not, therefore, surprising that the drama should be one of the oldest literary types and that the ancient Greeks should have produced the greatest dramas except those of William Shakespeare, nor is it surprising that the most popular literary art of our own times should be the dramatic motion picture.

A play is a story told through dialog and action. Because plays are meant to be seen and heard and not read, the reader of plays must imagine for himself the setting, the costumes, and the appearance, tone of voice, facial expression, feelings and actions of the characters. But when once you have trained yourself to pick up these details from the stage directions and from the hints dropped by the author in the dialog, you will find reading plays as enjoyable as reading fiction—and much faster, since the story is never slowed by description or comment but moves at the swift pace of conversation.

Indeed, a play moves more swiftly than ordinary conversation. Because the writer must compress a whole story into a few scenes and acts, he is forced to condense and select. The commonplace events in the lives of the characters are omitted. Only the events bearing on the plot of the play are presented. And these events have to follow each other quickly. Many more things must happen in one scene than occur in the same space of time in everyday life, and every remark made by the characters must explain the past, reveal character, or advance the plot. Thus in reading a play, we are getting the concentrated essence of life, just as in a drop of perfume we get the extracted essence of hundreds of flowers. This selection of just the significant acts and remarks of the characters and this compression of events into a brief space give to a play its brilliance, intensity, vitality, and effect of pulsating life. The characters in a play seem to live with extraordinary swiftness, fullness, and vividness.

As a play is an acted story, action is constant and important, and the plot [1] is always a major interest. Just as in a short story or novel the plot of a drama is a struggle of the main characters with conflicting forces. The leading character is called the protagonist and the principal character ranged against him is the antagonist. The opening scene must quickly acquaint us with the existing situation, the antecedent action, and the major characters, who seldom appear on the stage or screen until we are prepared to recognize them. As soon as this preliminary exposition (or explanation) is out of the way, the inciting force (or incident that starts the plot moving) occurs. From then on appear one after another the plot complications that keep the action going. Usually the things which complicate a plot are the familiar difficulties and personal reactions which we see around us in everyday life and which have already been used many times in literature; but the dramatist embodies them in new characters and weaves them together in a new story, so that they at once delight us by their novelty and appeal to us by their universality. These complicating elements often give rise to one or more sub-plots, and as the complications appear and the sub-plots unfold, they lead us through a series of minor crises up to a powerful, logical, and decisive climax (or turning point in the plot). This part of the play before the climax is called the rising action. The part after the climax is called the falling action, and leads us on to the dénouement or conclusion.

The location of the climax and the length of the falling action differ in different plays. In Shakespeare's long five-act plays, the climax comes in the third act about halfway through the play. In the more recent three-act play, the climax is usually at the first of the last act. In the one-act play, which bears the same relation to the full-length drama as the short story bears to the novel, the climax frequently closes the play. If the falling action is long, interest must be sustained by arousing suspense as to how the characters will take the climax and what results it will produce—either of which may create exciting scenes after the climax is over. The ending of the play must be logical and consistent with the nature of the story and the theme.

While these features are on the whole similar to those met in all fiction, there are some related considerations which are peculiar to the drama. The dramatist cannot speak for himself; he cannot tell

[1] See pages 1–3 and 238 for an explanation of what constitutes a plot.

us what he means by this or that scene or even by the play as a whole. Therefore he writes his scenes in such a way as to emphasize points he wishes us to notice. See whether you can tell what each scene in a play is intended to accomplish. Does it merely convey information, like so many opening scenes? Does it foreshadow, or forecast, coming events? Does it advance the action? Does it suggest the passing of time? Does it create atmosphere? Does it reveal character? Does it bring out the meaning of a preceding scene by contrast? Or is it a scene which merely meets some mechanical necessity of staging, like the short scenes before the curtain by which authors often cover the time it takes to change scenery back stage?

Although the uses of setting are the same in drama and in fiction, as plays are meant to be acted, the means of representing the setting are important. The Greek theater and the theater of Shakespeare's day had no stage scenery but only a permanent architectural background before which all plays must be presented. It is interesting to see how the Greek dramatists and Shakespeare suggest the time, place, and atmosphere of their scenes by the dialog itself. Indeed Shakespeare is a master scene painter in words, and he never misses a chance to revive in the mind of his audience the setting of the scene being enacted, not only by descriptive passages but by passing references and little touches unobtrusively woven into the lines of the actors. Modern theater managers have, however, many resources in scenery and lighting; and sometimes, especially in the motion picture, they are tempted to elaborate the scenic effects so that they overshadow the story and the characters.

Various styles of stage design have been used effectively at different periods: realistic, impressionistic, expressionistic, and constructivist. To study these various styles and the work of the great stage designers who have used them, and to imagine how you would stage each play you read—even perhaps to prepare stage designs for scenery and costume—is a fascinating pursuit.

The dialog of a play is even more interesting than the conversation which enlivens great works of fiction. As pointed out at the start, dialog in a play is highly selective. Every remark must either advance the action, depict setting, or reveal motives and character. Dialog must also be varied to suit the various characters. Shakespeare had the amazing power of adapting his speech to the education, vocabulary, phrasing, thought power, feeling, and personality of many hundreds of characters. Other writers can compose natural conversation for only a few types.

As has been pointed out by many critics, dramatic dialog is always exaggerated to help the dramatist depict his characters: no people are quite so stupid or witty or subtle or comical or silver-tongued as the characters in a play, and no conversation is so concentratedly good. But none the less the "goodness" must give the flavor of life. Because of this heightened quality of the conversation in a play, a great dramatist often produces speeches for his characters which are unforgettable and quotable—because of the eloquence, truth, pathos, or beauty of the lines. Shakespeare is the most quoted of all writers of any type, and of all books in the world except the *Bible*, his *Hamlet* has undoubtedly the most phrases, lines, and passages which have become almost household words.

A dramatist has one great disadvantage as compared with the writer of fiction: he cannot easily show the hidden thoughts of his characters. On the stage and screen, authors resort to various practices to give us these thoughts. In the movies, we often see what is called a fade-in or dissolve, in which the thoughts and feelings passing through the character's mind are pictured in a slightly different camera focus and at a more rapid speed. On the stage, several devices have been used. One modern dramatist has each character presented by two actors—one representing the outer, and the other the inner self. Eugene O'Neill in one play makes the same actor speak both parts—the inner self speaking in a slightly veiled voice. In another O'Neill play, the characters put masks on and off—assuming the mask when the lines are not entirely sincere.

On the whole, however, the most successful device for giving the characters' thoughts are the asides and soliloquies used by Shakespeare. Of course, people do not often talk aloud to themselves as the actor does in a soliloquy. However, all people think things over; and Shakespeare gives to his soliloquies the fragmentary quality of such thinking. The actor speaks in phrases, starts an idea without finishing it, jumps over the intermediate steps in a train of thought. Once accepted by the audience as a stage device, the soliloquy is the best method of seeing within a character.

The skill with which a dramatist introduces his characters and gets them on and off the stage is another interesting feature of the drama. Shakespeare's stage was very large and projected far out into the audience so that the characters had a long walk before they could join naturally in the dialog. He covers this long entrance with great skill, usually by comments from the other characters which explain who the newcomer is and how he fits into the plot. Exits were equally trying in the Shakespearean theater and are difficult on any stage. The actor must go off on a good line which finishes his part in the incident and is effective enough to bear the attention called to it by the exit. As Shakespeare's stage had no curtain, he had to provide some natural way for everyone left on the stage at the end of a scene to walk off and for dead bodies to be carried out.

Indeed the whole problem of characterization is as prominent in a play as in fiction; and we ask here as there whether the characters are real people with individualized personalities or whether they are merely colorless figures going through the actions required by the plot; whether the characters are few or many; whether they are drawn from one social class or from all classes; whether the play features one central character or whether a number of main characters claim attention; whether the motives and reactions of the characters are natural; and whether the plot grows out of the characters or the characters are forced into the lines of the plot and do things inappropriate to their real natures.

The dramatist cannot analyze his characters for us as does a novelist. But each time a character speaks, acts, or is spoken about, some trait of his personality is displayed. Owing to the recurrent crises in a play, the characters reveal themselves dramatically by their reactions to these crises and to the choices with which the crises confront them.

Plays fall into several classes. Most impressive is tragedy, in which we watch sympathetically, moved by pity and fear, the struggle with overwhelming odds of a noble nature who meets disaster, "not because of vice or depravity, but because of some frailty or error in judgment." A comedy is a play in which the hero triumphs. The comedy is thus lighter in tone and contains more gaiety and humor than a tragedy. A tragi-comedy gives a tragic ending for some characters and a happy ending for others, or else the leading characters lose in one way but gain in another. A farce is broadly humorous, since the characters are either themselves ridiculous in motives and appearance, or meet with ridiculous difficulties. A melodrama is a highly exciting play full of astonishing and improbable happenings, exaggerated characters, and crises, in which the favorite characters emerge triumphant and the villains are foiled at the last moment. All plays belong to one of these four already listed main classes. Historical or chronicle plays turn real historic characters and events into drama. Mystery, miracle, and morality plays dramatize respectively Bible stories, the lives of the saints, and stories which teach religious or moral lessons. The first

English plays were of this type.[2] The masque is an allegorical pageant in which spectacle, song, and dance predominate over plot and character. A problem play has as its theme the presentation or solution of some vital social or human problem of general application. Problem plays go out of date with the problem they present unless the problem serves to reveal characters who can compel permanent interest in themselves.

Sometimes a play belonging to one of these classes may be fantastic and allegorical, making its point about life through impossible plots and characters, as do the fantasies and allegories of fiction. And plays of any and all these classes may be written to be read, not acted. These are called closet[3] dramas; and are the work of poets who have a sense of dramatic situation but lack either the theatrical skill or interest to adapt their dramas for stage presentation.

To do this, indeed, requires both skill and experience. For the dramatist who expects his play to succeed on the stage or screen must consider expertly the taste and needs of the theatrical producer who will buy it, the abilities of the actors likely to present it, the physical features of the stage or studio where it must be acted, and the demands of the audience that will witness it. The story of great drama is the story of how the supreme dramatists have met each of these problems and yet given the world something finely entertaining—something noteworthy for its theme, its study of human nature, or its truthful portrayal of those great experiences which remain permanently and universally significant. The playwright who composes merely to sell his play, to exploit a certain actor or actors, to astonish the public by stage spectacle and theatrical tricks, or to cater to the lower impulses and tastes of the mass mind will never produce great art in the drama. But the dramatist who can make the available producer, actor, and stage a vehicle for profound and vital comment on life, understandable by and interesting to the audience, will ennoble the stage and screen and immortalize himself.

FOR FURTHER READING

Boas and Smith: *Introduction to Literature* (revised edition). Chapter V. "The Drama."

[2] See Weeks, Lyman and Hill, *English Literature,* pages 107–121 and 241–261 for the history of the English drama.

[3] *closet* was in earlier times the name of a private sitting room or study.

TWO CROOKS AND A LADY

Eugene Pillot (America)

Two Crooks and a Lady was written by a student in a course in play-writing formerly taught at Harvard University by Professor George Pierce Baker. This course graduated so many dramatists whose works were later produced on Broadway that the course and even its catalog number (47) became famous all over the United States. English 47 had a little theatre called The 47 Workshop, in which plays written by the class were acted by the class before an invited audience, each of whom paid his admission by writing a criticism of the play and the performance. Another famous dramatic course of the same kind is taught by Professor Frederick H. Koch at the University of North Carolina. Its students have produced plays of the mountain whites and the South, which have also found their way onto the stage.

Two Crooks and a Lady is based on a short story, *Fibre,* by Richard Washburn Child.

❋ ❋ ❋

Characters

MILLER, *The Hawk*
LUCILLE, *His accomplice*
MRS. SIMMS-VANE
MISS JONES, *Her companion*
POLICE INSPECTOR GARRITY
A POLICEMAN

SCENE: *Library in the old Fifth Avenue mansion of Mrs. Simms-Vane. It is an old-fashioned, thoroughly substantial room and an ideal setting for its owner. French windows, overlooking Fifth Avenue and extending to the floor, are in the middle of the rear wall. Bookcases on each side of them extend to a door at rear right and to a writing desk at left front. There is a chair near the window, one by the table, and one by the desk. Prominent among the usual desk fittings must be a small gold stamp box. A waste-paper basket stands beside the desk, in full view of the audience. Several porcelain vases are placed about the room. A long library table, holding two brass candlesticks, is at right front. Just above it, on the right wall, a large, long mirror hangs so that it reflects the opposite side of the room.*

PLACE: *New York City.* TIME: *The present. About three o'clock on a rainy afternoon.*

The curtain rises on an empty stage, rather dark because of the rainy day and the drawn curtains. The French window in the rear opens cautiously and MILLER *stealthily slips into the room. He is a tall, handsome man—the usual type of gentleman crook who has emerged from the bottom of his nefarious profession. He wears a dark raincoat and a soft black hat, pulled down a little over his eyes. As he starts to advance into the room, approaching footsteps are heard off right. Frightened, he slips behind the heavy curtains at the windows.*

LUCILLE *enters from the door at right. She is in the conventional white apron and cap of a well-groomed parlor maid. She stops for a moment to tidy the table, glances up at the mirror, and starts to make a slight readjustment of her cap. Suddenly she realizes that it is too dark for her to see, goes to the window, and quickly pulls back the curtains, flooding the room with light and revealing* MILLER. *The moment she sees* MILLER, *she jumps back frightened.*

LUCILLE. [*In a loud voice.*] Miller!

MILLER. [*Frightened, he comes forward cautiously.*] Don't shout!

LUCILLE. You nearly scared the life out of me!

MILLER. Don't tell it to the whole house. [*Glances toward door.*] Lucille, anybody about?

[*Throughout the following scene,* LUCILLE *and* MILLER *give their lines quickly, feverishly, for they fear that they may be interrupted at any moment.*]

LUCILLE. Not yet; but they wheel Mrs. Simms-Vaine in here every afternoon. You're not safe here! [*Tries to hurry him to the window.*]

MILLER. [*Catching her by the arm.*] Quick! Where does she keep the Thirty-three?

LUCILLE. [*Carelessly, as she jerks her arm away.*] Why should I tell you?

MILLER. Going to hog the necklace yourself 'stead of divvying up with me, huh?

LUCILLE. No.

MILLER. Then what's the matter with you?

LUCILLE. You've been taking that Minnie out again!

MILLER. Naw, I'm on the level with you.

LUCILLE. [*Scornfully.*] Huh!

MILLER. Didn't I say we'd get married soon's we cop the neck-lace?

LUCILLE. [*Arrogantly.*] I know you *said* that.

MILLER. Then, what's in your craw? Jealous again?

LUCILLE. Why not? I've got everything staked on you!

MILLER. And you can play it for all it's worth. It'll take both of us to steal the Thirty-three.

LUCILLE. Miller, it's a wonderful necklace.

MILLER. Worth forty thousand dollars.

LUCILLE. Thirty-three blue-white diamonds. Wouldn't think an old dame would be so stuck on it!

MILLER. No more than we are. [*Nudges her affectionately.*] Now, where does she keep it?

LUCILLE. In this room!

MILLER. This room?

LUCILLE. Yes, they say she comes in here to look at it; but no one's ever seen her do it!

MILLER. Good enough; we'll cop it this very afternoon!

LUCILLE. How?

MILLER. Listen, this is the dope.

LUCILLE. [*Eagerly.*] Uh-huh.

MILLER. Servants are off to-day, 'cept you, the cook, and the old dame's companion. Cook's way down in the kitchen—and I've fixed it to get the companion away.

LUCILLE. How?

MILLER. Dennis is across the street—watching this window.

LUCILLE. Why?

MILLER. When the time's ready, I'll signal him with this hand-kerchief and right off the phone here will ring. You answer it.

LUCILLE. [*Puzzled.*] What's the game?

MILLER. Dennis is going to send a fake message—something about a phony check—that'll get Miss Jones out of the house. Want you to answer the phone so's to be sure it's Dennis. Then call her, understand?

LUCILLE. Yes!

MILLER. After that it'll be plain sailing.

LUCILLE. But Dennis'll want some of the boot for doing that?

MILLER. Naw, I promised him a tenner if he'd send the phone message and then beat it to the station and get a couple of tickets for us. [*Murmur of voices from off right.*]

LUCILLE. Oh, they're coming now. Better get away in a hurry! [MILLER *runs to the window.*]

MILLER. Don't forget to answer that phone!

LUCILLE. I won't! They're almost here! Hurry up and get out!

MILLER. No, I'm going to stay right here.

LUCILLE. But they'll see you!

MILLER. No, they won't. I'll slide behind this curtain. [*He slips behind one of the window curtains, which remain partly open. He is completely concealed.* LUCILLE *pretends to arrange articles on the desk, furtively glancing at right door. From right enter* MISS JONES, *pushing an invalid's chair in which is seated* MRS. SIMMS-VANE.

MISS JONES, *the paid companion of* MRS. SIMMS-VANE, *is a rather dull, systematic English woman, not in the least understanding her mistress, but as a result of long service, obeying her to the letter.* MRS. SIMMS-VANE, *a hopeless paralytic for twenty years, cannot move her chin a quarter of an inch to left or right. Her body is rigid; her cheeks are webbed with the fine wrinkles of the years; her eyes are beautiful with patience; and her mouth is lovely with the firmness of suffering. Once very beautiful, she is now at the age of sixty, as inert as a faded flower. She wears a rich but simple dress of black silk with white lace at the throat.* MISS JONES *wheels the chair to left center, somewhat to rear, and facing the table and the mirror on the right wall. She lifts one of the invalid's hands and places it so that it rests easily on the arm of her chair. As she goes to the other side of the chair and arranges the other hand in a similar manner,* MILLER, *with his eye on* MISS JONES *and watched by* LUCILLE, *silently steps from behind the curtain, glances out the window, gives a quick wave of his handkerchief—the signal to the unseen Dennis—and slips behind the curtain again without being seen by either* MISS JONES *or* MRS. SIMMS-VANE.]

MRS. SIMMS-VANE. [*As* MISS JONES *starts to make a slight adjustment of the old lady's head against the back of her chair.*] No, to the right. [MISS JONES *moves the head slightly.*] Too much. More to the left. [MISS JONES *moves the head again.*]

MISS JONES. May I ask why you always want your head faced that way?

MRS. SIMMS-VANE. [*Coolly amused.*] You may *ask*.

[MRS. SIMMS-VANE's *tone causes* MISS JONES *to step back abashed, and she does not venture the question. The telephone on the desk rings.* MISS JONES *starts toward it; but* LUCILLE *has already picked it up.*]

LUCILLE. I'll answer it, Miss Jones. [*Speaks into the telephone.*] Hello—Yes—*Yes!* [*Glances in direction of* MILLER.]—All right, I'll call her. [*Turns to* MISS JONES.] It's for you, Miss Jones.

MISS JONES. Thank you. [*Goes to telephone.*] Hello—Yes—Oh, is that so?—Very well. I'll be right down to see about it.—Thank you. Good-bye. [*Hangs up the receiver and goes to* MRS. SIMMS-VANE.] Mrs. Simms-Vane, that was the Empire National Bank on the phone.

MRS. SIMMS-VANE. Yes?

MISS JONES. The cashier has discovered what appears to be an alteration in a check you gave Andrews, the grocer. They asked me to go immediately to their downtown offices; and I told them I would.

MRS. SIMMS-VANE. Very well.

MISS JONES. [*To* LUCILLE.] You will remain here with Mrs. Simms-Vane. There will be nothing to do for her. [*Goes to the door at right where she turns and says to* LUCILLE:] Even though it is raining, she will take her daily ride at four as usual. By that time, probably, I shall return.

LUCILLE. [*With a superior air.*] Very good, Miss Jones.

[*Exit* MISS JONES. *A moment's silence, then an outside door closes.* MILLER *steps out from behind the curtain and beckons for* LUCILLE *to come to him. She does so and together they step out into the room and look threateningly at* MRS. SIMMS-VANE *for a moment. They are now in her range of vision and she stares at them without the flicker of an eyelash.*]

MRS. SIMMS-VANE. [*Calmly.*] Lucille, who is this gentleman? [LUCILLE *fidgets.*] Why is he here? [LUCILLE *becomes more nervous.*]

MILLER. [*Brushing past* LUCILLE.] I'll do the talking!

MRS. SIMMS-VANE. I fear, Lucille, that I have been mistaken in you.

MILLER. [*To* MRS. SIMMS-VANE.] Now, there'll be no nonsense!

MRS. SIMMS-VANE. I think I understand.

MILLER. Better for you, if you do!

MRS. SIMMS-VANE. Sir, will you kindly step forward three or four steps?

MILLER. What for?

MRS. SIMMS-VANE. I am unable, because of my infirmity, to turn my head; and I prefer to talk looking into the eyes.

MILLER. [*Stepping in front of* MRS. SIMMS-VANE.] We'll not have much talk. [*Quickly, to* LUCILLE.] You mind that door.

[*Points to door, which* LUCILLE *closes as* MILLER *goes to the telephone and cuts its green cord. Resuming his position in front of* MRS. SIMMS-VANE.] Now, Mrs. Simms-Vane, I'll tell you why I'm here.

MRS. SIMMS-VANE. Yes?

MILLER. I come for the Thirty-three, and you're going to tell me where it is.

MRS. SIMMS-VANE. [*Slight surprise.*] So you call it the Thirty-three?

MILLER. Needn't pretend you don't understand what I'm talking about. I ain't got much time. Now, where is it? [*Points a menacing finger at* MRS. SIMMS-VANE's *face. She merely smiles and looks at him without making the slightest movement.*]

MRS. SIMMS-VANE. [*Firmly, but softly.*] Sir, you have made a mistake to come here.

MILLER. Mistake? Ha! [*Halfway laughs.*]

MRS. SIMMS-VANE. It is true that I am a helpless invalid and cannot call for assistance; but there is that which will cause you to fail. You shall have a disaster.

LUCILLE. [*As she comes to* MILLER, *frightened.*] Oh, Miller, what does she mean?

MILLER. [*Ignores* LUCILLE. *Speaks sneeringly to* MRS. SIMMS-VANE.] You mean you'll call on God? Well, my nerve's good for that stuff.

MRS. SIMMS-VANE. [*Referring to* LUCILLE.] Hers is not. [MILLER *turns and looks at* LUCILLE, *who has become very nervous.*]

LUCILLE. It's a lie! The old fossil!

MRS. SIMMS-VANE. [*A little, slow smile passes over her face as she continues in her calm voice.*] Nevertheless, I do not refer to divine assistance.

MILLER. Then, what do you mean?

MRS. SIMMS-VANE. I think you will fail, because you are not made of the material that succeeds. You are both of the base metals—unrestrained, passionate, and vulgar.

LUCILLE. [*Her vanity is hurt.*] The idea!

MRS. SIMMS-VANE. Yes, and that is why you made a mistake to come into conflict with me.

MILLER. Bah!

MRS. SIMMS-VANE. At the very outset, sir, you made a mistake.

MILLER. Mistake—what mistake?

MRS. SIMMS-VANE. Almost your first words disclosed the fact that you did not know where the necklace is laid away.

Miller. You're not very clever yourself. You've just as well as admitted the Thirty-three's in this room.

[*Jerks off his raincoat, throws it on the floor, and starts to search for the Thirty-three among the papers in the writing-desk drawers.* Lucille *still keeps guard at the door.* Mrs. Simms-Vane, *unable to turn her head, stares ahead at nothing.*]

Mrs. Simms-Vane. [*After a pause, in her same calm voice.*] Will you trust in one who has never broken her word to anyone?

Miller. [*Stops suddenly and looks at* Mrs. Simms-Vane.] What are you trying to get at?

Mr. Simms-Vane. Suppose I promise to reward you [Lucille *starts forward jealously*] both to the full? [Lucille *sinks back relieved.*]

Miller. What are you giving us?

Mrs. Simms-Vane. The necklace is my most treasured possession, not because of its money value, but because my dear, dead husband gave it to me when we were young and very happy. [Lucille *turns away, sickened by this expression of sentiment.*]

Miller. What's that got to do with us?

Mrs. Simms-Vane. That is why I will not have it taken from me.

Lucille. Listen to her!

Miller. [*Coarse laugh.*] Ha!

Mrs. Simms-Vane. Then look out for yourselves. I warn you.

[Miller *walks back until he stands in front of* Mrs. Simms-Vane. *Suddenly he takes a pistol from his pocket and thrusts the muzzle of it into her face.*]

Miller. [*Growling.*] Where's the thing hid? [Mrs. Simms-Vane *slowly closes her eyes and slowly opens them again. He pushes the revolver nearer her.*] Where's it hid?

Mrs. Simms-Vane. Do you think I fear that you will pull that trigger?

Miller. Why wouldn't I?

Mrs. Simms-Vane. Can you not see how beautiful that would be for me—a hopeless invalid?

Miller. [*Not understanding.*] Huh?

Mrs. Simms-Vane. But it is too much to hope. You would not shoot me.

Miller. I'll soon show you!

Mrs. Simms-Vane. Ah, no, that would make a noise.

Miller. [*Impatiently.*] What if it did?

Mrs. Simms-Vane. Then you could not continue your search. No, I cannot hope that you will pull that trigger.

Miller. [*Realizing the truth of her words, drops the pistol to his side.*] You're a tough old nut.

Mrs. Simms-Vane. Thank you, sir. That is very kind.

Miller. Bah! [*Then to* Lucille.] Pull out the books, girlie. We've got to frisk the whole room.

Lucille. [*Coming forward.*] All right!

Miller. Go through it systematic and fast; and look in the vases!

Lucille. Yes, yes! [*Begins to execute his commands.*]

Miller. Remember, she said it was "laid away"—that's the cue.

Lucille. Uh-huh.

[Miller *returns to the desk, tosses papers and boxes to the floor, opens the stamp box on the desk, finds a locked drawer, and feverishly splinters it open.* Lucille *is hastily pulling out the books from the shelves and searching the wall behind them for any secret hiding place of the necklace. The room is in a welter of disorder. Finally,* Miller *returns to his revolver which he left on the table as he made his rounds of the room, stares down at it, and bites his lip.*]

Miller. [*Growling.*] Time wasted! [*Looks at* Mrs. Simms-Vane *and takes a pair of steel pliers from his side pocket, opens them, and looks down at them.*] It's rough work; but it's got to be done. [*Goes to* Mrs. Simms-Vane *and closes his hand over one of her white wrists. Her fingers move a little.*] Huh! There's some feeling in this hand. I thought so. [*He slips the toothed jaws of the pliers between the thumb and forefinger down upon the soft flesh in the crotch of her thumb and closes the pliers upon it.*] Now, where's the necklace? [Mrs. Simms-Vane *silently stares at him.*] Better tell. [*She merely closes her eyes.*] You better tell! [Lucille *shudders as she sees that he is squeezing the pliers in his tightening grip.*] Curse you! Out with it! Where's the necklace?

Mrs. Simms-Vane. That is painful; but I do not think pain will ever be my master. I shall not tell you.

Lucille. Stop! Stop, Miller! The blood's coming!

Miller. Let it come.

Lucille. But she won't tell! Oh, you're crushing the flesh! Stop! [*Starts to pull him away.*]

Mrs. Simms-Vane. [*Opening her eyes.*] Ah, she's weakened! I said you were both made of inferior stuff. This French doll of yours, sir, was willing to see you torture an old lady who cannot move and yet a few drops of red blood make her cry out. What a pair you are—all boastfulness; but your nerves are made of shoddy. [MILLER *drops the pliers in his pocket, looks at* LUCILLE, *and sneers.*]

LUCILLE. [*To* MILLER.] Don't! Don't look at me like that!

MILLER. Why not? The old dame's right about us. [*Outside, a clock strikes three o'clock.*]

MRS. SIMMS-VANE. [*Fretfully.*] It's three. I ordered my hot milk for three.

MILLER. [*Wheeling toward* LUCILLE.] The cook'll bring it in?

LUCILLE. [*Sullenly.*] Perhaps.

MILLER. Quick, then! Go to the kitchen. Say she sent you for it. I'll take another look round the room. [LUCILLE *shrugs her shoulders and exits.* MILLER *starts to search in the desk drawers again.*]

MRS. SIMMS-VANE. [*Sees him in the mirror.*] Young man, I see you're searching in those drawers again. I would not waste my time doing that.

MILLER. [*Startled.*] Why not?

MRS. SIMMS-VANE. Perhaps I will tell you what you wish to know.

MILLER. What?

MRS. SIMMS-VANE. Come and stand in front of me.

MILLER. [*He does so, staring at her.*] Well?

MRS. SIMMS-VANE. You may be surprised, sir, to hear that I cannot help admiring the boldness you have shown in coming here.

MILLER. Aw, what are you giving me now?

MRS. SIMMS-VANE. I have always been attracted by ability, wherever it showed itself and——

MILLER. [*With contempt.*] Words, words.

MRS. SIMMS-VANE. No-o, but you are a handsome young man, and it is a pity that your magnetism and power should be thrown away on such a worthless young woman as Lucille.

MILLER. Aw, Lucille's all right.

MRS. SIMMS-VANE. Pah! You saw her cringe!

MILLER. Well?

MRS. SIMMS-VANE. A pretty face—that's all she is. And you are infatuated with her—you who could win women far above her class. She stands in your way. This very occasion is an example of it.

MILLER. What are you driving at?

MRS. SIMMS-VANE. In the next fifteen minutes she may cost you forty thousand dollars.

MILLER. [*Leaning nearer.*] How's it figured?

MRS. SIMMS-VANE. I don't trust her; but I could—trade with you.

MILLER. Trade?

MRS. SIMMS-VANE. Did it not occur to you, sir, that forty thousand dollars is very little to me? If I spent it, it would be charged to my heirs.

MILLER. What's that got to do with the Thirty-three?

MRS. SIMMS-VANE. I would willingly send you a check for the amount if you would go away.

MILLER. [*Scornfully.*] Huh!

MRS. SIMMS-VANE. But it is too much to ask you to take my word for that. However, I could take yours.

MILLER. [*Eagerly.*] Yes?

MRS. SIMMS-VANE. But not if Lucille were involved.

MILLER. Why not?

MRS. SIMMS-VANE. I love those stones the most of all material things—and I would not trust them to her.

MILLER. [*Glances toward door, then leans nearer to her, alert.*] How's that again? Talk faster.

MRS. SIMMS-VANE. I cannot. I meant that if I could trust you— you alone—with the necklace until I could arrange to buy it back from you, I would pay you more for it than its appraised value.

MILLER. How much more?

MRS. SIMMS-VANE. Twenty-five per cent more.

MILLER. I'll do it! Where's the necklace?

MRS. SIMMS-VANE. But I fear the girl.

MILLER. [*Discounting her.*] Oh, that girl?

MRS. SIMMS-VANE. Yes, you love her; and a man in love is not to be trusted.

MILLER. Aw, she's not the only girl I got.

MRS. SIMMS-VANE. O-oh—and still I've no doubt you have even agreed to share your gains with her.

MILLER. Well?

MRS. SIMMS-VANE. It is that which has invited my contempt.

MILLER. I never promised her a split. Besides, I know you're right about Lucille.

MRS. SIMMS-VANE. Then twenty thousand dollars is a high price to pay for this cheap little creature's favor.

MILLER. Don't have to pay it—unless she knows I've got the sparklers.

MRS. SIMMS-VANE. Would you then?

MILLER. Yes, she's a little wildcat, and she'd squeal on me.

MRS. SIMMS-VANE. Then you mean that you would not reveal to her that you have the necklace?

MILLER. Sure.

MRS. SIMMS-VANE. You mean that you would give me the chance to purchase back the diamonds from you?

MILLER. Yes.

MRS. SIMMS-VANE. You mean that you would promise to take nothing else from this house?

MILLER. What else is there?

MRS. SIMMS-VANE. There is a stamp box on the writing-desk. You opened it. I heard its click.

MILLER. What of it?

MRS. SIMMS-VANE. It is made of solid gold.

MILLER. [*Surprised that he should have missed such a valuable article, picks it up and stares at it.*] Gold? That made of gold?

MRS. SIMMS-VANE. Yes.

[*Thinking* MRS. SIMMS-VANE *cannot see him, he starts to pocket the stamp box. She sees his movement reflected in the mirror and gives a low chuckle of satisfaction. He is startled, not quite sure whether she saw his action or not. Quickly, but reluctantly, he puts the stamp box on the desk.*]

MILLER. [*In an over-generous tone.*] Well, what of it? I'd play straight; but how do I know that you——

MRS. SIMMS-VANE. You would have the word of Justinia Simms-Vane. Her honor has never been questioned. It would last as long as your own.

MILLER. [*Stares at her a moment.*] I'm no fool. Lucille's not worth the fuss. Where's the necklace?

MRS. SIMMS-VANE. Come near me. [*He does* so.] Open the buttons of my dress.

MILLER. [*Accusingly.*] But you said it was "laid away."

MRS. SIMMS-VANE. I chose my words carefully. Open my dress.

MILLER. [*Opens her dress and sees the necklace round her throat.*] Judas Garryowen! She wears them! What stones! What stones!

MRS. SIMMS-VANE. Take it quickly. [*He does so and at once begins to pick the stones from their settings.*] What are you doing?

MILLER. Aw— [*He is too busy to explain.*]

MRS. SIMMS-VANE. I say, what are you doing?

MILLER. Picking the stones from their settings.

MRS. SIMMS-VANE. But I don't understand——

MILLER. [*Picks out remaining stones.*] Just a way we have. [*Drops chain into wastebasket.*]

MRS. SIMMS-VANE. What was that noise?

MILLER. Chain going into the basket. I take no chances.

MRS. SIMMS-VANE. But you will do me the favor to button my dress. Lucille——

MILLER. Yes, yes; but look at them! [*Gloats over diamonds.*] Thirty-three perfect ones! A-ah, what a handful. Look! [*Holds them before her.*]

MRS. SIMMS-VANE. They are pretty; but my dress——

MILLER. All right. [*Drops stones in his right pocket, fastens her dress, and starts to adjust her lace collar.*]

MRS. SIMMS-VANE. I hear Lucille bringing——

MILLER. How you going to put her off the scent?

MRS. SIMMS-VANE. Leave that to me. If you are the gentleman I think you are, you will have her give me the milk.

MILLER. Well; but how will you fix her?

MRS. SIMMS-VANE. Just continue your search.

MILLER. But I've finished this room!

MRS. SIMMS-VANE. Then try the next; but leave the girl to me.

MILLER. [*Takes out the diamonds, looks at them a moment.*] All right. [*Walks away.*] But don't you play any tricks on me.

MRS. SIMMS-VANE. Sir, that will depend upon you.

[*He misses her inference and starts going through the drawers again. Suddenly, MRS. SIMMS-VANE hears him stop. Reflected in the mirror on the wall before her she sees him reach for the gold stamp box on the desk, slowly grasp it, and put it in his pocket. She sighs and closes her eyes. LUCILLE appears in the doorway, carrying a tray which holds a tall glass of hot milk.*]

MILLER. [*Seeing LUCILLE.*] You got the milk, huh?

LUCILLE. Yes, but the cook wanted to bring it in herself.

MILLER. Well, I've frisked the room all over again.

LUCILLE. What'd you find?

MILLER. No luck. The old lady's done us.

LUCILLE. Look some more. We got lots more time.

MRS. SIMMS-VANE. I want my hot milk.

LUCILLE. Forget it! [*Sets tray on the table.*]

MILLER. [*Over-generous.*] No, give her the milk.

LUCILLE. [*Surprised.*] What's come over you?

MILLER. Come here. [*LUCILLE does so. Half whisper.*] Listen, give her the milk and keep her busy. Do anything.

LUCILLE. What for?

MILLER. I want to see if there's anything worth picking up in the other rooms.

LUCILLE. But——?

MILLER. Go on; give her the milk.

[*Astounded,* LUCILLE *stares at him; but she takes the milk to* MRS. SIMMS-VANE. MILLER *wanders through the door into the adjoining room. Again and again his shadow appears near the doorway, as though he were watching the women.*]

MRS. SIMMS-VANE. You forget, my dear, that I cannot move. Put the glass to my lips. [LUCILLE *does so.*] A little nearer. [LUCILLE *puts the glass nearer* MRS. SIMMS-VANE'S *lips.*] The other side. [*Peeved,* LUCILLE *glances at her; but moves the glass to the other side of* MRS. SIMMS-VANE'S *mouth.*] What's that? Dirt? Is that dirt in my milk? [*Impatiently,* LUCILLE *looks at the milk. Whispering.*] Do not show any surprise, Lucille. Keep looking at the milk.

LUCILLE. [*Whispering.*] Yes.

MRS. SIMMS-VANE. [*Whispering.*] He has the necklace!

LUCILLE. [*Whispering.*] Oh!

MRS. SIMMS-VANE. [*Whispering.*] If you show him that you know, he will kill you. Don't move! [*Loudly.*] Is it dirt in my milk? Look again.

LUCILLE. I'm trying to see. [*Whispering.*] You're trying to make a fool of me!

MRS. SIMMS-VANE. [*Whispering.*] No, but he has tricked you and means to leave you to your fate. He has the diamonds!

LUCILLE. [*Whispering.*] Oh!

MRS. SIMMS-VANE. [*Whispering.*] The necklace without the stones is in the wastebasket. The revolver—is on the table.

LUCILLE. [*In hushed voice, as* MILLER *enters.*] Oh.

MILLER. [*Seeing* LUCILLE'S *suspicious attitude, turns to* MRS. SIMMS-VANE]. What are you trying to do—cut Lucille off from me? [LUCILLE *looks away.*]

MRS. SIMMS-VANE. [*Significantly.*] Did you find it—what you came for?

MILLER. [*Hesitates, then sullenly.*] No. [*Starts to look in the bookcases.* LUCILLE *sets glass on the table, runs to the wastebasket, looks in, and utters a cry of rage.* MILLER *turns swiftly.*]

LUCILLE. You've got it, you dog! [*Both rush for the revolver. She gets it.*] Stand back now!

MILLER. But Lucille——

LUCILLE. You double-crossed me—after I loved you so!

MILLER. Listen, girlie, the old lady's framed us. I love you, girlie. You know me. You get your share! This was the only way I could get the necklace! It was all for you!

MRS. SIMMS-VANE. Oh, Lucille, you little fool! The other woman is the one!

LUCILLE. I thought so! I'm going to kill you!

MILLER. [*Desperately.*] I love you!

LUCILLE. Oh! [*Pained, she closes her eyes.* MILLER *seizes a brass candlestick from the table and hurls it blindly at her, striking the wall behind her.*] You dog! [*She shoots. He falls to the floor.*] Oh, what have I done? What have I done? [*Covers her face. Outside a policeman's whistle is blown twice.* LUCILLE *is still too horrified by her crime to hear it; but* MRS. SIMMS-VANE *smiles knowingly and closes her eyes.*]

MRS. SIMMS-VANE. I said it would be disaster for him to cross me. He broke his agreement with me. He did not know that I could see him in the mirror over the table when he took the little stamp box. [*Outside the police whistle again.*]

LUCILLE. [*Hears whistle.*] O-oh, the police!

MRS. SIMMS-VANE. And now, you are a murderess.

LUCILLE. [*Running to her.*] No! No! Please save me!

MRS. SIMMS-VANE. I wonder if you are really bad. I doubt it. You are too young to be put in jail.

LUCILLE. You will save me?

MRS. SIMMS-VANE. I shall tell a little white lie for you, if you deserve it.

LUCILLE. [*Piteous fright.*] Oh, if you only would! [*Off right the doorbell rings.* LUCILLE *becomes more frightened and glances apprehensively toward the door.*]

MRS. SIMMS-LANE. I shall say you shot him in defending me. But we must hurry! That may be the police ringing now.

LUCILLE. Oh!

MRS. SIMMS-VANE. Put the revolver in my lap. [LUCILLE *does so.*]

LUCILLE. Oh, I don't deserve to be saved!

MRS. SIMMS-VANE. Never mind. Go put your hand in the young man's coat pocket.

LUCILLE. Oh, no! I'm afraid to touch him!

MRS. SIMMS-VANE. Do as I say.

[*Reluctantly,* LUCILLE *goes to* MILLER. *She starts to reach for his pocket, shudders, and recoils from him.*]

MRS. SIMMS-VANE. The right side. [LUCILLE *is startled that*

MRS. SIMMS-VANE *should know the correct pocket; but she quickly thrusts her hand into it.*] Do you feel the diamonds?

LUCILLE. [*Gloating.*] Yes; here they are. [*As she lifts the stones from* MILLER'S *pocket, she pauses, swiftly putting back a stray wisp of hair over her right ear.*]

MRS. SIMMS-VANE. Are you sure you have all of them?

LUCILLE. Yes!

MRS. SIMMS-VANE. You did not leave a single one?

LUCILLE. [*Overconfident.*] No, I'm sure!

MRS. SIMMS-VANE. Then count each one and drop it into my hand.

[LUCILLE *is startled, and fears that she has been trapped, but quickly recovers her composure.*]

LUCILLE. [*Counting the diamonds into* MRS. SIMMS-VANE'S *hand—the one that was not tortured by* MILLER]. One, two, three —how wonderful they are! [*Insistent ringing of the doorbell causes her to hasten her counting.*] Four, five, six— [*She quickly continues to count toward thirty.*]

[*The doorbell has ceased ringing. An outside door opens and closes. A growing murmur of voices. A man exclaims, "But we heard a shot fired!" A woman replies, "But it couldn't have been here!" The man, "We'll have a look anyway."*]

LUCILLE. [*Still counting.*] Thirty, thirty-one, thirty-two [*a pause of surprise*], thirty-three!

MRS. SIMMS-VANE. [*Suspiciously.*] Thirty-*three?*

LUCILLE. [*Bewildered, but relieved.*] Yes, thirty-three.

MRS. SIMMS-VANE. Then I have the stones my husband gave me,—all back again?

LUCILLE. All.

[*From right enter* MISS JONES, *in hat and raincoat, followed by Police Inspector.*]

MISS JONES. [*To Inspector.*] I'll prove to you there was nothing— [*Seeing* MRS. SIMMS-VANE, *rushes to her.*] Oh, Mrs. Simms-Vane, are you all right?

MRS. SIMMS-VANE. Yes.

MISS JONES. Nothing has happened?

MRS. SIMMS-VANE. No—everything.

[POLICEMAN GARRITY *appears in the doorway.*]

GARRITY. [*To* MISS JONES, *as he appears.*] Old lady safe?

[MILLER *stirs feebly.* MISS JONES *sees him.*]

MISS JONES. Yes, but, Inspector [*points to* MILLER], look!

MILLER. [*Feebly.*] Hello, Inspector.

INSPECTOR. [*To* GARRITY.] Miller, the Hawk! [*To* MRS. SIMMS-VANE:] Excuse me, ma'am, but who shot this man?

MRS. SIMMS-VANE. The maid.

LUCILLE. I was defending her!

MILLER. That's a lie! The little cat was the "inside" on this job. We messed it up, and she shot me. She thought I double-crossed her.

LUCILLE. Oh, how he talks! I never saw that man before in all my life! Did I, Mrs. Simms-Vane?

MRS. SIMMS-VANE. My dear young woman, I tried to give you a chance. Now I advise the officers to arrest you. You were his accomplice.

LUCILLE. But you said—you promised——

MRS. SIMMS-VANE. Certainly. But in my necklace there were not the number of stones you counted out to me. You kept one.

LUCILLE. No! No!

MRS. SIMMS-VANE. Yes, you did. The necklace was given to me by my husband on my thirty-fourth, not my thirty-third, birthday. You thought I did not know the number of my own stones; so you kept one.

MILLER. Ha! That serves the little devil proper. But it's just like her! I know her tricks! Look under the hair over her ears!

[INSPECTOR and GARRITY *start to examine her; but she breaks away from them.*]

LUCILLE. Keep away from me! I'll give her the stone! [*She reaches under the hair over her right ear and throws the diamond into* MRS. SIMMS-VANE's *lap.*] You old hag!

MRS. SIMMS-VANE. Miss Jones [MISS JONES *comes forward*], have the officers take these persons away.

[MISS JONES *nods to the officers to remove* LUCILLE *and* MILLER. GARRITY *takes* LUCILLE *into his custody and they exeunt right. The* INSPECTOR *helps* MILLER *up and starts toward the door with him, where* MILLER *turns round.*]

MILLER. [*Savagely to* MRS. SIMMS-VANE.] You'll not beat us again! [*The* INSPECTOR *pulls him out.*]

MRS. SIMMS-VANE. [*Serenely ignoring his remark.*] Miss Jones [MISS JONES *goes nearer to her, waiting*], you may order my carriage as usual.

[MISS JONES *is surprised, but quickly nods assent and starts toward the door.*]

CURTAIN

SICILIAN LIMES

Luigi Pirandello (Italy)

Translated by Elizabeth Abbott

Characters

Micuccio Bonavino, *a peasant,*
musician in a country band
Sina Marnis, *a singer*
Marta Marnis, *her mother*
Ferdinando, *a waiter*
Dorina, *a maid*
Guests

A room in a hotel, in a city in Sicily at the present time. Some one is snoring in the corner, left. Ferdinando *enters, followed by* Micuccio Bonavino. *The latter, from the country, is wearing high boots and his coat collar is turned up. In one hand, a dirty bag, and in the other an old valise and the case of a musical instrument which he can hardly carry, he is so tired and cold.* Dorina *speaks from behind the curtain.*

Dorina. Who's that?

Ferdinando. [*Setting the lamp on the table.*] Hey, Dorina! Signor Bonvicino's here!

Micuccio. [*Corrects him.*] Bonavino, really!

Ferdinando. Bonavino, Bonavino!

Dorina. [*Yawning behind the curtain.*] Well, who's he?

Ferdinando. A relative of the signora. [*To* Micuccio.] Just what relation did you say, please? Cousin, perhaps?

Micuccio. [*Embarrassed, hesitating.*] Well—not exactly—there's no relation! I am—I am . . . Micuccio Bonavino . . . she knows who I am! . . .

Dorina. A relative of the signora?

Ferdinando. [*Provoked.*] No, no! [*To* Micuccio.] Just from her town, eh? Then why did you ask me if Aunt Marta was here? [*To* Dorina.] Understand? I thought he meant a relative—a nephew! Sorry, I can't take you in, my good man.

Micuccio. What? How is that? I've come all the way from the country, on purpose to see her.

FERDINANDO. Well, she's not at home. You don't see people at this hour.

MICUCCIO. Is it my fault if the train only just got in? Could I tell it to run faster? It's a train, you see! It can't get here until it's due! I have been travelling for two days . . .

FERDINANDO. I can't let you in. Come back tomorrow, and you'll be able to see her. The signora is at the theater now.

MICUCCIO. What do you mean—come back? Where can I go this time of night, and a total stranger in the city? If she isn't here, I'll wait for her. A great note! Can't I wait for her here?

DORINA. We're having a party!—in her honor.

MICUCCIO. All right, all the better! I'm sure that as soon as Teresina sees me——

FERDINANDO. Do you hear that? He calls her Teresina, just plain Teresina! He asked me if the singer, Teresina, lived here!

MICUCCIO. Well, what of it? Isn't she a singer? And isn't that her name? Are you trying to tell *me* what to call her?

DORINA. Then you really know her so well?

MICUCCIO. Know her? Together ever since we were so high, she and I!

FERDINANDO. [*To* DORINA.] What shall we do?

DORINA. Oh, let him wait!

MICUCCIO. [*Annoyed.*] Oh, I'm going to wait all right! What's the idea? I came on purpose . . .

FERDINANDO. Well, sit down in that chair! I wash my hands of it. I must get things ready.

MICUCCIO. Well, this is a fine way to treat me! As if I was—but perhaps it's the way I look, all dust and smoke from the train. . . . But if I should let Teresina hear about it when she comes back from the theater . . . [*As if suddenly in doubt, he looks around the room.*] Excuse me, whose house is this?

DORINA. [*Watching him, and making fun of him.*] Ours as long as we stay here!

MICUCCIO. Well, then! [*He looks around again.*] A big house?

DORINA. So-so!

MICUCCIO. That's a parlor?

DORINA. Yes, for the reception. Tonight there's a banquet there.

MICUCCIO. Oh, what a spread! What bright lights! Then it's true!

DORINA. What's true?

MICUCCIO. Oh, you can see—they're getting along well. . . .

DORINA. You know who Sina Marnis is?

MICUCCIO. Sina? Oh! Of course! I remember! That's what she calls herself now. Aunt Marta wrote me about it—Teresina—of course—Teresina, Sina . . .

DORINA. Oh, wait a minute—now that I think of it, you are [*She calls to* FERDINANDO.] . . . Pst! . . . come here, Ferdinando! You know who he is? He's the fellow she's always writing to—the mother, I mean . . .

MICUCCIO. She doesn't know much about writing, poor thing . . .

DORINA. Yes! Yes! Bonavino.

MICUCCIO. Micuccio. It's all the same! We say Micuccio.

DORINA. You've been sick, haven't you? Recently?

MICUCCIO. Sick, yes, sick! Dead—you might say—with the candles lighted!

DORINA. Signora Marta sent you a money order, didn't she?

MICUCCIO. A money order, yes. And that's one thing I came for. I have the money here.

DORINA. You're bringing the money back to her?

MICUCCIO. [*Worried.*] Money, no! The money question doesn't come up! Don't even talk about it! Tell me, will it be long before they get here?

FERDINANDO. [*Coming back from the parlor to the door. Left, with dishes, shouting.*] Bravo! Bravo! Encore! Encore!

MICUCCIO. [*Smiling.*] Wonderful voice, eh? [*Rubbing his hands.*] I can take the credit for that! My work!

DORINA. Her voice?

MICUCCIO. I discovered her voice!

DORINA. You did? [*To* FERDINANDO.] Listen to that, Ferdinando! He discovered her voice!

MICUCCIO. I'm a musician, I am!

FERDINANDO. Oh! A musician! Bravo! And what do you play? The trombone?

MICUCCIO. [*Shaking his finger, quite earnestly.*] No, the idea! Trombone! I play the piccolo! I'm in the band. The town band, in our village, home!

DORINA. Tell us how it happened, boy! Listen to this, Ferdinando!

MICUCCIO. [*Shrugging his shoulders.*] How it happened! . . . She used to sing . . . She was always singing—sometimes spite songs, too . . . because—because . . .

FERDINANDO. Because what?

MICUCCIO. Hard times, troubles, poor little thing—in those days . . . Her father was dead. Me, yes, I helped her—her and her mother, Aunt Marta. But my mother was against it—and—in the end . . .

DORINA. You were in love with her?

MICUCCIO. Me? With Teresina? You make me laugh! My mother said I had to give her up, because she had nothing, poor little thing, and her father was dead—while, we, as for me, I had my little place, in the band . . .

FERDINANDO. But then, nothing . . . you weren't engaged?

MICUCCIO. My parents wouldn't let us, then! It was Heaven—I really believe it was an inspiration from Heaven! No one had ever paid any attention to her singing, not even me. Then all of a sudden—one morning . . . I'll never forget it! It was one morning in April. She was singing at the window, up in the garret—they lived in a garret then! . . . I had heard her sing once a little song of the folks in our neighborhood! . . . I had never paid any particular attention. But that morning—an angel—that's it—an angel, it was, singing! Quiet like, without saying a word to her nor to her mother, that day after dinner I took our band master to their garret—Saro Malaviti. Well, he heard her—and he knows what he's talking about, when it comes to music; he said, "Why, man, this is a voice of God!" Imagine me! Imagine her! So I rented a piano. I got the songs she needed, and the bandmaster began to give her lessons—not much, you know—he was satisfied with the little presents I could give him from time to time . . . Huh? What was I? Just what I am now—just a poor devil. The piano cost money, the music cost money—and then Teresina had to live well . . .

FERDINANDO. Eh, of course!

DORINA. . . . so she could keep in training—strong. . . .

MICUCCIO. Meat every day! That's something I can brag about!

FERDINANDO. I should say so!

DORINA. And then? . . .

MICUCCIO. She began to get on! And even that early you could tell . . . There she was up there, in the sky, you might say—and her voice carried—such a voice—pretty much all over town! And the people down in the street under her window—packed like this! . . . She was all on fire—fire is the word—and when she stopped singing, she would grab me by my two arms, like this [*He seizes* FERDINANDO.] and she would shake me! . . . Crazy! Crazy! Because she could see already—she knew what she would be some day! And the bandmaster, he told us so, too. And she couldn't find ways to thank me! Aunt Marta, on the other hand, poor soul . . .

DORINA. She was against it?

MICUCCIO. I wouldn't say she was against it—she didn't believe her eyes, that's all! She had seen so much in her life, poor old soul! She didn't want Teresina to get grand ideas, ideas about rising too high in the world—she'd been resigned to what she had for so long! Besides she knew what it was costing me . . . and she knew that my family . . . But I broke with all them, with my father, with my mother . . . That was when a *maestro* from outside heard Teresina sing, and he said it would be a shame not to have her go on studying in some conservatory. That set me off! I broke with them all. I sold the farm that an uncle of mine had left me in his will, and I sent Teresina to Naples to the Conservatory.

FERDINANDO. *You* did?

MICUCCIO. Me, me! Who else?

DORINA. [*To* FERDINANDO.] He paid, he means! . . .

MICUCCIO. Four years I kept her there, studying. Four years—and I haven't seen her since.

DORINA. Not once?

MICUCCIO. Not once? Because—because after that, she began singing in the theaters, you see. Here, there, from Naples to Rome, from Rome to Milan—then to Spain—then to Russia—then back here again! . . .

FERDINANDO. A sensation, everywhere! . . .

MICUCCIO. Oh, I know! I have all the newspapers, here in my valise. And then I have her letters here, too . . . [*He takes a packet of letters from an inside pocket.*] . . . from her and from her mother. Listen to this—what she wrote when she sent me the money, that time I was so sick. "Micuccio, dear, I haven't time to write, but I stand behind everything mother says. Take care of yourself, get well, and always be fond of me. Teresina."

FERDINANDO. And she sent you—a lot of money?

MICUCCIO. A thousand, yes.

FERDINANDO. And your farm—excuse me—the one you sold, how much was it worth?

MICUCCIO. How much could it be worth? Not much—a little strip of land like that . . . But I have the money here. I don't want the money. The little I did, I did for her. We agreed to wait, two, three years, so that she could get her start. Aunt Marta always kept repeating that in her letters. But I'll say it just as it is—I wasn't expecting money! But if Teresina sent it, it's a sign that she must be pretty well fixed, that she has made her way . . .

FERDINANDO. Yes, she has—what a way she has made!

MICUCCIO. And so it's time . . .

DORINA. . . . to get married!

MICUCCIO. I am here!

FERDINANDO. You came to marry Sina Marnis?

DORINA. [*To* FERDINANDO.] Quiet! There's a betrothal, donkey! Of course! To marry Sina Marnis!

MICUCCIO. I'm not the one to talk. I just say: here I am. I just dropped everything back there in the village, the family, the band, everything. The money came without my knowing, when I was more dead than alive. My mother wanted to keep it. I just had to pry it out of her hands. Money? No, sir! Micuccio Bonavino, money? No, sir! I'm all right any place—even at the end of the world. You can't starve me! My art, I have—the piccolo, I have, and . . .

DORINA. Really? You brought your piccolo with you?

MICUCCIO. The idea! Of course I brought it with me! My piccolo and me—you can't keep us apart!

DORINA. You play well, I imagine?

MICUCCIO. So-so—I have been at it only ten years!

FERDINANDO. What do you say—let's hear a tune. [*He goes and picks up the instrument in its case.*]

DORINA. Yes, yes! Good! Play something for us!

MICUCCIO. Oh, no! What do you want me to play—at this time of night?

DORINA. Just one little tune! Please do!

FERDINANDO. We've got to force you? [*He opens the case and takes out the instrument.*] Here you are! Now!

DORINA. Come, come! Just to show us!

MICUCCIO. Well, then— if you must have it—I'll play—what do you say?—the little song Teresina sang that day in the garret?

FERDINANDO AND DORINA. Yes, yes! Fine! That one!

[MICUCCIO *sits down and begins to play, very seriously.* FERDI-
NANDO *and* DORINA *do their best to keep from laughing.*
MICUCCIO's *tune is interrupted by a loud ring of the bell.*]

FERDINANDO. Oh! Here she is now!

DORINA. [*To the other waiter.*] Come, come! Go and open the door!

FERDINANDO. My coat—where did I put my coat?

DORINA. Over there! [*She points to the curtain and hurries out.*]

[MICUCCIO *gets up, the instrument in his hands, bewildered.*
FERDINANDO, *seeing that* MICUCCIO *is about to follow* DORINA,
halts him rudely.]

FERDINANDO. You stay here! I must let the signora know first.
[FERDINANDO *goes out.*]

[MICUCCIO *stands, humiliated, confused, depressed by anxious forebodings.*]

MARTA. [*From within.*] In there, Dorina! In the parlor! In the parlor!

[DORINA, FERDINANDO *enter, right, and cross the stage carrying imposing flowers, wreaths, etc.* MICUCCIO *cranes his neck to look into the drawing room and glimpses a confusion of men in dinner coats, talking, walking about.* DORINA *enters hurriedly, and crosses to the door, right.*]

MICUCCIO. [*Touching her arm.*] Who are they?

DORINA. [*Without stopping.*] The guests! [*She goes out.*]

[MICUCCIO *looks again. He is dazzled. In his amazement or his emotion he is scarcely conscious himself that his eyes are blurred with tears. He shut them behind one hand and strives to pull himself together, as if to master the anxiety, the stab of pain, that a burst of shrill laughter gives him. It is* SINA's *laugh! She is in there—in the drawing room!* DORINA *is back again with two more baskets of flowers.*]

DORINA. [*Hurrying toward the drawing room.*] Crying?

MICUCCIO. Me? No . . . but all those people! . . .

[AUNT MARTA *enters, right. The poor old lady is wearing a hat, and she does not know what to do with herself in the gorgeous velvet cloak she has on. At sight of* MICUCCIO, *she utters a cry, which she smothers at once.*]

MARTA. Why! Micuccio! . . . You here? . . .

MICUCCIO. [*Lowering his hand from his face and staring at her, almost in fear.*] Aunt Marta—you? Like that . . .?

MARTA. How? Like what?

MICUCCIO. With a hat! You?[1]

MARTA. Oh! [*She shakes her head and lifts one hand in gesture; then alarmed.*] But what's this? Without letting us know? What has happened?

MICUCCIO. I—I—have come! . . .

MARTA. But this evening, of all times! Dear, dear! Wait—what shall we do? What shall we do? You see all the people there are in there! Dear me, it's a party! They're giving a party, for Teresina!

MICUCCIO. I know! . . .

MARTA. Her evening, you see—in her honor. Wait—wait here a moment . . .

MICUCCIO. If you—if you think I ought to go away . . .

---

[1] *With a hat! You?:* peasant women in Europe go bareheaded or wear a little shawl tied under the chin.

MARTA. No, wait a moment. [*She starts toward the drawing room.*]

MICUCCIO. But I wouldn't know where . . . here . . . in this place . . .

[MARTA *returns and beckons to him with her gloved hand to wait. She goes in to the drawing room, where suddenly a deep silence falls. Words of* SINA MARNIS *come clearly, distinctly:* "*One moment, boys!*" MICUCCIO *again covers his face with his hands. But* SINA *does not appear. Instead, a little later,* AUNT MARTA *returns without the hat, without the gloves, without the cloak— and much more at her ease.*]

MARTA. So here I am, here I am! . . .

MICUCCIO. And—and—Teresina? . . .

MARTA. I announced you! I told her! . . . And in a minute, as soon as she possibly can . . . she'll come out. Meanwhile, we will stay in here for a little while by ourselves, eh? you and me. Is that all right?

MICUCCIO. As far as I'm concerned. . . .

MARTA. I'll stay with you! . . .

MICUCCIO. But no, not if—not if you'd rather—I mean, if you too ought to be in there . . .

MARTA. No, no! They're having supper in there now, see? Admirers of hers—the manager—her work, you know! Let's stay here, you and I! . . . Dorina will set this little table for us right away— and . . . and we'll have supper together, eh? you and I! We can talk about the good old days. [DORINA *enters.*] Come Dorina, quick—something for me, and this dear boy of mine. Dear, dear Micuccio! It doesn't seem real! You and I together again!

DORINA. Here you are! And there are the chairs!

MARTA. [*Sitting down.*] Yes, yes, here, like this, all cosy, off by ourselves! In there, you know—oh, so many people! Poor thing, you see she has to stand in with them, otherwise—well . . . her work—what else can she do? Have you seen the papers? Grand things, sonny, grand! And, you know, I'm—I'm all at sea—it don't seem real alone with you, tonight! [*Looking at him with affectionate pity.*]

MICUCCIO. [*With anguished voice.*] And—she—she will come, she said? . . . I mean—just to see her, at least! . . .

MARTA. Why, of course she'll come! The moment she has a chance to breathe—didn't I say so? And she too! Just imagine how much rather she'd be here with you and me—with you, after all this time! How many years is it? Such a long time, such a long time!

Oh, sonny, some ways it seems only the other day, then again it seems forever! How many things, how many things I've seen! Things, well—I hardly believe they're true. If anyone had told me so I'd have said they were crazy . . . when we were living back there in Palma, and you used to come up to our garret . . .

[DORINA *enters with the first course, and stops beside* MICUCCIO *that he may help himself.*]

MARTA. Oh, fine, Dorina . . . [MICUCCIO *looks at* AUNT MARTA, *confused, bashful, he raises his hands to take his helping, sees they are grimy from the journey, and drops them to his lap again, more embarrassed than ever.*] Here, here, Dorina, I'll do it—let me help you . . . [*She does so.*] There, sonny, is that all right?

MICUCCIO. Yes, yes, thank you.

MARTA. And here I am! [*She helps herself.*]

MICUCCIO. [*Winking one eye, and making an expressive gesture with his right hand on his cheek.*] Mm-mm! Good stuff! . . . First class! . . .

MARTA. Something special for the party tonight, you see. Well, let's eat! But first . . . [*She crosses herself.*] I can do that in here, with you? [MICUCCIO *also crosses himself.*] Good, sonny. Believe me, when I have to eat in there and can't cross myself, well, it just seems as though I couldn't get it down! Eat! Eat!

MICUCCIO. Oh, I am hungry, I am! Two days, not a bite!

MARTA. What! Didn't you eat, on the way?

MICUCCIO. I did take something along to eat. I still have it in my valise there. But, you know I was ashamed, there, Aunt Marta. It . . . it seemed so cheap, and I felt as if everyone was watching me.

MARTA. Silly! And you went without? Well, now, you can eat, my poor Micuccio! Eat! You must be starved! Two days! And drink, here, drink! [*She pours wine for him.*]

MICUCCIO. Thanks, I will have a swallow. [*From time to time* DORINA *goes back and forth through the room carrying courses. Whenever she opens the inner glass door, the buzz of laughter and merrymaking can be heard.* MICUCCIO *raises his head from his plate, disturbed, and looks into the affectionate pitying eyes of* AUNT MARTA, *as if to find an explanation there.*] They're laughing! . . .

MARTA. Yes. But drink, drink! Oh, our good home wine, Micuccio! You don't know how I miss it! The wine Michela used to have, the woman on the floor below us! What's become of Michela? What's she doing?

MICUCCIO. Michela? She's all right! She's all right.

MARTA. And her girl, Luzza?

MICUCCIO. Married—and two children!

MARTA. So Donna Mariangela—a grandmother, a grandmother already! Lucky woman! Two you said?

MICUCCIO. Two, yes! [*Another burst of merriment comes from the drawing room. He winces.*]

MARTA. You don't want your wine?

MICUCCIO. Yes! . . . I was just . . .

MARTA. Don't mind them! You know—noisy people! Besides, a great crowd of them! What can you do! It's just life, sonny. Her work, you know! . . . Her manager is there. [DORINA *appears with another course.*] Oh, Dorina, here! Pass your plate, Micuccio! You will like a little of this, too. [*Serving him.*]

MICUCCIO. What a lot you've learned! You make my eyes stand out.

MARTA. You have to learn, sonny!

MICUCCIO. When I saw you with that velvet coat, and that hat! . . .

MARTA. You have to! . . . But—don't make me think of that!

MICUCCIO. I know, you have to make a show! . . . But if the folks at home should see you, if they saw you dressed like that at Palma, Aunt Marta! . . .

MARTA. [*Hiding her face in her hands.*] Oh dear me, dear me! Don't make me think of it! When I do think of it, I'm so ashamed, so ashamed! . . . I look in the glass sometimes and I say, "Me, this way?" And it all seems as though I was dressing up for carnival at home. But what can I do? You have to! . . .

MICUCCIO. But . . . so then—so then, I say . . . she has really got somewhere! You can see it! . . . Huh, money! . . . They pay her well, I suppose!

MARTA. Oh yes, fairly well . . .

MICUCCIO. How much an evening?

MARTA. That depends—depends on the season—depends on the theater. But then you know, sonny, this life, it costs—it costs a lot. It takes all we get, and more too. And so many things, you know! It goes faster than it comes—clothes, jewels, bills of all kinds . . . [*She breaks off at a loud uproar of voices from the parlor.*]

VOICES. Where is he? Where is he? We want to see him! Where?

SINA'S VOICE. One moment, I tell you, one moment!

MARTA. There she is! That's she! She's coming!

[SINA *enters suddenly, all rustling in silk, sparkling with jewels,*

*her bosom, shoulders, and arms bare. The room seems sud-
denly to be brilliantly lighted.*]

MICUCCIO. [*Who has extended his hand toward his wine glass,
stops, petrified, dazzled, his face flaming, his eyes wide open, his
mouth agape, as if he were gazing at an apparition in some dream of
fairyland. He stammers.*] Teresina! . . .

SINA. Micuccio? Where are you? Oh, there he is! How are you?
How are you? Ah, well again? Good for you! So, you were sick!
Too bad! Listen, I'll be out again in a little while. Anyhow, mother
will keep you company. Don't forget eh? See you later! [*She trips
out again. MICUCCIO remains as he was. SINA's reappearance in the
parlor is greeted with noisy cries.*]

MARTA. [*After a long pause, timidly, with the thought of bringing
him out of the trance in which he seems to be imprisoned.*] Aren't
you going to finish what you have? [MICUCCIO *looks around at her,
in a stupor, unable to grasp the meaning of her words.*] Your supper,
I said . . . [*She points to his plate.*]

MICUCCIO. [*Forces a finger in between his neck and his dirty
collar and tugging at his shirt as if to make room for a deep breath.*]
Supper? [*He drums on his chin with his fingers, meaning that he
cannot eat any more. For a while he sits silent, humiliated, absorbed in the vision that has just left him. Then he murmurs:*] How
she has changed! Why no—I wouldn't have known her—all—all
like that . . . [*His gesture suggests, with surprise but without disdain, that SINA's arms and shoulders are bare.*] A dream—her voice
—her eyes—it isn't she—it isn't she any more—Teresina! . . .
[*Perceiving that AUNT MARTA is shaking her head sadly and has
stopped eating as if waiting for him to resume his meal.*] Why, of
course not! . . . No use—no use even thinking about it! All over
—and who knows how long since! . . . And me—what a fool!
What a fool! . . . They told me so, down at the village! And me—
me—broke my neck to get here—thirty-six hours—only just to . . .
to . . . So that was why the waiter—and that girl—Dorina—how
they must be laughing at me! [*Several times he brings his fore-
fingers together and smiles sadly, shaking his head.*] How—how
could I know? I came . . . because she—Teresina—had promised
to . . . to . . . But perhaps . . . of course, how could she have
known that some day—she would be . . . what she is now! While
I—back there—back there, in the village—with my piccolo—in the
town band—she—she—going on, going on, so far, so far! . . .
Huh! No use! No use even thinking about it any more! . . . [*He
turns on MARTA abruptly.*] If I have done anything for her—no-

body, Aunt Marta, nobody here now must suspect that I came here to—to sponge— [*He is more and more distressed, and gets to his feet.*] Or rather, wait! . . . [*He thrusts his hand into his inner pocket and pulls out a pocketbook.*] I came for this too—to give you back the money you sent me. You meant to pay me back? You meant to make good to me . . .? But what's all that! I see that Teresina has become a—a queen. I see that—well, never mind! No use even to think of it any more! But money—no! I never deserved this from her . . . What's the money for? . . . That's over! No! No money, to me! I am only sorry it isn't all there . . .

MARTA. [*Trembling, much moved, with tears in her eyes.*] What are you saying, what are you saying, my dear child!

MICUCCIO. [*Motioning to her to be quiet.*] I didn't spend it myself. They spent it while I was sick, without my knowing. But we can let that go for the little I spent for her, before—you remember? Not worth talking about! . . . We call it square! The rest is here . . . and . . . I am going!

MARTA. Oh no! So soon? At least wait till I tell Teresina. Didn't you hear her say—she wants to see you again! I'll go and tell her! . . .

MICUCCIO. [*Holding her down in her chair.*] No, it's no use. Listen! [*From the parlor comes a risqué [2] song from a musical comedy, sung boisterously in chorus by all the company and punctuated by bursts of laughter.*] Let her stay there! That's where she belongs! Me—poor fool—I've seen her, and that's enough! Or rather—you'd better go in there, too. Don't you hear them laughing? I don't want them to laugh at me . . . I'm going.

MARTA. [*Tearfully, interpreting* MICUCCIO's *sudden resolution in the worst sense, as if it were an act of anger and jealousy.*] But I—I can't control her any more, Micuccio . . .

MICUCCIO. [*Suddenly reading in her eyes a suspicion he has not yet had, violently, purple.*] Why?

MARTA. [*Bewildered, burying her face in her hands, but unable to keep back her tears. She is choking with sobs.*] Yes, yes, go, my boy, go! She isn't fit for you, you are right! . . . If you had listened to me, back there, then . . .!

MICUCCIO. [*Violently, bending over her and tearing her hands from her face.*] So—so she isn't fit for me? [*The singing and the playing continue to come from the other room.*]

MARTA. [*Heartbroken, weeping, she nods, then she raises her hands imploringly, with such simple and sincere sorrow that* MICUC-

[2] *risqué:* daring, not in good taste.

CIO's *anger cools.*] Micuccio, please, please, for my sake, Micuccio! . . .

MICUCCIO. Never mind, never mind! I am going just the same! . . . All the more reason, now! [*At this point* SINA *returns from the parlor.* MICUCCIO *drops* MARTA's *hand and turns to her. He seizes* SINA *by an arm and draws her out in front of him.*] So that's why! So that's why—like this! [*He motions with disgust at her bare shoulders.*] Arms—shoulders—everything!

MARTA. [*Frightened, imploringly.*] Micuccio, please!

MICUCCIO. Oh, don't be afraid! I'm not going to hurt her! I'm going away. What a fool, Aunt Marta! I didn't understand. Don't you cry, don't you cry! Anyway, what's the difference! Good luck, I say rather! Good luck! [*He picks up the little bag and starts toward the door. But it suddenly occurs to him that he has something in the little bag—some beautiful limes* [3] *which he had brought* TERESINA *from home.*] Oh, I forgot! Look, Aunt Marta, look!

[*He opens the bag and pours the fragrant fruit out on the table.*]

SINA. [*Starting to run for them.*] Oh! Limes! Limes!

MICUCCIO. [*Stopping her.*] Don't touch them! You're not fit to look at them, from a distance even! [*He takes one and holds it under* AUNT MARTA's *nose.*] Smell, smell, the smell of our valley at home! Suppose I was to take them one by one, and spot the heads of those pretty dudes in there?

MARTA. Micuccio, please!

MICUCCIO. Don't worry—I'm not going to! But mind, Aunt Marta, mind they're only for you . . . I brought them for her [*He points to* SINA.] . . . and to think I even paid the duty on them! [*His eyes fall on the money he had taken from his pocketbook and laid on the table. He seizes it, and thrusts it down the bosom of* SINA's *low-cut dress. She bursts into tears.*] For you! The money is for you! . . . Take it—there! Like that! And here's some more! . . . And don't cry—goodbye, Aunt Marta! Good luck to you!

[*He picks up his valise and his instrument, and goes out.*]

[3] *limes:* a small lemon-like fruit.

CURTAIN

A SUNNY MORNING

SERAFÍN AND JOAQUÍN ALVAREZ QUINTERO (SPAIN)

Translated by Lucretia Xavier Floyd

SCENE: *A sunny morning in a retired corner of a park in Madrid.*
TIME: *The present. Autumn. A bench at Right.*

DOÑA LAURA, *a handsome, white-haired old lady of about seventy, refined in appearance, her bright eyes and entire manner giving evidence that despite her age her mental faculties are unimpaired, enters leaning upon the arm of her maid,* PETRA. *In her free hand she carries a parasol, which serves also as a cane.*

DOÑA LAURA. I am so glad to be here. I feared my seat would be occupied. What a beautiful morning!

PETRA. The sun is hot.

DOÑA LAURA. Yes, you are only twenty. [*She sits down on the bench.*] Oh, I feel more tired today than usual. [*Noticing* PETRA, *who seems impatient.*] Go, if you wish to chat with your guard.

PETRA. He is not mine, señora; he belongs to the park.

DOÑA LAURA. He belongs more to you than he does to the park. Go find him, but remain within calling distance.

PETRA. I see him over there waiting for me.

DOÑA LAURA. Do not remain more than ten minutes.

PETRA. Very well, señora. [*Walks towards* R.]

DOÑA LAURA. Wait a moment.

PETRA. What does the señora wish?

DOÑA LAURA. Give me the bread crumbs.

PETRA. I don't know what is the matter with me.

DOÑA LAURA. [*Smiling.*] I do. Your head is where your heart is—with the guard.

PETRA. Here, señora.

[*She hands* DOÑA LAURA *a small bag. Exit* PETRA *by* R.]

DOÑA LAURA. Adiós. [*Glances toward trees at* R.] Here they come! They know just when to expect me. [*She rises, walks toward* R., *and throws three handfuls of bread crumbs.*] These are for the spryest, these for the gluttons, and these for the little ones which are the most persistent. [*Laughs. She returns to her seat and watches, with a pleased expression, the pigeons feeding.*] There, that big one is always first! I know him by his big head. Now one, now another, now two, now three— That little fellow is the least timid. I believe he would eat from my hand. That one takes his piece and flies up to that branch alone. He is a philosopher. But where do they all come from? It seems as if the news had spread. Ha, ha! Don't quarrel. There is enough for all. I'll bring more tomorrow.

[*Enter* DON GONZALO *and* JUANITO *from* L.C. DON GONZALO *is an old gentleman of seventy, gouty and impatient. He leans upon* JUANITO's *arm and drags his feet somewhat as he walks.*]

DON GONZALO. Idling their time away! They should be saying mass.

JUANITO. You can sit here, señor. There is only a lady. [DOÑA LAURA *turns her head and listens.*]

DON GONZALO. I won't, Juanito. I want a bench to myself.

JUANITO. But there is none.

DON GONZALO. That one over there is mine.

JUANITO. There are three priests sitting there.

DON GONZALO. Rout them out. Have they gone?

JUANITO. No, indeed. They are talking.

DON GONZALO. Just as if they were glued to the seat. No hope of their leaving. Come this way, Juanito. [*They walk toward the birds,* R.]

DOÑA LAURA. [*Indignantly.*] Look out!

DON GONZALO. Are you speaking to me, señora?

DOÑA LAURA. Yes, to you.

DON GONZALO. What do you wish?

DOÑA LAURA. You have scared away the birds who were feeding on my crumbs.

DON GONZALO. What do I care about the birds?

DOÑA LAURA. But I do.

DON GONZALO. This is a public park.

DOÑA LAURA. Then why do you complain that the priests have taken your bench?

DON GONZALO. Señora, we have not met. I cannot imagine why you take the liberty of addressing me. Come, Juanito. [*Both go out* R.]

DOÑA LAURA. What an ill-natured old man! Why must people get so fussy and cross when they reach a certain age? [*Looking toward* R.] I am glad. He lost that bench, too. Serves him right for scaring the birds. He is furious. Yes, yes; find a seat if you can. Poor man! He is wiping the perspiration from his face. Here he comes. A carriage would not raise more dust than his feet. [*Enter* DON GONZALO *and* JUANITO *by* R. *and walk toward* L.]

DON GONZALO. Have the priests gone yet, Juanito?

JUANITO. No, indeed, señor. They are still there.

DON GONZALO. The authorities should place more benches here for these sunny mornings. Well, I suppose I must resign myself and sit on the bench with the old lady. [*Muttering to himself, he sits at the extreme end of* DOÑA LAURA'S *bench and looks at her indignantly. Touches his hat as he greets her.*] Good morning.

DOÑA LAURA. What, you here again?

DON GONZALO. I repeat that we have not met.

DOÑA LAURA. I was responding to your salute.

DON GONZALO. "Good morning" should be answered by "good morning," and that is all you should have said.

DOÑA LAURA. You should have asked permission to sit on this bench, which is mine.

DON GONZALO. The benches here are public property.

DOÑA LAURA. Why, you said the one the priests have was yours.

DON GONZALO. Very well, very well. I have nothing more to say. [*Between his teeth.*] Senile old lady! She ought to be at home knitting and counting her beads.

DOÑA LAURA. Don't grumble any more. I'm not going to leave just to please you.

DON GONZALO. [*Brushing the dust from his shoes with his handkerchief.*] If the ground were sprinkled a little it would be an improvement.

DOÑA LAURA. Do you use your handkerchief as a shoe brush?

DON GONZALO. Why not?

DOÑA LAURA. Do you use a shoe brush as a handkerchief?

DON GONZALO. What right have you to criticize my actions?

DOÑA LAURA. A neighbor's right.

DON GONZALO. Juanito, my book. I do not care to listen to nonsense.

DOÑA LAURA. You are very polite.

DON GONZALO. Pardon me, señora, but never interfere with what does not concern you.

DOÑA LAURA. I generally say what I think.

DON GONZALO. And more to the same effect. Give me the book, Juanito.

JUANITO. Here, señor. [JUANITO *takes a book from his pocket, hands it to* DON GONZALO, *then exits by* R. DON GONZALO, *casting indignant glances at* DOÑA LAURA, *puts on an enormous pair of glasses, takes from his pocket a reading-glass, adjusts both to suit him and opens his book.*]

DOÑA LAURA. I thought you were taking out a telescope.

Don Gonzalo. Was that you?

Doña Laura. Your sight must be keen.

Don Gonzalo. Keener than yours is.

Doña Laura. Yes, evidently.

Don Gonzalo. Ask the hares and partridges.

Doña Laura. Ah! Do you hunt?

Don Gonzalo. I did, and even now——

Doña Laura. Oh, yes, of course!

Don Gonzalo. Yes, señora. Every Sunday I take my gun and dog, you understand, and go to one of my estates near Aravaca and kill time.

Doña Laura. Yes, kill time. That is all you kill.

Don Gonzalo. Do you think so? I could show you a wild boar's head in my study——

Doña Laura. Yes, and I could show you a tiger's skin in my boudoir. What does that prove?

Don Gonzalo. Very well, señora, please allow me to read. Enough conversation.

Doña Laura. Well, you subside, then.

Don Gonzalo. But first I shall take a pinch of snuff. [*Takes out snuffbox.*] Will you have some? [*Offers box to* Doña Laura.]

Doña Laura. If it is good.

Don Gonzalo. It is of the finest. You will like it.

Doña Laura. [*Taking pinch of snuff.*] It clears my head.

Don Gonzalo. And mine.

Doña Laura. Do you sneeze?

Don Gonzalo. Yes, señora, three times.

Doña Laura. And so do I. What a coincidence!

[*After taking the snuff, they await the sneezes, both anxiously, and sneeze alternately three times each.*]

Don Gonzalo. There, I feel better.

Doña Laura. So do I. [*Aside.*] The snuff has made peace between us.

Don Gonzalo. You will excuse me if I read aloud?

Doña Laura. Read as loud as you please; you will not disturb me.

Don Gonzalo. [*Reading.*] "All love is sad, but sad as it is, it is the best thing that we know." That is from Campoamor.

Doña Laura. Ah!

Don Gonzalo. [*Reading.*] "The daughters of the mothers I once loved kiss me now as they would a graven image." Those lines, I take it, are in a humorous vein.

Doña Laura. [*Laughing.*] I take them so, too.

Don Gonzalo. There are some beautiful poems in this book. Here. "Twenty years pass. He returns."

Doña Laura. You cannot imagine how it affects me to see you reading with all those glasses.

Don Gonzalo. Can you read without any?

Doña Laura. Certainly.

Don Gonzalo. At your age? You're jesting.

Doña Laura. Pass me the book, then. [*Takes book; reads aloud.*]

> "Twenty years pass. He returns.
> And each, beholding the other, exclaims—
> Can it be that this is he?
> Heavens, is it she?"

[Doña Laura *returns the book to* Don Gonzalo.]

Don Gonzalo. Indeed, I envy you your wonderful eyesight.

Doña Laura. [*Aside.*] I know every word by heart.

Don Gonzalo. I am very fond of good verses, very fond. I even composed some in my youth.

Doña Laura. Good ones?

Don Gonzalo. Of all kinds. I was a great friend of Espronceda, Zorrilla, Bécquer,[1] and others. I first met Zorrilla in America.

Doña Laura. Why, have you been in America?

Don Gonzalo. Several times. The first time I went I was only six years old.

Doña Laura. You must have gone with Columbus in one of his caravels!

Don Gonzalo. [*Laughing.*] Not quite as bad as that. I am old, I admit, but I did not know Ferdinand and Isabella. [*They both laugh.*] I was also a great friend of Campoamor. I met him in Valencia. I am a native of that city.

Doña Laura. You are?

Don Gonzalo. I was brought up there and there I spent my early youth. Have you ever visited that city?

Doña Laura. Yes, señor. Not far from Valencia there was a villa that, if still there, should retain memories of me. I spent several seasons there. It was many, many years ago. It was near the sea, hidden away among lemon and orange trees. They called it— let me see, what did they call it—Maricela.

Don Gonzalo. [*Startled.*] Maricela?

Doña Laura. Maricela. Is the name familiar to you?

Don Gonzalo. Yes, very familiar. If my memory serves me

[1] Spanish writers.

right, for we forget as we grow old, there lived in that villa the most beautiful woman I have ever seen, and I assure you I have seen many. Let me see—what was her name? Laura—Laura—Laura Llorente.

DOÑA LAURA. [*Startled.*] Laura Llorente?

DON GONZALO. Yes. [*They look at each other intently.*]

DOÑA LAURA. [*Recovering herself.*] Nothing. You reminded me of my best friend.

DON GONZALO. How strange!

DOÑA LAURA. It is strange. She was called "The Silver Maiden."

DON GONZALO. Precisely, "The Silver Maiden." By that name she was known in that locality. I seem to see her as if she were before me now, at that window with the red roses. Do you remember that window?

DOÑA LAURA. Yes, I remember. It was the window of her room.

DON GONZALO. She spent many hours there. I mean in my day.

DOÑA LAURA. [*Sighing.*] And in mine, too.

DON GONZALO. She was ideal. Fair as a lily, jet black hair and black eyes, with an uncommonly sweet expression. She seemed to cast a radiance wherever she was. Her figure was beautiful, perfect. "What forms of sovereign beauty God models in human clay!" She was a dream.

DOÑA LAURA. [*Aside.*] If you but knew that dream was now by your side, you would realize what dreams come to. [*Aloud.*] She was very unfortunate and had a sad love affair.

DON GONZALO. Very sad. [*They look at each other.*]

DOÑA LAURA. Did you hear of it?

DON GONZALO. Yes.

DOÑA LAURA. The ways of Providence are strange. [*Aside.*] Gonzalo!

DON GONZALO. The gallant lover, in the same affair——

DOÑA LAURA. Ah, the duel?

DON GONZALO. Precisely, the duel. The gallant lover was—my cousin, of whom I was very fond.

DONA LAURA. Oh, yes, a cousin? My friend told me in one of her letters the story of that affair, which was truly romantic. He, your cousin, passed by on horseback every morning down the rose path under her window, and tossed up to her balcony a bouquet of flowers which she caught.

DON GONZALO. And later in the afternoon the gallant horseman would return by the same path, and catch the bouquet of flowers she would toss him. Am I right?

Doña Laura. Yes. They wanted to marry her to a merchant whom she would not have.

Don Gonzalo. And one night, when my cousin waited under her window to hear her sing, this other person presented himself unexpectedly.

Doña Laura. And insulted your cousin.

Don Gonzalo. There was a quarrel.

Doña Laura. And later a duel.

Don Gonzalo. Yes, at sunrise, on the beach, and the merchant was badly wounded. My cousin had to conceal himself for a few days and later to fly.

Doña Laura. You seem to know the story well.

Don Gonzalo. And so do you.

Doña Laura. I have explained that a friend repeated it to me.

Don Gonzalo. As my cousin did to me. [Aside.] This is Laura!

Doña Laura. [Aside.] Why tell him? He does not suspect.

Don Gonzalo. [Aside.] She is entirely innocent.

Doña Laura. And was it you, by any chance, who advised your cousin to forget Laura?

Don Gonzalo. Why, my cousin never forgot her!

Doña Laura. How do you account, then, for his conduct?

Don Gonzalo. I will tell you. The young man took refuge in my house, fearful of the consequences of a duel with a person highly regarded in that locality. From my home he went to Seville, then came to Madrid. He wrote Laura many letters, some of them in verse. But undoubtedly they were intercepted by her parents, for she never answered at all. Gonzalo then, in despair, believing his love lost to him forever, joined the army, went to Africa, and there, in a trench, met a glorious death, grasping the flag of Spain and whispering the name of his beloved Laura——

Doña Laura. [Aside.] What an atrocious lie!

Don Gonzalo. [Aside.] I could not have killed myself more gloriously.

Doña Laura. You must have been prostrated by the calamity.

Don Gonzalo. Yes, indeed, señora. As if he were my brother. I presume, though, on the contrary, that Laura in a short time was chasing butterflies in her garden, indifferent to regret.

Doña Laura. No, señor, no!

Don Gonzalo. It is woman's way.

Doña Laura. Even if it were woman's way, "The Silver Maiden" was not of that disposition. My friend awaited news for days, months, a year, and no letter came. One afternoon, just at sunset, as the first stars were appearing, she was seen to leave the house, and with quickening steps wend her way toward the beach, the beach where her beloved had risked his life. She wrote his name on the sand, then sat down upon a rock, her gaze fixed upon the horizon. The waves murmured their eternal threnody and slowly crept up to the rock where the maiden sat. The tide rose with a boom and swept her out to sea.

DON GONZALO. Good heavens!

DOÑA LAURA. The fishermen of that shore who often tell the story affirm that it was a long time before the waves washed away that name written on the sand. [*Aside.*] You will not get ahead of me in decorating my own funeral.

DON GONZALO. [Aside.] She lies worse than I do.

DOÑA LAURA. Poor Laura!

DON GONZALO. Poor Gonzalo!

DOÑA LAURA. [*Aside.*] I will not tell him that I married two years later.

DON GONZALO. [*Aside.*] In three months I ran off to Paris with a ballet dancer.

DOÑA LAURA. Fate is curious. Here are you and I, complete strangers, met by chance, discussing the romance of old friends of long ago! We have been conversing as if we were old friends.

DON GONZALO. Yes, it is curious, considering the ill-natured prelude to our conversation.

DOÑA LAURA. You scared away the birds.

DON GONZALO. I was unreasonable, perhaps.

DOÑA LAURA. Yes, that was evident. [*Sweetly.*] Are you coming again tomorrow?

DON GONZALO. Most certainly, if it is a sunny morning. And not only will I not scare away the birds, but I will bring a few crumbs.

DOÑA LAURA. Thank you very much. Birds are grateful and repay attention. I wonder where my maid is? Petra! [*Signals for her maid.*]

DON GONZALO. [*Aside, looking at* LAURA, *whose back is turned.*] No, no, I will not reveal myself. I am grotesque now. Better that she recall the gallant horseman who passed daily beneath her window tossing flowers.

DOÑA LAURA. Here she comes.

DON GONZALO. That Juanito! He plays havoc with the nursemaids. [*Looks* R. *and signals with his hand.*]

DOÑA LAURA. [*Aside, looking at* GONZALO, *whose back is turned.*] No, I am too sadly changed. It is better he should remember me as the black-eyed girl tossing flowers as he passed among the roses in the garden.

[JUANITO *enters by* R., PETRA *by* L. *She has a bunch of violets in her hand.*]

DOÑA LAURA. Well, Petra! At last!

DON GONZALO. Juanito, you are late.

PETRA. [*To* DOÑA LAURA.] The guard gave me these violets for you, señora.

DOÑA LAURA. How very nice! Thank him for me. They are fragrant. [*As she takes the violets from her maid a few loose ones fall to the ground.*]

DON GONZALO. My dear lady, this has been a great honor and a great pleasure.

DOÑA LAURA. It has also been a pleasure to me.

DON GONZALO. Good-by until tomorrow.

DOÑA LAURA. Until tomorrow.

DON GONZALO. If it is sunny.

DOÑA LAURA. A sunny morning. Will you go to your bench?

DON GONZALO. No, I will come to this—if you do not object?

DOÑA LAURA. This bench is at your disposal.

DON GONZALO. And I will surely bring the crumbs.

DOÑA LAURA. Tomorrow, then?

DON GONZALO. Tomorrow!

[LAURA *walks away toward* R., *supported by her* MAID. GONZALO, *before leaving with* JUANITO, *trembling and with a great effort, stoops to pick up the violets* LAURA *dropped. Just then* LAURA *turns her head and surprises him picking up the flowers.*]

JUANITO. What are you doing, señor?

DON GONZALO. Juanito, wait——

DOÑA LAURA. [*Aside.*] Yes, it is he!

DON GONZALO. [*Aside.*] It is she, and no mistake.

[DOÑA LAURA *and* DON GONZALO *wave farewell.*]

DOÑA LAURA. Can it be that this is he?

DON GONZALO. Heavens, is it she?

[*They smile once more, as if she were again at the window and he below in the rose garden, and then disappear upon the arms of their servants.*]

CURTAIN

MARCO MILLIONS

Eugene O'Neill (America)

Though O'Neill is usually thought of as a tragic dramatist, he is the author of two brilliant farces each satirical of American life and culture. *Ah Wilderness* depicts with humorous and tender sympathy the struggle of the younger generation with its elders. *Marco Millions* contrasts Occident and Orient in the persons of Marco Polo [1] and the famous Chinese Emperor Kublai Khan. The play belongs to the class of literature which modernizes historical characters in order both to make the past seem more real and to satirize contemporary life. Marco Polo, a bustling go-getter interested only in material gain, can think and talk only of millions. Kublai Khan and his beautiful granddaughter typify the Oriental emphasis on spiritual values. Through two Venetian traders named Polo who had penetrated to China, Kublai has requested the Pope to send him a hundred wisemen of Christendom to debate religious issues with his Buddhists, Taoists, and Confucians. [2] The Pope humorously sends him Marco Polo—the son of one of these traders—as a sample of Western culture. The Khan is immensely interested in this "sample" and is particularly curious to discover whether Marco possesses "the thing called a soul which the West dreams lives after death." By the second act, Marco has been fifteen years in China, and has become Mayor of Yang-Chau, which he is rapidly making over on modern American lines!

✳   ✳   ✳

Act II—Scene 1

Scene: *The Little Throne Room in the Bamboo summer palace of the* Khan *at Xanadu, the City of Peace—smaller, more intimate than the one at Cambaluc, but possessing an atmosphere of aloof dignity and simplicity fitting to the philosopher ruler who retreats here to contemplate in peace the vanity of his authority. It is a beautiful sunlit morning in late June. The aged* Khan *reclines on his cushioned bamboo throne—his mask-like face full of philosophic calm. He has the detached air of an idol.* Kukachin, *a beautiful young girl of twenty, pale and delicate, is sitting at his feet. Her air is grief-stricken. A flute player in the garden is playing a melancholy song, whose words* Kukachin *murmurs to herself.* Kublai *looks down at her tenderly.*

[1] *Marco Polo:* a Venetian trader who spent twenty years in China in the thirteenth century.

[2] *Buddhists, Taoists, and Confucians:* adherents of three Oriental religions.

KUBLAI. [*Musingly.*] Sing while you can. When the voice fails, listen to song. When the heart fails, be sung asleep. [*Chidingly.*] That is a sad poem, Little Flower. Are you sad because you must soon become Queen of Persia? But Arghun is a great hero, a Khan of the blood of Chinghiz. You will be blessed with strong sons able to dare the proud destiny of our blood.

KUKACHIN. [*Dully.*] Your will is my law.

KUBLAI. Not my will. The will of life to continue the strong. [*Forcing a consoling tone.*] Come, Little Flower. You have been fading here. See how pale you have grown! Your eyes are listless! Your lips droop even in smiling! But life at the Court of Persia is gay. There will be feasts, celebrations, diverting pleasures. You will be their Queen of Beauty.

KUKACHIN. [*With a sigh.*] A Queen may be only a woman who is unhappy.

KUBLAI. [*Teasingly.*] What despair! You talk like the ladies in poems who have lost their lovers! [KUKACHIN *gives a violent start which he does not notice and a spasm of pain comes over her face.*] But, never mind, Arghun of Persia is a hero no woman could fail to love.

KUKACHIN. [*Starting to her feet—desperately.*] No! I can bear his children, but you cannot force me to—— [*She breaks down, weeping.*]

KUBLAI. [*Astonished—gazing at her searchingly.*] Have I ever forced you to anything? [*Then resuming his tone of tender teasing.*] I would say, rather, that ever since you were old enough to talk, the Ruler of Earth, as they innocently call your grandfather, has been little better than your slave.

KUKACHIN. [*Taking his hand and kissing it.*] Forgive me. [*Then smiling at him.*] Has my love for you, who have been both father and mother to me, brought you no happiness?

KUBLAI. [*With deep emotion.*] You have been a golden bird singing beside a black river. You took your mother's place in my heart when she died. I was younger then. The river was not so black—the river of man's life so deep and silent—flowing with an insane obsession—whither?—and why? [*Then sadly.*] But now you in your turn must leave me, the river seems black, indeed! [*Then after a pause—tenderly.*] If it will make you unhappy, you need not marry Arghun Khan.

KUKACHIN. [*Recovering herself—resolutely.*] No. Your refusal would insult him. It might mean war. [*Resignedly.*] And Arghun is as acceptable as any other. Forgive my weakness. You once told me a Princess must never weep. [*She forces a smile.*] It makes no difference whether I stay or go, except that I shall be homesick for you. [*She kisses his hand again.*]

KUBLAI. [*Gratefully.*] My little one. [*He strokes her hair. After a pause during which he looks at her thoughtfully—tenderly.*] We have never had secrets from each other, you and I. Tell me, can you have fallen in love?

KUKACHIN. [*After a pause—tremblingly.*] You must not ask that—if you respect my pride! [*With a pitiful smile.*] You see— he does not even know—— [*She is blushing and hanging her head with confusion.* CHU-YIN, *sage counselor of the* KHAN, *enters hurriedly from the right. He is very old but still upright. He is a bit breathless from haste but his face is wreathed in smiles.*]

CHU-YIN. [*Making an obeisance.*] Your Majesty, do you hear that martial music? His Honor, Marco Polo, Mayor of Yang-Chau, seems about to visit you in state! [*The strains of a distant band can be heard.*]

KUBLAI. [*Still looking at* KUKACHIN, *who has started violently at the mention of* MARCO'S *name—worriedly.*] Impossible! In love? . . . [*Then to* CHU-YIN *preoccupiedly.*] Eh? Marco? I have given no orders for him to return.

CHU-YIN. [*Ironically.*] No doubt he comes to refresh your humor with new copious notes on his exploits. Our Marco has made an active mayor. Yang-Chau, according to the petition for mercy you have received from its inhabitants, is the most governed of all your cities. I talked recently with a poet who had fled from there in horror. Yang-Chau used to have a soul, he said. Now it has a brand-new courthouse.

KUBLAI. [*Irritably.*] He is beginning to weary me with his grotesque antics. Marco's spiritual hump begins to disgust me. He has not even a mortal soul; he has only an acquisitive instinct. We have given him every opportunity to learn. He has memorized everything and learned nothing. He has looked at everything and seen nothing. He has lusted for everything and loved nothing. He is only a shrewd and crafty greed. I shall send him home to his native wallow.

CHU-YIN. [*In mock alarm.*] What? Must we lose our clown?

KUKACHIN. [*Who has been listening with growing indignation.*] How dare you call him a clown? Just because he is not a dull philosopher you think——

KUBLAI. [*Astounded—admonishingly.*] Princess!

KUKACHIN. [*Turns to him—on the verge of tears—rebelliously.*]

Why are you both so unjust? Has he not done well everything he has been appointed to do? Has he not always succeeded where others failed? Has he not by his will-power and determination risen to the highest rank in your service? [*Then her anger dying—more falteringly.*] He is strange, perhaps, to people who do not understand him, but that is because he is so different from other men, so much stronger! And he has a soul! I know he has!

KUBLAI. [*Whose eyes have been searching her face—aghast.*] Kukachin! [*She sees he has guessed her secret and at first quails and shrinks away, then stiffens regally and returns his gaze unflinchingly.* CHU-YIN *looks from one to the other comprehendingly. Finally* KUBLAI *addresses her sternly.*] So, because I have allowed this fool a jester's latitude, because I permitted him to amuse you when you were a little girl, and since then, on his returns, to speak with you—a Princess—— [*Then brusquely.*] I shall inform the ambassadors you will be ready to sail for Persia within ten days. You may retire. [*She bows with a proud humility and walks off left.* KUBLAI *sits in a somber study, frowning and biting his lips. The blaring of* MARCO'S *band grows steadily nearer.*]

CHU-YIN. [*Gently.*] I have suspected her love for him for a long time.

KUBLAI. Why didn't you warn me?

CHU-YIN. Love is to wisdom what wisdom seems to love—a folly. I reasoned, love comes like the breath of wind on water and is gone leaving calm and reflection. I reasoned, this is an enchanted moment for her and it will remain a poignant memory to recompense her when she is no longer a girl but merely a Queen. And I reasoned, who knows but some day this Marco may see into her eyes and his soul may be born, and that will make a very interesting study.

KUBLAI. [*Bewilderedly.*] I cannot believe it! Why, since she was a little girl, she has only talked to him once or twice every two years or so!

CHU-YIN. That was unwise, for thus he has remained a strange, mysterious dream-knight from the exotic West, an enigma with something about him of a likable boy who brought her home each time a humble foolish, touching little gift! And also remember that on each occasion he returned in triumph, having accomplished a task—a victor, more or less, acting the hero. [*The band has crashed and dinned its way into the courtyard.*] As now! Listen! [*He goes to the window and looks down—with ironical but intense amusement.*] Ah! He wears over his Mayor's uniform, the regalia of Cock of Paradise in his secret fraternal order of the Mystic Knights of Confucius! [3] The band of the Xanadu lodge is with him as well as his own! He is riding on a very fat white horse. He dismounts, aided by the steps of your Imperial Palace! He slaps a policeman on the back and asks his name! He chucks a baby under the chin and asks the mother its name. She lies and says "Marco" although the baby is a girl. He smiles. He is talking loudly so everyone can overhear. He gives the baby one yen to start a savings account and encourage its thrift. The mother looks savagely disappointed. The crowd cheers. He keeps his smile frozen as he notices an artist sketching him. He shakes hands with a one-legged veteran of the Manzi campaign and asks his name. The veteran is touched. Tears come to his eyes. He tells him— but Polo forgets his name even as he turns to address the crowd. He waves one hand for silence. The band stops. It is the hand on which he wears five large jade rings. The other hand rests upon— and pats—the head of a bronze dragon, our ancient symbol of Yang, the celestial male principle of the Cosmos. He clears his throat, the crowd stands petrified, he is about to draw a deep breath and open his mouth carefully in position one of the five phonetic exercises—— [*Here* CHU-YIN *chuckles.*] But I am an old man full of malice and venom and it embitters me to see others unreasonably happy so—— [*Here just as* MARCO *is heard starting to speak, he throws open the window and calls in a loud, commanding tone.*] Messer Polo, His Imperial Majesty commands that you stop talking, dismiss your followers, and repair to his presence at once!

MARCO'S VOICE. [*Very faint and crestfallen.*] Oh—all right— I'll be right there.

KUBLAI. [*Cannot control a laugh in spite of himself—help-lessly.*] How can one deal seriously with a child-actor?

[KUKACHIN *enters from the left, terribly alarmed, and throws herself at* KUBLAI's *feet.*] . . .

KUKACHIN. Why did you summon him? I told you he does not know. It is all my fault! Punish me, if you will! But promise me you will not harm him!

KUBLAI. [*Looking down at her—sadly.*] Is it my custom to take vengeance? [*Then as people are heard approaching—quickly.*] Compose yourself! Remember again, Princesses may not weep! [*She springs to her feet, turns away for a moment, then turns back,*

---

[3] *Mystic Knights of Confucius:* Confucius is a great Chinese philosopher, but needless to say, this is not a real Chinese organization. It is Marco's own invention.

her face rigidly calm and emotionless. KUBLAI *nods with appreciation of her control.*] Good. You will make a Queen. [*She bows and retires backward to the left side of the throne. At the same moment,* NICOLO *and* MAFFEO POLO [4] *enter ceremoniously from the right. They wear the regalia of officers in the Mystic Knights of Confucius over their rich merchant's robes. This costume is a queer jumble of stunning effects that recall the parade uniforms of our modern Knights Templar, of Columbus, of Pythias, Mystic Shriners, the Klan, etc. They are absurdly conscious and proud of this get-up—like two old men in a children's play.* KUBLAI *and* CHU-YIN *regard them with amused astonishment. Even* KUKACHIN *cannot restrain a smile. They prostrate themselves at the foot of the throne. Then just at the right moment, preceded by a conscious cough,* MARCO POLO *makes his entrance. Over his gorgeous uniform of Mayor, he wears his childishly fantastic regalia as chief of the Mystic Knights of Confucius. As he steps on, he takes off his gilded, laced hat with its Bird of Paradise plumes and bows with a mechanical dignity on all sides. He has the manner and appearance of a successful movie star at a masquerade ball, disguised so that no one can fail to recognize him. He moves in stately fashion to the throne and prostrates himself before the* KHAN. KUKACHIN *stares at him with boundless admiration, hoping to catch his eye. The* KHAN *looks from her to him and his face grows stern.* CHU-YIN *is enjoying himself.*]

KUBLAI. Rise. [MARCO *does so.* KUBLAI *continues dryly.*] To what do I owe the honor of this unexpected visit?

MARCO. [*Hastily, but with full confidence.*] Well, I was sending in to your treasury the taxes of Yang-Chau for the fiscal year, and I knew you'd be so astonished at the unprecedented amount I had sweated out of them that you'd want to know how I did it—so here I am. [*An awkward pause.* MARCO *is disconcerted at the* KHAN's *steady impersonal stare. He glances about—sees the Princess—welcomes this opportunity for diverting attention. Bowing with humble respect.*] Pardon me, Princess. I didn't recognize you before, you've gotten so grown up. [*Flatteringly.*] You look like a Queen.

KUKACHIN. [*Falteringly.*] I bid you welcome, Your Honor.

KUBLAI. [*As a warning to* KUKACHIN *to control her emotion.*] The Princess will soon be Queen of Persia.

MARCO. [*Flustered and awed, bowing to her again—flatteringly.*] Then—Your Majesty—if I may be humbly permitted

[4] *Nicolo and Maffeo:* Marco's uncle and father.

[*bowing to* KUBLAI] to offer my congratulations—and before I settle down to discussing business—if her Highness—Majesty— will accept a small token of my esteem—— [*Here he stamps his foot. An African Slave, dressed in a pink livery with green hat and shoes and stockings and carrying a golden wicker basket, enters. He kneels, presents the basket to* MARCO, *who lifts the cover and pulls out a small chow puppy with a pink ribbon tied around its neck. He steps forward and offers this to the Princess, with a boyish grin.*] A contribution to your zoo—from your most humble servant!

KUKACHIN. [*Taking it—flushing with pleasure.*] Oh, what a little darling! [*She cuddles the puppy in her arms.*]

MARCO. [*Boastfully.*] He's a genuine, pedigreed pup. I procured him at great cost—I mean he's extra well-bred.

KUKACHIN. Oh, thank you so much, Marco Polo! [*Stammering.*] I mean, Your Honor.

KUBLAI. [*Warningly.*] His Honor wishes to talk business, Princess.

KUKACHIN. [*Controlling herself.*] I ask pardon. [*She bows and retires to left, rear, where she stands fondling the puppy and watching* MARCO.]

MARCO. [*Plunging in confidently on what he thinks is a sure point of attack.*] My tax scheme, Your Majesty, that got such wonderful results is simplicity itself. I simply reversed the old system. For one thing I found they had a high tax on excess profits. Imagine a profit being excess! Why, it isn't humanly possible! I repealed it. And I repealed the tax on luxuries. I found out the great majority in Yang-Chau couldn't afford luxuries. The tax wasn't democratic enough to make it pay! I crossed it off and I wrote on the statute books a law that taxes every necessity in life, a law that hits every man's pocket equally, be he beggar or banker! And I got results!

CHU-YIN. [*Gravely.*] In beggars?

KUBLAI. [*With a chilling air.*] I have received a petition from the inhabitants of Yang-Chau enumerating over three thousand cases of your gross abuse of power!

MARCO. [*Abashed only for a moment.*] Oh, so they've sent that vile slander to you, have they? That's the work of a mere handful of radicals——

KUBLAI. [*Dryly.*] Five hundred thousand names are signed to it. [*Still more dryly.*] Half a million citizens accuse you of endeavoring to stamp out their ancient culture!

MARCO. What! Why, I even had a law passed that anyone caught interfering with culture would be subject to a fine! It was Section One of a blanket statute that every citizen must be happy or go to jail. I found it was the unhappy ones who were always making trouble and getting discontented. You see here's the way I figure it; if a man's good, he's happy—and if he isn't happy, it's a sure sign he's no good to himself or anyone else and he better be put where he can't do harm.

KUBLAI. [*A bit helplessly now.*] They complain that you have entirely prohibited all free expression of opinion.

MARCO. [*Feelingly.*] Well, when they go to the extreme of circulating such treasonable opinions against me, isn't it time to protect your sovereignty by strong measures? [KUBLAI *stares at this effrontery with amazement.* MARCO *watches this impression and hurries on with an injured dignity.*] I can't believe, Your Majesty, that this minority of malcontents can have alienated your long-standing high regard for me!

KUBLAI. [*Conquered—suddenly overpowered by a great smile.*] Not so! You are the marvel of mankind! And I would be lost without you!

MARCO. [*Flattered but at the same time nonplussed.*] I thank you! [*Hesitatingly.*] But, to tell the truth, I want to resign, anyhow. I've done all I could. I've appointed five hundred committees to carry on my work, and I retire confident that with the system I've instituted everything will go on automatically and brains are no longer needed.

KUBLAI. [*With mock seriousness.*] In behalf of the population of Yang-Chau I accept your resignation, with deep regret for the loss of your unique and extraordinary services. [*Then suddenly in a strange voice.*] Do you still possess your immortal soul, Marco Polo?

MARCO. [*Flustered.*] Ha-ha! Yes, of course—at least I hope so. But I see the joke. You mean that Yang-Chau used to be a good place to lose one. Well, you wouldn't know the old town now. Sin is practically unseen. [*Hurrying on to another subject—boisterously.*] But however much I may have accomplished there, it's nothing to the big surprise I've got in reserve for you. May I demonstrate? [*Without waiting for permission, takes a piece of printed paper like a dollar-bill from his pocket.*] What is it? Paper. Correct! What is it worth? Nothing. That's where you're mistaken. It's worth ten yen. No, I'm not a liar! See ten yen written on it, don't you? Well, I'll tell you the secret. This is money, legally valued at ten yens' worth of anything you wish to buy, by order of His Imperial Majesty, the Great Khan! Do you see my point? Its advantages over gold and silver coin are obvious. It's light, easy to carry, [*here he gives a prodigious wink*] wears out quickly, can be made at very slight expense and yields enormous profit. Think of getting ten yen for this piece of paper. Yet it can be done. If you make the people believe it's worth it, it is! After all, when you stop to think, who was it first told them gold was money? I'll bet anything it was some quick-thinker who'd discovered a gold mine! [KUBLAI *and* CHU-YIN *stare at him in petrified incredulity. He mistakes it for admiration and is flattered. Bows and lays his paper money on the* KHAN's *knee.*] You're stunned, I can see that. It's so simple—and yet, who ever thought of it before me? I was amazed myself. Think it over, Your Majesty, and let the endless possibilities dawn on you! And now I want to show another little aid to government that I thought out. [*He makes a sign to his uncle and father. The former takes a mechanical contrivance out of a box and sets it up on the floor. It is a working model of a clumsy cannon.* NICOLO, *meanwhile, takes children's blocks out of his box and builds them into a fortress wall.* MARCO *is talking. His manner and voice have become grave and portentous.*] It all came to me, like an inspiration, last Easter Sunday when Father and Uncle and I were holding a little service. Uncle read a prayer which spoke of Our Lord as the Prince of Peace. Somehow, that took hold of me. I thought to myself, well, it's funny there always have been wars and there always will be, I suppose, because I've never read much in any history about heroes who waged peace. Still, that's wrong. War is a waste of money which eats into the profits of life like thunder! Then why war, I asked myself? But how are you going to end it? Then the flash came! There's only one workable way and that's to conquer everybody else in the world so they'll never dare fight you again! An impossible task, you object? Not any more! This invention you see before you makes conquering easy. Let me demonstrate with these models. On our right, you see the fortress wall of a hostile capital. Under your present system with battering rams, to make an effective breach in this wall would cost you the lives of ten thousand men. Valuing each life conservatively at ten yen, this amounts to one hundred thousand yen! This makes the cost of breaching prohibitive. But all of this waste can be saved. How? Just keep your eyes on your right and permit my exclusive invention to solve this problem. [*He addresses the fortress in a matter-of-fact tone.*] So you won't surrender, eh? [*Then in a mock-heroic falsetto, answering himself like a ventriloquist.*] We die but we never surrender! [*Then matter-of-factly.*] Well, brother, those heroic sentiments do you a lot of credit, but this is war and not a tragedy. You're up against new methods this time, and you better give in and avoid wasteful bloodshed. [*Answering himself.*] No! Victory or death! [*Then again.*] All right, brother, don't blame me. Fire! [*His uncle fires the gun. There is a bang, and a leaden ball is shot out which knocks a big breach in the wall of blocks.* MARCO *beams,* KUKACHIN *gives a scream of fright, then a gasp of delight, and claps her hands.* MARCO *bows to her the more gratefully as* KUBLAI *and* CHU-YIN *are staring at him with a queer appalled wonder that puzzles him, although he cannot imagine it is not admiration.*] I see you are stunned again. What made it do that, you're wondering? This. [*He takes a little package out of his pocket and pours some black powder out of it on his palm.*] It's the same powder they've been using here in children's fireworks. They've had it under their noses for years without a single soul ever having creative imagination enough to visualize the enormous possibilities. But you can bet I did! It was a lad crying with a finger half blown off where he held a firecracker too long that first opened my eyes. I learned the formula, improved on it, experimented in secret, and here's the gratifying result! [*He takes the cannon ball from his father who has retrieved it.*] You see? Now just picture this little ball magnified into one weighing twenty pounds or so and then you'll really grasp my idea. The destruction of property and loss of life would be tremendous! No one could resist you!

KUBLAI. [*After a pause—musingly.*] I am interested in the hero of that city who preferred death to defeat. Did you conquer his immortal soul?

MARCO. [*With frankness.*] Well, you can't consider souls when you're dealing with soldiers, can you? [*He takes his model and places it on the* KHAN's *knee with the paper money.*] When you have time, I wish you'd look this over. In fact—and this is the big idea I've been saving for the last—consider these two inventions of mine in combination. You conquer the world with this [*he pats the cannon-model*] and you pay for it with this. [*He pats the paper money—rhetorically.*] You become the bringer of peace on earth and good-will to men, and it doesn't cost you a yen hardly. Your initial expense—my price—is as low as I can possibly make it out of my deep affection for your Majesty—only a million yen.

KUBLAI. [*Quickly.*] In paper?

MARCO. [*With a grin and a wink.*] No. I'd prefer gold, if you don't mind. [*Silence.* MARCO *goes on meaningly.*] Of course, I don't want to force them on you. I'm confident there's a ready market for them elsewhere.

KUBLAI. [*Grimly smiling.*] Oh, I quite realize that in self-protection I've got to buy them or kill you!

MARCO. [*Briskly.*] Then it's a bargain? But I've still got one proviso—that you give us permission to go home. [KUKACHIN *gives a little gasp.* MARCO *goes on feelingly.*] We're homesick, Your Majesty. We've served you faithfully, and, frankly, now that we've made our fortune we want to go home and enjoy it. There's no place like home, Your Majesty! I'm sure even a King in his palace appreciates that.

KUBLAI. [*With smiling mockery.*] But—who can play your part? And your mission—your example? What will your Pope say when you tell him I'm still unconverted?

MARCO. [*Confidently.*] Oh, you will be—on your death-bed, if not before—a man of your common sense.

KUBLAI. [*Ironically.*] Courtier! [*Then solemnly.*] But my last objection is insurmountable. You haven't yet proved you have an immortal soul!

MARCO. It doesn't need proving.

KUBLAI. If you could only bring forward one reliable witness.

MARCO. My Father and Uncle can swear——

KUBLAI. They think it is a family trait. Their evidence is prejudiced.

MARCO. [*Worried now—looks at* CHU-YIN *hopefully.*] Mr. Chu-Yin ought to be wise enough to acknowledge——

CHU-YIN. [*Smiling.*] But I believe that what can be proven cannot be true. [MARCO *stands puzzled, irritated, looking stubborn, frightened, and foolish. His eyes wander about the room, finally resting appealing on* KUKACHIN.]

KUKACHIN. [*Suddenly steps forward—flushed but proudly.*] I will bear witness he has a soul. [KUBLAI *looks at her with a sad wonderment,* CHU-YIN *smilingly,* MARCO *with gratitude,* NICOLO *and* MAFFEO *exchange a glance of congratulation.*]

KUBLAI. How can you know, Princess?

KUKACHIN. Because I have seen it—once, when he bound up my dog's leg, once when he played with a slave's baby, once when he listened to music over water and I heard him sigh, once when he looked at sunrise, another time at sunset, another at the stars, another at the moon, and each time he said that Nature was wonderful. And all the while, whenever he has been with me I have always felt—something strange and different—and that something must be His Honor's soul, must it not?

KUBLAI. [*With wondering bitterness.*] The eye sees only its own sight.

CHU-YIN. But a woman may feel life in the unborn.

KUBLAI. [*Mockingly but sadly.*] I cannot contest the profound intuitions of virgins and mystics. Go home, Your Honor, Immortal Marco, and live forever! [*With forced gaiety.*] And tell your Pope your example has done much to convert me to wisdom—if I could find the true one!

SPREADING THE NEWS

LADY GREGORY (IRELAND)

Lady Gregory is one of the Irish writers who helped secure home rule for Ireland by arousing Irish patriotism through pictures of Irish life in poem, play, and story.

❋   ❋   ❋

PERSONS

BARTLEY FALLON	TIM CASEY
MRS. FALLON	JAMES RYAN
JACK SMITH	MRS. TARPEY
SHAWN EARLY	MRS. TULLY

A POLICEMAN (JO MULDOON)

A REMOVABLE MAGISTRATE

SCENE: *The outskirts of a fair. An apple stall.* MRS. TARPEY *sitting at it.* MAGISTRATE *and* POLICEMAN *enter.*

MAGISTRATE. So that is the Fair Green. Cattle and sheep and mud. No system. What a repulsive sight!

POLICEMAN. That is so, indeed.

MAGISTRATE. I suppose there is a good deal of disorder in this place?

POLICEMAN. There is.

MAGISTRATE. Common assault?

POLICEMAN. It's common enough.

MAGISTRATE. Agrarian crime, no doubt? [1]

POLICEMAN. That is so.

MAGISTRATE. Boycotting? Maiming of cattle? Firing into houses?

POLICEMAN. There was one time, and there might be again.

MAGISTRATE. That is bad. Does it go any farther than that?

POLICEMAN. Far enough, indeed.

MAGISTRATE. Homicide, then! This district has been shamefully neglected! I will change all that. When I was in the Andaman Islands, [2] my system never failed. Yes, yes, I will change all that. What has that woman on her stall?

POLICEMAN. Apples mostly—and sweets.

MAGISTRATE. Just see if there are any unlicensed goods underneath—spirits or the like. We had evasions of the salt tax in the Andaman Islands.

POLICEMAN. [Sniffing cautiously and upsetting a heap of apples.] I see no spirits here—or salt.

MAGISTRATE. [To MRS. TARPEY.] Do you know this town well, my good woman?

MRS. TARPEY. [Holding out some apples.] A penny the half-dozen, your honor?

POLICEMAN. [Shouting.] The gentleman is asking do you know the town! He's the new magistrate!

MRS. TARPEY. [Rising and ducking.] Do I know the town? I do, to be sure.

MAGISTRATE. [Shouting.] What is its chief business?

MRS. TARPEY. Business, is it? What business would the people here have but to be minding one another's business?

MAGISTRATE. [Shouting.] I mean what trade have they?

MRS. TARPEY. Not a trade. No trade at all but to be talking.

MAGISTRATE. I shall learn nothing here.

[JAMES RYAN comes in, pipe in mouth. Seeing MAGISTRATE he retreats quickly, taking pipe from mouth.]

MAGISTRATE. The smoke from that man's pipe has a greenish look; he may be growing unlicensed tobacco at home. I wish I had brought my telescope to this district. Come to the post office; I will telegraph for it. I found it very useful in the Andaman Islands.

[MAGISTRATE and POLICEMAN go out left.]

MRS. TARPEY. Bad luck to Jo Muldoon, knocking my apples this

---

[1] *Agrarian crime:* disputes over the control of the land. [2] *Andaman Islands:* British penal colony in India.

way and that way. [*Begins arranging them.*] Showing off he was
to the new magistrate.

[*Enter* BARTLEY FALLON *and* MRS. FALLON.]

BARTLEY. Indeed it's a poor country and a scarce country to be
living in. But I'm thinking if I went to America it's long ago the
day I'd be dead!

MRS. FALLON. So you might, indeed.

[*She puts her basket on a barrel and begins putting parcels in it,
taking them from under her cloak.*]

BARTLEY. And it's a great expense for a poor man to be buried in
America.

MRS. FALLON. Never fear, Bartley Fallon, but I'll give you a
good burying the day you'll die.

BARTLEY. Maybe it's yourself will be buried in the graveyard of
Cloonmara before me, Mary Fallon, and I myself that will be dying
unbeknownst some night, and no one a-near me.

MRS. FALLON. Leave off talking of dying. It might be twenty
years you'll be living yet.

BARTLEY. [*With a deep sigh.*] I'm thinking if I'll be living at the
end of twenty years, it's a very old man I'll be then!

MRS. TARPEY. [*Turns and sees them.*] Good morrow, Bartley
Fallon; good morrow, Mrs. Fallon. Well, Bartley, you'll find no
cause for complaining today; they are all saying it was a good fair.

BARTLEY. [*Raising his voice.*] It was not a good fair, Mrs. Tarpey. It was a scattered sort of a fair. If we didn't expect more, we
got less. That's the way with me always; whatever I have to sell
goes down and whatever I have to buy goes up. If there's ever any
misfortune coming to this world, it's on myself it pitches, like a
flock of crows on seed potatoes.

MRS. FALLON. Leave off talking of misfortunes, and listen to Jack
Smith that is coming the way, and he singing.

[*Voice of* JACK SMITH *heard singing:*

"I thought, my first love,
    There'd be but one house between you and me,
And I thought I would find
    Yourself coaxing my child on your knee.
Over the tide
    I would leap with the leap of a swan,
Till I came to the side
    Of the wife of the red-haired man!"

[JACK SMITH *comes in; he is a red-haired man, and is carrying a hayfork.*]

MRS. TARPEY. That should be a good song if I had my hearing.

MRS. FALLON. [*Shouting.*] It's "The Red-haired Man's Wife."

MRS. TARPEY. I know it well. That's the song that has a skin on it!

[*She turns her back to them and goes on arranging her apples.*]

MRS. FALLON. Where's herself,[3] Jack Smith?

JACK SMITH. She was delayed with her washing; bleaching the clothes on the hedge she is, and she daren't leave them, with all the tinkers that do be passing to the fair. It isn't to the fair I came myself, but up to the Five Acre Meadow I'm going, where I have a contract for the hay. We'll get a share of it into tramps[4] today.

[*He lays down the hayfork and lights his pipe.*]

BARTLEY. You will not get it into tramps today. The rain will be down on it by evening, and on myself, too. It's seldom I eve started on a journey but the rain would come down on me befo I'd find any place of shelter.

JACK SMITH. If it didn't itself, Bartley, it is my belief you w carry a leaky pail on your head in place of a hat, the way you' be without some cause of complaining.

[*A voice heard, "Go on, now, go on out o' that. Go on I sa*

JACK SMITH. Look at that young mare of Pat Ryan's backing into Shaughnessy's bullocks with the dint of the Don't be daunted, Pat; I'll give you a hand with her.

[*He goes out, leaving his hayfork.*]

MRS. FALLON. It's time for ourselves to be going home all I bought put in the basket. Look at there, Jack Smith' he left after him. He'll be wanting it. [*Calls.*] Jack Sm Smith!—He's gone through the crowd—hurry after him, he'll be wanting it.

BARTLEY. I'll do that. This is no safe place to be leavir *takes up fork awkwardly and upsets the basket.*] Lo now! If there is any basket in the fair upset, it must l basket! [*He goes out to the right.*]

MRS. FALLON. Get out of that! It is your own fault of misfortunes and misfortunes will come. Glory be! new egg-cups rolling in every part—and my two pou with the paper broke——

MRS. TARPEY. [*Turning from stall.*] God help us, N what happened to your basket?

[3] *herself:* Mrs. Smith.

[4] *tramps:* boats for sh

MRS. FALLON. It's himself that knocked it down, bad manners to him. [*Putting things up.*] My grand sugar that's destroyed, and he'll not drink his tea without it. I had best go back to the shop for more; much good may it do him!

[*Enter* TIM CASEY.]

TIM CASEY. Where is Bartley Fallon, Mrs. Fallon? I want a word with him before he'll leave the fair. I was afraid he might have gone home by this, for he's a temperate man.

MRS. FALLON. I wish he did go home! It'd be best for me if he went home straight from the fair green, or if he never came with me at all! Where is he, is it? He's gone up the road [*jerks elbow*] following Jack Smith with a hayfork. [*She goes out to left.*]

TIM CASEY. Following Jack Smith with a hayfork! Did ever any one hear the like of that. [*Shouts.*] Did you hear that news, Mrs. Tarpey?

MRS. TARPEY. I heard no news at all.

TIM CASEY. Some dispute I suppose it was that rose between [Jac]k Smith and Bartley Fallon, and it seems Jack made off, and [Bart]ley is following him with a hayfork!

[Mr]S. TARPEY. Is he now? Well, that was quick work! It's not [m]inutes since the two of them were here, Bartley going home [Ja]ck going to the Five Acre Meadow; and I had my apples to [pick u]p, that Jo Muldoon of the police had scattered, and when I [looked] round again Jack Smith was gone, and Bartley Fallon was [there a]nd Mrs. Fallon's basket upset, and all in it strewed upon [the grou]nd—the tea here—the two pound of sugar there—the egg[s the]re—Look, now, what a great hardship the deafness puts [on me] that I didn't hear the commencement of the fight! Wait [till I tell] James Ryan that I see below. He is a neighbor of Bart[ley's, it] would be a pity if he wouldn't hear the news!

[*She go*]es out. *Enter* SHAWN EARLY *and* MRS. TULLY.]

[TIM C]ASEY. Listen, Shawn Early! Listen, Mrs. Tully, to the [news! Ja]ck Smith and Bartley Fallon had a falling out, and Jack [spilled M]rs. Fallon's basket into the road, and Bartley made an [end of] him with a hayfork, and away with Jack, and Bartley [after him.] Look at the sugar here yet on the road!

[SHAWN] EARLY. Do you tell me so? Well, that's a queer thing, [and] Fallon so quiet a man!

[MRS. TU]LLY. I wouldn't wonder at all. I would never think well [of a man th]at would have that sort of a moldering look. It's likely [he has t]aken Jack by this.

[*Enter JA*]MES RYAN *and* MRS. TARPEY.]

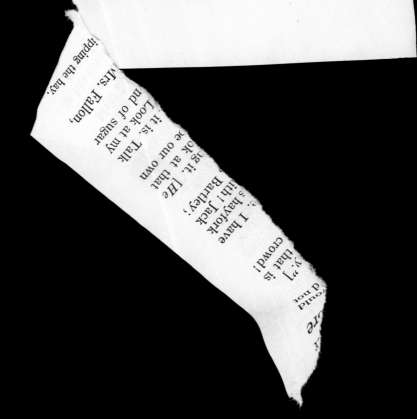

JAMES RYAN. That is great news Mrs. Tarpey was telling me! I suppose that's what brought the police and the magistrate up this way. I was wondering to see them in it a while ago.

SHAWN EARLY. The police after them? Bartley Fallon must have injured Jack so. They wouldn't meddle in a fight that was only for show!

MRS. TULLY. Why wouldn't he injure him? There was many a man killed with no more of a weapon than a hayfork.

JAMES RYAN. Wait till I run north as far as Kelly's bar to spread the news! [*He goes out.*]

TIM CASEY. I'll go tell Jack Smith's first cousin that is standing there south of the church after selling his lambs. [*Goes out.*]

MRS. TULLY. I'll go telling a few of the neighbors I see beyond to the west. [*Goes out.*]

SHAWN EARLY. I'll give word of it beyond at the east of the green.

[*Is going out when* MRS. TARPEY *seizes hold of him.*]

MRS. TARPEY. Stop a minute, Shawn Early, and tell me did you see red Jack Smith's wife, Kitty Keary, in any place?

SHAWN EARLY. I did. At her own house she was, drying clothes on the hedge as I passed.

MRS. TARPEY. What did you say she was doing?

SHAWN EARLY. [*Breaking away.*] Laying out a sheet on the hedge. [*He goes.*]

MRS. TARPEY. Laying out a sheet for the dead! The Lord have mercy on us! Jack Smith dead, and his wife laying out a sheet for his burying! [*Calls out.*] Why didn't you tell me that before, Shawn Early? Isn't the deafness the great hardship? Half the world might be dead without me knowing of it or getting word of it at all! [*She sits down and rocks herself.*] O my poor Jack Smith! To be going to his work so nice and so hearty, and to be left stretched on the ground in the full light of the day!

[*Enter* TIM CASEY.]

TIM CASEY. What is it, Mrs. Tarpey? What happened since?

MRS. TARPEY. O my poor Jack Smith!

TIM CASEY. Did Bartley overtake him?

MRS. TARPEY. O the poor man!

TIM CASEY. Is it killed he is?

MRS. TARPEY. Stretched in the Five Acre Meadow!

TIM CASEY. The Lord have mercy on us! Is that a fact?

MRS. TARPEY. Without the rites of the Church or a ha'porth!

TIM CASEY. Who was telling you?

Mrs. Tarpey. And the wife laying out a sheet for his corpse. [*Sits up and wipes her eyes.*] I suppose they'll wake [5] him the same as another?

[*Enter* Mrs. Tully, Shawn Early, *and* James Ryan.]

Mrs. Tully. There is great talk about this work in every quarter of the fair.

Mrs. Tarpey. Ochone! [6] cold and dead. And myself maybe the last he was speaking to!

James Ryan. The Lord save us! Is it dead he is?

Tim Casey. Dead surely, and the wife getting provision for the wake.

Shawn Early. Well, now, hadn't Bartley Fallon great venom in him?

Mrs. Tully. You may be sure he had some cause. Why would he have made an end of him if he had not? [*To Mrs. Tarpey, raising her voice.*] What was it rose the dispute at all, Mrs. Tarpey?

Mrs. Tarpey. Not a one of me knows. The last I saw of them, Jack Smith was standing there, and Bartley Fallon was standing there, quiet and easy, and he listening to "The Red-haired Man's Wife."

Mrs. Tully. Do you hear that, Tim Casey? Do you hear that, Shawn Early and James Ryan? Bartley Fallon was here this morning listening to red Jack Smith's wife, Kitty Keary that was! Listening to her and whispering with her! It was she started the fight so!

Shawn Early. She must have followed him from her own house. It is likely some person roused him.

Tim Casey. I never knew, before, Bartley Fallon was great with Jack Smith's wife.

Mrs. Tully. How would you know it? Sure it's not in the streets they would be calling it. If Mrs. Fallon didn't know of it, and if I that have the next house to them didn't know it, and if Jack Smith himself didn't know of it, it is not likely you would know of it, Tim Casey.

Shawn Early. Let Bartley Fallon take charge of her from this out so, and let him provide for her. It is little pity she will get from any person in this parish.

Tim Casey. How can he take charge of her? Sure he has a wife of his own. Sure you don't think he'd turn souper [7] and marry her in a Protestant church?

[5] *wake:* sit up with the body.   [6] *Ochone:* an exclamation of grief.
[7] *turn souper:* abandon his religious faith.

JAMES RYAN. It would be easy for him to marry her if he brought her to America.

SHAWN EARLY. With or without Kitty Keary, believe me it is for America he's making at this minute. I saw the new magistrate and Jo Muldoon of the police going into the post office as I came up— there was hurry on them—you may be sure it was to telegraph they went, the way he'll be stopped in the docks at Queenstown!

MRS. TULLY. It's likely Kitty Keary is gone with him, and not minding a sheet or a wake at all. The poor man, to be deserted by his own wife, and the breath hardly gone out yet from his body that is lying bloody in the field!

[*Enter* MRS. FALLON.]

MRS. FALLON. What is it the whole of the town is talking about? And what is it you yourselves are talking about? Is it about my man Bartley Fallon you are talking? Is it lies about him you are telling, saying that he went killing Jack Smith? My grief that ever he came into this place at all!

JAMES RYAN. Be easy now, Mrs. Fallon. Such there is no one at all in the whole fair but is sorry for you!

MRS. FALLON. Sorry for me, is it? Why would anyone be sorry for me? Let you be sorry for yourselves, and that there may be shame on you forever and at the day of judgment, for the words you are saying and the lies you are telling to take away the character of my poor man, and to take the good name off of him, and to drive him to destruction! That is what you are doing!

SHAWN EARLY. Take comfort now, Mrs. Fallon. The police are not so smart as they think. Sure he might give them the slip yet, the same as Lynchehaun.

MRS. TULLY. If they do get him, and if they do put a rope around his neck, there is no one can say he does not deserve it!

MRS. FALLON. Is that what you are saying, Bridget Tully, and is that what you think? I tell you it's too much talk you have, making yourself out to be such a great one, and to be running down every respectable person! A rope, is it? It isn't much of a rope was needed to tie up your own furniture the day you came into Martin Tully's house, and you never bringing as much as a blanket, or a penny, or a suit of clothes with you, and I myself bringing seventy pounds and two feather beds. And now you are stiffer than a woman would have a hundred pounds! It is too much talk the whole of you have. A rope, is it? I tell you the whole of this town is full of liars and schemers that would hang you up for half a glass of whiskey. [*Turning to go.*] Killing Jack Smith indeed! Where are you at all, Bartley, till I bring you out of this? My nice, quiet little man! My decent comrade! He that is as kind and as harmless as an innocent beast of the field! He'll be doing no harm at all if he'll shed the blood of some of you after this day's work! [*Calls out.*] Bartley! Bartley Fallon! Where are you? [*Going out.*] Did anyone see Bartley Fallon?

[*All turn to look after her.*]

JAMES RYAN. It is hard for her to believe any such a thing, God help her!

[*Enter* BARTLEY FALLON *from right, carrying hayfork.*]

BARTLEY. It is what I often said to myself, if there is ever any misfortune coming to this world, it is on myself it is sure to come!

[*All turn round and face him.*]

BARTLEY. To be going about with this fork, and to find no one to take it, and no place to leave it down, and I wanting to be gone out of this.—Is that you, Shawn Early? [*Holds out fork.*] It's well I met you. You have no call to be leaving the fair for a while the way I have, and how can I go till I'm rid of this fork? Will you take it and keep it until such time as Jack Smith——

SHAWN EARLY. [*Backing.*] I will not take it, Bartley Fallon, I'm very thankful to you!

BARTLEY. [*Turning to apple stall.*] Look at it now, Mrs. Tarpey; it was here I got it; let me thrust it in under the stall. It will lie there safe enough, and no one will take notice of it until such time as Jack Smith——

MRS. TARPEY. Take your fork out of that! Is it to put trouble on me and to destroy me you want? Putting it there for the police to be rooting out maybe. [*Thrusts him back.*]

BARTLEY. That is a very unneighborly thing for you to do, Mrs. Tarpey. Hadn't I enough care on me with that fork before this, running up and down with it and afeard to lay it down in any place. I wish I never touched it or meddled with it at all!

JAMES RYAN. It is a pity, indeed, you ever did.

BARTLEY. Will you yourself take it, James Ryan? You were always a neighborly man.

JAMES RYAN. [*Backing.*] There is many a thing I would do for you, Bartley Fallon, but I won't do that!

SHAWN EARLY. I tell you there is no man will give you any help or any encouragement for this day's work.

BARTLEY. If no one at all will take it, maybe it's best to give it up to the police.

TIM CASEY. There'd be a welcome for it with them, surely! [*Laughter.*]

Mrs. Fallon. It's himself that knocked it down, bad manners to him. [*Putting things up.*] My grand sugar that's destroyed, and he'll not drink his tea without it. I had best go back to the shop for more; much good may it do him!

[*Enter* Tim Casey.]

Tim Casey. Where is Bartley Fallon, Mrs. Fallon? I want a word with him before he'll leave the fair. I was afraid he might have gone home by this, for he's a temperate man.

Mrs. Fallon. I wish he did go home! It'd be best for me if he went home straight from the fair green, or if he never came with me at all! Where is he, is it? He's gone up the road [*jerks elbow*] following Jack Smith with a hayfork. [*She goes out to left.*]

Tim Casey. Following Jack Smith with a hayfork! Did ever any one hear the like of that. [*Shouts.*] Did you hear that news, Mrs. Tarpey?

Mrs. Tarpey. I heard no news at all.

Tim Casey. Some dispute I suppose it was that rose between Jack Smith and Bartley Fallon, and it seems Jack made off, and Bartley is following him with a hayfork!

Mrs. Tarpey. Is he now? Well, that was quick work! It's not ten minutes since the two of them were here, Bartley going home and Jack going to the Five Acre Meadow; and I had my apples to settle up, that Jo Muldoon of the police had scattered, and when I looked round again Jack Smith was gone, and Bartley Fallon was gone, and Mrs. Fallon's basket upset, and all in it strewed upon the ground—the tea here—the two pound of sugar there—the egg-cups there—Look, now, what a great hardship the deafness puts upon me, that I didn't hear the commincement of the fight! Wait till I tell James Ryan that I see below. He is a neighbor of Bartley's; it would be a pity if he wouldn't hear the news!

[*She goes out. Enter* Shawn Early *and* Mrs. Tully.]

Tim Casey. Listen, Shawn Early! Listen, Mrs. Tully, to the news! Jack Smith and Bartley Fallon had a falling out, and Jack knocked Mrs. Fallon's basket into the road, and Bartley made an attack on him with a hayfork, and away with Jack, and Bartley after him. Look at the sugar here yet on the road!

Shawn Early. Do you tell me so? Well, that's a queer thing, and Bartley Fallon so quiet a man!

Mrs. Tully. I wouldn't wonder at all. I would never think well of a man that would have that sort of a moldering look. It's likely he has overtaken Jack by this.

[*Enter* James Ryan *and* Mrs. Tarpey.]

[JACK SMITH *comes in ; he is a red-haired man, and is carrying a hayfork.*]

MRS. TARPEY. That should be a good song if I had my hearing.

MRS. FALLON. [*Shouting.*] It's "The Red-haired Man's Wife."

MRS. TARPEY. I know it well. That's the song that has a skin on it !

[*She turns her back to them and goes on arranging her apples.*]

MRS. FALLON. Where's herself,[3] Jack Smith?

JACK SMITH. She was delayed with her washing; bleaching the clothes on the hedge she is, and she daren't leave them, with all the tinkers that do be passing to the fair. It isn't to the fair I came myself, but up to the Five Acre Meadow I'm going, where I have a contract for the hay. We'll get a share of it into tramps [4] today. [*He lays down the hayfork and lights his pipe.*]

BARTLEY. You will not get it into tramps today. The rain will be down on it by evening, and on myself, too. It's seldom I ever started on a journey but the rain would come down on me before I'd find any place of shelter.

JACK SMITH. If it didn't itself, Bartley, it is my belief you would carry a leaky pail on your head in place of a hat, the way you'd not be without some cause of complaining.

[*A voice heard, "Go on, now, go on out o' that. Go on I say."*]

JACK SMITH. Look at that young mare of Pat Ryan's that is backing into Shaughnessy's bullocks with the dint of the crowd! Don't be daunted, Pat; I'll give you a hand with her.

[*He goes out, leaving his hayfork.*]

MRS. FALLON. It's time for ourselves to be going home. I have all I bought put in the basket. Look at there, Jack Smith's hayfork he left after him. He'll be wanting it. [*Calls.*] Jack Smith! Jack Smith!—He's gone through the crowd—hurry after him, Bartley; he'll be wanting it.

BARTLEY. I'll do that. This is no safe place to be leaving it. [*He takes up fork awkwardly and upsets the basket.*] Look at that now! If there is any basket in the fair upset, it must be our own basket ! [*He goes out to the right.*]

MRS. FALLON. Get out of that ! It is your own fault, it is. Talk of misfortunes and misfortunes will come. Glory be ! Look at my new egg-cups rolling in every part—and my two pound of sugar with the paper broke——

MRS. TARPEY. [*Turning from stall.*] God help us, Mrs. Fallon, what happened to your basket?

[3] *herself:* Mrs. Smith.   [4] *tramps:* boats for shipping the hay.

Mrs. Tully. And it is to the police Kitty Keary herself will be brought.

Mrs. Tarpey. [*Rocking to and fro.*] I wonder now who will take the expense of the wake for poor Jack Smith?

Bartley. The wake for Jack Smith!

Tim Casey. Why wouldn't he get a wake as well as another? Would you begrudge him that much?

Bartley. Red Jack Smith dead! Who was telling you?

Shawn Early. The whole town knows of it by this.

Bartley. Do they say what way did he die?

James Ryan. You don't know that yourself, I suppose, Bartley Fallon? You don't know he was followed and that he was laid dead with the stab of a hayfork?

Bartley. The stab of a hayfork!

Shawn Early. You don't know, I suppose, that the body was found in the Five Acre Meadow?

Bartley. The Five Acre Meadow!

Tim Casey. It is likely you don't know the police are after the man that did it?

Bartley. The man that did it!

Mrs. Tully. You don't know, maybe, that he was made away with for the sake of Kitty Keary, his wife?

Bartley. Kitty Keary, his wife! [*Sits down bewildered.*]

Mrs. Tully. And what have you to say now, Bartley Fallon?

Bartley. [*Crossing himself.*] I to bring that fork here, and to find that news before me! It is much if I can ever stir from this place at all, or reach as far as the road!

Tim Casey. Look, boys, at the new magistrate, and Jo Muldoon along with him! It's best for us to quit this.

Shawn Early. That is so. It is best not to be mixed in this business at all.

James Ryan. Bad as he is, I wouldn't like to be an informer against any man.

[*All hurry away except* Mrs. Tarpey, *who remains behind her stall. Enter* Magistrate *and* Policeman.]

Magistrate. I knew the district was in a bad state, but I did not expect to be confronted with a murder at the first fair I came to.

Policeman. I am sure you did not, indeed.

Magistrate. It was well I had not gone home. I caught a few words here and there that roused my suspicions.

Policeman. So they would, too.

Magistrate. You heard the same story from everyone you asked?

POLICEMAN. The same story—or if it was not altogether the same, anyway it was no less than the first story.

MAGISTRATE. What is that man doing? He is sitting alone with a hayfork. He has a guilty look. The murder was done with a hayfork!

POLICEMAN. [*In a whisper.*] That's the very man they say did the act; Bartley Fallon himself!

MAGISTRATE. He must have found escape difficult—he is trying to brazen it out. A convict in the Andaman Islands tried the same game, but he could not escape my system! Stand aside—Don't go far—Have the handcuffs ready. [*He walks up to* BARTLEY, *folds his arms, and stands before him.*] Here, my man, do you know anything of John Smith?

BARTLEY. Of John Smith! Who is he, now?

POLICEMAN. Jack Smith, sir, Red Jack Smith!

MAGISTRATE. [*Coming a step nearer and tapping him on the shoulder.*] Where is Jack Smith?

BARTLEY. [*With a deep sigh, and shaking his head slowly.*] Where is he, indeed?

MAGISTRATE. What have you to tell?

BARTLEY. It is where he was this morning, standing in this spot, singing his share of songs—no, but lighting his pipe—scraping a match on the sole of his shoe——

MAGISTRATE. I ask you, for the third time, where is he?

BARTLEY. I wouldn't like to say that. It is a great mystery, and it is hard to say of any man, did he earn hatred or love.

MAGISTRATE. Tell me all you know.

BARTLEY. All that I know— Well, there are the three estates; there is Limbo, and there is Purgatory, and there is——

MAGISTRATE. Nonsense! This is trifling! Get to the point.

BARTLEY. Maybe you don't hold with the clergy so? That is the teaching of the clergy. Maybe you hold with the old people. It is what they do be saying, that the shadow goes wandering, and the soul is tired, and the body is taking a rest— The shadow! [*Starts up.*] I was nearly sure I saw Jack Smith not ten minutes ago at the corner of the forge, and I lost him again. Was it his ghost I saw, do you think?

MAGISTRATE. [*To policeman.*] Conscience-struck! He will confess all now!

BARTLEY. His ghost to come before me! It is likely it was on account of the fork! I to have it and he to have no way to defend himself the time he met with his death!

MAGISTRATE. [*To policeman.*] I must note down his words. [*Takes out notebook.*] [*To* BARTLEY.] I warn you that your words are being noted.

BARTLEY. If I had ha' run faster in the beginning, this terror would not be on me at the latter end! Maybe he will cast it up against me at the day of judgment— I wouldn't wonder at all at that.

MAGISTRATE. [*Writing.*] At the day of judgment——

BARTLEY. It was soon for his ghost to appear to me—is it coming after me always by day it will be, and stripping the clothes off in the night time?— I wouldn't wonder at all at that, being as I am an unfortunate man!

MAGISTRATE. [*Sternly.*] Tell me this truly. What was the motive of this crime?

BARTLEY. The motive, is it?

MAGISTRATE. Yes; the motive; the cause.

BARTLEY. I'd sooner not say that.

MAGISTRATE. You had better tell me truly. Was it money?

BARTLEY. Not at all! What did poor Jack Smith ever have in his pockets unless it might be his hands that would be in them?

MAGISTRATE. Any dispute about land?

BARTLEY. [*Indignantly.*] Not at all! He never was a grabber or grabbed from anyone!

MAGISTRATE. You will find it better for you if you tell me at once.

BARTLEY. I tell you I wouldn't for the whole world wish to say what it was—it is a thing I would not like to be talking about.

MAGISTRATE. There is no use in hiding it. It will be discovered in the end.

BARTLEY. Well, I suppose it will, seeing that mostly everybody knows it before. Whisper here now. I will tell no lie; where would be the use? [*Puts his hand to his mouth, and* MAGISTRATE *stoops.*] Don't be putting the blame on the parish, for such a thing was never done in the parish before—it was done for the sake of Kitty Keary, Jack Smith's wife.

MAGISTRATE. [*To policeman.*] Put on the handcuffs. We have been saved some trouble. I knew he would confess if taken in the right way. [*Policeman puts on handcuffs.*]

BARTLEY. Handcuffs now! Glory be! I always said if there was ever any misfortune coming to this place it was on myself it would fall. I to be in handcuffs! There's no wonder at all in that.

[*Enter* MRS. FALLON, *followed by the rest. She is looking back at them as she speaks.*]

MRS. FALLON. Telling lies the whole of the people of this town are; telling lies, telling lies as fast as a dog will trot! Speaking against my poor respectable man! Saying he made an end of Jack Smith! There is no better man and no kinder man in the whole of the five parishes! It's little annoyance he ever gave to anyone! [*Turns and sees him.*] What in the earthly world do I see before me? Bartley Fallon in charge of the police! Handcuffs on him! O Bartley, what did you do at all at all?

BARTLEY. O Mary, there has a great misfortune come upon me! It is what I always said, that if there is ever any misfortune——

MRS. FALLON. What did he do at all, or is it bewitched I am?

MAGISTRATE. This man has been arrested on a charge of murder.

MRS. FALLON. Whose charge is that? Don't believe them! They are all liars in this place! Give me back my man!

MAGISTRATE. It is natural you should take his part, but you have no cause of complaint against your neighbors. He has been arrested for the murder of John Smith, on his own confession.

MRS. FALLON. The saints of heaven protect us! And what did he want killing Jack Smith?

MAGISTRATE. It is best you should know all. He did it on account of a love affair with the murdered man's wife.

MRS. FALLON. [*Sitting down.*] With Jack Smith's wife! With Kitty Keary!— Ochone, the traitor!

THE CROWD. A great shame, indeed. He is a traitor, indeed.

MRS. TULLY. To America he was bringing her, Mrs. Fallon.

BARTLEY. What are you saying, Mary? I tell you——

MRS. FALLON. Don't say a word! I won't listen to any word you'll say! [*Stops her ears.*] Oh, isn't he the treacherous villain? Ochone go deo!

BARTLEY. Be quiet till I speak! Listen to what I say!

MRS. FALLON. Sitting beside me on the ass car coming to the town, so quiet and so respectable, and treachery like that in his heart!

BARTLEY. Is it your wits you have lost, or is it I myself that have lost my wits?

MRS. FALLON. And it's hard I earned you, slaving, slaving—and you grumbling, and sighing, and coughing, and discontented, and the priest wore out anointing you, with all the times you threatened to die!

BARTLEY. Let you be quiet till I tell you!

MRS. FALLON. You to bring such a disgrace into the parish! A thing that was never heard of before!

BARTLEY. Will you shut your mouth and hear me speaking?

MRS. FALLON. And if it was for any sort of a fine handsome woman, but for a little fistful of a woman like Kitty Keary, that's not four feet high hardly, and not three teeth in her head unless she got new ones! May God reward you, Bartley Fallon, for the black treachery in your heart and the wickedness in your mind, and the red blood of poor Jack Smith that is wet upon your hand!

[*Voice of* JACK SMITH *heard singing:*]

"The sea shall be dry,
    The earth under mourning and ban!
Then loud shall he cry
    For the wife of the red-haired man!"

BARTLEY. It's Jack Smith's voice—I never knew a ghost to sing before—. It is after myself and the fork he is coming! [*Goes back. Enter* JACK SMITH.] Let one of you give him the fork and I will be clear of him now and for eternity!

MRS. TARPEY. The Lord have mercy on us! Red Jack Smith! The man that was going to be waked!

JAMES RYAN. Is it back from the grave you are come?

SHAWN EARLY. Is it alive you are, or is it dead you are?

TIM CASEY. Is it yourself at all that's in it?

MRS. TULLY. Is it letting on you were to be dead?

MRS. FALLON. Dead or alive, let you stop Kitty Keary, your wife, from bringing my man away with her to America!

JACK SMITH. It is what I think—the wits are gone astray on the whole of you. What would my wife want bringing Bartley Fallon to America?

MRS. FALLON. To leave yourself, and to get quit of you she wants, Jack Smith, and to bring him away from myself. That's what the two of them had settled together.

JACK SMITH. I'll break the head of any man that says that! Who is it says it? [*To* TIM CASEY.] Was it you said it? [*To* SHAWN EARLY.] Was it you?

ALL TOGETHER. [*Backing and shaking their heads.*] It wasn't I said it!

JACK SMITH. Tell me the name of any man that said it!

ALL TOGETHER. [*Pointing to* BARTLEY.] It was *him* that said it!

JACK SMITH. Let me at him till I break his head!

[BARTLEY *backs in terror. Neighbors hold* JACK SMITH *back.*]

JACK SMITH. [*Trying to free himself.*] Let me at him! Isn't he the pleasant sort of scarecrow for any woman to be crossing the ocean with! It's back from the docks of New York he'd be turned [*trying to rush at him again*], with a lie in his mouth and treachery in his heart, and another man's wife by his side, and he passing her off as his own! Let me at him, can't you. [*Makes another rush, but is held back.*]

MAGISTRATE. [*Pointing to* JACK SMITH.] Policeman, put the handcuffs on this man. I see it all now. A case of false impersonation, a conspiracy to defeat the ends of justice. There was a case in the Andaman Islands, a murderer of the Mopsa tribe, a religious enthusiast——

POLICEMAN. So he might be, too.

MAGISTRATE. We must take both these men to the scene of the murder. We must confront them with the body of the real Jack Smith.

JACK SMITH. I'll break the head of any man that will find my dead body!

MAGISTRATE. I'll call more help from the barracks. [*Blows policeman's whistle.*]

BARTLEY. It is what I am thinking, if myself and Jack Smith are put together in the one cell for the night, the handcuffs will be taken off him, and his hands will be free, and murder will be done that time surely!

MAGISTRATE. Come on! [*They turn to the right.*]

CURTAIN

A MARRIAGE PROPOSAL

ANTON CHEKHOV (RUSSIA)

Translated by Barrett H. Clark and H. R. Baukhage

The characters in this play are rich but not noble Russian land owners who illustrate the funny side of the extravagant Russian temperament. The heroine has passed her first youth.

❋   ❋   ❋

STEPAN. [*Going toward* IVAN *and greeting him.*] Who is this I see? My dear fellow! Ivan Vassiliyitch! I'm so glad to see you! [*Shakes hands.*] This is a surprise! How are you?

IVAN. Thank you! And how are you?

STEPAN. Oh, so-so, my friend. Please sit down. This is nice of you not to forget your neighbors. But tell me, why all this ceremony? Dress clothes, white gloves, and all? Are you on your way to some important engagement, my good fellow?

IVAN. No, I have no engagement except with you, Stepan Stepanovitch.

STEPAN. But why in evening clothes, my friend? This isn't New Year's!

IVAN. You see, it's simply this, that—[*Composing himself.*] I have come to you, Stepan Stepanovitch, to trouble you with a request. It is not the first time I have had the honor of turning to you for assistance, and you have always, that is—I beg your pardon, I am a bit excited! I'll have a drink of water first, dear Stepan Stepanovitch. [*He drinks.*]

STEPAN. [*Aside.*] He's come to borrow money! I won't give him any! [*To* IVAN.] What is it, then, dear Ivan?

IVAN. You see—dear—Stepanovitch, pardon me, Stepan—Stepan—dearvitch—I mean—I am terribly nervous, as you will be so good as to see! What I mean to say—you are the only one who can help me, though I don't deserve it, and—and I have no right whatever to make this request of you.

STEPAN. Oh, don't beat about the bush, my dear fellow. Tell me!

IVAN. Immediately—in a moment. Here it is, then: I have come to ask—for the hand of your daughter, Natalia Stepanovna.

STEPAN. [*Joyfully.*] Angel! Ivan Vassiliyitch! Say that once again! I didn't quite hear it!

IVAN. I have the honor to beg——

STEPAN. [*Interrupting.*] My dear, dear man! I am so happy that everything is so—everything! [*Embraces and kisses him.*] I have wanted this to happen for so long. It has been my dearest wish! [*He represses a tear.*] And I have always loved you, my dear fellow, as my own son! May God give you His blessings and His grace and—I always wanted it to happen. But why am I standing here like a blockhead? I am completely dumfounded with pleasure completely dumfounded. My whole being! I'll call Natalia!

IVAN. Dear Stepan Stepanovitch, what is your opinion? May I hope for Natalia Stepanovna's acceptance?

STEPAN. Really! A fine boy like you—and you think she won't accept on the minute? Lovesick as a cat and all that! [*He goes out.*]

IVAN. I'm cold. My body is trembling as though I were going to take my examination! But the chief thing is to settle matters! If a person meditates too much, or hesitates, or talks about it, waits for an ideal or for true love, he never gets it. *Brrr!* It's cold! Natalia is an excellent housekeeper, not bad-looking, well educated—what more could I ask? I'm so excited my ears are roaring!

[*He drinks water.*] And not to marry, that won't do! In the first place I'm thirty-five—a critical age, you might say. In the second place, I must live a well-regulated life. I have a weak heart and continual palpitating; I am very sensitive and always getting excited. My lips begin to tremble and the pulse in my right temple throbs terribly. But the worst of all is my insomnia. I hardly lie down and begin to doze before something in my left side begins to pull and tug, and something begins to hammer in my left shoulder —and in my head, too! I jump up like a madman, walk about a little and lie down again, but the moment I fall asleep I have a terrible cramp in the side. So it goes all night long!

[*Enter* NATALIA STEPANOVNA.]

NATALIA. Ah! It's you. Papa said to go in: there was a dealer here who'd come to buy something. Good afternoon, Ivan Vassiliyitch.

IVAN. Good day, my dear Natalia Stepanovna.

NATALIA. You must pardon me for wearing my apron and this old dress: we are working today. Why haven't you come to see us oftener? You've not been here for so long! Sit down. [*They sit down.*] Won't you have something to eat?

IVAN. Thank you, I have just had lunch.

NATALIA. Today it is beautiful, and only yesterday it rained so hard the workmen couldn't do a stroke of work. Think of it! I was so anxious that I had the whole field mowed, and now I'm sorry I did it, because I am afraid the hay will rot. But what on earth is this? You are in evening clothes! The latest cut! Are you on your way to a ball? And you seem to be looking better, too—really. Why are you dressed up so gorgeously?

IVAN. [*Excited.*] You see, my dear Natalia Stepanovna—it's simply this: I have decided to ask you to listen to me—of course it will be a surprise, and indeed you'll be angry, but I—[*Aside.*] How fearfully cold it is!

NATALIA. What is it? [*A pause.*] Well?

IVAN. I'll try to be brief. My dear Natalia Stepanovna, as you know—for many years—since my childhood, I have had the honor to know your family. My poor aunt and her husband, from whom, as you know, I inherited the estate, always had the greatest respect for your father and your poor mother. Furthermore my property, as you know, adjoins your own. If you will be so good as to remember, my meadows come up to your birch woods.

NATALIA. Pardon the interruption. You said "my meadows"— but are they your meadows?

IVAN. They belong to me.

NATALIA. What nonsense! The meadows belong to us—not to you.

IVAN. Now, my dear Natalia Stepanovna!

NATALIA. Well, that is certainly news to me. How do they belong to you?

IVAN. How? I am speaking of the meadows lying between your birch woods and my brick-earth.

NATALIA. Yes, exactly. They belong to us.

IVAN. No, you are mistaken, my dear Natalia Stepanovna, they belong to me.

NATALIA. Try to remember exactly, Ivan Vassiliyitch. Is it so long ago that you inherited them?

IVAN. Long ago! As far back as I can remember they have always belonged to us.

NATALIA. But that isn't true! You'll pardon my saying so.

IVAN. It is all a matter of record, my dear Natalia Stepanovna. It is true that at one time the title to the meadows was disputed, but now everyone knows they belong to me. There is no room for discussion. Be so good as to listen: my aunt's grandmother put these meadows, free of rent, into the hands of your father's grandfather's peasants for a certain time while they were making bricks for my grandmother. These people used the meadows for about forty years, living there as they would on their own property. Later, however, when——

NATALIA. There's not a word of truth in that! My grandfather, and my great-grandfather, too, knew that their estate reached back to the swamp, which proves that the meadows belong to us. What further discussion can there be? I can't understand it. It is really most annoying.

IVAN. I'll show you the papers, Natalia Stepanovna.

NATALIA. No, you are either joking or trying to lead me into a discussion. That's not at all nice! We have owned this property for nearly three hundred years, and now all at once we hear that it doesn't belong to us. Ivan Vassiliyitch, you will pardon me, but I really can't believe my ears. The meadows are worth very little! In all, they don't contain more than five acres, and they are worth only a few hundred rubles—say three hundred; but the injustice of the thing is what affects me. Say what you will, I can't bear injustice.

IVAN. Only listen until I have finished, please! The peasants of your respected father's grandfather, as I have already had the honor to tell you, baked bricks for my grandmother. My aunt's grandmother wished to do them a favor——

NATALIA. Grandfather! Grandmother! Aunt! I know nothing about them. All I know is that the meadows belong to us, and that ends the matter.

IVAN. No, they belong to me!

NATALIA. And if you keep on explaining it for two days, and put on five suits of evening clothes, the meadows are still ours—ours—ours! I don't want to take your property, but I refuse to give up what belongs to us!

IVAN. Natalia Stepanovna, I don't need the meadows, I am only concerned with the principle. If you are agreeable, I beg of you, accept them as a gift from me!

NATALIA. But *I* can give them to *you,* because they belong to me! This is most extraordinary, Ivan Vassiliyitch! Until now we have considered you as a good neighbor and a good friend; only last year we lent you our threshing machine, so that we couldn't thresh until November, and now you treat us like thieves! You offer to make me a present of my own land. Excuse me, but good neighbors don't treat each other that way. In my opinion, it's a very low trick—to speak frankly——

IVAN. According to you I'm a usurper, then, am I? My dear lady, I have never appropriated other peoples' property, and I shall permit no one to accuse me of such a thing! [*He goes quickly to the bottle and drinks water.*] The meadows are mine.

NATALIA. That's not the truth! They are mine!

IVAN. Mine!

NATALIA. I'll prove it to you! This afternoon I'll send my reapers into the meadows.

IVAN. W-h-a-t?

NATALIA. My reapers will be there today!

IVAN. I'll chase them off!

NATALIA. If you dare!

IVAN. The meadows are mine, you understand? Mine!

NATALIA. Really, you needn't scream so! If you want to scream and snort and rage you may do it at home, but here please keep yourself within the limits of common decency.

IVAN. My dear lady, if it weren't that I am suffering from palpitation of the heart and hammering of the arteries in my temples, I would deal with you very differently! [*In a loud voice.*] The meadows belong to me!

NATALIA. Us!

IVAN. Me!

[*Enter* STEPANOVITCH.]

STEPAN. What's going on here? What is he yelling about?

NATALIA. Papa, please tell this gentleman to whom the meadows belong—to us or to him?

STEPAN. [*To* IVAN.] My dear fellow, the meadows are ours, of course.

IVAN. But, merciful heavens, Stepan Stepanovitch, how do you make that out? You at least might be reasonable. My aunt's grandmother gave the use of the meadows free of rent to your grandfather's peasants; the peasants lived on the land for forty years and used it as their own, but later, when——

STEPAN. Permit me, my dear friend. You forget that your grandmother's peasants never paid, because there had been a lawsuit over the meadows, and everyone knows that the meadows belong to us. You haven't looked at the map.

IVAN. I'll prove to you that they belong to me!

STEPAN. Don't try to prove it, my dear fellow.

IVAN. I will!

STEPAN. My good fellow, what are you shrieking about? You can't prove anything by yelling, you know. I ask for nothing that belongs to you, nor do I intend to give up anything of my own. Why should I? If it has gone so far, my dear man, that you really intend to claim the meadows, I'd rather give them to the peasants than to you, and I certainly shall!

IVAN. I can't believe it! By what right can you give away property that doesn't belong to you?

STEPAN. Really, you must allow me to decide what I am to do with my own land! I'm not accustomed, young man, to have people address me in that tone of voice. I, young man, am twice your age, and I beg you to address me with respect.

IVAN. No! No! You think I'm a fool! You're making fun of me! You call my property yours and then expect me to stand quietly by and talk to you like a human being. That isn't the way a good neighbor behaves, Stepan Stepanovitch! You are no neighbor; you're no better than a land-grabber. That's what you are!

STEPAN. Wh-at? What did he say?

NATALIA. Papa, send the reapers into the meadows this instant!

STEPAN. [*To* IVAN.] What was that you said, sir?

NATALIA. The meadows belong to us and I won't give them up! I won't give them up! I won't give them up!

IVAN. We'll see about that! I'll prove in court that they belong to me.

STEPAN. In court! You may sue in court, sir, if you like! Oh, I know you; you are only waiting to find an excuse to go to law!

You're an intriguer, that's what you are! Your whole family are always looking for quarrels. The whole lot!

IVAN. Kindly refrain from insulting my family. Never has one been brought to trial for embezzlement, as your dear uncle was!

STEPAN. Your grandmother was a dipsomaniac,[1] and the younger aunt, Nastasia Michailovna, eloped with an architect!

IVAN. And your mother limped. [*He puts his hand over his heart.*] Oh, my side pains! My temples are bursting! Lord in Heaven! Water!

STEPAN. And your dear father was a gambler—and a glutton!

NATALIA. And your aunt was a gossip like few others!

IVAN. And you are an intriguer. Oh, my heart! And it's an open secret that you cheated at the elections—my eyes are blurred! Where is my hat?

NATALIA. Oh, how low! Liar! Disgusting thing!

IVAN. Where's my hat? My heart! Where shall I go? Where is the door? Oh—it seems—as though I were dying! I can't—my legs won't hold me— [*Goes to the door.*]

STEPAN. [*Following him.*] May you never darken my door again!

NATALIA. Bring your suit to court! We'll see!

[VASSILIYITCH *staggers out.*]

STEPAN. [*Angrily.*] The devil!

NATALIA. What a good-for-nothing! And they talk about being good neighbors!

STEPAN. Loafer! Scarecrow! Monster!

NATALIA. A swindler like that takes over a piece of property that doesn't belong to him and then dares argue about it!

STEPAN. And to think that this fool dares make a proposal of marriage!

NATALIA. What? A proposal of marriage?

STEPAN. Why, yes! He came here to make you a proposal of marriage.

NATALIA. Why didn't you tell me that before?

STEPAN. That's why he had on his evening clothes! The poor fool!

NATALIA. Proposal for me? Oh! [*Falls into an armchair and groans.*] Bring him back! Bring him back!

STEPAN. Bring whom back?

NATALIA. Faster, faster, I'm sinking! Bring him back! [*She becomes hysterical.*]

---

[1] *dipsomaniac:* drunkard.

STEPAN. What is it? What's wrong with you? [*His hands to his head.*] I'm cursed with bad luck! I'll shoot myself! I'll hang myself!

NATALIA. I'm dying! Bring him back!

STEPAN. Bah! In a minute! Don't bawl! [*He rushes out.*]

NATALIA. [*Groaning.*] What have they done to me? Bring him back! Bring him back!

STEPAN. [*Comes running in.*] He's coming at once! The devil take him! Ugh! Talk to him yourself; I won't!

NATALIA. [*Groaning.*] Bring him back!

STEPAN. He's coming, I tell you! O Lord! What a task it is to be the father of a grown daughter! I'll cut my throat! I really will cut my throat! We've argued with the fellow, insulted him, and now we've thrown him out!—and you did it all, you!

NATALIA. Why, it was you. You have no manners, you are brutal! If it weren't for you, he wouldn't have gone!

STEPAN. Oh, yes, I'm to blame! If I shoot or hang myself, remember you'll be to blame. You forced me to it! You! [IVAN *appears in the doorway.*] There, talk to him yourself! [*He goes out.*]

IVAN. Terrible palpitation! My leg is lamed! My side hurts me——

NATALIA. Pardon us, we were angry, Ivan Vassiliyitch. I remember now—the meadows really belong to you.

IVAN. My heart is beating terribly! My meadows—my eyelids tremble— [*They sit down.*] I was wrong. It was only the principle of the thing—the property isn't worth much to me, but the principle is worth a great deal.

NATALIA. Exactly, the principle! Let us talk about something else.

IVAN. Because I have proofs that my aunt's grandmother had, with the peasants of your good father——

NATALIA. Enough, enough. [*Aside.*] I don't know how to begin. [*To* IVAN.] Are you going hunting soon?

IVAN. Yes, heath-cock shooting, respected Natalia Stepanovna. I expect to begin after the harvest. Oh, did you hear? My dog Ugadi—you know him—he limps!

NATALIA. What a shame! How did that happen?

IVAN. I don't know. Perhaps it's a dislocation, or maybe he was bitten by some other dog. [*He sighs.*] The best dog I ever had— to say nothing of his price! I paid Mironov one hundred and twenty-five rubles for him.

NATALIA. That was too much, Ivan Vassiliyitch.

IVAN. In my opinion it was very cheap. A wonderful dog!

NATALIA. Papa paid eighty-five for Okatai, and Okatai is a much better dog than Ugadi!

IVAN. Really? Okatai better than Ugadi? What an idea! [*He laughs.*] Okatai better than Ugadi!

NATALIA. Of course. It is true Okatai is still young; he isn't full-grown yet, but in the pack or on the leash with two or three others there is none better, even——

IVAN. I really must beg your pardon, Natalia Stepanovna, but you quite overlook the fact that he has a short lower jaw, and a dog with a short lower jaw can't snap.

NATALIA. Short lower jaw? That's the first time I heard that!

IVAN. I assure you, his lower jaw is shorter than his upper.

NATALIA. Have you measured it?

IVAN. I have measured it. He is good at running, though.

NATALIA. In the first place, our Okatai is pure-bred, and as for your mongrel, nobody could ever figure out his pedigree; he's old and ugly, and as skinny as an old hag.

IVAN. Old, certainly! I wouldn't take five of your Okatais for him! Ugadi is a dog and Okatai is—it is laughable to argue it! Dogs like your Okatai can be found by the dozens at any dealer's, a whole poundful!

NATALIA. Ivan Vassiliyitch, you are very contrary today. First you say our meadows belong to you and then you declare Ugadi is better than Okatai. I don't like it when a person doesn't say what he really thinks. You know perfectly well that Okatai is a hundred times better than your silly Ugadi. What makes you keep on saying he isn't?

IVAN. I can see, Natalia Stepanovna, you consider me either a blind man or a fool. But at least you must admit that Okatai has a short lower jaw!

NATALIA. It isn't so!

IVAN. Yes, a short lower jaw!

NATALIA. [*Loudly.*] It's not so!

IVAN. What makes you scream, my dear lady?

NATALIA. What makes you talk such nonsense? It's disgusting! It is high time Ugadi was shot, and yet you compare him with Okatai!

IVAN. Pardon me, but I can't carry on this argument any longer. I have palpitation of the heart!

NATALIA. I have always noticed that the hunters who do the most talking know least about hunting.

IVAN. My dear lady, I beg you to be still. My heart is bursting! [*He shouts.*] Be still!

NATALIA. I won't be still until you admit that Okatai is the better of the two dogs.

[*Enter* STEPANOVITCH.]

STEPAN. Well, has it begun all over again?

NATALIA. Papa, say frankly, on your honor, which dog is the better: Okatai or Ugadi?

IVAN. Stepan Stepanovitch, I beg you, just answer this: has your dog a short lower jaw or not? Yes or no?

STEPAN. And what if he has? Is it of such importance? There is no better dog in the whole country.

IVAN. My Ugadi is better. Tell the truth, now!

STEPAN. Don't get so excited, my dear fellow! Permit me. Your Ugadi certainly has his good points. He is a good breed, has a good stride, strong haunches, and so forth. But the dog, if you really want to know it, has two faults: he is old and he has a short lower jaw.

IVAN. Pardon me, I have palpitation of the heart!—Let us keep to facts. Just remember, in Maruskin's meadows my Ugadi kept ear to ear with Count Rasvachai and your dog.

STEPAN. He was behind, because the Count struck him with his whip.

IVAN. Quite right. All the other dogs were on the scent, but Okatai took it into his head to bite a sheep.

STEPAN. That isn't so! I am sensitive about that and beg you to stop this argument. He struck him because everybody looks on a strange dog of good blood with envy. Even you, sir, aren't free from the sin. No sooner do you find a better dog than Ugadi than you begin to—this, that—his, mine—and so forth! I remember distinctly.

IVAN. I remember something too!

STEPAN. [*Mimicking him.*] I remember something too! What do you remember?

IVAN. Palpitation! My leg is lame—I can't——

NATALIA. Palpitation! What kind of hunter are you? You ought to stay in the kitchen by the stove and wrestle with the potato peelings, and not go fox-hunting! Palpitation!

STEPAN. And what kind of hunter are you? A man with your diseases ought to stay at home and not jolt around in the saddle. If you were a hunter—! But you only ride round in order to find out about other people's dogs, and make trouble for everyone. I am sensitive! Let's drop the subject. Besides, you're no hunter.

IVAN. And are you? You only ride around to flatter the Count!—My heart! You intriguer! Swindler!

STEPAN. And what of it? [*Shouting.*] Be still!

IVAN. Intriguer!

STEPAN. Baby! Puppy! Walking drug-store!

IVAN. Old rat! Oh, I know you!

STEPAN. Be still! Or I'll shoot you—with my worst gun, like a partridge! Fool! Loafer!

IVAN. Everyone knows—oh, my heart!—that your poor late wife used to beat you. My leg—my temples—Heavens—I'm dying—I——

STEPAN. And your housekeeper wears the trousers in your house!

IVAN. Here—here—there—there—my heart has burst! My shoulder is torn asunder. Where is my shoulder? I'm dying! [*He falls into a chair.*] Call the doctor! [*Faints.*]

STEPAN. Baby! Half-baked clam! Fool!

NATALIA. Nice sort of hunter you are! You can't even sit on a horse. [*To* STEPAN.] Papa, what's the matter with him? [*She screams.*] Ivan Vassiliyitch! He is dead!

IVAN. I'm ill! I can't breathe! Air!

NATALIA. He is dead! [*She shakes* IVAN.] Ivan Vassiliyitch! What have we done! He is dead! [*She sinks into a chair.*] The doctor—doctor! [*She goes into hysterics.*]

STEPAN. Ah-h! What is it? What's the matter with you?

NATALIA. [*Groaning.*] He's dead! Dead!

STEPAN. Who is dead? Who? [*Looking at* IVAN.] Yes, he *is* dead! Good Heavens! Water! The doctor! [*Holding the glass to* IVAN'S *lips.*] Drink! He won't drink! He's dead! What a terrible situation! Why didn't I shoot myself? Why have I never cut my throat? What am I waiting for now? Only give me a knife! Give me a pistol! [IVAN *moves.*] He's coming to! Drink some water—there!

IVAN. Sparks! Mists! Where am I?

STEPAN. Get married! Quick, and then go to the devil! She's willing! [*He joins the hands of* IVAN *and* NATALIA.] She's agreed! Only leave me in peace!

IVAN. Wh-what? [*Getting up.*] Who?

STEPAN. She's willing! Kiss each other and—devil take you both!

NATALIA. [*Groans.*] He lives! Yes, yes, I'm willing!

STEPAN. Kiss each other!

IVAN. Who? What? [NATALIA *and* IVAN *kiss.*] Very nice! Pardon me, but what is this for? Oh, yes, I understand! My heart—sparks—I am so happy, Natalia Stepanovna! [*He kisses her hand.*] My leg is lame!

NATALIA. I'm happy too!

STEPAN. Ah-h! A load off my shoulders! Ah-h!

NATALIA. And now at least you'll admit that Ugadi is not so good a dog as Okatai!

IVAN. Better!

NATALIA. Worse!

STEPAN. Now the domestic joys have begun—Champagne!

IVAN. Better!

NATALIA. Worse, worse, worse!

STEPAN. [*Trying to drown them out.*] Champagne, champagne!

CYRANO DE BERGERAC

EDMOND ROSTAND (FRANCE)

Translated by Howard Thayer Kingsbury

DRAMATIS PERSONAE

CYRANO DE BERGERAC
CHRISTIAN DE NEUVILLETTE } *Guardsmen*
CARBON DE CASTEL-JALOUX, *captain of the guard*
COMTE DE GUICHE, *a noble*
RAGUENEAU, *a pastry cook*
LE BRET, *friend of Cyrano*
BELLEROSE, *theater owner*
ROXANE, *Cyrano's cousin*
A Refreshment Girl
Sister Martha
Two Musicians

Also a crowd of tradesmen, nobles, Musketeers, Gascony cadets, pages, comedians, musicians, children, spectators, actresses, nuns, etc.

Cyrano de Bergerac is laid in the same period as Dumas' *Three Musketeers* and the characters display the same combination of adventurous courage, pride, gallantry, good swordsmanship, and sentiment. The Gascon hero, Cyrano, is both a soldier and a poet, and thus displays all sides of seventeenth-century character at its best.

The scene of the first act is a fashionable theater in Paris in the reign of Louis XIV. Just as the play is about to begin, a voice rings out forbidding the actor to proceed. The command is spoken by Cyrano de Bergerac, a poor but proud and dashing young officer in the King's Guard. Cyrano, a man of taste and himself a writer, disapproves the bad acting of the leading man, Montfleury. Nonchalantly tossing a bag of gold-pieces to the manager, and challenging anyone of the audience to oppose his wishes, Cyrano forces the crowd to disperse, for his prowess with the rapier is as famous as his wit. A group of noblemen remain to protest. Their leader is De Guiche, a foppish but powerful courtier in love with Cyrano's cousin, the beautiful Roxane. De Guiche is supported by the Viscount, his friend, and Cyrano is accompanied by Le Bret, his comrade. The following scene takes place.

❋　❋　❋

Act I. Scene IV

The Vicomte. [*Choking.*] These great and lofty airs!
　A rustic, who—who—even wears no gloves,
　And goes about without a single ribbon.
Cyrano. It is my character that I adorn.
　I do not deck me like a popinjay;　　　　　　　　　　　　　5
　But though less foppish, I am better dressed:
　I would not sally forth, through carelessness,
　With an insult ill wiped out, or with my conscience
　Sallow with sleep still lingering in its eyes,
　Honor in rags, or scruples dressed in mourning.　　　　10
　But I go out with all upon me shining,
　With liberty and freedom for my plume,
　Not a mere upright figure;—'t is my soul
　That I thus hold erect as if with stays,
　And decked with daring deeds instead of ribbons,　　　15
　Twirling my wit as it were my moustache,
　The while I pass among the crowd, I make
　Bold truths ring out like spurs.
The Vicomte.　　　　　　　　　　　　But, sir—
Cyrano.　　　　　　　　　　　　　　　　　　I have
　No gloves?—A pity!—I had just one left,　　　　　　　20
　One of a worn-out pair!—which troubled me!
　I left it recently in some one's face.
The Vicomte. Knave, rascal, booby, flat-foot, scum o' the earth!

CYRANO. [*Taking off his hat and bowing as if the* VICOMTE *had just introduced himself.*] Ah? And I—Cyrano-Savinien-Hercule de Bergerac.

[*Laughter.*]

THE VICOMTE. [*In a temper.*] Buffoon!

CYRANO. [*Giving a cry like one who feels a sudden pain.*] Oh!

THE VICOMTE. [*Who was going off, turning about.*] What's he saying now?

CYRANO. [*With grimaces of pain.*] I must   25
Shake it, because it fell asleep—the fault
Of leaving it long idle—

THE VICOMTE. What's the matter?

CYRANO. My sword-blade tingles!

THE VICOMTE. [*Drawing his own sword.*] Very well, come on!

CYRANO. I shall give you a charming little stroke.

THE VICOMTE. [*With disdain.*] Poet!—

CYRANO. A poet, yes! and such a one,
That, while I fence with you, I'll improvise   30
A ballade for you.   •

THE VICOMTE.   A ballade?

CYRANO.   I suppose
You do not e'en imagine what that is?

THE VICOMTE. But—

CYRANO. [*As if reciting a lesson.*] The ballade, then, is made up of three stanzas,
Of eight lines—

THE VICOMTE. [*Shuffling his feet.*] Oh!

CYRANO. [*Continuing.*] And a refrain of four.

THE VICOMTE. You—

CYRANO. I'll make one and fight you both at once.   35
And at the last verse touch you, sir.

THE VICOMTE.   No!

CYRANO.   No?
The ballade of Monsieur de Bergerac's duel
At the Hôtel de Bourgogne with a booby.

THE VICOMTE. What is that, if you please?

CYRANO.   That is the title.

THE HALL. [*Excited to the highest pitch.*] In place!—No noise!—
In line!—This is amusing.

[*Tableau. A circle of curious onlookers in the parterre, the* MARQUISES *and the* OFFICERS *mixed in with the* TRADESMEN *and common people. The* PAGES *climb on people's shoulders to see better. All the women stand up in the boxes. To the right* DE GUICHE *and his gentlemen. To the left* LE BRET, RAGUENEAU, CUIGY, *etc.*]

CYRANO. [*Closing his eyes for a moment.*] Wait, let me choose my
    rhymes—I have them now: 40

      My hat I toss lightly away;
      From my shoulders I slowly let fall
      The cloak which conceals my array,
      And my sword from my scabbard I call,
      Like Céladon, graceful and tall,   45
      Like Scaramouche, quick hand and brain,—
      And I warn you, my friend, once for all,
      I shall thrust when I end the refrain.

[*The swords meet.*]

      You were rash thus to join in the fray;
      Like a fowl I shall carve you up small;   50
      Your ribs, 'neath your doublet so gay,
      Your breast, where the blue ribbons fall,
      Ding dong! ring your bright trappings all;
      My point flits like a fly on the pane,
      As I clearly announce to the hall   55
      I shall thrust when I end the refrain.

      I need one more rhyme for "array"—
      You give ground, you turn white as the wall—
      And so lend me the word "runaway."
      There! you have let your point fall   60
      As I parry your best lunge of all;
      I begin a new line, the end's plain,
      Your skewer hold tight, lest it fall.
      I shall thrust when I end the refrain.

[*Announces solemnly.*]

REFRAIN

      Prince, on the Lord you must call!
      I gain ground, I advance once again,   65
      I feint, I lunge. [*Lunging.*] There! that is all!
[THE VICOMTE *staggers.* CYRANO *salutes.*]
      For I thrust as I end the refrain.
[*Shouts. Applause in the boxes. Flowers and handkerchiefs are*

"I GAIN GROUND, I ADVANCE ONCE AGAIN,
I FEINT, I LUNGE. THERE! THAT IS ALL!"

thrown. The Officers *surround* Cyrano *and congratulate him.* Ragueneau *dances with enthusiasm.* Le Bret *is dizzy with joy. The* Vicomte's *friends hold him up and lead him away.*]

The Crowd. [*In one long cry.*] Ah!

A Light Guardsman. Superb!

A Woman. A pretty stroke!

Ragueneau. Magnificent!

A Marquis. Something quite new!

Le Bret. Mad folly!

Voices. [*In the confusion about* Cyrano.] Compliments, congratulations, bravo! 70

Voice of a Woman. He's a hero!

A Musketeer. [*Advancing quickly toward* Cyrano *with outstretched hands.*] Will you allow me, sir?—'T was right well done,
  And these are things I think I understand;
  Besides, I have expressed my joy by stamping! [*Withdraws.*]

Cyrano. Who is this gentleman?

Le Bret.   He's D'Artagnan! 75
  [*To* Cyrano, *taking him by the arm.*] Come, let us talk—

Cyrano. Let the crowd go out first. [*To* Bellerose.] May I wait?

Bellerose. [*Respectfully.*] Certainly!
  [*Shouts are heard without.*]

A Voice. They hiss Montfleury!

Bellerose. [*Solemnly.*] "Sic transit"— [*Changing his tone, to the* Doorkeeper *and the* Candle-snuffer.] Sweep. Close up.
  But leave the lights.
  We shall return when we have had our supper,
  For a rehearsal of tomorrow's farce. 80
  [Bellerose *goes out, after low bows to* Cyrano.]

The Doorkeeper. [*To* Cyrano.] You do not dine?

Cyrano. I?—No!

Le Bret. [*To* Cyrano.] Because?

Cyrano. [*Proudly.*]   Because— [*Changing his tone when he sees that the* Doorkeeper *has gone.*]
  I have no money!

Le Bret. [*Making the gesture of throwing a bag.*] What! the bag of crowns?

Cyrano. Inheritance, in one day thou art spent!

Le Bret. How will you live this month, then?

Cyrano. Naught is left. 85

Le Bret. What folly 't was to throw away the bag!

Cyrano. But what a stroke.

The Orange-girl. [*Coughing behind her little counter.*] Hum! hum!

   [Cyrano *and* Le Bret *turn about. She advances timidly.*]
     To see you fasting—
     It breaks my heart.
     [*Showing the sideboard.*] I have all that is needed.
     [*With enthusiasm.*] Take what you wish!

Cyrano. [*Taking off his hat.*] My Gascon pride forbids me,
     My child, to take one dainty from your hands,
     And yet I fear that this may cause you pain,   90
     And so I shall accept—
     [*Goes to the sideboard and chooses.*] —oh, nothing much!
     A grape—
     [*She starts to give him the bunch; he picks one grape.*] But
       one! This glass of water!
   [*She starts to pour in some wine; he stops her.*] Clear!
     And half a macaroon! [*He returns the other half.*]

Le Bret.   But this is foolish!

The Orange-girl. Oh, something more!

Cyrano. Why, yes, your hand to kiss!   95

   [*He kisses the hand which she holds out, as he would the hand of
     a princess.*]

The Orange-girl. I thank you, sir. [*She curtsies.*] Good night!
                            [*She goes out.*]

(Cyrano confesses to Le Bret that he loves Roxane, the cleverest, prettiest, and most popular belle of Paris. He is hopeless, however, because he thinks his enormous nose makes him too hideous for any woman to love. Le Bret suggests that the orange girl admired his cleverness and courage, and that Roxane had applauded the duel. Just as Cyrano decides to woo her, his hopes in his really hopeless love for Roxane are raised briefly when she sends asking for an interview. When he meets her the next day at the shop of Ragueneau, pastry-cook, he learns that she is in love with Christian, a handsome but not brilliant young officer who has just joined Cyrano's company. Roxane wishes Cyrano to protect her sweetheart.

The cook shop quickly fills with the cadets of the Guard, most of them Gascons, who make it their *rendezvous*. Christian, being a newcomer in the Guard, must prove his courage to be accepted. Having been told that it was dangerous to mention a nose or even to sneeze in the presence of the fiery and sensitive Cyrano, Christian chooses a novel way of establishing his bravery. The cadets beg Cyrano to recount

how the evening before he had put to flight a hundred men who had
attacked a friend of his from an ambush.)

ACT II. SCENE IX

CYRANO, LE BRET, THE CADETS, CHRISTIAN DE NEUVILLETTE.

A CADET. [*Seated at a table in the background, glass in hand.*] Cyrano! [CYRANO *turns.*] The story!

CYRANO. In a moment.

THE CADET. [*Rising and coming forward.*] The story of the fight!
'T will be a lesson——

[*Stops before the table where* CHRISTIAN *is seated.*]
——For this untried recruit.

CHRISTIAN. [*Raising his head.*] Untried recruit?

ANOTHER CADET. Yes, northern weakling!

CHRISTIAN. Weakling, did you say?

FIRST CADET. [*Mockingly.*] Monsieur de Neuvillette, learn this
one thing:

There is one object which we do not mention   5
More than the rope in the household of one hanged.

CHRISTIAN. And what is that?

ANOTHER CADET. [*In an impressive voice.*] Behold me! [*Mysteriously touches his finger to his nose three times.*] Understand?

CHRISTIAN. Ah! 't is the——

ANOTHER. Hush—that word is never uttered! [*Indicates* CYRANO,
who is talking with LE BRET *in the background.*]
Or 't is with him there you will have to do.

ANOTHER. [*Who has silently sat down on the table behind him,
while he has been turning to face the others.*] Two men he
slew because he liked it not   10
That they talked through their noses.

ANOTHER. [*Rising from under the table where he has crawled on all
fours, in a hollow voice.*] And one cannot
Without departing, cut off in his youth,
Make one allusion to the fatal feature!

ANOTHER. [*Laying his hand on his shoulder.*] One word's enough!
I said a word?—a gesture!
To draw one's kerchief is to draw one's shroud.   15

[*Silence. All around him fold their arms and watch him. He rises
and walks toward* CARBON DE CASTEL-JALOUX, *who is talking
with an officer and seems to see nothing.*]

CHRISTIAN. Captain!

CARBON. [*Turning and looking him over.*] Monsieur?

CHRISTIAN. What is the thing to do,
When Southrons are too boastful?

CARBON.   Prove to them
One can be from the North, and brave. [*Turns his back on him.*]

CHRISTIAN. I thank you.

FIRST CADET. [*To* CYRANO.] Your story now!

ALL   His story!

CYRANO. [*Coming forward towards them.*] What, my story?
[*All draw their benches towards him, and form a group, craning their necks.* CHRISTIAN *straddles a chair.*]
Well: I was marching all alone, to meet them,   20
The moon shone in the sky like a great watch,
When suddenly some watchmaker, with care,
Starting to draw a piece of cloudy cotton
Across the silver case of this round watch,
The night became the blackest ever seen;   25
And as there are no lights upon the quays,
Good Lord! you could not see beyond—

CHRISTIAN.   Your nose?
[*Silence. Every one rises slowly. They look at* CYRANO *in terror. He breaks off in amazement. A pause.*]

CYRANO. Who is that man there?

A CADET. [*In an undertone.*] He's a man who came
This morning.

CYRANO. [*Taking a step towards* CHRISTIAN.] Did you say this morning?

CARBON. [*In an undertone.*] Named Baron de Neuvil—

CYRANO. [*Quickly stopping.*] Ah, 'tis well—
[*Turns pale, then red, and makes another movement as if to fling himself upon* CHRISTIAN.] I—   29
[*Then regains his composure and says in a quiet voice.*] Well—
[*Begins again.*] As I was saying—
[*With a burst of anger in his voice.*] God—
[*Continues in a natural tone.*] —you could not see.
[*Amazement. They take their seats, watching him.*]
And so I went, thinking that for a beggar
I was about to offend some mighty prince,
Who surely would bear me a bitter grudge;
In short, that rashly and without concern,   35
I was about to thrust—

CHRISTIAN.   Your nose?

CYRANO. —my fingers
Between the bark and tree, since this great man
Might well be strong enough to deal a blow
Upon—

CHRISTIAN. Your nose?

CYRANO. [*Wiping the sweat from his face.*] —upon my meddling
fingers.
But then I added: "Gascon, do your duty!
Cyrano, march!" Then, onward in the dark, 40
I go and feel—

CHRISTIAN. A fillip on the nose?

CYRANO. I parry. Suddenly I find myself—

CHRISTIAN. Nose against nose—

CYRANO. [*Leaping at him.*] Damnation!
  [*All the* GASCONS *rush forward to see; when* CYRANO *reaches*
  CHRISTIAN, *he regains his self-control and continues.*]
With a hundred
Roistering ruffians, stinking—

CHRISTIAN. 'Neath your nose— 45

CYRANO. [*Pale and smiling.*] —With sour wine and onions! Then
I rush
Head down—

CHRISTIAN. Nose on the scent—

CYRANO. And so I charge:
Two I rip up! I run another through!
Then some one lunges—Paf! I answer—

CHRISTIAN. Pif!

CYRANO. [*Exploding.*] The devil! Out with you!
  [*All the* CADETS *rush towards the doors.*]

FIRST CADET. The tiger wakes! 50

CYRANO. Every one! With this man leave me alone!

SECOND CADET. We'll find him cut in mincemeat.

RAGUENEAU. What, in mincemeat?

ANOTHER CADET. Filling one of your patties!

RAGUENEAU. I grow pale
And limp as any napkin.

CARBON. Let us go!

ANOTHER. He will not leave a single morsel of him! 55

ANOTHER. I die of fright thinking what will befall!

ANOTHER. [*Closing the door on the right.*] Something most terrible!
  [*They all go out, some by the rear, some by the sides, some by
  the stairway.* CYRANO *and* CHRISTIAN *remain face to face, and
  look at each other for a moment.*]

(Instead of fighting Christian, Cyrano extends his hand. Then begins a curious arrangement whereby Cyrano nobly sets aside his love for Roxane and helps Christian to further his suit by composing letters for him and by teaching him the witty speeches he is unable to compose himself. At last Christian wishes to stand on his own feet, and meeting Roxane in front of her home one evening, tries to make love to her without using memorized speeches supplied by Cyrano. She soon becomes irritated with his stupidity and runs into the house. Just then Cyrano arrives with two musicians, whom he has won on a bet.)

ACT III. SCENE VI

[CHRISTIAN, CYRANO; *the* PAGES, *for a moment.*]

CHRISTIAN. Help!

CYRANO. No, Sir!

CHRISTIAN. I shall die unless at once I win her smiles again—

CYRANO. And how the devil
    Can I teach you to do it on the spot?

CHRISTIAN. [*Seizing his arm.*] Oh! come now, see!
    [*The window of the balcony is lighted up.*]

CYRANO. [*With emotion.*] Her window!

CHRISTIAN. I shall die!

CYRANO. Lower your voice.

CHRISTIAN. [*In very low voice.*] Shall die—

CYRANO.   The night is dark— 5

CHRISTIAN. Well?

CYRANO. It may be helped, though you do not deserve it.
    Take your position there, unhappy wight!
    Before the balcony! I shall stand beneath
    And prompt you with your words.

CHRISTIAN.   But—

CYRANO.   Hold your tongue.

THE PAGES. [*Reappearing in the background, to* CYRANO.] Holloa!

CYRANO. Hush!— [*Signals to them to speak low.*]

FIRST PAGE. [*In a low voice.*] We've just given Montfleury 10
    His serenade—

CYRANO. [*Aside, quickly.*] Go, put yourselves in ambush.
    One at this end the street, the other there,
    And if some inconvenient passer comes
    Then play a tune.

SECOND PAGE. What tune, Gassendi's pupil?

CYRANO. Gay for a woman, mournful for a man. 15

[THE PAGES *disappear, one at each end of the street. To* CHRISTIAN.]

    Call her!

CHRISTIAN. Roxane!

CYRANO. [*Picking up some pebbles and throwing them at the panes.*] Wait till I throw a pebble.

ROXANE. [*Half opening the window.*] Who calls me?

CHRISTIAN. I.

ROXANE.   Who?

CHRISTIAN.   Christian.

ROXANE. [*With disdain.*] Is it you?

CHRISTIAN. I would speak with you.

CYRANO. [*Under the balcony.*] Good! Good! Almost whisper.

ROXANE. Oh, no! You speak too ill. Begone!

CHRISTIAN.   I beg you!—

ROXANE. No, you love me no longer.

CHRISTIAN. [CYRANO *prompting him.*] What a charge!—Ye gods! —to love no more—when—I love most! 20

ROXANE. [*Stopping, as she was about to close the window.*] That's better!

CHRISTIAN. [*Same action.*] Love grows—cradled in my soul— My troubled soul—the which this cruel babe Has taken for his cot.

ROXANE. [*Coming out on the balcony.*] That's better now! But since this love is cruel, you were foolish 25 That·in his cot you did not smother him.

CHRISTIAN. [*Same action.*] That did I try—but the attempt was vain; This new-born babe—is a little—Hercules.

ROXANE. That's better.

CHRISTIAN. [*Same action.*] So that in a trice—he strangled The serpents—Pride and—Doubt.

ROXANE. [*Leaning on the balcony rail.*] That's very good. 30 But why with halting accents do you speak? Your fancy's lame?

CYRANO. [*Pulling* CHRISTIAN *under the balcony and gliding into his place.*] Hush! This becomes too hard.

ROXANE. Today your words are faltering. Why is this?

CYRANO. [*Talking in an undertone, like* CHRISTIAN.] Because it now is night; and in the dark They grope about, striving to find your ear. 35

ROXANE. But mine encounter no such obstacles.

CYRANO. They find their way at once? That is not strange,
 Because 't is in my heart that I receive them—
 My heart is large—your ear is wondrous small.
 Besides, your words descend; their pace is swift,   40
 While mine must climb, Madame, a longer task.

ROXANE. But they climb better in these last few moments.

CYRANO. As they have practised, they have learned the way.

ROXANE. Truly, 't is from a height I speak to you.

CYRANO. And you would kill me, if you should let fall   45
 From such a height, a hard word on my heart.

ROXANE. [*With a motion.*] I'm coming down.

CYRANO. [*Quickly.*]   No!

ROXANE. [*Showing him the bench which is under the balcony.*]
 Climb upon the bench.
 Quickly!

CYRANO. [*Drawing back with alarm into the darkness.*] No!

ROXANE. What?—No?

CYRANO. [*His feelings gaining on him more and more.*] For a mo-
 ment let me
 Improve this chance which offers—to be able
 To talk in accents soft, but not to see.   50

ROXANE. But not to see?

CYRANO. Yes—'t is a sheer delight;
 We guess at one another in the dark,
 You see the blackness of a trailing cloak,
 I see the whiteness of a summer robe,
 And I am but a shadow, you a radiance.   55
 You know not what these moments mean for me!
 If ever I was eloquent—

ROXANE.   You were

CYRANO. Until this hour my words have never come
 From my own heart—

ROXANE. Why?

CYRANO.   Because, until now I spoke through—

ROXANE.   What?

CYRANO.   —the dizziness where swims   60
 Whome'er you look on— But tonight it seems
 That for the first time I shall speak to you.

ROXANE. 'T is true that you have quite another voice.

CYRANO. [*Drawing near, feverishly.*] Yes, quite another, for in the
 sheltering night
 I dare at last to be myself—I dare—   65
 [*Stops, and in bewilderment.*]

What was I saying—I know not—All of this—
Forgive my mounting passion—is so sweet—
And is so new for me.

ROXANE. So new?

CYRANO. [*Distracted and still trying to take back his words.*] So
new—
—Why, yes!—to be sincere—without constraint,
The fear of being mocked has wrung my heart. 70

ROXANE. Mocked about what?

CYRANO. Oh—but—about my ardor—
My heart for shame has ever clothed itself
With wit as with a garment. I start forth
To snatch a star from out the sky,—I stop
In fear of ridicule,—and pluck a flower. 75

ROXANE. The flower has charms.

CYRANO. This evening let us scorn it.

ROXANE. You never yet have talked to me like this!

CYRANO. Oh! far removed from Cupid's enginery
'T is pleasant to escape to greener things.
Instead of drinking from a golden thimble 80
Insipid syrups, slowly, drop by drop,
Shall we not let the soul allay its thirst
By drinking freely from the river's flood?

ROXANE. But your wit?

CYRANO. I used to make you stay.
But now to speak with a court poet's phrases 85
Would be to affront this night, these odors sweet,
This magic hour, and even Nature's self.
Let Heaven, with one glance of her gleaming stars,
Take away all our wonted artifice;
I fear, lest in our subtle alchemy 90
The heart's true feeling may dissolve in smoke,
The soul may spend itself in empty play,
And e'en refinement be refined to naught.

ROXANE. But your wit?

CYRANO. I hate, when it plays with love.
For when one truly loves, it is a crime 95
Too long to thrust and parry. The moment comes—
And those to whom it never comes I pity—
When in our hearts we feel a noble passion
Saddened by every clever phrase we turn.

ROXANE. If to us two this moment now has come,
What words will you speak to me?

CYRANO.   Every word   100
    That rises to my lips. I'll cast them all
    Before you in a heap, with no arrangement—
    I love you—I am smothered—I am mad—
    I love you—I am faint—it is too much;
    Your name hangs in my heart like a bell's tongue,   105
    And evermore, Roxane, with love I tremble,
    And the bell swings, and then your name rings out.
    And everything you do lives in my heart;
    Last year there was one day I well remember,
    The tenth of May, one morn you dressed your hair   110
    So that its radiance burnt into my soul;
    And just as he, who at the sun too long
    Has gazed, sees circles red where'er he looks;
    So when I left the flames in which I swam
    My eyes saw blots of gold on everything.   115
ROXANE. Yes, this indeed is love—
CYRANO.   Truly, this passion
    Jealous and terrible, which sweeps me on,
    Is love indeed, with all its mournful madness!
    Is love indeed, and yet it is not selfish!
    Ah, for your joy I'd gladly give my own,   120
    Even if you should never know; if I
    Might sometimes from afar hear the soft laugh
    Of happiness born from my sacrifice,—
    Your very look rouses new worth in me;
    Do you begin to understand it now?   125
    And feel my soul climb slowly through the dark?
    Ah! but this night is all too fair, too sweet!
    I say all this to you; and you, you listen;
    It is too much. E'en in my maddest hopes
    I never hoped so much. There's nothing left,   130
    Except for me to die at once. She trembles,
    There through the branches dark, and for my words,
    For you are trembling, a leaf among the leaves,
    For thou art trembling, and I plainly felt
    Whether thou wouldst or no, the trembling dear   135
    Of thy sweet hand descend the jasmine branch.
    [*Madly kisses the end of a hanging branch.*]
ROXANE. I tremble, I weep, I love thee, I am thine—
    Aye, drunk with love!
CYRANO. Then let death come at once.

Since it is I who mixed the cup for thee!
    I ask but one thing more—

CHRISTIAN. [*Under the balcony.*] A kiss!

ROXANE. [*Drawing back.*] What?

CYRANO.   Oh!   140

ROXANE. You're asking?

CYRANO.   Yes—I—
    [*To* CHRISTIAN, *aside.*] You go far too fast!

CHRISTIAN. Since she is moved, I must improve my chance!

CYRANO. [*To* ROXANE.] Yes, I—I asked, 't is true, but, gracious
        heavens!
    I understand, I was too bold by far.

ROXANE. [*Somewhat disappointed.*] You insist no more than that?

CYRANO. Yes, I insist—   145
    Without insisting. Yes! Your modesty
    Is saddened—Well, this kiss—grant me it not.

CHRISTIAN. [*To* CYRANO, *pulling his cloak.*] Why?

CYRANO. Hush, Christian.

ROXANE. [*Leaning over.*] What do you say so low?

CYRANO. I scold myself for having gone too far,
    And to myself I said, "Hush, Christian."
    [*The lutes begin to play.*] Wait!   150
    Some one is coming.

[ROXANE *closes the window.* CYRANO *listens to the lutes, one of
    which plays a lively air, the other a mournful one.*]
    Sad? Gay? What's their plan?
    Is it a man, or woman?—'t is a monk!

[A CAPUCHIN *enters, going from house to house, lantern in hand,
    looking at the doors.*]

Scene VII

[CYRANO, CHRISTIAN, *a* CAPUCHIN.]

CYRANO. [*To* THE CAPUCHIN.] Who's this new follower of Di-
        ogenes?

THE CAPUCHIN. I'm looking for the house.

CHRISTIAN.   He's in our way!

THE CAPUCHIN. Of Madame Roxane Robin.

CHRISTIAN.   What's he after?

CYRANO. [*Showing him a street leading away.*] This way, keep to
    the right,—still to the right.

THE CAPUCHIN. Thank you! I'll say for you a *pater noster.*   5
                                   [*Goes out.*]

CYRANO. Good luck. My prayers accompany your cowl!
                           [*Comes back to* CHRISTIAN.]

SCENE VIII

[CYRANO, CHRISTIAN.]

CHRISTIAN. Get me this kiss!—

CYRANO.   No!

CHRISTIAN.   Soon or late—

CYRANO.   'T is true!
    'T will come; this moment of supreme delight
    When your two mouths together shall be drawn
    Because of her red lips, and your moustache.
    [*To himself.*] I'd rather that it were because—
[*Noise of shutters reopening.* CHRISTIAN *hides under the bal-
    cony.*]

SCENE IX

[CYRANO, CHRISTIAN, ROXANE.]

ROXANE. [*Coming forward on the balcony.*] 'T is you?
    We were speaking of—of—of a—

CYRANO.   Of a kiss.
    The word is sweet, I see not why your lips
    So fear to speak it; if it burns them now
    What will it be itself? Be not afraid.
    Make not a terror of it. Did you not,   5
    Just now, unknowingly, without alarm,
    Leave off your mockery, and softly pass
    From sigh to sigh, and from a sigh to tears?
    Pass on yet further by the easy path—
    'Twixt tears and kiss there's but a moment's tremble. 10

ROXANE. Be still!

CYRANO. A kiss, when all is said, what is it?
    An oath sworn nearer by; a promise made
    With greater certainty; a vow which seeks
    To make itself more binding; a rosy dot
    Placed on the "i" in loving; 't is a secret   15
    Told to the mouth instead of to the ear;
    A moment of the infinite, which makes
    A sound like to the humming of bees' wings;
    A greeting like the sweet breath of a flower;
    A way to feel the heart beat for a space,   20
    And taste the soul a moment on the lips.
ROXANE. Be still!
CYRANO. A kiss, Madame, it is so noble.
    That e'en the Queen of France, the Queen herself,
    Let her most happy courtier take one!
ROXANE.   Well!
CYRANO. [*Growing more impassioned.*] Like Buckingham, I've
    suffered silent pangs;   25
    Like him, a Queen I worship—you, my Queen.
    Like him, I'm sad and faithful.
ROXANE.   And like him
    You're fair.
CYRANO. [*Aside, sobered.*] True, I am fair, I quite forgot.
ROXANE. Well, climb and pluck this flower without a peer!
CYRANO. [*Pushing* CHRISTIAN *toward the balcony.*] Climb!
ROXANE. This heart beat.
CYRANO.   Climb!
ROXANE. This humming of bees' wings.
CYRANO. Climb!   30
CHRISTIAN. [*Hesitating.*] But now it seems perhaps I'd better not!
ROXANE. This moment of the infinite.
CYRANO. [*Pushing him.*] Climb, fool!
    [CHRISTIAN *plunges forward, and by means of the bench, the
    branches, and the pillars reaches the balustrade, which he
    vaults.*]
CHRISTIAN. Ah! Roxane! [*Embraces her and bends over her lips.*]
CYRANO. [*Aside.*] Ah! My heart, what torture strange!
    Kiss, feast of love where I am Lazarus,
    There reach me in the dark some crumbs from thee;   35
    But still I feel my heart has something gained
    Since on these lips where Roxane now is caught
    It is the words I spoke just now she kisses.
    [*The lutes are heard.*]

Now sad, now gay, the Capuchin!

[*Pretends to run as if he were arriving from a distance, and calls in a loud voice.*] Halloa!

ROXANE. What is it?

CYRANO. It is I, I was just passing—

Christian's still there?

CHRISTIAN. [*Greatly astonished.*] What, Cyrano?

ROXANE. Good evening, Cousin!

CYRANO. Good evening, cousin!

ROXANE. I'm coming down.

[*Disappears in the house.* THE CAPUCHIN *re-enters in the background.*]

CHRISTIAN. [*Seeing him.*] Again!

(The interloper is a monk sent by De Guiche, who by this time has become commander-in-chief of the armies. To keep him from sending Christian's company to the wars, Roxane has pretended to welcome De Guiche's advances. The monk now bears word that De Guiche is coming in a few moments, to claim the love of Roxane. She, however, pretends that the letter instructs the monk to marry her and Christian, and the credulous monk goes inside with them to perform the ceremony. Cyrano remains outside, and when De Guiche arrives, detains him with a wild invented tale of having fallen from the moon. When the ceremony is over, the lovers appear. De Guiche discovers how he has been fooled and, furious, orders the Gascony Guard to the most dangerous place in the wars.

In the campaign which follows, Cyrano continues to act for Christian, writing love-letters to Roxane in which he pours out his own very real love in the name of Christian, and smuggling them through their besieged lines at the risk of his life. Roxane arrives at the front. Christian discovers Cyrano's concealed love for Roxane, but just as he is going to tell her that it was really Cyrano's brilliant love-making which had won her, he is killed and dies in Roxane's arms. Of course, Cyrano can never tell her the truth.

Fifteen years later, we see Roxane as a lay sister in a convent. We learn that Cyrano has come to see her every Saturday since her husband's death. He has made many enemies, however, with his wit and his fearless hatred of the hypocritical courtiers of Paris. One Saturday night, his friends, Le Bret and Ragueneau, learn that Cyrano has been seriously wounded by an enemy. They depart at once for his home. Roxane, however, does not hear of the accident, and she is waiting in the garden of the convent when Cyrano slowly enters, announced by a Sister.)

Act V. Scene V

[ROXANE, CYRANO; *and, a moment later,* SISTER MARTHA.]

ROXANE. [*Without turning.*] What was I saying?
  [*She sews.* CYRANO *appears, very pale, with his hat pulled down over his eyes. A* SISTER *ushers him in and retires. He starts to walk slowly down the steps, making a visible effort to hold himself erect, and leaning on his stick.* ROXANE *works at her embroidery.*]
    Ah, these faded shades!
    Into what pattern shall I fashion them?
  [*To* CYRANO, *in tones of friendly scolding.*]
CYRANO. [*Reaching the arm-chair, and sitting down; speaking with*
    Late—for the first time in full fourteen years!
    a cheerful voice, in contrast to his expression.] Yes, 'tis absurd, I am beside myself.
    I was detained.
ROXANE.   By what?
CYRANO.   Oh, by a most   5
    Untimely visitation!
ROXANE.   By some churl
    Troubling you with importunate demands?
CYRANO. Yes, cousin, and I soon must do his bidding.
ROXANE. You bade him go?
CYRANO. Yes. "This is Saturday,"
    I said: "a day when surely, rain or shine,   10
    I must betake me to a certain house
    And pay a visit there. So come again
    Within an hour."
ROXANE. [*Lightly.*] Well, this friend of yours
    Will have to wait for you a longer time—
    I shall not let you go till evening falls.   15
CYRANO. But I may be constrained to go away
    A little sooner.
  [*He closes his eyes, and is silent for a moment.* SISTER MARTHA *crosses the park, from the chapel to the steps.* ROXANE *sees her, and signals to her with a little nod of her head.*]
ROXANE. [*To* CYRANO.] Oh! You will not tease
    Poor Sister Martha?
CYRANO. [*Smartly, opening his eyes.*] Yes, I think I shall.
  [*With a big, comical voice.*] Sister, come here!

[The Sister *glides towards him.*] Ah, ha! You carry still
Your bright eyes always lowered!

Sister Martha. [*Lifting her eyes with a smile.*] But— [*Sees his
appearance, and makes a movement of surprise.*] Oh!

Cyrano. [*Aside, indicating* Roxane.] Hush!
'T is nothing. [*In a voice of burlesque boasting.*] Yesterday I
made a fast!

Sister Martha. I understand. [*Aside.*]
That's why he is so pale.
[*In a quick aside to* Cyrano.]
Come to the dining-hall, and you shall take
A fine great bowl of broth. You will come, now?

Cyrano. Yes, yes; of course.

Sister Martha. Now, I am glad to see
That for this once you can be reasonable.

Roxane. [*Hearing them whispering.*] She's trying to convert you?

Sister Martha. No, not I!

Cyrano. Yes, that is true! And yet the pious words
Fall from your lips in such a plenteous flow
I am amazed you do not preach to me.
[*With mock anger.*]
Thunder and Mars! I shall amaze you, too,
For I shall suffer you this very night—
[*Pretends to be looking for a subject of raillery and to find it.*]
To pray for me at chapel!

Roxane. Oh, oh, oh!

Cyrano. [*Laughing.*] The Sister's stricken dumb.

Sister Martha. [*Gently.*] I waited not
For your permission. [*Retires.*

Cyrano. [*Turning to* Roxane, *who bends over her work.*] When
shall I see the end
Of this interminable needlework?

Roxane. I waited for that jest.
[*At this moment a puff of wind starts the leaves falling.*]

Cyrano. Look at the leaves.

Roxane. [*Raising her head, and looking far off through the vista.*]
They are Venetian yellow. Watch them fall.

Cyrano. Yes, watch them well—how gracefully they fall!
And in their journey short, from branch to earth,
How they put on a final fleeting charm!
And, although loath to molder on the ground,
They strive to give their fall the grace of flight!

Roxane. What, are you sad?

CYRANO. [*Remembering himself.*] No, not at all, Roxane.

ROXANE. Let the leaves fall, and tell me all the news,— 45
My journal!

CYRANO.   Here it is.

ROXANE.   Ah!

CYRANO. [*Growing paler and paler, and struggling against his pain.*]
Saturday,
The nineteenth of the month, His Majesty,
Having partaken of too many sweets,
Suffered a touch of fever, and was bled.
His illness was found guilty of high treason; 50
And now his august pulse is calm again!
At the Queen's ball, on Sunday, there were burned
Wax candles seven hundred sixty-three!
They say our troops beat John of Austria!
Four witches have been hanged! The little dog 55
Of Madame Athis needed medicine—

ROXANE. Monsieur de Bergerac, will you be still!

CYRANO. Nothing on Monday, but Lygdamire's new lover;—

ROXANE. Oh!

CYRANO. Tuesday the whole Court went to Fontainebleau;—
Wednesday De Fiesque had "No" from La Montglat;— 60
Thursday Mancini is Queen of France—almost!—
Friday La Montglat to De Fiesque said "Yes";
And on the twenty-sixth, on Saturday—
                    [*Closes his eyes; his head drops. Silence.*

ROXANE. [*Surprised at hearing nothing more, turns, looks at him;
and getting up in fright.*] He's fainted? [*Rushes towards him,
exclaiming.*] Cyrano!

CYRANO. [*Opening his eyes; with muffled voice.*] What is it? What?
[*Sees ROXANE leaning over him; quickly settles his hat on his
head, and draws back in alarm in his chair.*]
No, no! 'T is nothing, nothing! Let me be! 65

ROXANE. Yet—

CYRANO.   'T is my wound—from Arras—which at times—
You know—

ROXANE. Poor friend—

CYRANO.   'T is naught. 'T will pass. [*Smiles, with an
effort.*] It has passed!

ROXANE. Each of us has his wound; and I have mine,—
An ancient wound that never heals,—just here.
[*Lays her hand on her breast.*]
Here!—'neath this letter, with its yellowing folds! 70

Where still you see commingled blood and tears.
[*Twilight begins to fall.*]

CYRANO. His letter! Once I think you promised me
    That I might some day read it—

ROXANE.   Do you wish?—

CYRANO. Yes, 't is my wish, today—

ROXANE. [*Giving him the little bag which hangs about her neck.*]
    Here—

CYRANO. [*Taking it.*] I may open?

ROXANE. Open and read.
[*She returns to her work, folds it, and arranges her worsteds.*]

CYRANO. [*Reading.*] :
    "Farewell, Roxane, my death is very near!"   75

ROXANE. [*Stopping in astonishment.*] Aloud?

CYRANO.   "This very night, my best-beloved,
    My soul is heavy with unuttered love;
    And now I die; and never, nevermore,
    Shall my eyes feast on you their yearning gaze!"

ROXANE. But how you read his letter—with what voice!   80

CYRANO.   "Drunk with your beauty; kissing as they flit
    Each little graceful movement that you make;
    And one familiar gesture still I see—
    The way you touched your forehead!"

ROXANE.   How you read
    This letter!
[*Night falls imperceptibly.*]

CYRANO. "And I fain would cry aloud 'Farewell!'"   85

ROXANE.   You read—

CYRANO. "My dearest! Oh, my love! My treasure"—

ROXANE.   With a voice—

CYRANO. "My best-beloved"—

ROXANE. A voice that I have somewhere heard before.
[*Approaches softly, without his noticing it; goes behind his chair,
leans over quietly, and looks at the letter. The darkness
deepens.*]

CYRANO.   "My heart has never left you for a breath;
    And here, and in the world beyond the grave,
    I am he whose love for you passed every bound."   90

ROXANE. [*Laying her hand on his shoulder.*] But how can you read
    now? The night has come.
[*He starts, turns; sees her close to him; makes a startled gesture,
lowers his head. A long silence. Then, after it has become quite
dark, she says slowly, clasping her hands.*]

And for these fourteen years he's played this part
Of the old friend who comes to cheer me up.

CYRANO. Roxane!

ROXANE.   'T was you!—

CYRANO.   Ah, no, Roxane; not I!   95

ROXANE I should have guessed it, when he spoke my name.

CYRANO. Ah, no! It was not I.

ROXANE.   'T was you.

CYRANO.   I swear—

ROXANE. At last I see it all—the generous cheat!
You wrote the letters—

CYRANO.   No!

ROXANE.   The dear mad words
Were yours—

CYRANO.   No!

ROXANE. The voice that night was yours.   100

CYRANO. I swear it was not!

ROXANE. And the soul was yours.

CYRANO. I loved you not!

ROXANE.   You loved me—

CYRANO.   It was he—

ROXANE. You loved me!

CYRANO.   No.

ROXANE. But now you speak more soft.

CYRANO. No, no; my best-beloved, I loved you not.

ROXANE. How many things since then have come and gone!   105
Why have you held your peace for fourteen years?
Since on this letter, which was naught to him,
These tears were yours?

CYRANO. But the blood was his.

ROXANE. Then why today should you decide to break
This noble silence?

CYRANO. Why?

[*Enter* LE BRET *and* RAGUENEAU, *running.*]

SCENE VI

[*The Same;* LE BRET *and* RAGUENEAU.]

LE BRET. What madness! I was sure— There he is!

CYRANO. [*Smiling and straightening up.*] Why, yes; of course!

LE BRET. Madame, he's killed himself
By rising.

ROXANE. But just now, this weakness—

CYRANO.　　　　　　　　　　　　　　True,
　My news was not yet finished : Saturday,
　The twenty-sixth, an hour before he dined,
　Monsieu de Bergerac was foully murdered.
[*Uncovers. His head is seen to be bandaged.*]　　　5

ROXANE. What says he? Cyrano! Look at his head,
　Wrapped in a bandage! Oh! what have they done
　To you! Why?

CYRANO. *"By the good sword's thrust,
　Struck by a hero, fall with point in heart!"*—
　Yes, I said that. But Destiny's a mocker.
　And here I am, caught by a coward's trick ;　　　10
　Struck from behind ; felled by a faggot's blow
　Wielded by hireling hands,—indeed 'tis well :
　I shall have failed in all things—e'en in death.

RAGUENEAU. Oh, sir !

CYRANO.　　　　　　What are you doing now, my colleague?　　　15

RAGUENEAU. I now am candle-snuffer—for Molière.

CYRANO. Molière ?

RAGUENEAU. But I shall surely leave tomorrow !
　Yes, I am angry with him. Yesterday
　Scapin was acted ; and I plainly saw
　He'd stolen a scene from you—

LE BRET.　　　　　　　　　　A scene entire !

RAGUENEAU. The famous—"What the devil did he there?"　　　20

LE BRET. Molière [1] stole it from you !

CYRANO.　　　　　　　　　　　　Tush ! He's done well !
　The scene went off, I trust, with good effect ?

RAGUENEAU. [*Sobbing.*] Oh, sir, they laughed, they laughed !

CYRANO.　　　　　　　　　　　　　　Yes, all my life
　My part has been to prompt—and be forgot.　　　25
[*To* ROXANE.]
　Rememberest thou the night when Christian wooed,
　Under the balcony?— All my life is there !
　While I remained below, hid in the dark,
　Others have climbed to kisses and to fame !
　'T is just ; and on the threshold of my tomb,　　　30
　I own Molière a genius—Christian fair.
[*At this moment the chapel-bell rings, and the nuns are seen passing through the avenue in the background, going to mass.*]
　Their bell has sounded ; let them go to prayers.

[1] *Molière:* see Molière's *Doctor in Spite of Himself* on page 567.

ROXANE. [*Rising to call for help.*] Come! Sister, Sister!

CYRANO.   No, no! Go for no one.
> When you return, I shall have gone away.

[*The nuns have entered the chapel. The organ plays.*]
> Music was all I needed—there it is!   35

ROXANE. I love you! Live!

CYRANO.   No, in the fairy-tale
> 'T is plainly written that when the humbled Prince
> Had heard the words—"I love you," his disguise
> Of horror fled like snow before the sun:
> But you will see that I remain the same.   40

ROXANE. And I have wrought your sorrow—even I!

CYRANO. You? No, not you! 'T is quite the opposite.
> I ne'er knew woman's kindness. E'en my mother
> Thought me not fair. I never had a sister.
> Then I feared sweethearts with their mocking eyes!
> But, thanks to you, I've had at least a friend;   45
> And through my life a woman's robe has passed.

LE BRET. [*Pointing out the moonbeams falling through the
branches.*] There comes your other friend to see you.

CYRANO. [*Smiling at the moon.*] Yes!

ROXANE. I loved but one—and now I lose him twice.

CYRANO. Le Bret, I'm going,—up to the shining moon,   50
> And need devise no engine for this flight!

ROXANE. What did you say?

CYRANO. Yes, it is there, on high,
> There am I sent to make my paradise.
> More than one soul I love is exiled there:
> Socrates—Galileo. I'll find them all.   55

LE BRET. [*Rebelliously.*] No, no!
> 'T is too absurd! 'T is too unjust!
> So great a poet! Such a noble heart!
> To die this way! To die—

CYRANO.   Hear Le Bret scold!

LE BRET. [*Bursting into tears.*] Dear friend!

CYRANO. [*Rising, his eyes wandering.*]
> "These be Cadets of Gascony"—
> The elemental substance— Yes—the "*hic.*"   60

LE BRET. List to his science, even in his ravings.

CYRANO. Copernicus said—

ROXANE.   Oh!

CYRANO. "What did he there?
> And what the devil did he in the galley?"

> *Philosopher, physician,*
> *Poet, swordsman, and musician,*
> ***And** a traveller through the heavens to the moon!* 65
> *His sword-point always ready,*
> *His sword-arm always steady,*
> ***And** a lover to whom love was not a boon!*
>
> *Here lies Hercule-Savinien de Cyrano de Bergerac;*
> *All things in turn he tried; and all things did he lack!* 70

But pardon—I must go, I may not wait:
You see the moonbeams come to take me hence!
[*Falls back into his seat. Roxane's tears bring him back to reali-*
ties. He looks at her, and caresses her veil.]
I would not have you shed one tear the less
For Christian—fair and noble. All I ask
Is, when my body shall lie cold in death, 75
You give a double meaning to these weeds—
And let his mourning be my mourning too!
ROXANE. I swear it!
CYRANO. [*Shaken with a great tremor, rises quickly.*] No, not
there! Not in a chair!
[*They rush towards him.*]
Let no one hold me up. [*Leans against the tree.*] Only the tree
—[*Silence.*]
He comes! I feel already shod with stone, 80
And gloved with lead. [*Stiffens himself.*] But since he's on the
way,
I'll meet him standing upright—[*Draws his sword.*]—sword
in hand—
LE BRET. Cyrano!
ROXANE. [*Fainting.*] Cyrano!
[*All draw back in terror.*]
CYRANO.   He sees my nose!
Well! Let the flat-nose look me in the face!
[*Raises his sword.*]
You say 't is useless. That I know full well! 85
But I have never fought with hope to win.
No,—it is finer when 't is all in vain.
Now, who are these—a thousand thronged about me?
I know you well— You are all ancient foes:
Falsehood! [*Strikes with his sword in the air.*] There, there!
Ha, ha! And Compromise! 90

Bigotry! Cowardice! [*Strikes.*] Shall I make terms?
No, never! never! There is Folly, too!
I knew that in the end you'd lay me low.
No matter. Let me fight! and fight! and fight!
[*Swings his sword in circles, and stops, panting.*]
   You snatch them all away—laurel and rose!   95
Snatch on! One thing is left in spite of you,
Which I take with me: and this very night,
When I shall cross the threshold of God's house,
And enter, bowing low, this I shall take
Despite you, without wrinkle, without spot—   100
[*Rushes forward with brandished sword.*]
   And that is—
[*The sword falls from his hands. He staggers, and falls into the arms of* LE BRET *and* RAGUENEAU.]
ROXANE. [*Leaning over him, and kissing his forehead.*] What?
CYRANO. [*Opens his eyes, recognizes her, and says with a smile.*]
   My stainless soldier's crest!

CURTAIN.

THE DOLL'S HOUSE

HENRIK IBSEN (NORWAY)

Translated by William Archer

Nora and Torvald Helmer, a young married couple with three children, have met with luck in Torvald's appointment as director of a bank. Previously their means have been very modest. Early in their marriage, Torvald's life was despaired of, and the doctors said only a year in Italy could save him. Torvald disapproves of debt, so Nora secretly borrows the money for the trip from a money lender named Krogstadt, telling her husband that her father gave it to her. As her father died just then, Torvald never discovers the truth. For years Nora struggles to pay Krogstadt by economies in housekeeping and even by secret work. She is a child in business matters and does not even know how much she still owes. Her husband, who knows nothing of all this, thinks she is extravagant. He seems very fond of her and calls her his "little squirrel" and treats her like a plaything, never discussing any serious matters with her. She plays up to his idea of her beautifully, and they seem very happy in what Ibsen calls their "doll house" marriage.

The man from whom she borrowed the money, however, had once

committed a forgery and had a hard time getting a job again. Now at last he has a job in Torvald's bank and feels he can reestablish himself. But Torvald discharges him to make a place for a friend of Nora's. Krogstadt thereupon threatens Nora that unless she persuades Torvald to reemploy him, he will reveal not only the debt but the fact that Nora had forged her father's name on the note as security. Her father was dying at the time and to spare him worry, she signed his name herself—not realizing that this was a crime. She dated the signature three days after her father's death, which gave her away, of course, to Krogstadt. She tries in vain to influence Torvald, and he explains to her that Krogstadt is a criminal, a forger, who will probably poison the lives of his children by his influence. Poor Nora is frantic, wondering if she, too, is unfit to rear her children; and fearing to have Torvald's pride hurt by discovering he owes his life to his "little frisking squirrel."

Finally, Krogstadt writes Torvald the facts, but Nora keeps him from opening his mail during the Christmas holidays. In the meantime, Nora's friend turns out to be Krogstadt's old sweetheart and persuades him not to expose Nora, but Nora does not yet know this. New Year's Eve, as they return from a masquerade ball, they learn that their best friend is dying. Nora, who idolizes her husband, has decided to commit suicide to save Torvald from scandal through the exposure of her crime, and tells him that now he may read his letters. As the last scene begins, Torvald is speaking of his dying friend.

❊   ❊   ❊

HELMER. [*Walking up and down.*] He had so grown into our lives, I can't realize that he is gone. He and his sufferings and his loneliness formed a sort of cloudy background to the sunshine of our happiness.—Well, perhaps it's best as it is—at any rate for him. [*Stands still.*] And perhaps for us too, Nora. Now we two are thrown entirely upon each other. [*Takes her in his arms.*] My darling wife! I feel as if I could never hold you close enough. Do you know, Nora, I often wish some danger might threaten you, that I might risk body and soul, and everything, everything for your dear sake.

NORA. [*Tears herself from him and says firmly.*] Now you shall read your letters, Torvald.

HELMER. [*Kissing her forehead.*] Good night, my little songbird. Sleep well, Nora. Now I shall go and read my letters.

[*He goes with the letters in his hand into his room and shuts the door.*]

NORA. [*With wild eyes, gropes about her, seizes* HELMER'S *domino,*[1] *throws it round her, and whispers quickly, hoarsely, and*

---

[1] *domino:* mantle he wore at the masked ball.

brokenly.] Never to see him again. Never, never, never. [*Throws her shawl over her head.*] Never to see the children again. Never, never.—Oh that black, icy water! Oh that bottomless——! If it were only over! Now he has it; he's reading it. Oh, no, no, no, not yet. Torvald, goodbye——! Good-by, my little ones——!

[*She is rushing out by the hall; at the same moment* HELMER *flings his door open, and stands there with an open letter in his hand.*]

HELMER. Nora!

NORA. [*Shrieks.*] Ah——!

HELMER. What is this? Do you know what is in this letter?

NORA. Yes, I know. Let me go! Let me pass!

HELMER. [*Holds her back.*] Where do you want to go?

NORA. [*Tries to break away from him.*] You shall not save me, Torvald.

HELMER. [*Falling back.*] True! Is what he writes true? No, no, it is impossible that this can be true.

NORA. It is true. I have loved you beyond all else in the world.

HELMER. Pshaw—no silly evasions!

NORA. [*A step nearer him.*] Torvald——!

HELMER. Wretched woman—what have you done?

NORA. Let me go—you shall not save me! You shall not take my guilt upon yourself!

HELMER. I don't want any melodramatic airs. [*Locks the outer door.*] Here you shall stay and give an account of yourself. Do you understand what you have done? Answer! Do you understand it?

NORA. [*Looks at him fixedly, and says with a stiffening expression.*] Yes; now I begin fully to understand it.

HELMER. [*Walking up and down.*] Oh! what an awful awakening! During all these eight years—she who was my pride and my joy—a hypocrite, a liar—worse, worse—a criminal. Oh, the unfathomable hideousness of it all! Ugh! Ugh!

[NORA *says nothing, and continues to look fixedly at him.*]

HELMER. I ought to have known how it would be. I ought to have foreseen it. All your father's want of principle—be silent!—all your father's want of principle you have inherited—no religion, no morality, no sense of duty. How I am punished for screening him! I did it for your sake; and you reward me like this.

NORA. Yes—like this.

HELMER. You have destroyed my whole happiness. You have ruined my future. Oh, it's frightful to think of! I am in the power of a scoundrel; he can do whatever he pleases with me, demand whatever he chooses; he can domineer over me as much as he likes, and I must submit. And all this disaster and ruin is brought upon me by an unprincipled woman!

NORA. When I am out of the world, you will be free.

HELMER. Oh, no fine phrases. Your father, too, was always ready with them. What good would it do me, if you were "out of the world," as you say? No good whatever! He can publish the story all the same; I might even be suspected of collusion. People will think I was at the bottom of it all and egged you on. And for all this I have you to thank—you whom I have done nothing but pet and spoil during our whole married life. Do you understand now what you have done to me?

NORA. [*With cold calmness.*] Yes.

HELMER. The thing is so incredible, I can't grasp it. But we must come to an understanding. Take that shawl off. Take it off, I say! I must try to pacify him in one way or another—the matter must be hushed up, cost what it may.—As for you and me, we must make no outward change in our way of life—no outward change, you understand. Of course, you will continue to live here. But the children cannot be left in your care. I dare not trust them to you.—Oh, to have to say this to one I have loved so tenderly—whom I still——! But that must be a thing of the past. Henceforward there can be no question of happiness, but merely of saving the ruins, the shreds, the show—— [*A ring; HELMER starts.*] What's that? So late! Can it be the worst? Can he——? Hide yourself, Nora; say you are ill.

[NORA *stands motionless.* HELMER *goes to the door and opens it.*]

ELLEN. [*Half-dressed, in the hall.*] Here is a letter for you, ma'am.

HELMER. Give it to me. [*Seizes the letter and shuts the door.*] Yes, from him. You shall not have it. I shall read it.

NORA. Read it!

HELMER. [*By the lamp.*] I have hardly the courage to. We may both be lost, both you and I. Ah! I must know. [*Hastily tears the letter open; reads a few lines, looks at an enclosure; with a cry of joy.*] Nora!

[NORA *looks inquiringly at him.*]

HELMER. Nora!—Oh! I must read it again.—Yes, yes, it is so. I am saved! Nora, I am saved!

NORA. And I?

HELMER. You too, of course; we are both saved, both of us. Look here—he sends you back your promissory note. He writes that he regrets and apologizes that a happy turn in his life—— Oh, what matter what he writes. We are saved, Nora! No one can harm you. Oh, Nora, Nora——; but first to get rid of this hateful thing. I'll just see—— [*Glances at the I.O.U.*] No, I will not look at it; the whole thing shall be nothing but a dream to me. [*Tears the I.O.U. and both letters in pieces. Throws them into the fire and watches them burn.*] There! it's gone!—He said that ever since Christmas Eve—— Oh, Nora, they must have been three terrible days for you!

NORA. I have fought a hard fight for the last three days.

HELMER. And in your agony you saw no other outlet but—— No; we won't think of that horror. We will only rejoice and repeat —it's over, all over! Don't you hear, Nora? You don't seem able to grasp it. Yes, it's over. What is this set look on your face? Oh, my poor Nora, I understand; you cannot believe that I have forgiven you. But I have, Nora; I swear it. I have forgiven everything. I know that what you did was all for love of me.

NORA. That is true.

HELMER. You loved me as a wife should love her husband. It was only the means that, in your inexperience, you misjudged. But do you think I love you the less because you cannot do without guidance? No, no. Only lean on me; I will counsel you, and guide you. I should be no true man if this very womanly helplessness did not make you doubly dear in my eyes. You mustn't dwell upon the hard things I said in my first moment of terror, when the world seemed to be tumbling about my ears. I have forgiven you, Nora—I swear I have forgiven you.

NORA. I thank you for your forgiveness. [*Goes out, to the right.*]

HELMER. No, stay——! [*Looking through the doorway.*] What are you going to do?

NORA. [*Inside.*] To take off my masquerade dress.

HELMER. [*In the doorway.*] Yes, do, dear. Try to calm down, and recover your balance, my scared little songbird. You may rest secure. I have broad wings to shield you. [*Walking up and down near the door.*] Oh, how lovely—how cozy our home is, Nora! Here you are safe; here I can shelter you like a hunted dove whom I have saved from the claws of the hawk. I shall soon bring your poor beating heart to rest; believe me, Nora, very soon. Tomorrow all this will seem quite different—everything will be as before. I shall not need to tell you again that I forgive you; you will feel for yourself that it is true. How could you think I could find it in my heart to drive you away, or even so much as to reproach you? Oh, you don't know a true man's heart, Nora. There is something indescribably sweet and soothing to a man in having forgiven his wife—honestly forgiven her, from the bottom of his heart. She becomes his property in a double sense. She is as though born again; she has become, so to speak, at once his wife and his child. That is what you shall henceforth be to me, my bewildered, helpless darling. Don't be troubled about anything, Nora; only open your heart to me, and I will be both will and conscience to you. [Nora *enters in everyday dress.*] Why, what's this? Not gone to bed? You have changed your dress?

Nora. Yes, Torvald; now I have changed my dress.

Helmer. But why now, so late——?

Nora. I shall not sleep tonight.

Helmer. But, Nora dear——

Nora. [*Looking at her watch.*] It's not so late yet. Sit down, Torvald; you and I have much to say to each other. [*She sits at one side of the table.*]

Helmer. Nora—what does this mean? Your cold, set face——

Nora. Sit down. It will take some time. I have much to talk over with you. [Helmar *sits at the other side of the table.*]

Helmer. You alarm me, Nora. I don't understand you.

Nora. No, that is just it. You don't understand me; and I have never understood you—till tonight. No, don't interrupt. Only listen to what I say.—We must come to a final settlement, Torvald.

Helmer. How do you mean?

Nora. [*After a short silence.*] Does not one thing strike you as we sit here?

Helmer. What should strike me?

Nora. We have been married eight years. Does it not strike you that this is the first time we two, you and I, man and wife, have talked together seriously?

Helmer. Seriously! What do you call seriously?

Nora. During eight whole years, and more—ever since the day we first met—we have never exchanged one serious word about serious things.

Helmer. Was I always to trouble you with the cares you could not help me to bear?

Nora. I am not talking of cares. I say that we have never yet set ourselves seriously to get to the bottom of anything.

Helmer. Why, my dearest Nora, what have you to do with serious things?

Nora. There we have it! You have never understood me.—I have had great injustice done me, Torvald; first by father, and then by you.

HELMER. What! By your father and me?—By us, who have loved you more than all the world?

NORA. [*Shaking her head.*] You have never loved me. You only thought it amusing to be in love with me.

HELMER. Why, Nora, what a thing to say!

NORA. Yes, it is so, Torvald. While I was at home with Father, he used to tell me all his opinions, and I held the same opinions. If I had others I said nothing about them, because he wouldn't have liked it. He used to call me his doll-child, and played with me as I played with my dolls. Then I came to live in your house——

HELMER. What an expression to use about our marriage!

NORA. [*Undisturbed.*] I mean I passed from Father's hands into yours. You arranged everything according to your taste; and I got the same tastes as you; or I pretended to—I don't know which—both ways, perhaps; sometimes one and sometimes the other. When I look back on it now, I seem to have been living here like a beggar, from hand to mouth. I lived by performing tricks for you, Torvald. But you would have it so. You and Father have done me a great wrong. It is your fault that my life has come to nothing.

HELMER. Why, Nora, how unreasonable and ungrateful you are! Have you not been happy here?

NORA. No, never. I thought I was; but I never was.

HELMER. Not—not happy!

NORA. No; only merry. And you have always been so kind to me. But our house has been nothing but a play-room. Here I have been your doll-wife, just as at home I used to be Papa's doll-child. And the children, in their turn, have been my dolls. I thought it fun when you played with me, just as the children did when I played with them. That has been our marriage, Torvald.

HELMER. There is some truth in what you say, exaggerated and overstrained though it be. But henceforth it shall be different. Play-time is over; now comes the time for education.

NORA. Whose education? Mine, or the children's?

HELMER. Both, my dear, Nora.

NORA. Oh, Torvald, you are not the man to teach me to be a fit wife for you.

HELMER. And you can say that?

NORA. And I—how have I prepared myself to educate the children?

HELMER. Nora!

NORA. Did you not say yourself, a few minutes ago, you dared not trust them to me?

HELMER. In the excitement of the moment! Why should you dwell upon that?

NORA. No—you were perfectly right. That problem is beyond me. There is another to be solved first—I must try to educate myself. You are not the man to help me in that. I must set about it alone. And that is why I am leaving you.

HELMER. [*Jumping up.*] What—do you mean to say——?

NORA. I must stand quite alone if I am ever to know myself and my surroundings; so I cannot stay with you.

HELMER. Nora! Nora!

NORA. I am going at once. I dare say Christina will take me in for tonight——

HELMER. You are mad! I shall not allow it! I forbid it!

NORA. It is of no use your forbidding me anything now. I shall take with me what belongs to me. From you I will accept nothing, either now or afterwards.

HELMER. What madness this is!

NORA. Tomorrow I shall go home—I mean to what was my home. It will be easier for me to find some opening there.

HELMER. Oh, in your blind inexperience——

NORA. I must try to gain experience, Torvald.

HELMER. To forsake your home, your husband, and your children! And you don't consider what the world will say.

NORA. I can pay no heed to that. I only know that I must do it.

HELMER. This is monstrous! Can you forsake your holiest duties in this way?

NORA. What do you consider my holiest duties?

HELMER. Do I need to tell you that? Your duties to your husband and your children.

NORA. I have other duties equally sacred.

HELMER. Impossible! What duties do you mean?

NORA. My duties toward myself.

HELMER. Before all else you are a wife and a mother.

NORA. That I no longer believe. I believe that before all else I am a human being, just as much as you are—or at least that I should try to become one. I know that most people agree with you, Torvald, and that they say so in books. But henceforth I can't be satisfied with what most people say, and what is in books. I must think things out for myself, and try to get clear about them.

HELMER. Are you not clear about your place in your own home? Have you not an infallible guide in questions like these? Have you not religion?

NORA. Oh, Torvald, I don't really know what religion is.

HELMER. What do you mean?

NORA. I know nothing but what Pastor Hansen told me when I was confirmed. He explained that religion was this and that. When I get away from all this and stand alone, I will look into that matter too. I will see whether what he taught me is right, or, at any rate, whether it is right for me.

HELMER. Oh, this is unheard of! And from so young a woman! But if religion cannot keep you right, let me appeal to your conscience—for I suppose you have some moral feeling? Or, answer me: perhaps you have none?

NORA. Well, Torvald, it's not easy to say. I really don't know— I am all at sea about these things. I only know that I think quite differently from you about them. I hear, too, that the laws are different from what I thought; but I can't believe that they can be right. It appears that a woman has no right to spare her dying father, or to save her husband's life! I don't believe that.

HELMER. You talk like a child. You don't understand the society in which you live.

NORA. No, I do not. But now I shall try to learn. I must make up my mind which is right—society or I.

HELMER. Nora, you are ill; you are feverish; I almost think you are out of your senses.

NORA. I have never felt so much clearness and certainty as tonight.

HELMER. You are clear and certain enough to forsake husband and children?

NORA. Yes, I am.

HELMER. Then there is only one explanation possible.

NORA. What is that?

HELMER. You no longer love me.

NORA. No; that is just it.

HELMER. Nora!—Can you say so!

NORA. Oh, I'm so sorry, Torvald; for you've always been so kind to me. But I can't help it. I do not love you any longer.

HELMER. [*Mastering himself with difficulty.*] Are you clear and certain on this point too?

NORA. Yes, quite. That is why I will not stay here any longer.

HELMER. And can you also make clear to me how I have forfeited your love?

NORA. Yes, I can. It was this evening, when the miracle did not happen; for then I saw you were not the man I had imagined.

HELMER. Explain yourself more clearly; I don't understand.

NORA. I have waited so patiently all these eight years; for of course I saw clearly enough that miracles don't happen every day. When this crushing blow threatened me, I said to myself so confidently, "Now comes the miracle!" When Krogstad's letter lay in the box, it never for a moment occurred to me that you would think of submitting to that man's conditions. I was convinced that you would say to him, "Make it known to all the world"; and that then——

HELMER. Well? When I had given my own wife's name up to disgrace and shame——?

NORA. Then I firmly believed that you would come forward, take everything upon yourself, and say, "I am the guilty one."

HELMER. Nora——!

NORA. You mean I would never have accepted such a sacrifice? No, certainly not. But what would my assertions have been worth in opposition to yours?—That was the miracle that I hoped for and dreaded. And it was to hinder that that I wanted to die.

HELMER. I would gladly work for you day and night, Nora—bear sorrow and want for your sake. But no man sacrifices his honor, even for one he loves.

NORA. Millions of women have done so.

HELMER. Oh, you think and talk like a silly child.

NORA. Very likely. But you neither think nor talk like the man I can share my life with. When your terror was over—not for what threatened me, but for yourself—when there was nothing more to fear—then it seemed to you as though nothing had happened. I was your lark again, your doll, just as before—whom you would take twice as much care of in future, because she was so weak and fragile. [*Stands up.*] Torvald—in that moment it burst upon me that I had been living here these eight years with a strange man, and had borne him three children.—Oh, I can't bear to think of it! I could tear myself to pieces!

HELMER. [*Sadly.*] I see it, I see it; an abyss has opened between us.—But, Nora, can it never be filled up?

NORA. As I am now, I am no wife for you.

HELMER. I have strength to become another man.

NORA. Perhaps—when your doll is taken away from you.

HELMER. To part—to part from you! No, Nora, no; I can't grasp the thought.

NORA. [*Going into room on the right.*] The more reason for the thing to happen.

[*She comes back with outdoor things and a small traveling-bag, which she places on a chair.*]

HELMER. Nora, Nora, not now! Wait till tomorrow.

NORA. [*Putting on cloak.*] I can't spend the night in a strange man's house.

HELMER. But can we not live here, as brother and sister——?

NORA. [*Fastening her hat.*] You know very well that wouldn't last long. [*Puts on the shawl.*] Good-by, Torvald. No, I won't go to the children. I know they are in better hands than mine. As I now am, I can be nothing to them.

HELMER. But some time, Nora—some time——?

NORA. How can I tell? I have no idea what will become of me.

HELMER. But you are my wife, now and always!

NORA. Listen, Torvald—when a wife leaves her husband's house, as I am doing, I have heard that in the eyes of the law he is free from all duties toward her. At any rate, I release you from all duties. You must not feel yourself bound, any more than I shall. There must be perfect freedom on both sides. There, I give you back your ring. Give me mine.

HELMER. That too?

NORA. That too.

HELMER. Here it is.

NORA. Very well. Now it is all over. I lay the keys here. The servants know about everything in the house—better than I do. Tomorrow, when I have started, Christina will come to pack up the things I brought with me from home. I will have them sent after me.

HELMER. All over! all over! Nora, will you ever think of me again?

NORA. Oh, I shall often think of you, and the children, and this house.

HELMER. May I write to you, Nora?

NORA. No—never. You must not.

HELMER. But I must send you——

NORA. Nothing, nothing.

HELMER. I must help you if you need it.

NORA. No, I say. I take nothing from strangers.

HELMER. Nora—can I never be more than a stranger to you?

NORA. [*Taking her traveling-bag.*] Oh, Torvald, then the miracle of miracles would have to happen——

HELMER. What is the miracle of miracles?

NORA. Both of us would have to change so that—— Oh, Torvald, I no longer believe in miracles.

HELMER. But *I* will believe. Tell me! We must so change that——?

Nora. That communion between us shall be a marriage. Good-by. [*She goes out by the hall door.*]

Helmar. [*Sinks into a chair by the door with his face in his hands.*] Nora! Nora! [*He looks around and rises.*] Empty. She is gone. [*A hope springs up in him.*] Ah! The miracle of miracles——?!

[*From below is heard the reverberation of a heavy door closing.*]

THE END

THE RIVALS

Richard Brinsley Sheridan (England)

The Rivals, Sheridan's laughable farce of the brocade and powder period in the Eighteenth Century, deals with the age-old question of who shall select their future mates—the young people themselves or their parents. The joke in this play is that after violently quarreling over the point, both sides find they have selected the same persons! The lovely heroine, Lydia Languish, has three main suitors, dashing Captain Absolute, a fiery Irishman named Sir Lucius O'Trigger, and a country cousin named Bob Acres. Sir Lucius has been writing letters to Lydia, addressing her as Delia. Her elderly aunt, Mrs. Malaprop, gets them by mistake and answers them, thinking they are for her. Mrs. Malaprop has a large vocabulary and misuses most of it, thereby raising many laughs. Sir Lucius convinces Bob Acres that his chances with Lydia have been injured by a certain Lieutenant Beverly whom they do not know but of whose attentions to Lydia they have heard. Sir Lucius persuades Bob to challenge Beverly to a duel. Bob has never fought a duel, and in the following scene we see him unwillingly dragged to the dueling ground by O'Trigger, who is acting as his second. Beverley turns out to be Acre's good friend, Captain Absolute, who is going under the name of Beverley while he secretly courts Lydia.

The scene is Bath, England, a fashionable health resort.

✳   ✳   ✳

Act V. Scene III

King's-Mead-Fields

Enter Sir Lucius O'Trigger *and* Acres, *with pistols*

Acres. By my valor! then, Sir Lucius, forty yards is a good distance. Odds levels and aims!—I would say it is a good distance.

Sir Lucius. Is it for muskets or small field-pieces? Upon my con-

science, Mr. Acres, you must leave those things to me.—Stay now
—I'll show you.—[*Measures paces along the stage.*] There now,
that is a very pretty distance—a pretty gentleman's distance.

ACRES. Zounds! we might as well fight in a sentry-box! I tell
you, Sir Lucius, the farther he is off, the cooler I shall take my aim.

SIR LUCIUS. Faith! then I suppose you'ld aim at him best of all
if he was out of sight!

ACRES. No, Sir Lucius; but I should think forty or eight-and-
thirty yards——

SIR LUCIUS. Pho! pho! nonsense! three or four feet between the
mouths of your pistols is as good as a mile.

ACRES. Odds bullets, no!—by my valor! there is no merit in
killing him so near: do, my dear Sir Lucius, let me bring him down
at a long shot:—a long shot, Sir Lucius, if you love me!

SIR LUCIUS. Well, the gentleman's friend and I must settle that.
—But tell me now, Mr. Acres, in case of an accident, is there any
little will or commission I could execute for you?

ACRES. I am much obliged to you, Sir Lucius—but I don't understand——

SIR LUCIUS. Why, you may think there's no being shot at without a little risk—and if an unlucky bullet should carry a quietus [1]
with it—I say it will be no time to be bothering you about family
matters.

ACRES. A quietus!

SIR LUCIUS. For instance, now—if that should be the case—
would you choose to be pickled and sent home?—or would it be
the same to you to lie here in the Abbey? [2]—I'm told there is very
snug lying in the Abbey.

ACRES. Pickled!—Snug lying in the Abbey!—Odds tremors! Sir
Lucius, don't talk so!

SIR LUCIUS. I suppose, Mr. Acres, you never were engaged in an
affair of this kind before.

ACRES. No, Sir Lucius, never before.

SIR LUCIUS. Ah! that's a pity!—there's nothing like being used
to a thing.—Pray now, how would you receive the gentleman's
shot?

ACRES. Odds files!—I've practised that—there, Sir Lucius—
there.— [*Puts himself in an attitude.*] A sidefront, hey? Odd!
I'll make myself small enough: I'll stand edgeways.

SIR LUCIUS. Now—you're quite out—for if you stand so when I
take my aim—— [*Levelling at him.*]

ACRES. Zounds! Sir Lucius—are you sure it is not cocked?

[1] *quietus*: death, *i.e.*, permanent quiet.　　　[2] *Abbey*: the church in Bath.

Sir Lucius. Never fear.

Acres. But—but—you don't know—it may go off of its own head!

Sir Lucius. Pho! be easy.—Well, now if I hit you in the body, my bullet has a double chance—for if it misses a vital part of your right side—'twill be very hard if it don't succeed on the left!

Acres. A vital part?

Sir Lucius. But, there—fix yourself so—[*Placing him.*]—let him see the broad-side of your full front—there—now a ball or two may pass clean through your body, and never do any harm at all.

Acres. Clean through me!—a ball or two clean through me!

Sir Lucius. Ay, may they—and it is much the genteelest attitude into the bargain.

Acres. Look'ee! Sir Lucius—I'd just as lieve be shot in an awkward posture as a genteel one; so, by my valor! I will stand edgeways.

Sir Lucius. [*Looking at his watch.*] Sure they don't mean to disappoint us—Hah!—no, faith—I think I see them coming.

Acres. Hey!—what!—coming!——

Sir Lucius. Ay.—Who are those yonder getting over the stile?

Acres. There are two of them indeed!—well—let them come—hey, Sir Lucius!—we—we—we—we—won't run.

Sir Lucius. Run!

Acres. No—I say—we won't run, by my valor!

Sir Lucius. What the devil's the matter with you?

Acres. Nothing—nothing—my dear friend—my dear Sir Lucius —but I—I—I don't feel quite so bold, somehow, as I did.

Sir Lucius. O fy!—consider your honor.

Acres. Ay—true—my honor. Do, Sir Lucius, edge in a word or two every now and then about my honor.

Sir Lucius. Well, here they're coming. [*Looking.*]

Acres. Sir Lucius—if I wa'n't with you, I should almost think I was afraid.—If my valor should leave me!—Valor will come and go.

Sir Lucius. Then pray keep it fast, while you have it.

Acres. Sir Lucius—I doubt it is going—yes—my valor is certainly going!—it is sneaking off!—I feel it oozing out as it were at the palms of my hands!

Sir Lucius. Your honor—your honor!—Here they are.

Acres. O mercy!—now—that I was safe at Clod-Hall! or could be shot before I was aware!

[*Enter* FAULKLAND *and* CAPTAIN ABSOLUTE.]

SIR LUCIUS. Gentlemen, your most obedient.—Hah!—what, Captain Absolute!—So, I suppose, sir, you are come here, just like myself—to do a kind office, first for your friend—then to proceed to business on your own account.[3]

ACRES. What, Jack!—my dear Jack!—my dear friend!

ABSOLUTE. Hark'ee, Bob, Beverley's at hand.

SIR LUCIUS. Well, Mr. Acres—I don't blame your saluting the gentleman civilly.—[*To Faulkland.*] So, Mr. Beverley, if you'll choose your weapons, the captain and I will measure the ground.

FAULKLAND. My weapons, sir!

ACRES. Odds life! Sir Lucius, I'm not going to fight Mr. Faulkland; these are my particular friends.

SIR LUCIUS. What, sir, did you not come here to fight Mr. Acres?

FAULKLAND. Not I, upon my word, sir.

SIR LUCIUS. Well, now, that's mighty provoking. But I hope, Mr. Faulkland, as there are three of us come on purpose for the game, you won't be so cantankerous as to spoil the party by sitting out.

ABSOLUTE. O pray, Faulkland, fight to oblige Sir Lucius.

FAULKLAND. Nay, if Mr. Acres is so bent on the matter——

ACRES. No, no, Mr. Faulkland;—I'll bear my disappointment like a Christian.—Look'ee, Sir Lucius, there's no occasion at all for me to fight; and if it is the same to you, I'd as lieve let it alone.

SIR LUCIUS. Observe me, Mr. Acres—I must not be trifled with. You have certainly challenged somebody—and you came here to fight him. Now, if that gentleman is willing to represent him, I can't see, for my soul, why it isn't just the same thing.

ACRES. Why no—Sir Lucius—I tell you, 'tis one Beverley I've challenged—a fellow, you see, that dare not show his face!—If he were here, I'd make him give up his pretensions directly!

ABSOLUTE. Hold, Bob—let me set you right—there is no such man as Beverley in the case.—The person who assumed that name is before you; and as his pretensions are the same in both characters, he is ready to support them in whatever way you please.

SIR LUCIUS. Well, this is lucky.—Now you have an opportunity——

ACRE. What, quarrel with my dear friend Jack Absolute?—not

[3] Sir Lucius supposes Absolute has come as Beverley's second, and thinks Faulkland is Beverley.

if he were fifty Beverleys! Zounds! Sir Lucius, you would not have me so unnatural.

SIR LUCIUS. Upon my conscience, Mr. Acres, your valor has oozed away with a vengeance!

ACRES. Not in the least! Odds backs and abettors! I'll be your second with all my heart—and if you should get a quietus, you may command me entirely. I'll get you snug lying in the Abbey here; or pickle you, and send you over to Blunderbuss-hall, or anything of the kind, with the greatest pleasure.

SIR LUCIUS. Pho! pho! you are little better than a coward.

ACRES. Mind, gentlemen, he calls me a coward; coward was the word, by my valor!

SIR LUCIUS. Well, sir?

ACRES. Look'ee, Sir Lucius, 'tisn't that I mind the word coward —coward may be said in joke—but if you had called me a poltroon, odds daggers and balls——

SIR LUCIUS. Well, sir?

ACRES. I should have thought you a very ill-bred man.

SIR LUCIUS. Pho! you are beneath my notice.

ABSOLUTE. Nay, Sir Lucius, you can't have a better second than my friend Acres.—He is a most determined dog—called in the country, Fighting Bob.—He generally kills a man a week—don't you, Bob?

ACRES. Ay—at home!

SIR LUCIUS. Well, then, captain, 'tis we must begin—so come out, my little counsellor—[*Draws his sword.*]—and ask the gentleman whether he will resign the lady, without forcing you to proceed against him?

ABSOLUTE. Come on then, sir—[*Draws.*]; since you won't let it be an amicable suit, here's my reply.

[*Enter* SIR ANTHONY ABSOLUTE,[4] SERVANT, MRS. MALAPROP, *and* LYDIA.]

SERVANT. Knock 'em all down, sweet Sir Anthony; knock down my master's in particular; and bind his hands over to their good behavior!

SIR ANTHONY. Put up, Jack, put up, or I shall be in a frenzy— how came you in a duel, sir?

ABSOLUTE. Faith, sir, that gentleman can tell you better than I; 'twas he called on me, and you know, sir, I serve his majesty.

SIR ANTHONY. Here's a pretty fellow; I catch him going to cut

[4] *Sir Anthony Absolute:* Captain Absolute's father.

a man's throat, and he tells me he serves his majesty!—Zounds! sirrah, then how durst you draw the king's sword against one of his subjects?

ABSOLUTE. Sir, I tell you! that gentleman called me out, without explaining his reasons.

SIR ANTHONY. Gad! sir, how came you to call my son out, without explaining your reasons?

SIR LUCIUS. Your son, sir, insulted me in a manner which my honor could not brook.

SIR ANTHONY. Zounds! Jack, how durst you insult the gentleman in a manner which his honor could not brook?

MRS. MALAPROP. Come, come, let's have no honor before ladies. —Captain Absolute, come here—How could you intimidate us so? —Here's Lydia has been terrified to death for you.

ABSOLUTE. For fear I should be killed, or escape, ma'am?

MRS. MALAPROP. Nay, no delusions to the past—Lydia is convinced; speak, child.

SIR LUCIUS. With your leave, ma'am, I must put in a word here: I believe I could interpret the young lady's silence. Now mark——

LYDIA. What is it you mean, sir?

SIR LUCIUS. Come, come, Delia, we must be serious now—this is no time for trifling.

LYDIA. 'Tis true, sir; and your reproof bids me offer this gentleman my hand, and solicit the return of his affections.

ABSOLUTE. O! my little angel, say you so!—Sir Lucius—I perceive there must be some mistake here, with regard to the affront which you affirm I have given you. I can only say, that it could not have been intentional. And as you must be convinced, that I should not fear to support a real injury, you shall now see that I am not ashamed to atone for an inadvertency—I ask your pardon. —But for this lady, while honored with her approbation, I will support my claim against any man whatever.

SIR ANTHONY. Well said, Jack, and I'll stand by you, my boy.

ACRES. Mind, I give up all my claim—I make no pretensions to any thing in the world; and if I can't get a wife without fighting for her, by my valor! I'll live a bachelor.

SIR LUCIUS. Captain, give me your hand: an affront handsomely acknowledged becomes an obligation; and as for the lady, if she chooses to deny her own handwriting, here——[*Takes out letters.*]

MRS. MALAPROP. O, he will dissolve my mystery!—Sir Lucius, perhaps there's some mistake—perhaps I can illuminate——

Sir Lucius. Pray, old gentlewoman, don't interfere where you have no business.—Miss Languish, are you my Delia, or not?

Lydia. Indeed, Sir Lucius, I am not. [*Walks aside with* Captain Absolute.]

Mrs. Malaprop. Sir Lucius O'Trigger—ungrateful as you are— I own the soft impeachment—pardon my blushes, I am Delia.

Sir Lucius. You Delia—pho! pho! be easy.

Mrs. Malaprop. Why, thou barbarous Vandyke—those letters are mine—When you are more sensible of my benignity—perhaps I may be brought to encourage your addresses.

Sir Lucius. Mrs. Malaprop, I am extremely sensible of your condescension; and whether you or Lucy [5] have put this trick on me, I am equally beholden to you.—And, to show you I am not ungrateful, Captain Absolute, since you have taken that lady from me, I'll give you my Delia into the bargain.

Absolute. I am much obliged to you, Sir Lucius; but here's my friend, Fighting Bob, unprovided for.

Sir Lucius. Hah! little Valor—here, will you make your fortune?

Acres. Odds wrinkles! No.—But give me your hand, Sir Lucius, forget and forgive; but if ever I give you a chance of pickling me again, say Bob Acres is a dunce, that's all.

Sir Anthony. Come, Mrs. Malaprop, don't be cast down—you are in your bloom yet.

Mrs. Malaprop. O Sir Anthony—men are all barbarians.

[5] *Lucy:* Lydia's maid, who misdelivered Sir Lucius' letters on purpose to Mrs. Malaprop.

THE DOCTOR IN SPITE OF HIMSELF

Molière (France)

Translated by Barrett H. Clark

Persons in the Play

SGANARELLE, *Martine's husband*
MARTINE, *Sganarelle's wife*
M. ROBERT, *Sganarelle's neighbor*
VALÈRE, *Géronte's servant*
LUCAS, *Jacqueline's husband*
JACQUELINE, *Lucas' wife, and nurse in Géronte's home*
LUCINDE, *Géronte's daughter*
GÉRONTE, *A country gentleman*
LÉANDRE, *Lucinde's lover*

TIME: *Late seventeenth century*

ACT FIRST

SCENE: *A wood.*

[*Enter* SGANARELLE *and* MARTINE, *quarreling.*]

SGANARELLE. No, I tell you, I will do nothing of the kind: I am master here.

MARTINE. And I tell you you shall live as I want you to. I didn't marry you to put up with your nonsense.

SGANARELLE. Oh, what a plague it is to have a wife!

MARTINE. Cursed be the day when I took it into my head to say "Yes."

SGANARELLE. Cursed be the notary who made me sign my own ruination!

MARTINE. What right have you to complain of that? Oughtn't you rather to be thanking heaven that you have me for a wife?

SGANARELLE. It's true you honored me too greatly. Goodness! don't provoke me—I might tell you something——

MARTINE. Come, now, what could you say?

SGANARELLE. Enough; let us stop right here. It's enough that I know what I know; and I repeat you were very lucky to get me.

MARTINE. What do you mean by your "very lucky to get you"?

A man who will drive me into the gutter, a drunkard who eats up all I have!

SGANARELLE. Now, that's a lie: I drink part of it.

MARTINE. Who sells everything in the house.

SGANARELLE. That's what I call living on one's income.

MARTINE. Who has taken away my very bed from under me!

SGANARELLE. You will get up earlier.

MARTINE. Who leaves me nothing in the whole house.

SGANARELLE. There won't be so much trouble when we move.

MARTINE. Who from morning to night does nothing but eat and drink.

SGANARELLE. That's to keep me occupied.

MARTINE. And what do you think I shall do with my family meanwhile?

SGANARELLE. Whatever you please.

MARTINE. I have four poor little children on my hands.

SGANARELLE. Put them on the ground.

MARTINE. Who are continually begging me for bread.

SGANARELLE. Give them the rod. When I have enough to eat and drink, the family ought to be satisfied.

MARTINE. And do you mean to say, you drunkard, that——?

SGANARELLE. Gently, please.

MARTINE. I am forever to put up with your insolence and——?

SGANARELLE. Let's keep calm, wife.

MARTINE. Who could, with you for a husband!

SGANARELLE. My dear, you know my patience is very short-lived, and my arm knows how to wield a club.

MARTINE. I laugh at your silly threats. See, I'm not at all afraid of you.

SGANARELLE. My better half, you desire a beating, I see.

MARTINE. You think I'm frightened at your talk!

SGANARELLE. Sweet object of my love, I shall box your ears.

MARTINE. Drunkard!

SGANARELLE. [*He beats her; she screams.*] That is the best way to make you keep still.

[*Enter* M. ROBERT.]

M. ROBERT. Here, here, here! What's this? What a disgraceful affair!

[MARTINE *comes up to him, looks him in the face, and after a short pause, deliberately slaps him.*]

MARTINE. I like to have him beat me.

M. Robert. Very well, then; I don't object.

Martine. What business is it of yours?

M. Robert. None whatsoever.

Martine. Impertinent fellow, to interfere with a husband who is beating his wife!

M. Robert. I am very sorry, indeed.

Martine. Mind your own business.

M. Robert. I shall say nothing more.

Martine. I tell you, I wish to be beaten.

M. Robert. Very well, then.

Martine. You are a fool to interfere with other people's business.

[M. Robert *goes to* Sganarelle, *who hits him and drives him off.*]

M. Robert. Neighbor, I beg your pardon. Go on, whack your wife as much as you please; I'll help you if you like.

Sganarelle. I do not like.

M. Robert. Oh, that's a different matter.

Sganarelle. I'll beat her if I like; and I won't beat her if I don't like.

M. Robert. All right; it's not my fault.

Sganarelle. She is my wife, and not yours.

M. Robert. I don't doubt it in the least, Monsieur!

Sganarelle. And you are exceedingly impudent to meddle in other people's concerns. [M. Robert *goes out.* Sganarelle *goes to his wife and takes her hand.*] Come, now, let's make up and be happy.

Martine. I won't.

Sganarelle. What!

Martine. No, I won't.

Sganarelle. Now, now.

Martine. I won't do anything of the kind.

Sganarelle. Come, come, come.

Martine. No, I *will* be angry.

Sganarelle. Come, now; it's only a trifle.

Martine. Let me be, I tell you!

Sganarelle. I ask your forgiveness.

Martine. Well, I forgive you this time. [*Aside.*] But you shall pay for it!

Sganarelle. A little row now and then between those who truly love only increases affection. There now, I'm going to the wood, and I promise you more than a hundred faggots to-day. [*He goes out.*]

MARTINE. I shan't forget what I owe him for that beating. I'll get him a trouncing he won't soon forget. [*She retires to the rear of the stage, apparently planning.*]

(At this moment enter Lucas and Valère, who are seeking a skilled physician to cure their master's daughter, Lucinde, who has been stricken dumb. We learn from their talk that Lucinde is being forced by her father to marry a rich old man instead of the young Léandre whom she loves. Martine, to get her revenge, tells them that Sganarelle is a great doctor but that he is a little mad and pretends to be a wood-cutter, and must be soundly beaten before he will treat a patient. By administering a cudgeling to Sganarelle and telling him he will receive any fee he wishes, Lucas and Valère compel the bogus doctor to accompany them to Géronte's home and introduce him as a distinguished physician. Sganarelle—a clever rascal—scents profit and enters into the part.)

ACT SECOND

SCENE: *Before* GÉRONTE'S *house.*

[*Enter* GÉRONTE, VALÈRE, LUCAS, *and* JACQUELINE.]

VALÈRE. Yes, Monsieur, I'm sure you will be satisfied; we have brought you the most illustrious doctor in the world.

LUCAS. He has mended folks that's dead; that's what he's done.

VALÈRE. He is rather peculiar, as I said. Lucas says he is a little mad.

LUCAS. Yes, that's what I said.

VALÈRE. But really, this is only a pretense to conceal his great learning.

GÉRONTE. I should very much like to see him; send for him at once.

VALÈRE. Very well. [*He goes out.*]

JACQUELINE. You can take my word for it, Monsieur, this doctor'll be just like the rest of them. I tell you, a husband to her liking is the only cure for her.

GÉRONTE. Come, now, you do a lot of meddling, nurse.

JACQUELINE. All the same, it's a husband she wants, it is.

GÉRONTE. Who would take her as she is now? I offered to let her marry Cléante, but she refused.

JACQUELINE. And no wonder; you wanted to give her to a man she didn't like. Why don't you give her to Léandre? She likes him.

GÉRONTE. I don't like Léandre; he has no money; Cléante has.

JACQUELINE. Ah, parents nowadays always ask: "How much has he?" What's the use of anything, if you can't be happy, I say?

[*Enter* VALÈRE *and* SGANARELLE.]

VALÈRE. Here comes the doctor, Monsieur.

GÉRONTE. I am delighted to see you, Monsieur. We have great need of you. [*Removing his hat and bowing.*]

SGANARELLE. [*In a black gown and high hat.*] Hippocrates says —that both of us should put on our hats.

GÉRONTE. Hippocrates says that?

SGANARELLE. Yes.

GÉRONTE. In what chapter does he say that?

SGANARELLE. In his chapter—on hats.

GÉRONTES. Well, if Hippocrates says so, it must be.

SGANARELLE. Now, doctor, since I have——

GÉRONTE. Whom are you speaking to, Monsieur?

SGANARELLE. To you.

GÉRONTES. I am not a doctor.

SGANARELLE. What, you are not a doctor?

GÉRONTE. Certainly not.

SGANARELLE. [*Beating him.*] Really?

GÉRONTE. Oh, oh,—really! I tell you I am no doctor.

SGANARELLE. *Now* you are a doctor. I have no other degree than you have.

GÉRONTE. What sort of fellow is this you have brought me?

VALÈRE. Didn't I tell you he was rather eccentric?

GÉRONTE. Yes, but I don't like his eccentricities.

VALÈRE. Never mind, Monsieur, he was only joking.

GÉRONTE. I don't like his kind of joking.

SGANARELLE. Pardon the liberty I have taken. I am very sorry——

GÉRONTE. Don't say any more about it. I have a daughter who was stricken with a strange disease.

SGANARELLE. I am delighted to know it, I can assure you.

GÉRONTE. Many thanks.

SGANARELLE. What is your daughter's name?

GÉRONTE. Lucinde.

SGANARELLE. Lucinde? A nice name!

GÉRONTE. I shall go and see what she is doing. [*He goes out.*]

SGANARELLE. An interesting case, upon my word.—Ha! someone

is coming. [*Walks up and down a moment, then re-enter* GÉRONTE, *leading* LUCINDE *by the hand.*]

GÉRONTE. Here is my daughter.

SGANARELLE. Is this the patient?

GÉRONTE. Yes: my only child. I should never recover if anything were to happen to her. If she should die——

SGANARELLE. Impossible, Monsieur. She cannot die without a regular prescription from the Academy.

GÉRONTE. Bring a chair, there. [*A chair is brought.*]

SGANARELLE. Not so bad, this patient!

GÉRONTE. She smiles, Monsieur; you have made her smile.

SGNARELLE. Of course, Monsieur, it's my business. This is fine. It is a very good symptom. Well, Mademoiselle, what ails you? What pains do you feel?

LUCINDE. [*Making gesticulations.*] Ouh, oi, oi!

SGANARELLE. What's that?

LUCINDE. Oi, oi.

SGANARELLE. Ouh, ouh, oi, oi, I don't understand your language!

GÉRONTE. That's just what's the matter, Monsieur. She is dumb, and I have been compelled to put off the marriage.

SGANARELLE. Why was that?

GÉRONTE. The man she is to marry wants to wait for her recovery.

SGANARELLE. Show me the man who doesn't want his wife dumb! I only wish mine had that malady! I should see that she wasn't soon cured!

GÉRONTE. Well, cure this case, at any rate.

SGANARELLE. Don't worry, Monsieur. Is her pain very acute?

GÉRONTE. Yes—very.

SGANARELLE. That's right. [*To* LUCINDE.] Let me feel your pulse. [*To* GÉRONTE.] Monsieur, I am enlightened as to your daughter's condition: she is dumb!

GÉRONTE. Yes; that's just it. You found it out immediately.

SGANARELLE. Of course! We great doctors know things at once. A fool would have been disturbed and puzzled, and would have beat about the bush. But I tell you plainly: your daughter is dumb.

GÉRONTE. Yes; but how did it happen?

SGANARELLE. Very simply: she lost her speech.

GÉRONTE. Very good; but why?

SGANARELLE. Our best authorities seem to agree that it arises from an impediment of the tongue.

GÉRONTE. Yes, but tell me the causes. The authorities must surely——

SGANARELLE. Well, Aristotle says—many fine things.

GÉRONTE. I can readily believe it.

SGANARELLE. He was a great man.

GÉRONTE. No doubt of it.

SGANARELLE. A *very* great man; a man who was far greater than I am. But to return to the question: I am of the opinion that this impediment arises from certain peccant humors. Peccant—that is to say—a—a—peccant. For, as the vapors exhumed are formed by a certain exhalation of circuitous—a—you understand Latin?

GÉRONTE. No.

SGANARELLE. What, you don't understand Latin?

GÉRONTE. No.

SGANARELLE. Carborias influxoriorum arci thrumbi thantrat——

GÉRONTE. Ah, why didn't I study when I was young?

SGANARELLE. So these vapors, passing from the left to the right side, come into contact with the lungs—Latin armyan—Hebrew, polyglum—and from there they proceed immediately to the—please follow me more closely.

GÉRONTE. I am.

SGANARELLE. And have a certain malignity by a—pay attention to me.

GÉRONTE. I am, Monsieur.

SGANARELLE. Which is always caused by the sharpness of these, and the concavity of the diaphragm—nequaquam in uterque imibus. And therefore your daughter is dumb.

GÉRONTE. No one could possibly argue better. But, Monsieur, what do you think should be done?

SGANARELLE. What do I think should be done?

GÉRONTE. Yes.

SGANARELLE. Well, I suggest that she be put immediately to bed, and take plenty of bread and wine.

GÉRONTE. Why, if you please?

SGANARELLE. Because this wonderful combination often produces speech.

GÉRONTE. What a great man you are! Quick, bring some bread and wine!

SGANARELLE. I shall soon return to see how the patient is getting on. I wish you good-day.

GÉRONTE. One moment, please.

SGANARELLE. What do you want?

GÉRONTE. To give you your fee.

SGANARELLE. [*Holding out his hand.*] I shall not take it.

GÉRONTE. Ah, Monsieur!

SGANARELLE. Not at all.

GÉRONTE. I beg of you——

SGANARELLE. I will not. I do not practise for money.

GÉRONTE. I'm quite sure of that.

SGANARELLE. [*Taking the money.*] Is it full weight?

GÉRONTE. Certainly.

SGANARELLE. I am not a mercenary doctor.

GÉRONTE. I can readily believe it.

SGANARELLE. I am not inspired by any base desire for gold. No, not at all.

GÉRONTE. I don't doubt it in the least. Well, I bid you good-day.

SGANARELLE. Good-day, Monsieur. Don't forget. I never practise for money.

[GÉRONTE *goes out. Enter* LÉANDRE.]

SGANARELLE. Well, this isn't so bad after all——

(Léandre confides to Sganarelle that Lucinde is just pretending to be dumb to escape marrying Cléante. He begs the supposed doctor to help him win the lady. They disguise Léandre in an apothecary's gown.)

LÉANDRE. I wish I knew five or six long Latin words to mix with my conversation. Then I should be a learned man.

SGANARELLE. Nonsense; it's not necessary. The dress is sufficient. I don't know any more about medicine than you do.

LÉANDRE. How's that?

SGANARELLE. Deuce take me if I know a thing about it. I shall confide in you, Monsieur.

LÉANDRE. What! you're not really——?

SGANARELLE. Of course not. They made me a doctor. I don't know anything, I tell you. I left school at the end of the sixth form. But now I'm a doctor. A shoemaker who spoils a pair of shoes is blamed for it. But when we doctors make a slip, our dead patients never blame us. They can never tell what medicine killed them. Here come some people who want to be cured. Let's get out of their way. Go and wait for me near Lucinde's home. [LÉANDRE *goes out. Enter* JACQUELINE *and* LUCAS.] Here is a monster nurse! Ah, nurse of my heart, I am charmed to meet you; the sight of you is like cassia, rhubarb and senna to me, and when you——

JACQUELINE. Gracious me, Mr. Doctor, it's no use talkin' to me that way. I don't understand a single word of your Latin.

SGANARELLE. It is not necessary for one to know Latin nowadays. Who's this? [*Hides.*]

[*Enter* GÉRONTE.]

GÉRONTE. Lucas, have you seen our doctor lately?

LUCAS. Yes, Monsieur, I've seen him.

GÉRONTE. Where is he?

LUCAS. I don't know.

GÉRONTE. Go and see what my daughter is doing. [LUCAS *goes out. Enter* SGANARELLE *and* LÉANDRE.] Ah, Monsieur, I was looking for you.

SGANARELLE. Well, I was coming. How is the patient?

GÉRONTE. She is somewhat worse since taking your remedy.

SGANARELLE. So much the better; she is going to be cured.

GÉRONTE. Possibly, but I think she will choke before then.

SGANARELLE. Don't be anxious about her. I have some further remedies in case all others fail.

GÉRONTE. Who is that man with you?

SGANARELLE. He is an apothecary.

GÉRONTE. Ah, I see.

SGANARELLE. Your daughter will need him, I feel sure.

[*Enter* JACQUELINE *and* LUCINDE.]

JACQUELINE. Here is your daughter, master; she wished to walk about a little.

SGANARELLE. That is the best thing for her. Feel her pulse, Apothecary, I shall consult about further measures. [*He draws* GÉRONTE *over to the opposite side of the stage and turns him away from* LUCINDE *and* LÉANDRE. *Each time* GÉRONTE *starts to turn round,* SGANARELLE *prevents him.*] Monsieur, it is a grave question among us doctors. For, Monsieur, as I said before, I think it highly probable that—with the inequality of such peccant——

[LUCINDE *is heard muttering.*]

GÉRONTE. Listen! my daughter spoke! Oh, great doctor, excellent doctor! What miracles you perform! How can I ever repay you for the great service you have done me!

SGANARELLE. [*Strutting about and stroking his beard.*] Hem! Hem! This has been a very troublesome case indeed.

LUCINDE. Yes, Father, I have recovered my speech, but only to tell you that I will marry no one but Léandre, and that it is useless to try to force me to accept Cléante——

GÉRONTE. But I shall——

LUCINDE. Nothing can shake my resolution.

GÉRONTE. What is this? Am I to——?

LUCINDE. All your arguments are useless.

GÉRONTE. But I will force you to marry him, and if you don't——

LUCINDE. I will not submit to such tyranny. No, no, no! [*She says this last in a shrill and piercing voice.*]

GÉRONTE. My, oh, my! Doctor, I beseech you to make her dumb again! My fortune will be yours if you do it.

SGANARELLE. My utmost skill can but make *you* deaf, which is some consolation.

GÉRONTE. Many thanks! [*To* LUCINDE.] And as for you, you will marry Cléante this very evening.

LUCINDE. I would sooner die!

SGANARELLE. Stop this wrangling at once. I know a remedy that will cure her.

GÉRONTE. Is is possible?

SGANARELLE. Certainly. Just let me arrange it. I shall need the apothecary. [*To* LÉANDRE, *aside.*] One word, Monsieur. The only remedy I know of in this case is one matrimonium pill. You must persuade her to take the medicine at once. Give her also a dose of elopement. Go into the garden now and persuade her to take these remedies. I shall speak with her father meanwhile. [LUCINDE *and* LÉANDRE *go out.*]

GÉRONTE. What are those drugs you just mentioned, monsieur? I don't think I ever heard of them before.

SGANARELLE. They are used in extreme cases.

GÉRONTE. Did you ever see such impudence?

SGANARELLE. Indeed, never.
with him.

GÉRONTE. I think she is just the kind of girl who would elope

SGANARELLE. You don't believe that?

GÉRONTE. I shall take good care that they don't see each other.

SGANARELLE. Believe me, that is a very prudent step.

[*Enter* LUCAS.]

LUCAS. Oh, Master, here's a pretty mess! Your daughter's run away with her Léandre! It was him as played the 'pothecary, and this is the doctor that gave the remedy.

GÉRONTE. What! Abuse me in this shameful manner! Quick, fetch the police. Here, you hold this rascal! [GÉRONTE *goes out.*]

LUCAS. [*Collaring* SGANARELLE.] Take my word for it, you'll hang for this!

[*Enter* MARTINE.]

MARTINE. Goodness me! What's become of that doctor I recommended to you?

LUCAS. Here he is. He's just going to be hanged.

MARTINE. My husband hanged! Why?

LUCAS. He helped someone elope with the Master's daughter.

MARTINE. Alas, my dear husband, are you going to be hanged?

SGANARELLE. Don't you see? What can I do?

MARTINE. Unhappy me! If you had only finished chopping the wood, there might have been some consolation!

SGANARELLE. Go away, you grieve me.

MARTINE. No, no, I shall stay and encourage you to die; I'll not leave you until I see you hanged.

SGANARELLE. Thanks, my dear wife.

[*Enter* GÉRONTE.]

GÉRONTE. The police officer will soon be here and you will be sent to prison!

SGANARELLE. Ah, my dear Monsieur, [*Bowing and taking off his hat*] wouldn't a few blows from that stick be sufficient to allay your wrath?

GÉRONTE. No, it is a matter of law.—But what's this?

[*Enter* LÉANDRE, LUCINDE, JACQUELINE *and* LUCAS.]

LÉANDRE. I appear now as Léandre, and bring you back your daughter. We intended to elope and marry. But I shall not steal your daughter; I shall only receive her from your own hands.— I *also* wish to let you know that I just received word of the death of my uncle, who has made me heir to a large fortune and——

GÉRONTE. A large—? Ah, my son, your virtue appeals to me! I give you my daughter with the greatest of pleasure.

MARTINE. Since you are not going to be hanged, thank me for making you a doctor; I gained you that honor.

SGANARELLE. And also the honor of a severe thrashing. But come, I forgive you this time.

CURTAIN.

ROMEO AND JULIET

William Shakespeare (England)

The world famous tragedy of *Romeo and Juliet* is based on an Italian legend of the year 1303. Shakespeare's story is compressed into five days. "The lovers meet for the first time on Sunday; they are married on Monday; they part at dawn on Tuesday; they are reunited in death on Thursday night." The swiftness and violence of the action—"too like the lightning," as Juliet says—belong to the South, to Italy. But Shakespeare's tender and beautiful picture of youthful love belongs to every place and time.

❀ ❀ ❀

Dramatis Personæ

Prince of Verona.

Paris, *a young nobleman, kinsman to the prince.*

Montague, ⎰ *heads of two houses at variance*
Capulet, ⎱ *with each other.*

Romeo, *son to Montague.*

Mercutio, *kinsman to the prince, and friend to Romeo.*

Benvolio, *nephew to Montague, and friend to Romeo.*

Tybalt, *nephew to Lady Capulet.*

Friar Laurence, *a Franciscan.*

Balthasar, *servant to Romeo.*

Sampson, ⎰ *servants to Capulet.*
Gregory, ⎱

Abraham, *servant to Montague.*

An Apothecary.

Lady Montague, *wife to Montague.*

Lady Capulet, *wife to Capulet.*

Juliet, *daughter to Capulet.*

Nurse *to Juliet.*

Citizens of Verona; kinsfolk of both houses;
Maskers, Guards, Watchmen, Servants
and Attendants.
Chorus.

The Prologue

Two households, both alike in dignity,
   In fair Verona, where we lay our scene,
From ancient grudge break to new mutiny,
   Where civil blood makes civil hands unclean.
From forth the fatal loins of these two foes   5
   A pair of star-cross'd lovers take their life;
Whose misadventured piteous overthrows
   Do with their death bury their parents' strife.
The fearful passage of their death-mark'd love,
   And the continuance of their parents' rage,   10
Which, but their children's end, nought could remove,
   Is now the two hours' traffic of our stage;
The which if you with patient ears attend,
What here shall miss, our toil shall strive to mend.

Act I. Scene I

Verona. A public place.

[*Enter* Sampson *and* Gregory, *of the house of Capulet, with swords and bucklers.*]

Sam. I strike quickly, being moved.
Gre. But thou art not quickly moved to strike.
Sam. A dog of the house of Montague moves me.
Gre. To move is to stir, and to be valiant is to stand: therefore, if thou art moved, thou runn'st away.
Sam. A dog of that house shall move me to stand: I will take the wall of any man or maid of Montague's.   5
Gre. Draw thy tool; here comes two of the house of Montagues.

[*Enter* Abraham *and* Balthasar.]

Sam. My naked weapon is out: quarrel; I will back thee.
Gre. How! turn thy back and run?
Sam. Fear me not.
Gre. No, marry; I fear thee!   10
Sam. Let us take the law of our sides; let them begin.
Gre. I will frown as I pass by, and let them take it as they list.
Sam. Nay, as they dare. I will bite my thumb at them; which is a disgrace to them, if they bear it.

ABR. Do you bite your thumb at us, sir? 15
SAM. I do bite my thumb, sir.
ABR. Do you bite your thumb at us, sir?
SAM. [*Aside to* GRE.] Is the law of our side, if I say ay?
GRE. No.
SAM. No, sir, I do not bite my thumb at you, sir; but I bite my
thumb, sir. 20
GRE. Do you quarrel, sir?
ABR. Quarrel, sir! no, sir.
SAM. But if you do, sir, I am for you: I serve as good a man as you.
ABR. No better.
SAM. Well, sir. 25

[*Enter* BENVOLIO.]

GRE. [*Aside to* SAM.] Say "better": here comes one of my master's
kinsmen.
SAM. Yes, better, sir.
ABR. You lie.
SAM. Draw, if you be men. Gregory, remember thy swashing blow.
[*They fight.*]
BEN. Part, fools! [*Beating down their weapons.*] 30
Put up your swords; you know not what you do.

[*Enter* TYBALT.]

TYB. What, art thou drawn among these heartless hinds?
Turn thee, Benvolio, look upon thy death.
BEN. I do but keep the peace: put up thy sword,
Or manage it to part these men with me. 35
TYB. What, drawn, and talk of peace! I hate the word,
As I hate hell, all Montagues, and thee:
Have at thee, coward! [*They fight.*

[*Enter several of both houses, who join the fray; then enter
Citizens and Peace-officers, with clubs.*]

FIRST OFF. Clubs, bills, and partisans! strike! beat them down!
Down with the Capulets! down with the Montagues! 40
[*Enter old* CAPULET *in his gown, and* LADY CAPULET.]
CAP. What noise is this? Give me my long sword, ho!
LA. CAP. A crutch, a crutch! why call you for a sword?
CAP. My sword, I say! Old Montague is come,
And flourishes his blade in spite of me.

[*Enter old* MONTAGUE *and* LADY MONTAGUE.]

ON. Thou villain Capulet!—Hold me not, let me go.   45
A. MON. Thou shalt not stir one foot to seek a foe.

[*Enter* PRINCE OF VERONA *with his train.*]

PRIN. Rebellious subjects, enemies to peace,
 Profaners of this neighbor-stained steel,—
 Will they not hear? What, ho! you men, you beasts,
 That quench the fire of your pernicious rage   50
 With purple fountains issuing from your veins,
 On pain of torture, from those bloody hands
 Throw your mistemper'd weapons to the ground.
 And hear the sentence of your movèd prince.
 Three civil brawls, bred of an airy word,   55
 By thee, old Capulet, and Montague,
 Have thrice disturb'd the quiet of our streets.
 And made Verona's ancient citizens
 Cast by their grave beseeming ornaments,
 To wield old partisans, in hands as old,   60
 Canker'd with peace, to part your canker'd hate.
 If ever you disturb our streets again,
 Your lives shall pay the forfeit of the peace.
 For this time, all the rest depart away.
 You, Capulet, shall go along with me;   65
 And, Montague, come you this afternoon,
 To know our farther pleasure in this case,
 To old Free-town, our common judgment-place.
 Once more, on pain of death, all men depart.

(We first see Romeo in love with love rather than with any particular girl. However, he fancies himself deeply smitten by Rosaline, who disdains him. To distract his mind, his cousin Benvolio persuades him to go masked to a ball at the house of Capulet, his hereditary enemy. Here he sees the fourteen-year-old Juliet, and all thought of Rosaline vanishes from his mind.)

From Scene V

ROM. [*To a Servingman.*] What lady's that, which doth enrich
 the hand
  Of yonder knight?
SERV. I know not, sir.

Rom. O, she doth teach the torches to burn bright!
It seems she hangs upon the cheek of night
Like a rich jewel in an Ethiop's ear;
Beauty too rich for use, for earth too dear!
So shows a snowy dove trooping with crows,
As yonder lady o'er her fellows shows.
The measure done, I'll watch her place of stand,
And, touching hers, make blessed my rude hand.
Did my heart love till now? forswear it, sight!
For I ne'er saw true beauty till this night.

Tyb. This, by his voice, should be a Montague.
Fetch me my rapier, boy. What dares the slave
Come hither, cover'd with an antic face,
To fleer and scorn at our solemnity?   15
Now, by the stock and honor of my kin,
To strike him dead I hold it not a sin.

Cap. Why, how now, kinsman! wherefore storm you so?

Tyb. Uncle, this is a Montague, our foe;
A villain, that is hither come in spite,   20
To scorn at our solemnity this night.

Cap. Young Romeo is it?

Tyb.   'Tis he, that villain Romeo.

Cap. Content thee, gentle coz, let him alone,
He bears him like a portly gentleman;
And, to say truth, Verona brags of him   25
To be a virtuous and well-govern'd youth:
I would not for the wealth of all this town
Here in my house do him disparagement:
Therefore be patient, take no note of him:
It is my will, the which if thou respect,   30
Show a fair presence and put off these frowns,
An ill-beseeming semblance for a feast.

Tyb. It fits, when such a villain is a guest:
I'll not endure him.

Cap.   He shall be endured: 35
What, goodman boy! I say, he shall: go to;
Am I the master here, or you? go to.
You'll not endure him! God shall mend my soul,
You'll make a mutiny among my guests!
You will set cock-a-hoop! you'll be the man!   40

Tyb. Why, uncle, 'tis a shame.

CAP. Go to, go to;
  You are a saucy boy: is't so, indeed?
  This trick may chance to scathe you, I know what:
  You must contrary me! marry, 'tis time.
  Well said, my hearts! You are a princox; go: 45
  Be quiet, or— More light, more light! For shame!
  I'll make you quiet. What, cheerly, my hearts!

TYB. Patience perforce with wilful choler meeting
  Makes my flesh tremble in their different greeting.
  I will withdraw: but this intrusion shall,   50
  Now seeming sweet, convert to bitterest gall.   [*Exit.*]

ROM. [*To* JULIET.] If I profane with my unworthiest hand
  This holy shrine, the gentle fine is this,
  My lips, two blushing pilgrims, ready stand
  To smooth that rough touch with a tender kiss.   55

JUL. Good pilgrims, you do wrong your hand too much,
  Which mannerly devotion shows in this;
  For saints have hands that pilgrims' hands do touch,
  And palm to palm is holy palmers' kiss.

ROM. Have not saints lips, and holy palmers too?   60

JUL. Ay, pilgrim, lips that they must use in prayer.

ROM. O, then, dear saint, let lips do what hands do;
  They pray, grant thou, lest faith turn to despair.

JUL. Saints do not move, though grant for prayers' sake.

ROM. Then move not, while my prayer's effect I take.   65
  Thus from my lips by thine my sin is purged.   [*Kissing her.*]

JUL. Then have my lips the sin that they have took.

ROM. Sin from my lips? O trespass sweetly urged!
  Give me my sin again.

JUL.   You kiss by the book.

NURSE. Madam, your mother craves a word with you.   70

ROM. What is her mother?

NURSE.   Marry, bachelor,
  Her mother is the lady of the house,
  And a good lady, and a wise and virtuous:
  I nursed her daughter, that you talk'd withal;
  I tell you, he that can lay hold of her   75
  Shall have the chinks.

ROM.   Is she a Capulet?
  O dear account! my life is my foe's debt.

BEN. Away, be gone; the sport is at the best.

  59. *palmer:* pilgrim.

Rom. Ay, so I fear; the more is my unrest.

Cap. Nay, gentlemen, prepare not to be gone; 　　　80
　　We have a trifling foolish banquet towards,
　　Is it e'en so? why, then, I thank you all;
　　I thank you, honest gentlemen; good night.
　　More torches here! Come on then, let's to bed.
　　Ah, sirrah, by my fay, it waxes late:
　　I'll to my rest. 　　[*Exeunt all but Juliet and Nurse.*] 85

Jul. Come hither, nurse. What is yond gentleman?

Nurse. The son and heir of old Tiberio.

Jul. What's he that now is going out of door?

Nurse. Marry, that, I think, be young Petruchio.

Jul. What's he that follows there, that would not dance? 　90

Nurse. I know not.

Jul. Go ask his name. If he be married,
　　My grave is like to be my wedding bed.

Nurse. His name is Romeo, and a Montague,
　　The only son of your great enemy. 　　95

Jul. My only love sprung from my only hate!
　　Too early seen unknown, and known too late!
　　Prodigious birth of love it is to me,
　　That I must love a loathèd enemy.

Nurse. What's this? what's this?

Jul. 　　　　　　　　A rhyme I learn'd even now 100
　　Of one I danced withal. 　　[*One calls within "Juliet."*]
　　　　　　　　Anon, anon!
　　Come, let's away; the strangers all are gone.

Act II. Scene II

Capulet's orchard.

[*Enter Romeo.*]

Rom. He jests at scars that never felt a wound.
　　　　　　　[Juliet *appears above at a window*.]
　　But, soft! what light through yonder window breaks?
　　It is the east, and Juliet is the sun!
　　Arise, fair sun, and kill the envious moon,
　　Who is already sick and pale with grief, 　　5
　　That thou her maid art far more fair than she:
　　Be not her maid, since she is envious;

Her vestal livery is but sick and green,
And none but fools do wear it; cast it off.
It is my lady; O, it is my love! 10
O, that she knew she were!
She speaks, yet she says nothing: what of that?
Her eye discourses, I will answer it.
I am too bold, 'tis not to me she speaks:
Two of the fairest stars in all the heaven, 15
Having some business, do intreat her eyes
To twinkle in their spheres till they return.
What if her eyes were there, they in her head?
The brightness of her cheek would shame those stars,
As daylight doth a lamp; her eyes in heaven 20
Would through the airy region stream so bright
That birds would sing and think it were not night.
See, how she leans her cheek upon her hand!
O, that I were a glove upon that hand,
That I might touch that cheek!

JUL.   Ay me!

ROM.   She speaks: 25
O, speak again, bright angel! for thou art
As glorious to this night, being o'er my head,
As is a winged messenger of heaven
Unto the white-upturned wondering eyes
Of mortals that fall back to gaze on him, 30
When he bestrides the lazy-pacing clouds
And sails upon the bosom of the air.

JUL. O Romeo, Romeo! wherefore art thou Romeo?
Deny thy father and refuse thy name;
Or, if thou wilt not, be but sworn my love, 35
And I'll no longer be a Capulet.

ROM. [Aside.] Shall I hear more, or shall I speak at this?

JUL. 'Tis but thy name that is my enemy;
Thou art thyself, though not a Montague.
What's Montague? it is nor hand, nor foot, 40
Nor arm, nor face, nor any other part
Belonging to a man. O, be some other name!
What's in a name? That which we call a rose
By any other name would smell as sweet;
So Romeo would, were he not Romeo call'd, 45
Retain that dear perfection which he owes
Without that title. Romeo, doff thy name,

And for thy name, which is no part of thee,
Take all myself.

ROM.   I take thee at thy word:
Call me but love, and I'll be new baptized;   50
Henceforth I never will be Romeo.

JUL. What man art thou, that, thus bescreen'd in night,
So stumblest on my counsel?

ROM.   By a name
I know not how to tell thee who I am:
My name, dear saint, is hateful to myself,   55
Because it is an enemy to thee;
Had I it written, I would tear the word.

JUL. My ears have yet not drunk a hundred words
Of thy tongue's uttering, yet I know the sound:
Art thou not Romeo, and a Montague?   60

ROM. Neither, fair maid, if either thee dislike.

JUL. How camest thou hither, tell me, and wherefore?
The orchard walls are high and hard to climb,
And the place death, considering who thou art,
If any of my kinsmen find thee here.   65

ROM. With love's light wings did I o'er-perch these walls,
For stony limits cannot hold love out:
And what love can do, that dares love attempt;
Therefore thy kinsmen are no let to me.

JUL. If they do see thee, they will murder thee.   70

ROM. Alack, there lies more peril in thine eye
Than twenty of their swords: look thou but sweet,
And I am proof against their enmity.

JUL. I would not for the world they saw thee here.

ROM. I have night's cloak to hide me from their eyes;   75
And but thou love me, let them find me here:
My life were better ended by their hate,
Than death prorogued, wanting of thy love.

JUL. By whose direction found'st thou out this place?

ROM. By love, that first did prompt me to inquire;   80
He lent me counsel, and I lent him eyes.
I am no pilot; yet, wert thou as far
As that vast shore wash'd with the farthest sea,
I would adventure for such merchandise.

JUL. Thou know'st the mask of night is on my face,   85
Else would a maiden blush bepaint my cheek

78. *prorogued:* postponed.

For that which thou hast heard me speak tonight.
Fain would I dwell on form, fain, fain deny
What I have spoke: but farewell compliment!
Dost thou love me? I know thou wilt say "Ay," 90
And I will take thy word: yet, if thou swear'st,
Thou mayst prove false: at lovers' perjuries,
They say, Jove laughs. O gentle Romeo,
If thou dost love, pronounce it faithfully:
Or if thou think'st I am too quickly won, 95
I'll frown and be perverse and say thee nay,
So thou wilt woo; but else, not for the world.
In truth, fair Montague, I am too fond;
And therefore thou mayst think my 'havior light:
But trust me, gentleman, I'll prove more true 100
Than those that have more cunning to be strange.
I should have been more strange, I must confess,
But that thou overheard'st, ere I was ware,
My true love's passion: therefore pardon me,
And not impute this yielding to light love, 105
Which the dark night hath so discovered.

Rom. Lady, by yonder blessed moon I swear,
That tips with silver all these fruit-tree tops,—

Jul. O, swear not by the moon, th' inconstant moon,
That monthly changes in her circled orb, 110
Lest that thy love prove likewise variable.

Rom. What shall I swear by?

Jul.   Do not swear at all;
Or, if thou wilt, swear by thy gracious self,
Which is the god of my idolatry,
And I'll believe thee.

Rom.   If my heart's dear love— 115

Jul. Well, do not swear: although I joy in thee,
I have no joy of this contract tonight:
It is too rash, too unadvised, too sudden,
Too like the lightning, which doth cease to be
Ere one can say "It lightens." Sweet, good night! 120
This bud of love, by summer's ripening breath,
May prove a beauteous flower when next we meet.
Good night, good night! as sweet repose and rest
Come to thy heart as that within my breast!

Rom. O, wilt thou leave me so unsatisfied? 125

92. *perjuries:* false oaths.

Jul. What satisfaction canst thou have tonight?
Rom. The exchange of thy love's faithful vow for mine.
Jul. I gave thee mine before thou didst request it:
    And yet I would it were to give again.
Rom. Wouldst thou withdraw it? for what purpose, love?   130
Jul. But to be frank, and give it thee again.
    And yet I wish but for the thing I have:
    My bounty is as boundless as the sea,
    My love as deep; the more I give to thee,
    The more I have, for both are infinite.   135
    I hear some noise within; dear love, adieu!

                         [*Nurse calls within.*]

    Anon, good nurse! Sweet Montague, be true.
    Stay but a little, I will come again.   [*Exit.*]
Rom. O blessed, blessed night! I am afeard,
    Being in night, all this is but a dream,
    Too flattering-sweet to be substantial.

             [*Re-enter* Juliet, *above.*]

Jul. Three words, dear Romeo, and good night indeed.
    If that thy bent of love be honorable,
    Thy purpose marriage, send me word tomorrow,
    By one that I'll procure to come to thee,   145
    Where and what time thou wilt perform the rite,
    And all my fortunes at thy foot I'll lay,
    And follow thee my lord throughout the world.
Nurse. [*Within.*] Madam!
Jul. I come, anon.—But if thou mean'st not well,
    I do beseech thee—
Nurse. [*Within.*] Madam!
Jul.   By and bye, I come:—   150
    To cease thy suit, and leave me to my grief:
    Tomorrow will I send.
Rom.   So thrive my soul,—
Jul. A thousand times good night!   [*Exit.*]
Rom. A thousand times the worse, to want thy light.

                        [*Retiring slowly.*]

             [*Re-enter* Juliet, *above.*]

Jul. Hist! Romeo, hist!
Rom. It is my soul that calls upon my name: 155
    How silver-sweet sound lovers' tongues by night,
    Like softest music to attending ears!

JUL. Romeo!

ROM.   My dear?

JUL.   At what o'clock tomorrow
  Shall I send to thee?

ROM.   At the hour of nine.

JUL. I will not fail: 'tis twenty years till then.   160
  I have forgot why I did call thee back.

ROM. Let me stand here till thou remember it.

JUL. I shall forget, to have thee still stand there,
  Remembering how I love thy company.

ROM. And I'll still stay, to have thee still forget,   165
  Forgetting any other home but this.

JUL. 'Tis almost morning; I would have thee gone:
  And yet no farther than a wanton's bird,
  Who lets it hop a little from her hand,
  Like a poor prisoner in his twisted gyves,   170
  And with a silk thread plucks it back again,
  So loving-jealous of his liberty.

ROM. I would I were thy bird.

JUL.   Sweet, so would I:
  Yet I should kill thee with much cherishing.
  Good night, good night! parting is such sweet sorrow 175
  That I shall say good night till it be morrow.   [*Exit.*]

ROM. Sleep dwell upon thine eyes, peace in thy breast!
  Would I were sleep and peace, so sweet to rest!

(The next day JULIET sends her old nurse, who still acts as her
maid and companion, to sound ROMEO's intentions.)

SCENE V

CAPULET's *orchard.*

JUL. The clock struck nine when I did send the nurse;
  In half an hour she promised to return.
  Perchance she cannot meet him: that's not so.
  O, she is lame! love's heralds should be thoughts,
  Which ten times faster glide than the sun's beams,   5
  Driving back shadows over louring hills:
  Therefore do nimble-pinion'd doves draw love,

170. *gyves:* fetters.
7. *doves:* The car of Venus, goddess of love, was drawn by doves.

And therefore hath the wind-swift Cupid wings.
Now is the sun upon the highmost hill
Of this day's journey, and from nine till twelve   10
Is three long hours; yet she is not come.
Had she affections and warm youthful blood,
She would be as swift in motion as a ball;
My words would bandy her to my sweet love,
And his to me: 15
But old folks, many feign as they were dead;
Unwieldly, slow, heavy and pale as lead.

[*Enter* NURSE, *with* PETER.]

O God, she comes! O honey nurse, what news?
Hast thou met with him? Send thy man away.

NURSE. Peter, stay at the gate.   [*Exit* PETER.] 20

JUL. Now, good sweet nurse,— O Lord, why look'st thou sad?
Though news be sad, yet tell them merrily;
If good, thou shamest the music of sweet news
By playing it to me with so sour a face.

NURSE. I am a-weary; give me leave a while.
Fie, how my bones ache! what a jaunce have I had!   25

JUL. I would thou hadst my bones and I thy news:
Nay, come, I pray thee, speak; good, good nurse, speak.

NURSE. Jesu, what haste? can you not stay a while?
Do you not see that I am out of breath?   30

JUL. How art thou out of breath, when thou hast breath
To say to me that thou art out of breath?
The excuse that thou dost make in this delay
Is longer than the tale thou dost excuse.
Is thy news good, or bad? answer to that;   35
Say either, and I'll stay the circumstance:
Let me be satisfied, is't good or bad?

NURSE. Well, you have made a simple choice; you know not
how to choose a man: Romeo! no, not he; though his face
be better than any man's, yet his leg excels all men's; and 40
for a hand, and a foot, and a body, though they be not to be
talked on, yet they are past compare: he is not the flower
of courtesy, but, I'll warrant him, as gentle as a lamb. Go
thy ways, wench; serve God. What, have you dined at
home?   45

JUL. No, no, but all this did I know before.
What says he of our marriage? what of that?

8. *Cupid:* god of love.   26. *jaunce:* jaunt.

Nurse. Lord, how my head aches! what a head have I!
 It beats as it would fall in twenty pieces.
 My back o' t' other side,—ah, my back, my back!
 Beshrew your heart for sending me about,   50
 To catch my death with jauncing up and down!
Jul. I' faith, I am sorry that thou art not well.
 Sweet, sweet, sweet nurse, tell me, what says my love?
Nurse. Your love says, like an honest gentleman, and a courte-
 ous, and a kind, and a handsome, and, I warrant, a vir-
 tuous,—Where is your mother?   55
Jul. Where is my mother! why, she is within;
 Where should she be? How oddly thou repliest!
 "Your love says, like an honest gentleman,
 Where is your mother?"
Nurse.   O God's lady dear!   60
 Are you so hot? marry, come up, I trow;
 Is this the poultice for my aching bones?
 Henceforward do your messages yourself.
Jul. Here's such a coil! come, what says Romeo?
Nurse. Have you got leave to go to shrift today?   65
Jul. I have.
Nurse. Then hie you hence to Friar Laurence's cell;
 There stays a husband to make you a wife:
 Now comes the wanton blood up in your cheeks,
 They'll be in scarlet straight at any news.   70
 Hie you to church; I must another way,
 To fetch a ladder, by the which your love
 Must climb a bird's nest soon when it is dark;
 I am the drudge, and toil in your delight.
 Go; I'll to dinner; hie you to the cell.   75
Jul. Hie to high fortune! Honest nurse, farewell.   [*Exeunt.*]

(Romeo and Juliet are secretly wedded by Friar Laurence.)

Act III, Scene I

A public place.

[*Enter* Mercutio, Benvolio, *Page, and Servants.*]

Ben. I pray thee, good Mercutio, let's retire:
 The day is hot, the Capulets abroad,

And, if we meet, we shall not 'scape a brawl;
For now these hot days is the mad blood stirring.

MER. Thou art like one of those fellows that when he enters the ⁵
confines of a tavern claps me his sword upon the table, and
says "God send me no need of thee!" and by the operation
of the second cup draws it on the drawer, when indeed
there is no need.

BEN. Am I like such a fellow? ¹⁰

MER. Come, come, thou art as hot a Jack in thy mood as any
in Italy, and as soon moved to be moody, and as soon
moody to be moved.

BEN. And what to?

MER. Nay, an there were two such, we should have none ¹⁵
shortly, for one would kill the other. Thou! why, thou wilt
quarrel with a man that hath a hair more, or a hair less, in
his beard than thou hast: thou wilt quarrel with a man
for cracking nuts, having no other reason but because thou
hast hazel eyes; what eye, but such an eye, would spy ²⁰
out such a quarrel? thy head is as full of quarrels as an
egg is full of meat, and yet thy head hath been beaten as
addle as an egg for quarrelling: thou hast quarrelled with
a man for coughing in the street, because he hath wakened
thy dog that hath lain asleep in the sun: did'st thou not ²⁵
fall out with a tailor for wearing his new doublet before
Easter? with another, for tying his new shoes with old
riband? and yet thou wilt tutor me from quarrelling!

BEN. An I were so apt to quarrel as thou art, any man should
buy the fee-simple of my life for an hour and a quarter. ³⁰

MER. The fee-simple! O simple!

[*Enter* TYBALT *and others.*]

BEN. By my head, here comes the Capulets.

MER. By my heel, I care not.

TYB. Follow me close, for I will speak to them.
Gentlemen, good den: a word with one of you. ³⁵

MER. And but one word with one of us? couple it with something; make it a word and a blow.

TYB. You shall find me apt enough to that, sir, and you will
give me occasion.

MER. Could you not take some occasion without giving? ⁴⁰

TYB. Mercutio, thou consort'st with Romeo,—

30. *fee-simple:* ownership.

MER. Consort! what, dost thou make us minstrels? an thou
    make minstrels of us, look to hear nothing but discords:
    here's my fiddlestick; here's that shall make you dance.
    'Zounds, consort!   45

BEN. We talk here in the public haunt of men:
    Either withdraw into some private place,
    Or reason coldly of your grievances,
    Or else depart; here all eyes gaze on us.

MER. Men's eyes were made to look, and let them gaze;   50
    I will not budge for no man's pleasure, I.

[Enter ROMEO.]

TYB. Well, peace be with you, sir: here comes my man.

MER. But I'll be hang'd, sir, if he wear your livery:
    Marry, go before to field, he'll be your follower;
    Your worship in that sense may call him man.   55

TYB. Romeo, the love I bear thee can afford
    No better term than this,—thou art a villain.

ROM. Tybalt, the reason that I have to love thee
    Doth much excuse the appertaining rage
    To such a greeting: villain am I none;   60
    Therefore farewell; I see thou know'st me not.

TYB. Boy, this shall not excuse the injuries
    That thou hast done me; therefore turn and draw.

ROM. I do protest, I never injured thee,
    But love thee better than thou canst devise   65
    Till thou shalt know the reason of my love:
    And so, good Capulet,—which name I tender
    As dearly as mine own,—be satisfied.

MER. O calm, dishonorable, vile submission!   70
    Alla stoccata carries it away.   *[Draws.]*
    Tybalt, you rat-catcher, will you walk?

TYB. What wouldst thou have with me?

MER. Good king of cats, nothing but one of your nine lives,
    that I mean to make bold withal, and, as you shall use me   75
    hereafter, dry-beat the rest of the eight. Will you pluck
    your sword out of his pilcher by the ears? make haste, lest
    mine be about your ears ere it be out.

TYB. I am for you.   *[Drawing.]*

ROM. Gentle Mercutio, put thy rapier up.   80

MER. Come, sir, your passado.   *[They fight.]*

Rom. Draw, Benvolio; beat down their weapons.
　　　Gentlemen, for shame, forbear this outrage!
　　　Tybalt, Mercutio, the prince expressly hath
　　　Forbid this bandying in Verona streets:　　　　　85
　　　Hold, Tybalt! good Mercutio!

　　　[Tybalt *under* Romeo's *arm stabs* Mercutio *and flies
　　　　with his followers.*]

Mer.　　　　　　　　　　　　　I am hurt;
　　　A plague o' both your houses! I am sped:
　　　Is he gone, and hath nothing?

Ben.　　　　　　　　　　　What, art thou hurt?

Mer. Ay, ay, a scratch, a scratch, marry, 'tis enough.
　　　Where is my page? Go, villain, fetch a surgeon.　90

　　　　　　　　　　　　　　　　　[*Exit* Page.]

Rom. Courage, man; the hurt cannot be much.

Mer. No, 'tis not so deep as a well, nor so wide as a church-
　　　door; but 'tis enough, 'twill serve: ask for me tomorrow,
　　　and you shall find me a grave man. I am peppered, I
　　　warrant, for this world. A plague o' both your houses!　96
　　　'Zounds, a dog, a rat, a mouse, a cat, to scratch a man to
　　　death! a braggart, a rogue, a villain, that fights by the book
　　　of arithmetic! Why the devil came you between us? I
　　　was hurt under your arm.

Rom. I thought all for the best.　　　　　　　　　100

Mer. Help me into some house, Benvolio,
　　　Or I shall faint. A plague o' both your houses!
　　　They have made worms' meat of me: I have it,
　　　And soundly, too: your houses!

　　　　　　　　　[*Exeunt* Mercutio *and* Benvolio.]

Rom. This gentleman, the prince's ally,　　　　　105
　　　My very friend, hath got this mortal hurt
　　　In my behalf; my reputation stain'd
　　　With Tybalt's slander,—Tybalt, that an hour
　　　Hath been my kinsman: O sweet Juliet,
　　　Thy beauty hath made me effeminate,　　　　　110
　　　And in my temper soften'd valour's steel.

　　　　　　　　　　[*Re-enter* Benvolio.]

Ben. O Romeo, Romeo, brave Mercutio's dead!
　　　That gallant spirit hath aspired the clouds,
　　　Which too untimely here did scorn the earth.

Rom. This day's black fate on more days doth depend;　115
　　　This but begins the woe others must end.

[Re-enter TYBALT.]

BEN. Here comes the furious Tybalt back again.

ROM. Alive, in triumph! and Mercutio slain.
Away to heaven, respective lenity,
And fire-eyed fury be my conduct now! 120
Now, Tybalt, take the "villain" back again
That late thou gavest me; for Mercutio's soul
Is but a little way above our heads,
Staying for thine to keep him company:
Either thou, or I, or both, must go with him. 125

TYB. Thou, wretched boy, that didst consort him here.
Shalt with him hence.

ROM.   This shall determine that.

[They fight; TYBALT *falls.]*

BEN. Romeo, away, be gone!
The citizens are up, and Tybalt slain:
Stand not amazed: the prince will doom thee death 130
If thou art taken: hence, be gone, away!

ROM. O, I am fortune's fool!

BEN.   Why dost thou stay? *[Exit* ROMEO.]

[Enter CITIZENS.]

FIRST CIT. Which way ran he that kill'd Mercutio?
Tybalt, that murderer, which way ran he?

BEN. There lies that Tybalt.

FIRST CIT.   Up, sir, go with me; 135
I charge thee in the prince's name, obey.

[Enter PRINCE, *attended;* MONTAGUE, CAPULET, *their
Wives, and others.]*

PRIN. Where are the vile beginners of this fray?

BEN. O noble prince, I can discover all
The unlucky manage of this fatal brawl:
There lies the man, slain by young Romeo, 140
That slew thy kinsman, brave Mercutio.

LA. CAP. Tybalt, my cousin! O my brother's child!
O prince! O cousin! husband! O, the blood is spilt
Of my dear kinsman! Prince, as thou art true,
For blood of ours, shed blood of Montague. 145
O cousin, cousin!

PRIN. Benvolio, who began this bloody fray?

BEN. Tybalt, here slain, whom Romeo's hand did slay,
    Romeo that spoke him fair, bid him bethink
    How nice the quarrel was, and urged withal
    Your high displeasure: all this uttered   150
    With gentle breath, calm look, knees humbly bow'd,
    Could not take truce with the unruly spleen
    Of Tybalt deaf to peace, but that he tilts
    With piercing steel at bold Mercutio's breast;
    Who, all as hot, turns deadly point to point,   155
    And, with a martial scorn, with one hand beats
    Cold death aside, and with the other sends
    It back to Tybalt, whose dexterity
    Retorts it: Romeo he cries aloud,
    "Hold, friends! friends, part!" and, swifter than his tongue, 160
    His agile arm beats down their fatal points,
    And 'twixt them rushes; underneath whose arm
    An envious thrust from Tybalt hit the life
    Of stout Mercutio, and then Tybalt fled:
    But by and by comes back to Romeo,   165
    Who had but newly entertain'd revenge,
    And to 't they go like lightning: for, ere I
    Could draw to part them, was stout Tybalt slain;
    And, as he fell, did Romeo turn and fly;
    This is the truth, or let Benvolio die.   170
LA. CAP. He is a kinsman to the Montague,
    Affection makes him false, he speaks not true:
    Some twenty of them fought in this black strife,
    And all those twenty could but kill one life.
    I beg for justice, which thou, prince, must give;   175
    Romeo slew Tybalt, Romeo must not live.
PRIN. Romeo slew him, he slew Mercutio;
    Who now the price of his dear blood doth owe?
MON. Not Romeo, prince, he was Mercutio's friend;
    His fault concludes but what the law should end,   180
    The life of Tybalt.
PRIN.   And for that offence
    Immediately we do exile him hence:
    I have an interest in your hate's proceeding,
    My blood for your rude brawls doth lie a-bleeding,
    But I'll amerce you with so strong a fine,   185
    That you shall all repent the loss of mine:

185. *amerce:* punish.

I will be deaf to pleading and excuses;
Nor tears nor prayers shall purchase out abuses:
Therefore use none: let Romeo hence in haste,
Else, when he's found, that hour is his last. 190
Bear hence this body, and attend our will:
Mercy but murders, pardoning those that kill. [*Exeunt.*]

SCENE II

CAPULET'S *orchard.*

[*Enter* JULIET.]

JUL. Gallop apace, you fiery-footed steeds,
Towards Phœbus' lodging: such a wagoner
As Phaethon would whip you to the west,
And bring in cloudy night immediately.
Spread thy close curtain, love-performing night, 5
That runaways' eyes may wink, and Romeo
Leap to these arms, untalk'd of and unseen.
Come, night, come, Romeo, come, thou day in night;
For thou wilt lie upon the wings of night
Whiter than new snow on a raven's back. 10
Come, gentle night, come, loving, black-brow'd night,
Give me my Romeo; and, when he shall die,
Take him and cut him out in little stars,
And he will make the face of heaven so fine,
That all the world will be in love with night, 15
And pay no worship to the garish sun.
O, I have bought the mansion of a love,
But not possess'd it, and tedious is this day
As is the night before some festival
To an impatient child that hath new robes 20
And may not wear them. O, here comes my nurse,
And she brings news, and every tongue that speaks
But Romeo's name speaks heavenly eloquence.

(At this moment the nurse arrives bringing the rope ladder by
which Romeo was to have climbed that night to Juliet's balcony room.
She brings also the news of Tybalt's death at Romeo's hand and of
Romeo's banishment. Juliet is distracted with grief.)

2-3. *Phœbus* is the sun-god, whose son, *Phœthon*, once drove his father's fiery
chariot with reckless speed.

SCENE III

Friar Laurence's cell.

[*Enter* FRIAR LAURENCE.]

FRI. L. Romeo, come forth; come forth, thou fearful man:
　　　Affliction is enamor'd of thy parts,
　　　And thou art wedded to calamity.

[*Enter* ROMEO.]

ROM. Father, what news? what is the prince's doom?
　　　What sorrow craves acquaintance at my hand,　　　5
　　　That I yet know not?
FRI. L. 　　　　　　　　Too familiar
　　　Is my dear son with such sour company:
　　　I bring thee tidings of the prince's doom.
ROM. What less than dooms-day is the prince's doom?
FRI. L. A gentler judgment vanish'd from his lips,　　　10
　　　Not body's death, but body's banishment.
ROM. Ha, banishment! be merciful, say "death;"
　　　For exile hath more terror in his look,
　　　Much more than death: do not say "banishment."
FRI. L. Here from Verona art thou banishèd:　　　15
　　　Be patient, for the world is broad and wide.
ROM. There is no world without Verona walls,
　　　But purgatory, torture, hell itself.
　　　Hence banishèd is banish'd from the world,
　　　And world's exile is death: then "banishèd"　　　20
　　　Is death mis-term'd: calling death "banishèd"
　　　Thou cut'st my head off with a golden axe,
　　　And smilest upon the stroke that murders me.
FRI. L. O deadly sin! O rude unthankfulness!
　　　Thy fault our law calls death; but the kind prince,　　　25
　　　Taking thy part, hath brush'd aside the law,
　　　And turned that black word death to banishment.
　　　This is dear mercy, and thou seest it not.
ROM. 'Tis torture, and not mercy: heaven is here,
　　　Where Juliet lives; and every cat and dog　　　30
　　　And little mouse, every unworthy thing,
　　　Live here in heaven and may look on her,

But Romeo may not. More validity,
More honorable state, more courtship lives
In carrion-flies than Romeo. They may seize 35
On the white wonder of dear Juliet's hand,
And steal immortal blessing from her lips;
Who, even in pure and vestal modesty,
Still blush, as thinking their own kisses sin;
But Romeo may not; he is banishèd. 40
This may flies do, but I from this must fly;
They are free men, but I am banishèd;
And say'st thou yet, that exile is not death?
Hadst thou no poison mix'd, no sharp-ground knife,
No sudden mean of death, though ne'er so mean, 45
But "banishèd" to kill me?—"Banishèd"?
O friar, the damned use that word in hell;
Howling attends it: how hast thou the heart,
Being a divine, a ghostly confessor,
A sin-absolver, and my friend profess'd, 50
To mangle me with that word "banishèd"?

FRI. L. Thou fond mad man, hear me but speak a word.

ROM. O, thou wilt speak again of banishment.

FRI. L. I'll give thee armour to keep off that word;
Adversity's sweet milk, philosophy, 55
To comfort thee, though thou art banishèd.

ROM. Yet "banishèd"? Hang up philosophy!
Unless philosophy can make a Juliet,
Displant a town, reverse a prince's doom,
It helps not, it prevails not: talk no more. 60

FRI. L. O, then I see that madmen have no ears.

ROM. How should they, when that wise men have no eyes?

FRI. L. Let me dispute with thee of thy estate.

ROM. Thou can'st not speak of that thou dost not feel:
Wert thou as young as I, Juliet thy love, 65
An hour but married, Tybalt murdered,
Doting like me, and like me banishèd,
Then mightst thou speak, then mightst thou tear thy hair,
And fall upon the ground, as I do now,
Taking the measure of an unmade grave. 70

[*Drawing his sword.*]

FRI. L. Hold thy desperate hand:
Art thou a man? thy form cries out thou art:
Thy tears are womanish; thy wild acts denote

The unreasonable fury of a beast:
Unseemly woman in a seeming man!   75
Or ill-beseeming beast in seeming both!
Thou hast amazed me. By my holy order,
I thought thy disposition better temper'd.
Hast thou slain Tybalt? wilt thou slay thyself?
And slay thy lady that in thy life lives,   80
By doing damnèd hate upon thyself?
What, rouse thee, man! thy Juliet is alive,
For whose dear sake thou wast but lately dead;
There art thou happy. Tybalt would kill thee,
But thou slew'st Tybalt; there art thou happy too.   85
The law, that threaten'd death, becomes thy friend,
And turns it to exile; there art thou happy.
A pack of blessings lights upon thy back;
Happiness courts thee in her best array;
But, like a misbehaved and sullen wench,   90
Thou pout'st upon thy fortune and thy love.
Take heed, take heed, for such die miserable.
Go, get thee to thy love, as was decreed,
Ascend her chamber, hence and comfort her;
But look thou stay not till the watch be set,   95
For then thou canst not pass to Mantua,
Where thou shalt live till we can find a time
To blaze your marriage, reconcile your friends,
Beg pardon of the prince, and call thee back
With twenty hundred thousand times more joy   100
Than thou went'st forth in lamentation.

Scene V

Capulet's *orchard*.

[*Enter* Romeo *and* Juliet, *above, at the Window.*]

Jul. Wilt thou be gone? It is not yet near day:
    It was the nightingale, and not the lark,
    That pierced the fearful hollow of thine ear;
    Nightly she sings on yond pomegranate-tree:
    Believe me, love, it was the nightingale.   5
Rom. It was the lark, the herald of the morn,
    No nightingale: look, love, what envious streaks

Do lace the severing clouds in yonder east:
Night's candles are burnt out, and jocund day
Stands tiptoe on the misty mountain tops: 10
I must be gone and live, or stay and die.

JUL. Yond light is not day-light, I know it, I:
It is some meteor that the sun exhales,
To be to thee this night a torch-bearer,
And light thee on thy way to Mantua: 15
Therefore stay yet; thou need'st not to be gone.

ROM. Let me be ta'en, let me be put to death;
I am content, so thou wilt have it so.
I'll say yon grey is not the morning's eye,
'Tis but the pale reflex of Cynthia's brow; 20
Nor that is not the lark, whose notes do beat
The vaulty heaven so high above our heads.
I have more care to stay than will to go:
Come, death, and welcome! Juliet wills it so.
How is 't, my soul? let's talk: it is not day. 25

JUL. It is, it is: hie hence, be gone, away!
It is the lark that sings so out of tune,
Straining harsh discords and unpleasing sharps.
Some say the lark makes sweet division;
This doth not so, for she divideth us. 30
O, now be gone; more light and light it grows.

ROM. More light and light: more dark and dark our woes!

[Enter NURSE, *to the chamber.]*

NURSE. Madam!

JUL. Nurse?

NURSE. Your lady mother is coming to your chamber: 35
The day is broke; be wary, look about. *[Exit.]*

JUL. Then, window, let day in, and let life out.

ROM. Farewell, farewell! one kiss, and I'll descend. *[Descends.]*

JUL. Art thou gone so? my lord, my love, my friend!
I must hear from thee every day in the hour, 40
For in a minute there are many days:
O, by this count I shall be much in years
Ere I again behold my Romeo!

ROM. Farewell!
I will omit no opportunity 45
That may convey my greetings, love, to thee.

20. *Cynthia's:* the moon's.

JUL. O, think'st thou we shall ever meet again?
ROM. I doubt it not; and all these woes shall serve
    For sweet discourses in our time to come.
JUL. O God! I have an ill-divining soul.   60
    Methinks I see thee, now thou art below,
    As one dead in the bottom of a tomb:
    Either my eyesight fails or thou look'st pale.
ROM. And trust me, love, in my eye so do you:
    Dry sorrow drinks our blood. Adieu, adieu!   55

(Juliet weeps so violently—her family supposing it to be over
Tybalt's death—that her father decides to check her grief by marrying her at once to a very desirable suitor, Count Paris. She pleads
at least for time, but her father is inexorable. She flies to Friar
Laurence for advice, and seeing she is ready to kill herself to avoid
this marriage, he gives her a potion which will throw her into a death-
like trance for two days. He tells her that when she awakens in the
Capulet vault, he and Romeo will be at her side to carry her away
to Mantua, where Romeo has gone into exile. Juliet then appears to
consent to her father's demand, and preparations for the marriage
go forward.)

ACT IV. SCENE III

JULIET'S *Chamber.*

[*Enter* JULIET *and* NURSE.]

JUL. Ay, those attires are best: but, gentle nurse,
    I pray thee, leave me to myself tonight;
    For I have need of many orisons
    To move the heavens to smile upon my state,
    Which, well thou know'st, is cross and full of sin.   5

[*Enter* LADY CAPULET.]

LA. CAP. What, are you busy, ho? need you my help?
JUL. No, madam; we have cull'd such necessaries
    As are behoveful for our state tomorrow:
    So please you, let me now be left alone,
    And let the nurse this night sit up with you,   10
    For I am sure you have your hands full all
    In this so sudden business.

LA. CAP.   Good night!
> Get thee to bed and rest, for thou hast need.
>> *[Exeunt* LADY CAPULET *and* NURSE.]

JUL. Farewell! God knows when we shall meet again.
> I have a faint cold fear thrills through my veins,   15
> That almost freezes up the heat of life:
> I'll call them back again to comfort me.
> Nurse!—What should she do here?
> My dismal scene I needs must act alone.
> Come, vial.   20
> What if this mixture do not work at all?
> Shall I be married then tomorrow morning?
> No, no: this shall forbid it. Lie thou there.
>> *[Laying down a dagger.]*
> What if it be a poison, which the friar
> Subtly hath minister'd to have me dead,   25
> Lest in this marriage he should be dishonor'd,
> Because he married me before to Romeo?
> I fear it is: and yet, methinks, it should not,
> For he hath still been tried a holy man.
> How if, when I am laid into the tomb,   30
> I wake before the time that Romeo
> Come to redeem me? there's a fearful point.
> Shall I not then be stifled in the vault,
> To whose foul mouth no healthsome air breathes in,
> And there die strangled ere my Romeo comes?   35
> Or, if I live, is it not very like,
> The horrible conceit of death and night,
> Together with the terror of the place,
> As in a vault, an ancient receptacle,
> Where for this many hundred years the bones   40
> Of all my buried ancestors are pack'd;
> Where bloody Tybalt, yet but green in earth,
> Lies festering in his shroud; where, as they say,
> At some hours in the night spirits resort;
> Alack, alack, is it not like that I   45
> So early waking, what with loathsome smells
> And shrieks like mandrakes' torn out of the earth,
> That living mortals hearing them run mad:
> O, if I wake, shall I not be distraught,
> Environed with all these hideous fears?   50
> And madly play with my forefathers' joints?

And pluck the mangled Tybalt from his shroud?
And, in this rage, with some great kinsman's bone,
As with a club, dash out my desperate brains?
O, look! methinks I see my cousin's ghost   55
Seeking out Romeo, that did spit his body
Upon a rapier's point: stay, Tybalt, stay!
Romeo, I come! this do I drink to thee.

[She falls upon her bed, within the curtains.]

Scene V

Juliet's chamber.

[Enter Nurse.]

Nurse. Mistress! what, mistress! Juliet! fast, I warrant her, she.
Why, lamb! why, lady! fie, you slug-a-bed!
Why, love, I say! madam! sweet-heart! why, bride!
What, not a word? you take your pennyworths now:
Sleep for a week; God forgive me,
Marry, and amen, how sound is she asleep!   5
I needs must wake her. Madam, madam, madam!
Ay, let the county take you in your bed;
He'll fright you up, i' faith. Will it not be?

[Undraws the curtains.]
What, dress'd! and in your clothes! and down again!   10
I must needs wake you. Lady! lady! lady!
Alas, alas! Help, help! my lady's dead!
O, well-a-day, that ever I was born!
Some aqua-vitæ, ho! My lord! my lady!

(All goes as the Friar planned, except that his messenger to Romeo
is detained on the way and never reaches Romeo. Romeo, however,
hears from a trusty servant that Juliet is dead and buried. Romeo
buys poison from an apothecary and sets out for Verona, saying,
"Juliet, I will lie with thee tonight.")

Act V, Scene III

A churchyard; in it a monument belonging to the Capulets.

[Enter Romeo and Balthasar, with a torch, mattock, &c.]

Rom. Give me that mattock and the wrenching iron.
Hold, take this letter; early in the morning

See thou deliver it to my lord and father.
Give me the light: upon thy life, I charge thee,
Whate'er thou hear'st or seest, stand all aloof, 5
And do not interrupt me in my course.
Why I descend into this bed of death
Is partly to behold my lady's face,
But chiefly to take thence from her dead finger
A precious ring, a ring that I must use
In dear employment: therefore hence, be gone:
But if thou, jealous, dost return to pry
In what I farther shall intend to do,
By heaven, I will tear thee joint by joint
And strew this hungry churchyard with thy limbs:
The time and my intents are savage-wild, 15
More fierce and more inexorable by far
Than empty tigers or the roaring sea.

BAL. I will be gone, sir, and not trouble you.

ROM. So shalt thou show me friendship. Take thou that:
Live, and be prosperous: and farewell, good fellow. 20

BAL. [*Aside.*] For all this same, I'll hide me hereabout:
His looks I fear, and his intents I doubt. [*Retires.*]

ROM. Thou detestable maw, thou womb of death,
Gorged with the dearest morsel of the earth,
Thus I enforce thy rotten jaws to open, 25
And in despite I'll cram thee with more food.
[*Opens the tomb.*]

(At this point PARIS comes to lay flowers on JULIET's Tomb.)

PAR. This is that banish'd haughty Montague
That murder'd my love's cousin, with which grief,
It is supposed, the fair creature died,
And here is come to do some villainous shame 30
To the dead bodies: I will apprehend him. [*Comes forward.*]
Stop thy unhallow'd toil, vile Montague!
Can vengeance be pursued further than death?
Condemned villain, I do apprehend thee:
Obey, and go with me; for thou must die. 35

ROM. I must indeed, and therefore came I hither.
Good gentle youth, tempt not a desperate man;
Fly hence and leave me: think upon these gone;
Let them affright thee. I beseech thee, youth,
Put not another sin upon my head, 40
By urging me to fury: O, be gone!

By heaven, I love thee better than myself,
For I come hither arm'd against myself:
Stay not, be gone: live, and hereafter say,
A madman's mercy bid thee run away.

PAR. I do defy thy conjurations   45
And apprehend thee for a felon here.

ROM. Wilt thou provoke me? then have at thee, boy!

                                                    [*They fight.*]

PAGE. O Lord, they fight! I will go call the watch.   [*Exit.*]

PAR. O, I am slain! [*Falls.*] If thou be merciful,   50
Open the tomb, lay me with Juliet.
                                                          [*Dies.*]

ROM. In faith, I will. Let me peruse this face:
Mercutio's kinsman, noble County Paris!
What said my man, when my betossed soul
Did not attend him as we rode? I think
He told me Paris should have married Juliet: 55
Said he not so? or did I dream it so?
Or am I mad, hearing him talk of Juliet,
To think it was so? O, give me thy hand,
One writ with me in sour misfortune's book!
I'll bury thee in a triumphant grave;   60
A grave? O, no, a lantern, slaughter'd youth;
For here lies Juliet, and her beauty makes
This vault a feasting presence full of light.
Death, lie thou there, by a dead man interr'd.   65

                    [*Laying* PARIS *in the monument.*]

O my love! my wife!
Death, that hath suck'd the honey of thy breath,
Hath had no power yet upon thy beauty:
Thou art not conquer'd; beauty's ensign yet
Is crimson in thy lips and in thy cheeks,
And death's pale flag is not advanced there.   70
Tybalt, liest thou there in thy bloody sheet?
O, what more favor can I do to thee
Than with that hand that cut thy youth in twain
To sunder his that was thine enemy?
Forgive me, cousin! Ah, dear Juliet,   75
Why art thou yet so fair? shall I believe
That unsubstantial death is amorous,
And that the lean abhorred monster keeps
Thee here in dark to be his paramour?
For fear of that, I still will stay with thee,   80
And never from this palace of dim night

Depart again: here, here will I remain
With worms that are thy chamber-maids; O, here
Will I set up my everlasting rest,   85
And shake the yoke of inauspicious stars
From this world-wearied flesh. Eyes, look your last!
Arms, take your last embrace! and, lips, O you
The doors of breath, seal with a righteous kiss
A dateless bargain to engrossing death!   90
Come, bitter conduct, come, unsavory guide!
Thou desperate pilot, now at once run on
The dashing rocks thy sea-sick weary bark.
Here's to my love! [*Drinks.*] O true apothecary!
Thy drugs are quick. Thus with a kiss I die.   95
        [*Dies.*]

(Meanwhile, Friar Laurence has heard that his messenger missed
Romeo, and he goes to the cemetery to open the Capulet vault and
be with Juliet when she wakes. He has just discovered Romeo's
body as Juliet opens her eyes.)

JUL. O comfortable friar! where is my lord?
    I do remember well where I should be,
    And there I am: where is my Romeo?   [*Noise within.*]
FRI. L. I hear some noise. Lady, come from that nest
    Of death, contagion and unnatural sleep: 100
    A greater power than we can contradict
    Hath thwarted our intents: come, come away:
    Thy husband in thy bosom there lies dead;
    And Paris too: come, I'll dispose of thee
    Among a sisterhood of holy nuns: 105
    Stay not to question, for the watch is coming;
    Come, go, good Juliet; I dare no longer stay.
JUL. Go, get thee hence, for I will not away.   [*Exit* FRI. L.]
    What's here? a cup, closed in my true love's hand?
    Poison, I see, hath been his timeless end: 110
    O churl! drunk all, and left no friendly drop
    To help me after? I will kiss thy lips;
    Haply some poison yet doth hang on them,
    To make me die with a restorative.   [*Kisses him.*]
    Thy lips are warm.   115
FIRST WATCH. [*Within.*] Lead, boy: which way?
JUL. Yea, noise? then I'll be brief. O happy dagger!
        [*Snatching* ROMEO's *dagger.*]

This is thy sheath [*Stabs herself*] ; there rust, and let me die.
[*Falls on* ROMEO's *body, and dies.*]

(Meanwhile the servant of Paris has raised the night watch, and the rumor noised through the town brings both the Montagues and the Capulets, together with the Prince of Verona and a throng of attendants, to the tomb. From Friar Laurence they hear the story of the lovers.)

PRIN. Capulet! Montague!
    See, what a scourge is laid upon your hate,
    That heaven finds means to kill your joys with love!   120
    And I, for winking at your discords too,
    Have lost a brace of kinsmen: all are punish'd.
CAP. O brother Montague, give me thy hand:
    This is my daughter's jointure, for no more
    Can I demand.
MON.   But I can give thee more: 125
    For I will raise her statue in pure gold;
    That whiles Verona by that name is known,
    There shall no figure at such rate be set
    As that of true and faithful Juliet.
CAP. As rich shall Romeo's by his lady's lie;   130
    Poor sacrifices of our enmity!
PRIN. A glooming peace this morning with it brings;
    The sun for sorrow will not show his head:
    Go hence, to have more talk of these sad things;
    Some shall be pardon'd and some punished: 135
    For never was a story of more woe
    Than this of Juliet and her Romeo.

ALCESTIS

EURIPIDES (GREECE)

Translated by Gilbert Murray

Ancient Greece produced the greatest dramatic literature of any nation except the English. The center of the Greek drama was in Athens where the works of Aeschylus, Sophocles, Euripedes, and Meleager (the tragic dramatists) and of Aristophanes (the witty writer of comedies) were enacted during semiannual religious festivals in a civic open-air theater. The actors were all men and wore masks—either comic or tragic, according to the play—in which was concealed a sort of amplifier to carry the voice to the vast assemblage of citizens which crowded the amphitheater.

A Greek drama differed from a modern play in several ways. The subject was likely to be legendary or historical and brought out some great lesson of religious or civic importance. When the characters had become so involved in difficulty that escape seemed well-nigh impossible, a god or demi-god often appeared to rescue them. This deity was usually brought onto the stage from above in a car swung from a great crane which lowered it to the ground. A divinity who thus appeared to unravel a tangled complication was thus called the *deus ex machina* (or god from the machine).

The action in a Greek play was continuous and took place in one spot in less than a day. What happened off stage had to be reported by an entering character. Scenery was limited to a fixed architectural background.

The place of minor characters was largely filled by a chorus of interested persons, who remained on the stage during the entire play, sometimes exchanging words with the major characters, and filling in the time between the episodes in the play by comments among themselves on the action and characters, and by choruses which were spoken rhythmically to music somewhat as a modern verse-speaking choir recites a poem. Sometimes the whole chorus spoke in unison; sometimes one group answered another; sometimes individuals spoke alone. This recitation was accompanied by rhythmic movement and pantomime. During the dialog of the main characters, the chorus remained silent on a lower level of the stage called the orchestra. In the intervals between the episodes, when the main actors had left the scene, the chorus often surged up to the upper level of the stage where the action took place. The chorus thus furnished a picturesque variation from the dramatic dialog, and also from its superior knowledge gave the audience through its comments information about characters and past events, which helped explain the plot.

The play which follows was written in the fifth century B.C. during the golden age of Greek culture.

❋ ❋ ❋

The scene represents the ancient Castle of ADMETUS *near Pherae in Thessaly. It is the dusk before dawn;* APOLLO, *radiant in the darkness, looks at the Castle.*

APOLLO. Admetus' House! 'Twas here I bowed my head
　　　　Of old, and chafed not at the bondman's bread,
　　　　Though born in heaven. Aye, Zeus to death had hurled
　　　　My son, Asclepios, Healer of the World,

Piercing with fire his heart; and in mine ire 5
I slew his Cyclop churls, who forged the fire,
Whereat Zeus cast me forth to bear the yoke
Of service to a mortal. To this folk
I came, and watched a stranger's herd for pay,
And all his house I have prospered to this day. 10
For innocent was the Lord I chanced upon
And clean as mine own heart, King Pheres' son,
Admetus. Him I rescued from the grave,
Beguiling the Grey Sisters till they gave
A great oath that Admetus should go free, 15
Would he but pay to Them Below in fee
Another living soul. Long did he prove
All that were his, and all that owed him love,
But never a soul he found would yield up life
And leave the sunlight for him, save his wife: 20
Who, even now, down the long galleries
Is borne, death-wounded; for this day it is
She needs must pass out of the light and die.
And, seeing the stain of death must not come nigh
My radiance, I must leave this house I love. 25
But ha! The Headsman of the Pit, above
Earth's floor, to ravish her! Aye, long and late
He hath watched, and cometh at the fall of fate.

[*Enter from the other side* THANATOS *or Death, a crouching
black-haired and winged figure, carrying a drawn sword. He
starts in revulsion on seeing* APOLLO.]

THANATOS. Aha!
    Why here? What mak'st thou at the gate, 30
        Thou Thing of Light? Wilt overtread
The eternal judgment, and abate
        And spoil the portions of the dead?
'Tis not enough for thee to have blocked
        In other days Admetus' doom 35
With craft of magic wine, which mocked
        The three Grey Sisters of the Tomb;
            But now once more
    I see thee stand at watch, and shake
    That arrow-armèd hand to make 40
    This woman thine, who swore, who swore,
        To die now for her husband's sake.

14. *Grey Sisters*: fates.

Apollo. Fear not.
    I bring fair words and seek but what is just.

Thanatos. [*Sneering.*] And if words help thee not, an arrow
        must?   45

Apollo. 'Tis ever my delight to bear this bow.

Thanatos. And aid this house unjustly? Aye, 'tis so.

Apollo. I love this man, and grieve for his dismay.

Thanatos. And now wilt rob me of my second prey!

Apollo. I never robbed thee, neither then nor now.   50

Thanatos. Why is Admetus here then, not below?

Apollo. He gave for ransom his own wife, for whom . . .

Thanatos. [*Interrupting.*] I am come; and straight will bear her
        to the tomb.

Apollo. Go, take her.—I can never move thine heart.

Thanatos [*Mocking.*] To slay the doomed?—Nay; I will do my
        part.   55

Apollo. Thou wilt not grant me, then, this boon? 'Tis so?

Thanatos. Thou knowest me, what I am: I tell thee, no!
        Talk on, talk on! Thy threats shall win no bride
        From me.—This woman, whatsoe'er betide,
        Shall lie in Hades' house. Even at the word   60
        I go to lay upon her hair my sword.
        For all whose head this grey sword visiteth
        To death are hallowed and the Lords of death.

    [Thanatos *goes into the house. Presently, as the day grows
    lighter, the* Chorus *enters; it consists of Citizens of Pherae,
    who speak severally.*]

(As the chorus enters, speaking among themselves, we learn they
have gathered out of sympathy and admiration for the noble wife
who is about to die in order to prolong her husband's life. A maid
comes out from the castle almost in tears.)

Leader. But see, a handmaid cometh, and the tear
        Wet on her cheek! What tidings shall we hear? . . .   65
            Thy grief is natural, daughter, if some ill
            Hath fallen today. Say, is she living still
            Or dead, your mistress? Speak, if speak you may.

Maid. Alive. No, dead. . . . Oh, read it either way.

Leader. Nay, daughter, can the same soul live and die?   70

Maid. Her life is broken; death is in her eye.

    60. *Hades:* the land of the dead.

LEADER. Poor King, to think what she was, and what thou!

MAID. He never knew her worth. . . . He will know it now.

LEADER. There is no hope, methinks, to save her still?

MAID. The hour is come, and breaks all human will. 75

LEADER. She hath such tendance as the dying crave?

MAID. For sure: and rich robes ready for her grave.

LEADER. 'Fore God, she dies high-hearted, aye, and far
 In honour raised above all wives that are!

MAID. Far above all! How other? What must she 80
 Who seeketh to surpass this woman be?
 Or how could any wife more shining make
 Her lord's love, than by dying for his sake?
 But thus much all the city knows. 'Tis here,
 In her own rooms, the tale will touch thine ear 85
 With strangeness. When she knew the day was come,
 She rose and washed her body, white as foam,
 With running water; then the cedarn press
 She opened, and took forth her funeral dress
 And rich adornment. So she stood arrayed 90
 Before the Hearth-Fire of her home, and prayed:
 "Mother, since I must vanish from the day,
 This last, last time I kneel to thee and pray;
 Be mother to my children! Find some dear
 Helpmate for him, some gentle lord for her. 95
 And let not them, like me, before their hour
 Die; let them live in happiness, in our
 Old home, till life be full and age content."
  To every household altar then she went
 And made for each his garland of the green 100
 Boughs of the wind-blown myrtle, and was seen
 Praying, without a sob, without a tear.
 She knew the dread thing coming, but her clear
 Cheek never changed: till suddenly she fled
 Back to her own chamber and bridal bed: 105
 Then came the tears and she spoke all her thought.
  "O bed, whereon my laughing girlhood's knot
 Was severed by this man, for whom I die,
 Farewell! 'Tis thou . . . I speak not bitterly . . .
 'Tis thou hast slain me. All alone I go
 Lest I be false to him or thee. And lo,
 Some woman shall lie here instead of me—
 Happier perhaps; more true she cannot be."

    She kissed the pillow as she knelt, and wet
With flooding tears was that fair coverlet.   115
    At last she had her fill of weeping; then
She tore herself away, and rose again,
Walking with downcast eyes; yet turned before
She had left the room, and cast her down once more
Kneeling beside the bed. Then to her side   120
The children came, and clung to her and cried;
And her arms hugged them, and a long good-bye
She gave to each, like one who goes to die.
The whole house then was weeping, every slave
In sorrow for his mistress. And she gave   125
Her hand to all; aye, none so base was there
She gave him not good words and he to her.
    So on Admetus falls from either side
Sorrow. 'Twere bitter grief to him to have died
Himself; and being escaped, how sore a woe   130
He hath earned instead—Ah, some day he shall know!

LEADER. Surely Admetus suffers, even today,
    For this true-hearted love he hath cast away?

MAID. He weeps; begs her not leave him desolate,
    And holds her to his heart—too late, too late!   135
She is sinking now, and there, beneath his eye
Fading, the poor cold hand falls languidly,
And faint is all her breath. Yet still she fain
Would look once on the sunlight—once again
And never more. I will go in and tell   140
Thy presence. Few there be, will serve so well
My master and stand by him to the end.
But thou hast been from olden days our friend.

[THE MAID *goes in. The chorus comments critically on the willingness of the husband to accept such a sacrifice. During their last words,* ADMETUS *and* ALCESTIS *come from the castle door.* ALCESTIS *is supported by her Handmaids and followed by her two children.*]

LEADER. And who hath said that Love shall bring
    More joy to man than fear and strife?   145
I knew his perils from of old,
I know them now, when I behold
    The bitter faring of my King,
Whose love is taken, and his life
    Left evermore an empty thing.   150

ALCESTIS. O Sun, O light of the day that falls!
    O running cloud that races along the sky!

ADMETUS. They look on thee and me, a stricken twain,
    Who have wrought no sin that God should have thee slain.

ALCESTIS. Dear Earth, and House of sheltering walls,   155
    And wedded homes of the land where my fathers lie!

ADMETUS. Fail not, my hapless one. Be strong, and pray
    The o'er-mastering Gods to hate us not alway.

ALCESTIS. [*Faintly, her mind wandering.*] A boat two-oared, upon
        water; I see, I see.
            And the Ferryman of the Dead,   160
        His hand that hangs on the pole, his voice that cries;
    "Thou lingerest; come. Come quickly, we wait for thee."
    He is angry that I am slow; he shakes his head.

ADMETUS. Alas, a bitter boat-faring for me,
    My bride ill-starred.—Oh, this is misery!   165

ALCESTIS. [*As before.*] Drawing, drawing! 'Tis some one that
        draweth me . . .
        To the Palaces of the Dead.
    So dark. The wings, the eyebrows and ah, the eyes! . . .
        Go back! God's mercy! What seekest thou? Let me
        be! . . .
    [*Recovering.*] Where am I? Ah, and what paths are these I
        tread?   170

ADMETUS. Grievous for all who love thee, but for me
    And my two babes most hard, most solitary.

ALCESTIS. Hold me not; let me lie.—
    I am too weak to stand; and Death is near,
    And a slow darkness stealing on my sight.
        My little ones, good-bye.   175
    Soon, soon, and mother will be no more here . . .
    Good-bye, two happy children in the light.

ADMETUS. Oh, word of pain, oh, sharper ache
        Than any death of mine had brought!   180
        For the Gods' sake, desert me not,
    For thine own desolate children's sake.
    Nay, up! Be brave. For if they rend
        Thee from me, I can draw no breath;
        In thy hand are my life and death,   185
    Thine, my belovèd and my friend!

ALCESTIS. Admetus, seeing what way my fortunes lie,
    I fain would speak with thee before I die.

I have set thee before all things; yea, mine own
Life beside thine was naught. For this alone 190
I die . . . Dear Lord, I never need have died.
I might have lived to wed some prince of pride,
Dwell in a king's house. . . . Nay, how could I torn
From thee, live on, I and my babes forlorn?
I have given to thee my youth—not more nor less. 195
But all—though I was full of happiness.
Thy father and mother both—'tis strange to tell—
Had failed thee, though for them the deed was well,
The years were ripe, to die and save their son.
The one child of the house: for hope was none, 200
If thou shouldst pass away, of other heirs.
So thou and I had lived through the long years,
Both. Thou hadst not lain sobbing here alone
For a dead wife and orphan babes. . . . 'Tis done
Now, and some God hath wrought out all his will. 205
    Howbeit I now will ask thee to fulfill
One great return-gift—not so great withal
As I have given, for life is more than all;
But just and due, as thine own heart will tell.
For thou hast loved our little ones as well 210
As I have. . . . Keep them to be masters here
In my old house; and bring no stepmother
Upon them. She might hate them. She might be
Some baser woman, not a queen like me,
And strike them with her hand. For mercy, spare 215
Our little ones that wrong. It is my prayer . . .
They come into a house; they are all strife
And hate to any child of the dead wife . . .
Better a serpent than a stepmother!
    A boy is safe. He has his father there 220
To guard him. But a little girl! [*Taking the Little Girl to
her.*] What good
And gentle care will guide thy maidenhood?
What woman wilt thou find at father's side?
One evil word from her, just when the tide
Of youth is full, would wreck thy hope of love. 225
And no more mother near, to stand above
Thy marriage-bed, nor comfort thee pain-tossed
In travail, when one needs a mother most!
Seeing I must die. . . . 'Tis here, across my way,

Not for the morrow, not for the third day, 230
But now— Death, and to lie with things that were.
    Farewell. God keep you happy.—Husband dear,
Remember that I failed thee not; and you,
My children, that your mother loved you true.

LEADER. Take comfort. Ere thy lord can speak, I swear 235
If truth is in him, he will grant thy prayer.

ADMETUS. He will, he will! Oh never fear for me.
Mine hast thou been, and mine shalt ever be,
Living and dead, thou only. None in wide
Hellas but thou shalt be Admetus' bride. 240
No race so high, no face so magic-sweet
Shall ever from this purpose turn my feet.
And children . . . if God grant me joy of these,
'Tis all I ask; of thee no joy nor ease
He gave me. And thy mourning I will bear 245
Not one year of my life but every year,
While life shall last. . . . My mother I will know
No more. My father shall be held my foe.
They brought the words of love but not the deed,
While thou hast given thine all, and in my need 250
Saved me. What can I do but weep alone,
Alone always, when such a wife is gone? . . .
Oh, I will find some artist wondrous wise
Shall mould for me thy shape, thine hair, thine eyes,
And lay it in thy bed; and I will lie 255
Close, and reach out mine arms to thee, and cry
Thy name into the night, and wait and hear
My own heart breathe: "Thy love, thy love is near."
A cold delight; yet it might ease the sum
Of sorrow. . . . And good dreams of thee will come 260
Like balm. 'Tis sweet, even in a dream, to gaze
On a dear face, the moment that it stays.
    But now, wife, wait for me till I shall come
Where thou art, and prepare our second home.
These ministers in that same cedar sweet 265
Where thou art laid will lay me, feet to feet,
And head to head, oh, not in death from thee
Divided, who alone art true to me!

LEADER. This life-long sorrow thou hast sworn, I too,
Thy friend, will bear with thee. It is her due. 270

ALCESTIS. Children, ye heard his promise? He will wed
    No other woman nor forget the dead.

ADMETUS. Again I promise. So it shall be done.

ALCESTIS. [*Giving the children into his arms one after the other.*]
    On that oath take my daughter: and my son.

ADMETUS. Dear hand that gives, I accept both gift and vow. 275

ALCESTIS. Thou, in my place, must be their mother now.

ADMETUS. And how can I, forlorn of thee, live on?

ALCESTIS. Time healeth; and the dead are dead and gone.

ADMETUS. Oh, take me with thee to the dark below,
    Me also!

ALCESTIS. 'Tis enough that one should go. 280

ADMETUS. O Fate, to have cheated me of one so true!

ALCESTIS. [*Her strength failing.*] There comes a darkness: a great
      burden, too.

ADMETUS. I am lost if thou wilt leave me. . . . Wife! Mine own!

ALCESTIS. I am not thy wife; I am nothing. All is gone.

ADMETUS. Thy babes! Thou wilt not leave them.—Raise thine
      eye. 285

ALCESTIS. I am sorry. . . . But good-bye, children; good-bye.

ADMETUS. Look at them! Wake and look at them!

ALCESTIS. I must go.

ADMETUS. What? Dying!

ALCESTIS. Farewell, husband! [*She dies.*]

ADMETUS. [*With a cry.*] Ah! . . . Woe, woe!

LEADER. Admetus' Queen is dead!

[*While* ADMETUS *is weeping silently, and the* CHORUS *veil their
faces, the* LITTLE BOY *runs up to his dead Mother.*]

LITTLE BOY. Oh, what has happened? Mummy has gone away, 290
    And left me and will not come back any more!
    Father, I shall be lonely all the day . . .
    Look! Look! Her eyes . . . and her arms not like before,
    How they lie . . .
    Mother! Oh, speak a word!
    Answer me, answer me, Mother! It is I. 295
    I am touching your face. It is I, your little bird.

ADMETUS. [*Recovering himself and going to the child.*]
    She hears us not, she sees us not. We lie
    Under a heavy grief, child, thou and I.

LITTLE BOY. I am so little Father, and lonely and cold
    Here without Mother. It is too hard. . . . And you, 300
      Poor little sister, too.

Oh Father!
Such a little time we had her. She might have stayed
   On till we all were old . . .
Everything is spoiled when Mother is dead.   305

[THE LITTLE BOY *is taken away, with his sister, sobbing.*]

LEADER. My King, thou needs must gird thee to the worst.
   Thou shalt not be the last, nor yet the first,
   To lose a noble wife. Be brave, and know
   To die is but a debt that all men owe.

ADMETUS. I know. It came not without doubts and fears,   310
   This thing. The thought hath poisoned all my years.
      Howbeit, I now will make the burial due
   To this dead Queen. Be assembled, all of you;
   And after, raise your triumph-song to greet
   This pitiless Power that yawns beneath our feet.   315
      Meantime let all in Thessaly who dread
   My sceptre join in mourning for the dead
   With temples sorrow-shorn and sable weed.
   Ye chariot-lords, ye spurrers of the steed,
   Shear close your horses' manes! Let there be found   320
   Through all my realm no lute, nor lyre, nor sound
   Of piping, till twelve moons are at an end.
   For never shall I lose a closer friend,
   Nor braver in my need. And worthy is she
   Of honour, who alone hath died for me.   325

[*The body of* ALCESTIS *is carried into the house by mourners;*
ADMETUS *follows it.*]

(The Chorus sings a hymn in praise of Alcestis. As the song ceases,
Heracles enters and asks lodging of Admetus for the night. He is on
his way to perform one of his labors and has not heard of Admetus'
bereavement. Admetus, knowing Heracles will go on wearily in search
of shelter if he knows the truth, tells him a distant relative has died.
Heracles is installed in the most distant guest quarters so as not to
be disturbed by the funeral, and a feast is spread for him.)

CHORUS. Oh, a House that loves the stranger,
      And a House for ever free!
   Where Apollo, the Song-changer,
      Was a herdsman in thy fee. . . .
   He hath opened wide his dwelling   330
      To the stranger, though his ruth
   For the dead was fresh and welling,
      For the loved one of his youth.

'Tis the brave heart's cry:
"I will fail not, though I die!"　　335
Doth it win, with no man's telling,
　Some high vision of the truth?
　We may marvel. Yet I trust,
　When man seeketh to be just
And to pity them that wander, God will raise him from the
　dust.　　340

[As the song ceases the doors are thrown open and ADMETUS
*comes before them: a great funeral procession is seen moving
out.]*

(Admetus' father, Pheres, arrives with funeral gifts and praise for
Alcestis, but Admetus rails at him bitterly because though aged, he
was unwilling to die to save his son. Pheres aptly points out that
Admetus has himself been unwilling to die to save his wife, and retorts:

> Be silent, loving thine own life, and know
> All men love theirs.

As the funeral moves off the stage, it is followed by the Chorus chanting:)

CHORUS. Ah me!
　Farewell, unfalteringly brave!
　　Farewell, thou generous heart and true!
　　May Pluto give thee welcome due,
　And Hermes love thee in the grave.　　345
　Whate'er of blessèd life there be
　　For high souls to the darkness flown,
　　Be thine for ever, and a throne
　Beside the crowned Persephonê.

(Heracles now suddenly discovers that Alcestis is dead, and in
gratitude for Admetus' hospitality, goes forth to fight with Death for
Alcestis' soul. Meanwhile Admetus returns from the funeral, and the
audience has the satisfaction of hearing him at last repent his selfishness.)

ADMETUS. *[Erect and facing them.]*
　Behold, I count my wife's fate happier,　　350
　Though all gainsay me, than mine own. To her
　Comes no more pain for ever; she hath rest
　And peace from all toil, and her name is blest.

341. *Pluto:* king of the dead. 345. *Hermes:* revenger of the gods who guides the
souls of the dead to Hades. 348. *Persephonê:* queen of the dead.

But I am one who hath no right to stay
Alive on earth; one that hath lost his way
In fate, and strays in dreams of life long past . . .   355
Friends, I have learned my lesson at the last.

    I have my life. Here stands my house. But now
How dare I enter in? Or, entered, how
Go forth again? Go forth, when none is there   360
To give me a parting word, and I to her? . . .
    Where shall I turn for refuge? There within,
The desert that remains where she hath been
Will drive me forth, the bed, the empty seat
She sat in; nay, the floor beneath my feet   365
Unswept, the children crying at my knee
For mother; and the very thralls will be
In sobs for the dear mistress that is lost.

    That is my home! If I go forth, a host
Of feasts and bridal dances, gatherings gay   370
Of women, will be there to fright me away
To loneliness. Mine eyes will never bear
The sight. They were her friends; they played with her.

    And always, always, men who hate my name
Will murmur: "This is he who lives in shame   375
Because he dared not die! He gave instead
The woman whom he loved, and so is fled
From death. He counts himself a man withal!
And seeing his parents died not at his call
He hates them, when himself he dared not die!"   380
    Such mocking beside all my pain shall I
Endure. . . . What profit was it to live on,
Friend, with my grief kept and mine honor gone?

(As the Chorus sings a second tribute to Alcestis, Heracles enters,
his festal robes deranged as by a struggle. Behind him two attendants
lead a veiled woman, who seems like one asleep or unconscious. She
remains in the background while Heracles comes forward, reproaches
Admetus for concealing his sorrow from a friend, and asks Admetus
to keep a captive maid for him till he returns from the labor on which
he is bound. Admetus refuses ever again to admit a woman to his
house, vowing to remain faithful to Alcestis. Gradually the veiled
woman begins to hear his words. Heracles unveils her and urges Admetus to look at her. He refuses even to turn his head. The woman
reaches out her arms to Admetus, and Heracles begs him to take her
hand and lead her in. Reluctantly without looking Admetus reaches

his hand backward and clasps hers. Suddenly he turns and sees—
Alcestis. Heracles has fought with Death for her at the brink of the
grave and brought her back to her sorrowing husband.)

ADMETUS. [*In an awed whisper, looking towards* ALCESTIS.]
    Why standeth she so still? No sound, no word!
HERACLES. She hath dwelt with Death. Her voice may not be
      heard   385
    Ere to the Lords of Them Below she pay
    Due cleansing, and awake on the third day.
    [*To the Attendants*.] So; guide her home.
    [*They lead* ALCESTIS *to the doorway*.]
                And thou, King, for the rest
    Of time, be true; be righteous to thy guest,   390
    As he would have thee be. But now farewell!
    My task yet lies before me, and the spell
    That binds me to my master; forth I fare.
ADMETUS. Stay with us this one day! Stay but to share
    The feast upon our hearth!   395
HERACLES.   The feasting day
    Shall surely come; now I must needs away.
                          [HERACLES *departs*.]
ADMETUS. Farewell! All victory attend thy name
    And safe home-coming!
                    Lo I make proclaim
    To the Four Nations and all Thessaly;   400
    A wondrous happiness hath come to be:
    Therefore pray, dance, give offerings and make full
    Your altars with the life-blood of the Bull!
    For me . . . my heart is changed; my life shall mend
    Henceforth. For surely Fortune is a friend.   405
                [*He goes with* ALCESTIS *into the house*.]
CHORUS. There be many shapes of mystery;
    And many things God brings to be,
        Past hope or fear.
    And the end men looked for cometh not,
    And a path is there where no man thought.   410
        So hath it fallen here.

READING PROBLEMS ON THE DRAMA

1. *Two Crooks and a Lady:* Who is the dominant character in this
play? What does Mrs. Simms-Vane mean by saying that Lucille and Miller

are not made of material that succeeds? In how many ways does Mrs. Simms-Vane show her superiority? For what dramatic purpose has the author made her a paralytic? In how many ways do Lucille and Miller show that they are made of "base metal"? How does each of them forfeit the chance offered by Mrs. Simms-Vane? What do you think is the climax (or turning point) of the play? Why does Mrs. Simms-Vane sit each afternoon alone before the mirror? What part does the mirror play in the drama? Is the same idea expressed in Mr. Child's title, *Fibre*, and Mr. Pillot's *Two Crooks and a Lady?* Explain from this play (1) why a crook is a crook; and (2) why he is almost certain to fail.

2. *Sicilian Limes:* Did you guess from the start how the play would end? How is the end foreshadowed in the conversation first with the servants, then with Marta, and at last with Sina? Do you think the attitude of the servants toward Micuccio undergoes any change during the opening conversation? How does the old mother fit into her new life? Where does the climax or turning point occur? What effect does the appearance of Sina produce on Micuccio? Why was he unwilling to keep the money? Note the steps by which Micuccio's character is gradually revealed. Which character in the play most commands your respect? Why?

3. *A Sunny Morning:* How are the characters and the age of the couple indicated in the opening conversation with the servants and each other? How is the revelation of their former acquaintance foreshadowed? How do they recognize each other? Why do they not reveal their identity? Carry the story beyond the curtain.

4. *Marco Millions:* Explain what Kublai means by Marco's spiritual hump. Do you think Kukachin or Kublai correctly estimates Marco? What does Kublai mean at the end of the scene by "the eye sees only its own sight"? What is O'Neill burlesquing in Chu-Yin's description of Marco's arrival? Analyze the points in Marco's character and ideas that are revealed by each detail of his arrival, his grammar, his government, and his discussion of the two inventions. What is O'Neill satirizing in Marco's discussion of war and firearms? Do you think Marco fairly represents the Western viewpoint? Find illustrations in American or European life of points satirized in this scene. What is Kublai's reaction to the idea of paper money and firearms? Explain Kublai's final remark; is it serious or ironical?

5. *Spreading the News:* Why are the magistrate and policeman introduced at the beginning? How does Lady Gregory make real personalities out of them instead of just puppets in the plot? How is the Irish dialect different from English? Why is Mrs. Tarpey made deaf? Trace the steps by which the rumor grows. Why does Bartley think Jack's ghost appeared to him? How is the interest kept up at the end of the play after Jack reappears? How does Bartley's character heighten the humor of the situations? What happens after the curtain?

6. *The Marriage Proposal:* What is more vital to these characters— love or personal pride and practical advantage? Is this a love match? Why does Natalia cry hysterically, "Bring him back"? Why does Chekhov get the characters into *two* arguments? What difference is there between the

situations as the two arguments start? At least what will this family never lack?

7. *Cyrano de Bergerac:* In what ways does Cyrano show in the first scene his literary taste, his courage, his skill as a poet, and his extravagant pride? Why does Cyrano despair of being loved? How does Christian command our respect on his first appearance? How does Cyrano show his unselfish generosity on the same occasion? In the famous balcony scene, what consolation does Cyrano have? Why is it artistic that Roxane should discover only after many years that it was Cyrano she loved? How does she discover it? How are the circumstances of his death typical of Cyrano?

8. *The Doll's House:* Ibsen was the inventor of the so-called problem play. With what problem does this play deal and how is it handled? Is a solution given? What startling contrast is offered by Helmer's speeches before and after reading the letter? Note next the change that takes place in Helmer's attitude when he gets Krogstadt's second letter. What is it Helmer objects to: Nora's crime, or its becoming public? What does Nora mean by, "Yes, Torvald, I have changed my dress"? What does Nora think has been wrong with their married life? Whom does she blame? What three reasons cause her to leave home? Do you think she will return? Is Nora really a stupid little feather-brain, as Torvald once called her? Frame what you think would be Ibsen's definition of an ideal relation between husband and wife. This play was written many years ago and has been called woman's first declaration of independence. Have conditions changed completely since then?

9. *The Rivals:* What is so entertaining about the names in this play? What is amusing in Bob Acres' oaths? In what amusing way is Acres' alarm over the duel displayed? Does he make any comeback at O'Trigger? Locate Mrs. Malaprop's slips in word usage and see if you can supply the correct expression.

10. *The Doctor in Spite of Himself:* Select good bits of repartee from these scenes. What diverting contrast in action occurs in the first act? Why does Sganarelle consent to impersonate a doctor? Is he a stupid man? Prove. Why does he ask Géronte whether he understands Latin? Sganarelle knows a few Latin words but he makes up the rest; is the counterfeit clever? By what trait does Sganarelle succeed in passing himself off as a doctor? What is the only sort of patient a fake doctor can cure? Does this doctor find such a patient? Does the doctor take a fee? What is amusing in the end of the play? Is such medical quackery practised now?

11. *Romeo and Juliet:* How does the first scene introduce the force that is to dominate the play? How is this same element touched upon in the ballroom scene? Why do you suppose Shakespeare makes Romeo and Juliet speak in rhyme at their first meeting? Which of the many comparisons used by Romeo to describe the beauty of Juliet in the orchard scene seems to you best to convey her charm? his love? How do Juliet's speeches reveal her youth, sweetness, innocence, and love? How does she maintain her youthful dignity in spite of having revealed her love before it was

sought? Why is it so suitable and artistic to surround the lovers by the night, the moonbeams, the lovely garden—and yet to separate them by the balcony? Select lines from this scene that strike you as poetic or true to universal feeling. What humorous scenes and characters does the play contain and how is the humor obtained? Where is the turning point in the play? Through whose fault does it turn to tragedy? Is the Prince justified in his punishment for the outbreak? Why does Shakespeare show us Juliet waiting for Romeo, and then Romeo crying out against his banishment? What is particularly sweet and natural in the parting between the lovers? How are Juliet's love and heroism shown in the potion scene? What is so effective in the sudden last line? For what does the audience wait and hope throughout Romeo's death speech? Is it appropriate that the tragic ending of the play should be accidental? Why? Is it true to life that only tragedy can move us to reform?

12. *Alcestis:* What does the poetic form add to the effect of this play? What do the choruses add? What dramatic contrast is presented at the first of the play? Select other scenes which will make striking or beautiful stage pictures. How do we learn of what is passing in the palace? What impression of Alcestis do we receive before we actually see her? What features of the death scene are most human and appealing? Compare this scene with Hector's farewell (page 392). Does Alcestis ever reproach her husband? What is our feeling toward Admetus? Who finally expresses this? What good traits does Admetus have? When does he finally recognize the mistake he has made? Why does Heracles (Hercules) bring Alcestis in veiled? What is the purpose of the conversation in her presence? Would you have returned to Admetus? Compare this last scene with the statue scene in *The Winter's Tale*.

FURTHER READINGS IN THE DRAMA

Baker: *Modern American Plays*
Barker: *Forty Minute Plays from Shakespeare*
Coffman: *A Book of Modern Plays*
Cohen: *Longer Modern Plays*
Hubbel and Beatty: *Introduction to the Drama*
Pence: *Dramas by Present Day Writers*
Pollard: *Miracle and Mystery Plays*
Thomas, C. T.: *Atlantic Book of Junior Plays*
Thomas, R.: *Plays and the Theatre*
Webber and Webster: *Typical Plays*
Andreyev: *Love of One's Neighbor*
Barrie: *The Admirable Crichton*
Bennett: *Milestones*
Besier: *The Barretts of Wimpole Street*
Capek: *R. U. R.*
Chekhov: *The Boor*

Down: *The Maker of Dreams*
Drinkwater: *Abraham Lincoln*
Dunsany: *Gods of the Mountain*
    The Lost Silk Hat
Euripides: *Iphigenia in Tauris*
Galsworthy: *The Mob*
Gilbert: *Trial by Jury*
    The Mikado
Gillette: *Secret Service*
Gogol: *The Government Inspector*
Goldsmith: *She Stoops to Conquer*
Gregory: *The Workhouse Ward*
Green: *In Abraham's Bosom*
Jerome: *The Passing of the Third Floor Back*
Maeterlinck: *The Blue Bird*
Milne: *Dover Road*
Molière: *The Imaginary Invalid*
O'Neill: *Ah Wilderness*
    Emperor Jones
Pinero: *Trelawny of the Wells*
Rostand: *The Romances*
Schiller: *William Tell*
Shakespeare: *Merchant of Venice*
    Taming of the Shrew
    Midsummer Night's Dream
Shaw: *Pygmalion*
Sheridan: *School for Scandal*
Sophocles: *Antigone*
Synge: *Riders to the Sea*
Tagore: *The Post Office*
Tarkington: *The Trysting Place*
Wilde: *The Importance of Being Ernest*
Yeats: *The Hour Glass*
Zangwill: *The Melting Pot*

SUGGESTIONS FOR ORIGINAL DRAMATIZATIONS

1. Divide the class into groups each of which will enact for the class a scene from one of the plays in this unit.

2. Individuals or groups working together may wish to write short plays based on tales or short stories in this volume. The test of your success will be your ability to condense events into one or two scenes; make conversation natural and yet make each remark advance the action, reveal character, or create atmosphere; and end each scene on a high point of interest.

3. The class may wish to enact interesting original plays written by its members.

IX

The Fable

S O FAR we have been studying story-telling whether in prose or in verse and whether in the form of fiction or of drama. We noted, however, that all these types of narrative often had themes or ideas behind them. In other words, even in telling a story, an author cannot resist giving you his opinions on life. There are stories which are written for no other purpose than to convey such an opinion.

A fable is a story, in which all the characters, acts and objects are allegorical; that is, they stand for types of people, things, or experiences in the real world. While some fables are of novel length, the fable is usually short, often a mere anecdote, since the interest is in the idea, not the narrative, and the more swiftly the point can be made, the better.

Such stories are called fables because Aesop, who was the great original writer of this type of story, wrote animal stories in which he made his animals talk; and the French named them *fabliaux* from the word in that language which meant "to talk."

Fables go back in history to the primitive days of animal worship, when the sacred tribal animal, or his priest in animal garb, instructed his people in right and successful living. This he would no doubt do through appropriate stories.

The talking animal was preserved in later days as a quaint and convenient device behind which an author who wished to express dangerous and inconvenient opinions could hide. In the Middle Ages, most of the criticism of social, political, and religious institutions appeared in fable form, and Renard the Fox was one of the favorite characters of the satirists.

Today fables may have either animal or human characters.

SOUR GRAPES, THE SWAN AND THE GOOSE, AND THE ASS IN THE LION'S SKIN

Aesop (Greece)

Translated by (1) Ruth Mary Weeks and (2-3) William Ellery Leonard

I

A hungry fox one day sees tempting grapes
Hang far above. At which he sadly gapes.
He jumps for them again and yet again,
But all his weary efforts are in vain.
"Sour things," says Mr. Fox as off he goes, 5
"And quite unfit for eating, heaven knows."

2

A rich man bought a Swan and Goose—
That for song, and this for use.
It chanced his simple-minded cook
One night the Swan for Goose mistook. 10

But in the dark about to chop
The Swan in two above the crop,
He heard the lyric note, and stayed
The action of the fatal blade.

And thus we see a proper tune 15
Is sometimes very opportune.

3

An Ass put on a Lion's skin and went
About the forest with much merriment,
Scaring the foolish beasts by brooks and rocks,
Till at last he tried to scare the Fox. 20
But Reynard, hearing from beneath the mane
That raucous voice so petulant and vain,
Remarked, "O Ass, I too would run away,
But that I know your old familiar bray."

That's just the way with asses, just the way.

THE WOLF AND THE DOG, THE DOG AND THE SHADOW, THE BEAR AND THE TWO COMPANIONS

Jean de la Fontaine (France)

Translated by Elizur Wright

La Fontaine retold in clever French verse many of the anecdotes of older fable writers such as the Greek Phaedrus and Aesop, the Italian Faerno and Astemio, and the French Rabelais. To whatever he retells, he gives a turn of his own that makes the fable original.

❋ ❋ ❋

I

A prowling wolf, whose shaggy skin
(So strict the watch of dogs had been)
    Hid little but his bones,
Once met a mastiff dog astray.
A prouder, fatter, sleeker Tray,   5
    No human mortal owns.
Sir Wolf, in famished plight,
    Would fain have made a ration
    Upon his fat relation;
But then he first must fight;   10
    And well the dog seemed able
    To save from wolfish table
His carcass snug and tight.
    So then, in civil conversation,
    The wolf expressed his admiration   15
Of Tray's fine case. Said Tray, politely,
"Yourself, good sir, may be as sightly;
    Quit but the woods, advised by me.
    For all your fellows here, I see,
Are shabby wretches, lean and gaunt,   20
Belike to die of haggard want.
With such a pack, of course, it follows,
One fights for every bit he swallows.
    Come, then, with me, and share
    On equal terms our princely fare."   25
    "But what with you
    Has one to do?"

Inquires the wolf. "Light work indeed,"
Replies the dog; "you only need
> To bark a little now and then,   30
> To chase off duns and beggar men,
To fawn on friends that come or go forth,
Your master please, and so forth;
> For which you have to eat
> All sorts of well-cooked meat,—   35
Cold pullets, pigeons, savoury messes,—
Besides unnumbered fond caresses."
> The wolf, by force of appetite,
> Accepts the terms outright,
Tears glistening in his eyes.   40
But faring on, he spies
> A galled spot on the mastiff's neck.
"What's that?" he cries. "Oh, nothing but a speck."
"A speck?" "Ay, ay; 'tis not enough to pain me;
Perhaps the collar's mark by which they chain me."   45
> "Chain! chain you! What! run you not, then,
> Just where you please, and when?"
"Not always, sir; but what of that?"
"Enough, for me, to spoil your fat!
It ought to be a precious price   50
Which could to servile chains entice;
For me, I'll shun them while I've wit."
> So ran Sir Wolf, and runneth yet.

2

This world is full of shadow-chasers,
Most easily deceived.   55
> Should I enumerate these racers,
> I should not be believed.
I send them all to Aesop's dog,
Which, crossing water on a log,
Espied the meat he bore, below;   60
> To seize its image, let it go;
Plunged in; to reach the shore was glad,
With neither what he hoped, nor what he'd had.

3

Two fellows, needing funds, and bold,
A bearskin to a furrier sold,   65

Of which the bear was living still,
But which they presently would kill,—
    At least they said they would.
    And, if their word was good,
It was a king of bears,—an Ursa Major,—   70
    The biggest bear beneath the sun.
Its skin, the chaps would wager,
    Was cheap at double cost;
      'Twould make one laugh at frost,
      And make two robes as well as one.   75
Old Dindenaut, in sheep who dealt,
Less prized his sheep than they their pelt
    (In their account 'twas theirs,
    But in his own, the bear's).
By bargain struck upon the skin,   80
Two days at most must bring it in,
Forth went the two. More easy found than got,
    The bear came growling at them on the trot.
    Behold our dealers both confounded,
      As if by thunderbolt astounded!   85
Their bargain vanished suddenly in air;
For who could plead his interest with a bear?
    One of the friends sprung up a tree;
The other, cold as ice could be,
Fell on his face, feigned death,   90
And closely held his breath,—
He having somewhere heard it said
The bear ne'er preys upon the dead.
Sir Bear, sad blockhead, was deceived,
The prostrate man a corpse believed;   95
But, half suspecting some deceit,
He feels and snuffs from head to feet,
    And in the nostrils blows.
The body's surely dead, he thinks.
"I'll leave it," says he, "for it stinks";   100
    And off into the woods he goes.
The other dealer, from his tree
Descending cautiously, to see
His comrade lying in the dirt,
    Consoling, says, "It is a wonder   105
    That, by the monster forced asunder,
We're, after all, more scared than hurt.

But," added he, "what of the creature's skin?
He held his muzzle very near;
What did he whisper in your ear?"   110
"He gave this caution: 'Never dare
Again to sell the skin of bear
Its owner has not ceased to wear.'"

THE MAKING OF MAN

A MYTH OF THE MIWAK INDIANS (AMERICA)

Translated by Stephen Powers

After the Coyote had finished all the work on the world and the inferior creatures, he called a council of them to deliberate on the creation of Man. They sat down in an open space in the forest, all in a circle with the Mountain-Lion at the head. On his right sat the Grizzly Bear, next the Cinnamon Bear, and so on around, according to the rank, ending with the little Mouse, which sat at the Lion's left.

The Lion was the first to speak, and he declared he should like to see Man created with a mighty voice like himself, wherewith he could frighten all animals. For the rest, he would have him well-covered with hair, with terrible fangs in his jaws, strong talons, etc.

The Grizzly Bear said it was ridiculous to have such a voice as his neighbor, for he was always roaring with it, and scared away the very prey he wished to capture. He said the Man ought to have prodigious strength, and move about silently but very swiftly, if necessary, and be able to grip his prey without making a noise.

The Buck said that the Man would look very foolish, in his way of thinking, unless he had a magnificent pair of antlers on his head to fight with. He also thought it was very absurd to roar so loudly, and he would pay less attention to the Man's throat than he would to his ears and eyes, for he would have the first like a spider's web and the second like fire.

The Mountain Sheep protested he never could see what sense there was in such antlers, branching every way, only to get caught in the thickets. If the Man had horns, mostly rolled up, they would be like a stone on each side of his head, giving it weight, and enabling him to butt a great deal harder.

When it came to the Coyote's turn to speak, he declared all these were the stupidest speeches he ever heard, and that he could hardly keep awake while listening to such a pack of noodles and nincom-poops. Every one of them wanted to make the Man like himself. They might just as well take one of their own cubs and call it a Man. As for himself, he was not the best animal that could be made, and he could make one better than himself or any other. Of course, the Man would have to be like himself in having four legs, five fingers, etc. It was well enough to have a voice like the Lion, only the Man need not roar all the while with it. The Grizzly Bear had also some good points, one of which was the shape of his feet, which enabled him easily to stand erect; and he was in favor, there-fore, of making the Man's feet nearly like the Grizzly's. The Grizzly was also happy in having no tail, for he had learned from his own experience that that organ was only a harbor for fleas. The Buck's eyes and ears were pretty good, perhaps better than his own. Then there was the Fish, which was naked, and which he envied, because hair was a burden most of the year; and he, therefore, favored a Man without hair. His claws ought to be as long as the Eagle's so that he could hold things in them. But, after all, with all their separate gifts, they must acknowledge that there was no animal besides himself that had wit enough to supply the Man; and he should be obliged, therefore, to make him like himself in that respect also,—cunning and crafty.

After the Coyote had made an end, the Beaver said he never heard such twaddle and nonsense in his life. No tail, indeed! He would make a Man with a broad flat tail so that he could haul mud and sand on it. The Owl said all the animals seemed to have lost their senses. None of them wanted to give the Man wings. For himself, he could not see of what use anything on earth could be to himself without wings.

The Mole said it was perfect folly to talk about wings, for with them the Man would be certain to bump his head against the sky. Besides that, if he had eyes and wings both, he would get his eyes burnt out by flying too near the sun; but, without eyes, he could burrow in the cool soft earth and be happy.

Last of all, the little Mouse squeaked out that he would make a Man with eyes, of course, so he could see what he was eating; but, as for burrowing in the ground, that was absurd.

So the animals disagreed among themselves, and the council broke up in a row. The Coyote flew at the Beaver and nipped a piece out of his cheek; the Owl jumped on top of the Coyote's head, and commenced lifting his scalp, and there was a high time.

Every animal set to work to make a Man according to his own

ideas; and taking a lump of earth, each one commenced moulding
it like himself; but the Coyote began to make one like that he had
described in the council.

It was so late before they fell to work, that night-fall came on
before anyone had finished his model, and they all lay down and
fell asleep. But the cunning Coyote stayed awake and worked
hard on his model all night. Thus it was that Man was made by
the Coyote.

BAHRĀM GŪR

Nizami (Persia)

Translated by Edward Granville Browne

Bahrām Gūr had a favorite handmaiden whom he used to take with
him on his hunting expeditions, where she would beguile him, during
the intervals of repose, with the strains of the harp. One day the
King had displayed his prowess in the chase and in archery to the
utmost, expecting to win from his favorite some expression of admiration and wonder; but—

*   *   *

The maiden, prompted by mere wantonness,
Refused her admiration to express.
The King was patient, till a wild ass broke
Forth from its lair, then thus to her he spoke:
"My skill, O Tartar maid, thy narrow eyes   5
Behold not, or beholding do despise.
My skill, which knoweth neither bound nor end,
Entereth not thy narrow eyes, O friend!
Behold this beast, and bid my skill impale
What spot thou wilt between its head and tail."   10
"Wouldst thou," said she, "thy skill to me make clear?
Then with one shaft transfix its hoof and ear."
The King, when this hard test was offered him,
Prepared to gratify her fancy's whim;
Called for a cross-bow, and forthwith did lay   15
Within the groove thereof a ball of clay.
Straight to the quarry's ear the pellet shot,
Whereat the beast, to soothe the smarting spot,
And to remove the clay, its foot on high
Did raise, whereon the King at once let fly   20

An arrow like a lightning-flash, which sped
Straight to the hoof, and nailed it to the head.
Then to the maid of China said the King:
"Success is mine! What think you of this thing?"
"For long," said she, "the King this art hath wrought,   25
In tricks long practised to succeed is naught!
What man hath studied long, he does with ease,
And solves the hardest problems, if he please.
That thus my lord the quarry's hoof should hit
Proves not so much his courage as his wit."   30

THE DANCING BEAR

CHRISTIAN GELLERT (GERMANY)

Translated by Edward Z. Davis

A bear, who long had danced for bread,
One morning from his keeper fled;
Back to his native woods retreated,
And, by his brother brutes, was kindly greeted.
Their joy to see him made the forest roar,   5
They lick'd his chaps, they stroked him with the paw;
And when each bear his neighbor saw,
Their news was, So!—Our Bruin's here once more.
     Straightway the travelled youth went on
All his adventures to relate,   10
And whatsoever he had seen, or done,
Or heard, in foreign parts to state.
And when it came the turn to tell
His dancing deeds, to capering he fell,
As though his former master's chain   15
Were fasten'd round his neck again.

     Bears of the woods are seldom trained to dance;
Yet, seeing Bruin throw his limbs about,
The fancy seiz'd them all, themselves to prance,
And strive, with clumsy aim, his motions to make out.   20

     Scarce one of all the brood but quickly tripped,
And stumbling, staggering, fell his whole length down;
The more they fail'd, the brisker Bruin skipped,
To show their skill at fault and prove his own.

But no, their fury kindles at his play; 25
Away! Begone, you tumbling fool! they bawl;
Must you forsooth, be wiser than us all?
And straight, with one accord, they hooted him away.

Your neighbor's hatred would you shun?
His talents to surpass beware! 30
And still the higher your attainments run,
Conceal them still with greater care.
For though, at first, the voice of fame
Shall sound your praises to the sky:
Anon shall Envy blast your name, 35
And turn your fairest arts to crimes of deepest dye.

THE CITIZEN AND THE TRAVELLER

ROBERT LOUIS STEVENSON (SCOTLAND)

"Look round you," said the citizen. "This is the largest market in the world."

"Oh, surely not," said the traveller.

"Well, perhaps not the largest," said the citizen, "but much the best."

"You are certainly wrong there," said the traveller. "I can tell you——"

They buried the stranger at the dusk.

THE GOOD FLEA AND THE WICKED KING

VICTOR HUGO (FRANCE)

Once upon a time there was a wicked king, who made his people very unhappy. Everybody detested him, and those whom he had put in prison and beheaded would have liked to whip him. But how? He was the strongest, he was the master, he did not have to give account to any one, and when he was told his subjects were not content, he replied:

"Well, what of it? I don't care a rap!" Which was an ugly answer.

As he continued to act like a king, and as every day he became a little more wicked than the day before, this set a certain little flea to thinking over the matter. It was a little bit of a flea, who was of no consequence at all, but full of good sentiments. This is not the nature of fleas in general; but this one had been very well brought up; it bit people with moderation, and only when it was very hungry.

"What if I were to bring the king to reason?" it said to itself. "It is not without danger. But no matter—I will try."

That night the wicked king, after having done all sorts of naughty things during the day, was calmly going to sleep when he felt what seemed to be the prick of a pin.

"Bite!"

He growled, and turned over on the other side.

"Bite! Bite! Bite!"

"Who is it that bites me so?" cried the king in a terrible voice.

"It is I," replied a very little voice.

"You? Who are you?"

"A little flea who wishes to correct you."

"A flea? Just you wait! Just you wait, and you shall see!"

And the king sprang from his bed, twisted his coverings, and shook the sheets, all of which was quite useless, for the good flea had hidden itself in the royal beard.

"Ah," said the king, "it has gone now, and I shall be able to get a sound sleep."

But scarcely had he laid his head on the pillow, when—

"Bite!"

"How? What? Again?"

"Bite! Bite!"

"You dare to return, you abominable little flea? Think for a moment what you are doing! You are no bigger than a grain of sand, and you dare to bite one of the greatest kings on earth!"

"Well, what of it? I don't care a rap!" answered the flea in the very words of the king.

"Ah, if I only had you!"

"Yes, but you haven't got me!"

The wicked king did not sleep all that night, and he arose the next morning in a killing ill humor. He resolved to destroy his enemy. By his orders, they cleaned the palace from top to bottom, and particularly his bedroom; his bed was made by ten old women very skillful in the art of catching fleas. But they caught nothing, for the good flea had hidden itself under the collar of the king's coat.

That night, this frightful tyrant, who was dying for want of sleep, lay back on both his ears, though this is said to be very difficult. But

he wished to sleep double, and he knew no better way. I wish you
may find a better. Scarcely had he put out his light, when he felt the
flea on his neck.

"Bite! Bite!"

"Ah, zounds! What is this?"

"It is I—the flea of yesterday."

"But what do you want, you rascal—you tiny pest?"

"I wish you to obey me, and to make your people happy."

"Ho, there, my soldiers, my captain of the guard, my ministers,
my generals! Everybody! The whole lot of you!"

The whole lot of them came in. The king was in a rage, which
made everybody tremble. He found fault with all the servants of
the palace. Everybody was in consternation. During this time the
flea, quite calm, kept itself hid in the king's nightcap.

The guards were doubled; laws and decrees were made; ordi-
nances were published against all fleas; there were processions and
public prayers to ask of Heaven the extermination of the flea, and
sound sleep for the king. It was all of no avail. The wretched king
could not lie down, even on the grass, without being attacked by his
obstinate enemy, the good flea, who did not let him sleep a single
minute.

"Bite! Bite!"

It would take too long to tell the many hard knocks the king gave
himself in trying to crush the flea; he was covered with bruises and
contusions. As he could not sleep, he wandered about like an uneasy
spirit. He grew thinner. He would certainly have died if, at last,
he had not made up his mind to obey the good flea.

"I surrender," he said at last, when it began to bite him again.
"I ask for quarter. I will do what you wish."

"So much the better. On that condition only shall you sleep,"
replied the flea.

"Thank you. What must I do?"

"Make your people happy!"

"I have never learned how. I do not know how——"

"Nothing more easy: you have only to go away."

"Taking my treasures with me?"

"Without taking anything."

"But I shall die if I have no money," said the king.

"Well, what of it? I don't care!" replied the flea.

But the flea was not hard-hearted, and it let the king fill his
pockets with money before he went away. And the people were
able to be very happy by setting up a republic.

READING PROBLEMS ON THE FABLE

As the point of interest in all fables is to apply the story to human life, questions on each fable would duplicate those on any other. The following questions are therefore suggested for all selections in the fable unit.

1. What types of character or social classes do the characters represent? If the fable in an animal story, are the animals well chosen for the point made?

2. Is the situation in the fable also typical and if so, of what?

3. Is the incident interesting enough to stand alone as a story without the allegory embodied in it or does it depend for interest on the hidden meaning?

4. How is the incident shaped by the author to develop the desired point? Note especially clever details.

5. Does the author point the moral or leave you to work it out?

FURTHER READINGS

Broun: *The Fifty-first Dragon*
Stevenson: *Faith, Half Faith, and No Faith at All*
Chaucer: *The Nun's Priest's Tale*
Emerson: *The Mountain and the Squirrel*
Saxe: *The Blind Men and the Elephant*
Harris: *Uncle Remus*

Parables from the *New Testament*, such as "The Prodigal Son," "The Good Samaritan," "The Grain of Mustard Seed," "The Talent," "The Foolish Virgins," "The House Builded on the Sands," "The Lost Sheep," etc.

SUGGESTIONS FOR ORIGINAL FABLES

Write anecdotes based on first hand observation to illustrate the truth expressed in one of the foregoing fables; or else compose a fable of your own in prose or verse on some such topic as: 1. The Constant Borrower. 2. The Over-Confident Athlete. 3. The Delayed Preparation. 4. Cramming versus Reviewing. 5. The Exacting Good Teacher. 6. The Expensive Date. 7. The Chronic Cheater.

X

The Essay

THERE is nothing people like better than to express their opinions, and a literary type devoted entirely to this purpose was certain sooner or later to appear. We owe its modern form to a cultivated French gentleman named Montaigne. Montaigne spent his young manhood in political and court circles, but in middle life withdrew to his country estate where, lacking society as clever as himself, he began the chatty, informal, and entertaining conversations with the public which he called *Essais*, and of which he issued the first volume in 1580. Montaigne selected the name *essay* (or "first try") for his little prose pieces, because, just as we do in conversation, he started a topic, gave his opinions on it from one or two angles, and then dropped it without exhausting the subject as a writer would do in a scholarly treatise.

The Biblical writers, the Greek Plato and Aristotle, and the Roman Cicero, had written essays long before Montaigne's time, but of these authors, only Plato had given his essays a conversational turn. But Plato's reports of the conversations of Socrates with his followers on various topics were the discussions of a teacher with a pupil, and pursued the matter in hand to a thorough finish. It remained for this witty sixteenth century Frenchman to give the essay the happy manner of playful discussion without instruction or tedium, which is the mark of cultivated conversation.

Montaigne's conversations were one-sided, as are the conversations with their readers of all his charming imitators since he sat in his château library amusing himself with his ideas and creating the literary type which in one form or another largely fills our current magazines today. For the good magazine article is just such another brief conversation of author and reader upon some topic of mutual interest. Now you know that to enjoy a conversation, you have to take part in it. You get quickly bored if some one else monopolizes the talk. So to enjoy an essay you must keep up your end of the conversation. You must talk back as you read, by thinking of what you would say to the author if he were there in person. Sometimes you will agree with him and think of good illustrations of his points or of new angles of the subject that he has not developed. Sometimes you will disagree and answer him with arguments. In any case, you will be mentally alive and keeping up your end of the conversation, and hence you will be having a good time!

To be able to have fun playing thus with your mind is a mark of intellectual maturity, and to read essays well and be interested in ideas as such will stamp you as mentally adult. Psychologists tell us that during adolescence the mind develops for the first time the capacity for abstract thought and generalization. The bright child is interested in things. The adolescent begins to have ideas and theories, the pursuit of which he finds even more fascinating than his childhood games. It is at this moment that he first begins to discuss life problems with his friends. At this moment he begins to enjoy the conversation of brilliant men and women whom he can never meet but with whom he can chat intimately through the medium of their essays.

The essay is, then, a brief prose selection expressing the author's own thoughts, moods, or feelings. It therefore has a strong personal flavor. It treats the subject just from the angle that happens to interest the author, and opens up the subject rather than covering it completely. The essay is, none the less, a finished whole; whatever aspect of the topic it treats must be covered in a systematic way. A chapter in a textbook designed to give you mere information is seldom noted for its style. Clearness is all you ask of it. The style of an essay, however, is usually one of its principal charms. The writer strives to be delightful in every way—he keeps up a flow of ideas, he sparkles with anecdote, he uses amusing descriptive words, he raises a laugh or a smile at some novel or whimsical phrase, he flashes into poetic and imaginative passages. Being well read and well bred, the essayist illustrates his ideas by allusions (or half references [1]) to things in art, literature, music, science or history, and expects you to be familiar with the things to which he alludes and grasp the point without explanation. Like a gay guest at a

[1] When a columnist speaks of a movie actor as a young Adonis, he expects you to know that Adonis was a handsome Greek youth beloved by the ladies—and that this actor is ditto, ditto. When Mr. Crothers says, "The man with a literal mind moves in a perpetual comedy of errors. It is not a question of two Dromios. There are half a dozen Dromios under one hat," he expects us to to remember the story of Shakespeare's *Comedy of Errors.* When Arnold says of Pope's translation of Homer, "Bless me, thou art translated indeed," he expects us to recollect that that is what some one said to Bottom in *A Midsummer Night's Dream,* after Bottom had been turned by magic into a donkey.

party, he is always at his sparkling best. But like a charming social favorite, he is always sincere and natural and unaffected.

There are essays on every imaginable subject that has ever interested a lively mind. According to their center of interest, subject, or style, essays may be classified as follows:

1. The character sketch: a study of the appearance, character, and personality of a real or imaginary person

2. The descriptive essay: a picture of a place, building, object, etc. as seen through the author's eyes and mind

3. The familiar or personal essay: an intimate, informal revelation of the author's own personality, whims, tastes, and habits

4. The reflective or philosophic essay: a more serious discussion of deeper problems of life

5. The editorial essay: a discussion (often argumentative) of current issues, such as we find in the magazines, giving not just the news but a point of view toward it

6. The critical essay: a review which passes judgment on a play, a movie, a book, a musical composition or concert, a picture, or other work of art. The aim of the writer is to give one a clear idea of the subject, style, and value of the work of art, to place it in the history of the art, and to compare it with other works of its author and type

7. The scientific essay: an interpretation, not a mere explanation, of scientific facts, and intended to show the bearing on philosophy or progress of the scientific point discussed

8. The semi-narrative essay: an essay largely in narrative form but written for the idea, not the story

9. The biographical essay: an analysis of the life of some important person, not just narrating the events but explaining them and weighing their significance and influence

An essay is great if it:

1. Makes a vital point

2. Widens our intellectual range

3. Reveals an interesting personality in its author

4. Has an original style marked by appropriate beauty, wit, humor or imagination.

WITH THE PHOTOGRAPHER

STEPHEN LEACOCK (CANADA)

"I want my photograph taken," I said. The photographer looked at me without enthusiasm. He was a drooping man in a gray suit, with the dim eye of a natural scientist. But there is no need to describe him. Everybody knows what a photographer is like.

"Sit there," he said, "and wait."

I waited an hour. I read the *Ladies Companion* for 1912, the *Girls Magazine* for 1902 and the *Infants Journal* for 1888. I began to see that I had done an unwarrantable thing in breaking in on the privacy of this man's scientific pursuits with a face like mine.

After an hour the photographer opened the inner door.

"Come in," he said severely.

I went into the studio.

"Sit down," said the photographer.

I sat down in a beam of sunlight filtered through a sheet of factory cotton hung against a frosted skylight.

The photographer rolled a machine into the middle of the room and crawled into it from behind.

He was only in it a second,—just time enough for one look at me, —and then he was out again, tearing at the cotton sheet and the window panes with a hooked stick, apparently frantic for light and air.

Then he crawled back into the machine again and drew a little black cloth over himself. This time he was very quiet in there. I knew that he was praying and I kept still.

When the photographer came out at last, he looked very grave and shook his head.

"The face is quite wrong," he said.

"I know," I answered quietly; "I have always known it."

He sighed.

"I think," he said, "the face would be better three-quarters full."

"I'm sure it would," I said enthusiastically, for I was glad to find that the man had such a human side to him. "So would yours. In fact," I continued, "how many faces one sees that are apparently hard, narrow, limited, but the minute you get them three-quarters full they get wide, large, almost boundless in——"

But the photographer had ceased to listen. He came over and took my head in his hands and twisted it sideways. I thought he meant to kiss me, and I closed my eyes.

But I was wrong.

He twisted my face as far as it would go and then stood looking at it.

He sighed again.

"I don't like the head," he said.

Then he went back to the machine and took another look.

"Open the mouth a little," he said.

I started to do so.

"Close it," he added quickly.

Then he looked again.

"The ears are *bad*," he said; "droop them a little more. Thank you. Now the eyes. Roll them in under the lids. Put the hands on the knees, please, and turn the face just a little upward. Yes, that's better. Now just expand the lungs! So! And hump the neck— that's it—and just contract the waist—ha!—and twist the hip up toward the elbow—now! I still don't quite like the face, it's just a trifle *too* full, but——"

I swung myself round on the stool.

"Stop," I said with emotion but, I think, with dignity. "This face is *my* face. It is not yours, it is mine. I've lived with it for forty years and I know its faults. I know it's out of drawing. I know it wasn't made for me, but it's *my* face, the only one I have—" I was conscious of a break in my voice but I went on—"such as it is, I've learned to love it. And this is my mouth, not yours. These ears are *mine*, and if your machine is too narrow—" Here I started to rise from the seat.

Snick!

The photographer had pulled a string. The photograph taken, I could see the machine still staggering from the shock.

"I think," said the photographer, pursing his lips in a pleased smile, "that I caught the features just in a moment of animation."

"So!" I said bitingly,—"features, eh? You didn't think I could animate them, I suppose? But let me see the picture."

"Oh, there's nothing to see yet," he said, "I have to develop the negative first. Come back on Saturday and I'll let you see a proof of it."

On Saturday I went back.

The photographer beckoned me in. I thought he seemed quieter and graver than before. I think, too, there was a certain pride in his manner.

He unfolded the proof of a large photograph, and we both looked at it in silence.

"Is it me?" I asked.

"Yes," he said quietly, "it is you," and we went on looking at it.

"The eyes," I said hesitatingly, "don't look very much like mine."

"Oh, no," he answered, "I've retouched them. They come out splendidly, don't they?"

"Fine," I said, "but surely my eyebrows are not like that?"

"No," said the photographer, with a momentary glance at my

face, "the eyebrows are removed. We have a process now—the Delphide—for putting in new ones. You'll notice here where we've applied it to carry the hair away from the brow. I don't like the hair low on the skull."

"Oh, you don't, don't you?" I said.

"No," he went on, "I don't care for it. I like to get the hair clear back and make out a new brow line."

"What about the mouth?" I said with a bitterness that was lost on the photographer; "is that mine?"

"It's adjusted a little," he said, "yours is too low. I found I couldn't use it."

"The ears, though," I said, "strike me as a good likeness; they're just like mine."

"Yes," said the photographer thoughtfully, "that's so; but I can fix that all right in the print. We have a process now—the Sulphide—for removing the ears entirely. I'll see if——"

"Listen!" I interrupted, drawing myself up and animating my features to their full extent and speaking with a withering scorn that should have blasted the man on the spot. "Listen! I came here for a photograph—a picture—something which (mad though it seems) would have looked like me. I wanted something that would depict my face as Heaven gave it to me, humble though the gift may have been. I wanted something that my friends might keep after my death, to reconcile them to my loss. It seems that I was mistaken. What I wanted is no longer done. Go on, then, with your brutal work. Take your negative, or whatever it is you call it,—dip it in sulphide, bromide, oxide, cowhide,—anything you like,—remove the eyes, correct the mouth, adjust the face, restore the lips, reanimate the necktie and reconstruct the waistcoat. Coat it with an inch of gloss, shade it, emboss it, gild it, till even you acknowledge that it is finished. Then when you have done all that —keep it for yourself and your friends. They may value it. To me it is but a worthless bauble."

I broke into tears and left.

LOVE'S MINOR FRICTIONS

Frances and Gertrude Warner (America)

Minor friction is the kind that produces the most showy results with the smallest outlay. You can stir up more electricity in a cat by stroking her fur the wrong way than you can by dropping her into the well. You can ruffle the dearest member of your family more by asking him twice if he is *sure* that he locked the back door than his political opponents could stir him with a libel. We have direct access to the state of mind of the people with whom we share household life and love. Therefore, in most homes, no matter how congenial, a certain amount of minor friction is inevitable.

Four typical causes of minor friction are questions of *tempo,* the brotherly reform measure, supervised telephone conversations, and tenure of parental control. These are standard group-irritants that sometimes vex the sweetest natures.

The matter of *tempo,* broadly considered, covers the whole process of adjustment between people of hasty and deliberate moods. It involves alertness of spiritual response, alacrity in taking hints and filling orders, timely appreciations, considerate delays, and all the other delicate retards and accelerations that are necessary if hearts are to beat as one. But it also includes such homely questions as the time for setting out for places, the time consumed in getting ready to set out, and the swiftness of our progress thither. When a man who is tardy is unequally yoked with a wife who is prompt, the family moves from point to point with an irregularity of rhythm that lends suspense to the mildest occasions.

A certain architect and his wife Sue are a case in point. Sue is always on time. If she is going to drive at four, she has her children ready at half-past three, and she stations them in the front hall, with muscles flexed, at ten minutes to four, so that the whole group may emerge from the door like food shot from guns, and meet the incoming automobile accurately at the curb. Nobody ever stops his engine for Sue. Her husband is correspondingly late. Just after they were married, the choir at their church gambled quietly on the chances— whether she would get him to church on time, or whether he would make her late. The first Sunday they came five minutes early, the second ten minutes late, and every Sunday after that, Sue came early, Prescott came late, and the choir put their money into the contribution-box. In fact, a family of this kind can solve its problem most neatly by running on independent schedules, except when they are to ride in the same automobile or on the same train. Then, there is likely to be a breeze.

The matter of *tempo* involves also the sense of the fortunate moment, and the timing of deeds to accord with moods. In almost every group there is one member who is set at a slightly different velocity from the others, with a momentum not easily checked.

When the rest of the household settles down to pleasant conversation, this member thinks of something pressing that must be done at once.

The mother of three college boys is being slowly trained out of this habit. Her sons say that she ought to have been a fire-chief, so brisk is she when in her typical hook-and-ladder mood. Whenever her family sit talking in the evening, she has flitting memories of things that she must run and do. One night, when she had suddenly rushed out to see if the maid had remembered to put out the milk tickets, one of the boys was dispatched with a warrant for her arrest. He traced her to the door of the side porch, and peered out at her in the darkness. "What's little pussy-foot doing now?" he inquired affectionately. "Can she see better in the dark? Come along back." But her blood was up. She thought of several other duties, still waiting, and went at once to the kitchen and filled the dipper. With this she returned to the room where sat the waiting conversationalists, and systematically watered the fern. At the chorus of reproach she only laughed, the scornful laugh of the villain on the stage. Six determined hands seized her at once. The boys explained that, when they wanted to talk to her, it was not time to water ferns. As habitual breaker-up of public meetings, she was going to be reformed.

But the reform measure, a group-irritant second to none, is generally uphill business in the home. Welfare work among equals is sometimes imperative, but seldom popular. Any program of social improvement implies agitation and a powerful leverage of public opinion not wholly tranquillizing to the person to be reformed.

There is one family that has worked for years upon the case of one of its members who reads aloud out of season. When this brother William finds a noble bit of literature, he is fired to share it with his relatives, regardless of time and circumstances. He comes eagerly out of his study, book in hand, when his public is trying on a dress. Or he begins to read without warning, when all the other people in the room are reading something else. Arguments and penalties never had the slightest effect, until one of the company hit upon a device that proves a defensive measure in emergencies.

Brother William started suddenly to read aloud from a campaign speech. His youngest sister was absorbed in that passage in *Edwin Drood* called "A Night with Durdles," where Jasper and Durdles are climbing the cathedral spire. In self-defense she also began to read in a clear tone as follows: "Anon, they turn into narrower and steeper staircases, and the night air begins to blow upon them, and the chirp of some startled jackdaw or frightened rook precedes the heavy beating of wings in a confined space, and the beating down of dust and straws upon their heads."

The idea spread like wildfire. All the others opened their books and magazines and joined her in reading aloud from the page where they had been interrupted. It was a deafening medley of incongruous material—a very telling demonstration of the distance from which their minds had jumped when recalled to the campaign speech. Brother William was able to distinguish in the uproar such fragments as these: "Just at that moment I discovered four Spad machines far below the enemy planes"; " 'Thankyou, thankyou,' cried Mr. Salteena—"; "Thomas Chatterton Jupiter Zeus, a most dear woodrat"; and " 'It is natural,' Gavin said slowly, 'that you, sir, should wonder why I am here with this woman at such an hour.' "

This method did not work a permanent cure, because nothing ever cures the reader-aloud. His impulse is generosity—a mainspring of character, not a passing whim. But at a crisis, his audience can read aloud in concert.

The reform measure is more hopeful when directed, not at a rooted trait, but at a surface phase or custom. Even here success is not without its battles. My sister Barbara and I were once bent upon teaching our younger brother Geoffrey to rise when ladies entered the room. Geoffrey, then at the brigand age, looked at this custom as the mannerism of an effete civilization. He rose, indeed, for guests, but not as to the manner born. One day he came home and reported that the lady next door had introduced him to an aunt of hers who had just arrived on a visit. "And," said he, with speculative eye upon his sisters, *"I didn't get up to be introduced."*

The effect was all that heart could wish. Tongues flew. Geoffrey listened with mournful dignity, offering no excuse. He waited until our sisterly vocabulary was exhausted.

"Why didn't you ask me where I was when she introduced me?" he asked at length. "I was crawling along the ridgepole of her garage catching her cat for her, and I couldn't get up."

But we were not easily diverted from our attempts to foster in him the manly graces. We even went so far as to invite Geoffrey to afternoon tea parties with our friends. But a Tea-Lion, he said, was one thing that he was not. On such occasions he would be found sitting on the kitchen table dourly eating up the olives and refusing to come in. We were too young in those days to know that you cannot hurry a certain phase. But now, when we meet our brother at receptions, we smile at our former despair. Reformers often find their hardest tasks taken out of their hands by time.

Few brothers and sisters, however, are willing to trust to time to work its wonders. There is a sense of fraternal responsibility that goads us to do what we can for each other in a small way. The friction that ensues constitutes an experience of human values that the hermit in his cell can never know. Whenever people of decided views feel personally responsible for each other's acts, a type of social unrest begins to brew that sometimes leads to progress and sometimes leads to riots.

For this reason, in any home that aspires to peace at any price, the telephone should be installed in a soundproof box-office with no glass in the door. There is nothing that so incenses a friendly nature as a family grouped in the middle-distance offering advice when a telephone conversation is going on. The person at the receiver looks so idle; there seems to be no reason why he should not listen with his unoccupied ear; and, when he is so evidently in need of correct data, it seems only kind to help him out. It is the most natural thing in the world to listen. The family listens, in the first place, to find out which one of them is wanted, and they continue to listen to find out what is said. When the wrong thing is said, all loyal relatives feel responsible.

The person telephoning is unfairly handicapped by necessary politeness, because he can be heard through the transmitter and his advisers cannot. Only extreme exasperation can unleash his tongue, as happened once when Geoffrey, in our father's absence, undertook to answer a telephone call while Barbara, in the next room, corrected his mistakes.

Geoffrey, pricking both ears, was doing very well, until the lady at the other end of the line asked a question at the exact moment when Barbara offered a new thought. "What did you say?" inquired Geoffrey. Both Barbara and the lady repeated. "What is it?" said Geoffrey, waving one foot at Barbara. Barbara, not seeing the foot, repeated, and so did the lady, this time more distinctly. "I beg your pardon," said Geoffrey anxiously, "but what did you say?" Like an incredible nightmare the thing happened again. "Shut up!" roared Geoffrey; "what did you say?"

Barbara, recognizing instantly that part of the message directed to her, wrote her suggestion on the telephone pad and stole prudently away. Minor friction, she had learned, can sometimes lead to action on a large scale. Only after some such experience as this do we allow a kinsman to conduct his own telephone conversations, taking his own responsibilities, running his own dark risks.

But the sense of mutual responsibility is, after all, the prime educational factor in family life. Every good parent has a feeling of accountability for the acts of his children. He may believe in self-determination for the small States about him, but after all he holds a mandate.[1] The delightful interweaving of parental suggestion with the original tendencies of the various children is the delicate thing that makes each family individual. It is also the delicate thing that makes parenthood a nervous occupation. When parental suggestion is going to interweave delightfully as planned, and when it is not going to interweave at all, is something not foretold in the prophets.

The question of parental influence becomes more complex as the family grows older and more informally organized. Sometimes a son or daughter wants to carry out a pet project without any advice or warning or help from anybody. There is nothing rash or guilty about his plan. He simply happens to be in the mood to act, not in committee, but of himself. To achieve this, surrounded by a united and conversational family, becomes a game of skill. To dodge advice, he avoids the most innocent questions. At such times as these, the wisest parents wonder what they have done to forfeit confidence. They see this favorite son of theirs executing the most harmless plans with all the secrecy of the young poisoning princes of the Renaissance.

When this happens, the over-sensitive parent grieves, the dictatorial parent rails, but the philosophical parent picks up whatever interesting morsels he can on the side, and cocks a weather eye.

"Robert seems to have a good many engagements," wrote the mother of a popular son in a letter to an absent daughter, "but whether the nature of the engagements is social, athletic, or philanthropic, we can only infer from the equipment with which he sets out. I inferred the first this morning when he asked me to have his dress-suit sent to be pressed; but I could not be certain until Mrs. Stone said casually that Robert was to be a guest at Mrs. Gardiner's dinner next week. Don't you love to see such tender intimacy between mother and son?"

Secrecy of this kind is not the monopoly of sons. Excellent young women have chopped ice and frozen sherbet behind closed doors because they did not want to be told again not to get the ice all over the back piazza. Certain warnings go with certain projects as inevi-

---

[1] *mandate:* protectorate.

tably as rubbers with the rain. The practiced mother has so often found the warnings necessary that the mere sight of the act produces the formula by rote. Model sons and daughters should accept these hints with gratitude, thus avoiding all friction, however minor. But rather than be advised to do that which they were planning to do already, the most loyal of daughters will resort to clandestine measures, and go stealthily with the ice-pick as with a poniard beneath a cloak. This annoys an affectionate and capable mother very much. And she has a right to be annoyed, has she not? After all, it is her ice-pick.

There is something of spirited affection about the memory of all these early broils. They were heated enough at the time, for the most violent emotions can fly out at a trifling cause. Remarks made in these turbulent moments are often taken as a revelation of your true and inward self. The sentiments that you express in your moment of wrath sound like something that you have been repressing for years and are now turning loose upon an enlightened world.

With friends, after such an outburst, you could never feel quite the same again. But with your relatives, such moments can be lived down—as once occurred in our own family when our father one hot summer day sent Geoffrey back to town to perform a forgotten errand. I had not heard of the event until I took my place at table.

"Where's Geoffrey?" said I.

"I sent him back to get a letter he forgot," said my father.

"In all this heat?" I protested. "Well, if I had been in his place, I'd have gone away and stayed away."

"Well, you could," said my father serenely.

"Well, I will," said Little Sunshine, and walked out of the door and up the street in a rage.

After you have left your parental home as suddenly as this, there comes a moment when you have the sensation of being what is termed "all dressed up with no place to go." You feel that your decision, though sudden, is irrevocable, because going back would mean death to your pride. Therefore, when Geoffrey met his eloping sister at the corner, it was with some little diplomacy that he learned my history and took me back to the table under his wing. The conversation barely paused as we took our places. Our father went on affably serving the salad to the just and the unjust alike. If, at this point, I had been treated with the contumely that I deserved, the memory would be unpleasant in the minds of all. As it is, the family now mentions it as the time when Margaret ran away to sea.

The only thing that can make minor friction hurtful is the disproportionate importance that it can assume when it is treated as a major issue, or taken as an indication of mutual dislike. It is often an indication of the opposite, though at the moment the contestants would find this hard to believe. Kept in its place, however, we find in it later a great deal of humorous charm, because it belongs to a period when we dealt with our brethren with a primitive directness not possible in later years. An intricate ambition, this matter of harmony in the home. Ideally, every family would like to have a history of uninterrupted adorations and exquisite accord. But growth implies change, change implies adjustment, and adjustment among varied personalities implies friction. Kept at the minimum, kept in its place, such friction does not estrange. Instead, it becomes a means to an intimate acquaintance with one another's traits and moods—an intimacy of understanding not far remote from love.

THE SEARCHINGS OF JONATHAN

Elisabeth Woodbridge (America)

"What I find it hard to understand is, why a person who can see a spray of fringed gentian in the middle of a meadow can't see a book on the sitting-room table."

"The reason why I can see the gentian," said Jonathan, "is because the gentian is there."

"So is the book," I responded.

"Which table?" he asked.

"The one with the lamp on it. It's a red book, about so big."

"It isn't there; but, just to satisfy you, I'll look again."

He returned in a moment with an argumentative expression of countenance. "It isn't there," he said firmly. "Will anything else do instead?"

"No, I wanted you to read that special thing. Oh, dear! And I have all these things in my lap! And I know it is there."

"And I know it isn't there." He stretched himself out in the hammock and watched me as I rather ostentatiously laid down thimble, scissors, needle, cotton, and material and set out for the sitting-room table. There were a number of books on it, to be sure. I glanced rapidly through the piles, fingered the lower books, pushed aside a magazine, and pulled out from beneath it the book I wanted. I returned to the hammock and handed it over. Then, after possessing myself, again rather ostentatiously, of material, cotton, needle, scissors, and thimble, I sat down.

"It's the second essay I specially thought we'd like," I said.

"Just for curiosity," said Jonathan, with an impersonal air, "where did you find it?"

"Find what?" I asked innocently.

"The book."

"Oh! On the table."

"Which table?"

"The one with the lamp on it."

"I should like to know where."

"Why—just there—on the table. There was an *Atlantic* on top of it, to be sure."

"I saw the *Atlantic*. Blest if it looked as though it had anything under it! Besides, I was looking for it on top of things. You said you laid it down there just before luncheon, and I didn't think it could have crawled in under so quick."

"When you're looking for a thing," I said, "you mustn't think; you must look. Now go ahead and read."

If this were a single instance, or even if it were one of many illustrating a common human frailty, it would hardly be worth setting down. But are not all the Jonathans in the world continually being sent to some sitting-room table for something, and coming back to assert, with more or less pleasantness, according to their temperament, that it is not there? The incident, then, is not isolated; it is typical of a vast group. For Jonathan, read Everyman; for the red book, read any particular thing that you want Him to bring; for the sitting-room table, read the place where you know it is and Everyman says it isn't.

Is it necessary to recount instances? Every family can furnish them. As I allow myself to float off into a reminiscent dream I find my mind possessed by a continuous series of dissolving views in which Jonathan is always coming to me saying, "It isn't there," and I am always saying, "Please look again."

Though everything in the house seems to be in a conspiracy against him, it is perhaps with the fishing-tackle that he has most constant difficulties.

"My dear, have you any idea where my rod is? No, don't get up—I'll look if you'll just tell me where——"

"Probably in the corner behind the chest in the orchard room."

"I've looked there."

"Well, did you take it in from the wagon last night?"

"Yes, I remember doing it."

"The dining-room? You came in that way."

He goes and returns. "Not there." I reflect deeply.

"Jonathan, are you sure it's not in that corner of the orchard room?"

"Yes, I'm sure; but I'll look again." He disappears, but in a moment I hear his voice calling, "No! Yours is here, but not mine."

I perceive that it is a case for me, and I get up. "You go and harness. I'll find it," I call.

There was a time when, under such conditions, I should have begun by hunting in all the unlikely places I could think of. Now I know better. I go straight to the corner of the orchard room. Then I call to Jonathan, just to relieve his mind.

"All right! I've found it."

"Where?"

"Here in the orchard room."

"Where in the orchard room?"

"In the corner."

"What corner?"

"The usual corner—back of the chest."

"The devil!" Then he comes back to put his head in at the door. "What are you laughing at?"

If it isn't the rod, it is the landing net, which has hung itself on a nail a little to the left or right of the one he had expected to see it on; or his reel, which has crept into a corner of the tackle drawer and held a ball of string in front of itself to distract his vision; or a bunch of snell hooks, which, aware of its protective coloring, has snuggled up against the shady side of the drawer and tucked its pink-papered head underneath a gay pickerel spoon.

Fishing tackle is, clearly, "possessed," but in other fields Jonathan is not free from trouble. Finding anything on a bureau seems to offer peculiar obstacles. It is perhaps a big, black-headed pin that I want. "On the pincushion, Jonathan."

He goes, and returns with two sizes of safety pins and one long hatpin.

"No, dear, those won't do. A small, black-headed one—at least small compared with an ordinary pin."

"Common or house pin?" he murmurs, quoting a friend's phrase.

"Do look again! I hate to drop this to go myself."

"When a man does a job, he gets his tools together first."

"Yes; but they say women shouldn't copy men, they should develop along their own lines. Please go."

He goes, and comes back. "You don't want fancy gold pins, I suppose?"

"No, no! Here, you hold this, and I'll go." I dash to the bureau. Sure enough, he is right about the cushion. I glance hastily about. There, in a little saucer, are a half dozen of the sort I want. I snatch some and run back.

"Well, it wasn't in the cushion, I bet."

"No," I admit; "it was in a saucer just behind the cushion."

"You said cushion."

"I know. It's all right."

"Now, if you had said simply 'bureau,' I'd have looked in other places on it."

"Yes, you'd have looked in other places!" I could not forbear responding. There is, I grant, another side to this question. One evening when I went upstairs I found a partial presentation of it, in the form of a little newspaper clipping, pinned on my cushion. It read as follows:

"My dear," said she, "please run and bring me the needle from the haystack."

"Oh, I don't know which haystack."

"Look in all the haystacks—you can't miss it; there's only one needle."...

When we travel, the same thing happens with the tickets, especially if they chance to be costly and complicated ones, with all the shifts and changes of our journey printed thick upon their faces. The conductor appears at the other end of the car. Jonathan begins vaguely to fumble without lowering his paper. Pocket after pocket is browsed through in this way. Then the paper slides to his knee and he begins a more thorough investigation, with all the characteristic clapping and diving motions that seem to be necessary. Some pockets must always be clapped and others dived into to discover their contents.

No tickets. The conductor is halfway up the car. Jonathan's face begins to grow serious. He rises and looks on the seat and under it. He sits down and takes out packet after packet of papers and goes over them with scrupulous care. At this point I used to become really anxious—to make hasty calculations as to our financial resources, immediate and ultimate—to wonder if conductors ever really put nice people like us off trains. But that was long ago. I know now that Jonathan has never lost a ticket in his life. So I glance through the paper that he has dropped or watch the landscape until he reaches a certain stage of calm and definite pessimism, when he says, "I must have pulled them out when I took out those postcards in the other car. Yes, that's just what has happened." Then, the conductor being only a few seats away, I beg Jonathan to look once more in his vest pocket, where he always puts them. To oblige me he looks, though without faith, and lo! this time the tickets fairly fling themselves upon him, with smiles almost curling up their corners.

In the matter of the home haystacks Jonathan's confidence in himself has at last been shaken. For a long time, when he returned to me after some futile search, he used to say, "Of course you can look for it if you like, but it is not there." But man is a reasoning, if not altogether reasonable being, and with a sufficient accumulation of evidence, especially when there is some one constantly at hand to interpret its teachings, almost any set of opinions, however fixed, may be shaken. So here.

Once when we shut up the farm for the winter I left my fountain pen behind. This was little short of a tragedy, but I comforted myself with the knowledge that Jonathan was going back that week-end for a day's hunt.

"Be sure you get the pen first of all," I said, "and put it in your pocket."

"Where is it?" he asked.

"In the little medicine cupboard over the fireplace in the orchard room, standing up at the side of the first shelf."

"Why not on your desk?" he asked.

"Because I was writing tags in there, and set it up so it would be out of the way."

"And it was out of the way. All right. I'll collect it."

He went, and on his return I met him with eager hand—"My pen!"

"I'm sorry," he began.

"You didn't forget!" I exclaimed.

"No. But it wasn't there."

"But—did you look?"

"Yes, I looked."

"Thoroughly?"

"Yes, I lit three matches."

"Matches! Then you didn't get it when you first got there!"

"Why—no—I had the dog to attend to—and—but I had plenty of time when I got back, and it wasn't there."

"Well—Dear me! Did you look anywhere else? I suppose I may be mistaken. Perhaps I did take it back to the desk."

"That's just what I thought myself," said Jonathan. "So I went there, and looked, and then I looked on all the mantelpieces and your bureau. You must have put it in your bag the last minute—bet it's there now!"

"Bet it isn't."

It wasn't. For two weeks more I was driven to using other pens —strange and distracting to the fingers and the eyes and the mind. Then Jonathan was to go up again.

"Please look once more," I begged, "and don't expect not to see it. I can fairly see it myself, this minute, standing up there on the right-hand side, just behind the machine-oil can."

"Oh, I'll look," he promised. "If it's there, I'll find it."

He returned penless. I considered buying another. But we were planning to go up together the last week of the hunting season, and I thought I would wait on the chance.

We got off at the little station and hunted our way up, making great sweeps and jogs, as hunters must, to take in certain spots we thought promising—certain ravines and swamp edges where we are always sure of hearing the thunderous whir of partridge wings, or the soft, shrill whistle of woodcock. At noon we broiled chops and rested in the lee of the wood edge, where, even in the late fall, one can usually find spots that are warm and still. It was dusk by the time we came over the crest of the farm ledges and saw the huddle of the home buildings below us, and quite dark when we reached the house. Fires had been made and coals smoldered on the hearth in the sitting-room.

"You light the lamp," I said, "and I'll just take a match and go through to see if that pen should happen to be there."

"No use doing anything tonight," said Jonathan. "Tomorrow morning you can have a thorough hunt."

But I took my match, felt my way into the next room, past the fireplace, up to the cupboard, then struck my match. In its first flare-up I glanced it. Then I chuckled.

Jonathan had gone out to the dining-room, but he has perfectly good ears.

"NO!" he roared, and his tone of dismay, incredulity, rage, sent me off into gales of unscrupulous laughter. He was striding in, candle in hand, shouting, "It was not there!"

"Look yourself," I managed to gasp.

This time, somehow, he could see it.

"You planted it! You brought it up and planted it!"

"I never! Oh, dear me! It pays for going without it for weeks!"

"Nothing will ever make me believe that that pen was standing there when I looked for it!" said Jonathan, with vehement finality.

"All right," I sighed happily. "You don't have to believe it."

But in his heart perhaps he does believe it. At any rate, since that time he has adopted a new formula: "My dear, it may be there, of course, but I don't see it." And this position I regard as unassailable.

One triumph he has had. I wanted something that was stored away in the shut-up town house.

"Do you suppose you could find it?" I said, as gently as possible.

"I can try," he said.

"I think it is in a box about this shape—see?—a gray box, in the attic closet, the farthest-in corner."

"Are you sure it's in the house? If it's in the house, I think I can find it."

"Yes, I'm sure of that."

When he returned that night, his face wore a look of satisfaction very imperfectly concealed beneath a mask of nonchalance.

"Good for you! Where was it? Was it where I said?"

"No."

"Where?"

"It wasn't in a corner at all. It wasn't in that closet."

"It wasn't! Where, then?"

"Downstairs in the hall closet." He paused, then could not forbear adding, "And it wasn't in a gray box; it was in a big hatbox with violets all over it."

"Why, Jonathan! Aren't you grand! How did you ever find it? I couldn't have done better myself. Why, you've lived down the fountain pen—and we'll forget the pen——"

"Oh, no, you won't forget the pen either," he said with a certain pleasant grimness.

"Well, perhaps not—of course it would be a pity to forget that. Suppose I say, then, that we'll always regard the pen in the light of the violet hatbox?"

"I think that might do." Then he had an alarming afterthought. "But see here—you won't expect me to do things like that often?"

"Dear me, no! People can't live always on their highest levels. Perhaps you'll never do it again." Jonathan looked distinctly relieved. "I'll accept it as a unique effort—like Dante's angel and Raphael's sonnet."

"Jonathan," I said that evening, "what do you know about St. Anthony of Padua?"

"Not much."

"Well, you ought to. He helped you today. He's the saint who helps the people to find lost articles. Every man ought to take him as a patron saint."

"And do you know which saint it is who helps people to find lost virtues—like humility, for instance?"

"No. I don't really."

"I didn't suppose you did," said Jonathan.

DINNER TABLE TALK

Charles Dudley Warner (America)

Many people suppose that it is the easiest thing in the world to dine if you can get plenty to eat. This error is the foundation of much social misery. The world that never dines, and fancies it has a grievance justifying anarchy on that account, does not know how much misery it escapes. A great deal has been written about the art of dining. From time to time geniuses have appeared who knew how to compose a dinner; indeed, the art of doing it can be learned, as well as the art of cooking and serving it. It is often possible, also, under extraordinarily favorable conditions, to select a company congenial and varied and harmonious enough to dine together successfully. The tact for getting the right people together is perhaps rarer than the art of composing the dinner. But it exists. And an elegant table with a handsome and brilliant company about it is a common conjunction in this country. It is universally admitted that the number must be small. While there is nothing in social intercourse so agreeable and inspiring as a dinner of the right sort, society has invented no infliction equal to a large dinner that does not "go," as the phrase is. Why it does not go when the viands are good and the company is bright, is one of the acknowledged mysteries.

There need be no mystery about it. The social instinct and the social habit are wanting to a great many people of uncommon intelligence and cultivation—that sort of flexibility or adaptability that makes agreeable society. But even this does not account for the

failure of so many promising dinners. The secret of this failure always is that the conversation is not general. The sole object of the dinner is talk—and private talk at a table is not the sort that saves a dinner; however good it is, it always kills it. The chance of arrangement is that the people who would like to talk together are not neighbors; and if they are, they exhaust each other to weariness in an hour, at least of topics which can be talked about with the risk of being overheard. A duet to be agreeable must be to a certain extent confidential, and the dinner-table duet admits of little except generalities, and generalities between two have their limits of entertainment. Then there is the awful possibility that the neighbors at table may have nothing to say to each other; and in the best-selected company one may sit beside a stupid man—that is, stupid for the purpose of a *tête-à-tête*.

But this is not the worst of it. No one can talk well without an audience; no one is stimulated to say bright things except by the attention and questioning and interest of other minds. There is little inspiration in side talk to one or two. Nobody ought to go to a dinner who is not a good listener, and, if possible, an intelligent one. To listen with a show of intelligence is a great accomplishment. It is not absolutely essential that there should be a great talker or a number of good talkers at a dinner if all are good listeners, and able to "chip in" a little to the general talk that springs up. For the success of the dinner does not necessarily depend upon the talk being brilliant, but it does depend upon its being general, upon keeping the ball rolling round the table; the old-fashioned game becomes flat when the balls all disappear into private pockets. There are dinners where the object seems to be to pocket all the balls [1] as speedily as possible. We have learned that that is not the best game; the best game is when you not only depend on the carom,[2] but on going to the cushion [3] before you carom; that is to say, including the whole table, and making things lively. The hostess succeeds who is able to excite this general play of all the forces at the table, even using the silent but non-elastic material as cushions, if one may continue the figure.

Is not this, O brothers and sisters, an evil under the sun, this dinner as it is apt to be conducted? Think of the weary hours you have

---

[1] *pocket all the balls:* In pool, when a ball is knocked into one of the pockets at the edge of the table, it is removed from play and the person who knocked it in scores a point. The game ends when all balls have been pocketed.

[2] *carom:* a play in pool in which one strikes other balls with his own.

[3] *cushion:* Players purposely drive their balls against the cushioned edge of the pool table when they wish to give them a new direction.

given to a rite that should be the highest social pleasure! How often when a topic is started that promises well, and might come to something in a general exchange of wit and fancy, and some one begins to speak on it, and speak very well, too, have you not had a lady at your side cut in and give you her views on it—views that might be amusing if thrown out into the discussion, but which are simply impertinent as an interruption! How often when you have tried to get a "rise" out of somebody opposite, have you not had your neighbor cut in across you with some private depressing observation to your next neighbor! Private talk at a dinner-table is like private chat at a parlor musical, only it is more fatal to the general enjoyment.

There is a notion that the art of conversation, the ability to talk well, has gone out. That is a great mistake. Opportunity is all that is needed. There must be the inspiration of the clash of minds and the encouragement of good listening. In an evening round the fire, when couples begin to whisper or talk low to each other, it is time to put out the lights. Inspiring interest is gone. The most brilliant talker in the world is dumb. People whose idea of a dinner is private talk between seat-neighbors should limit the company to two. They have no right to spoil what can be the most agreeable social institution that civilization has evolved.

A SMALL VOCABULARY MAY HAVE A BIG KICK

RING W. LARDNER (AMERICA)

Ring Lardner ran a series of articles in *The Saturday Evening Post* representing the reactions to various current topics of the uneducated, almost illiterate man. The vocabulary, sentence structure, and spelling of the articles was intended to place the imaginary speaker in the social and intellectual scale. Don't absent-mindedly imitate any of these intentional mistakes of Mr. Lardner's!

❊　　❊　　❊

The other night I was to a party where they had a argument in regards to how many wds. is in the average man or lady's vocabulary which they meant how many wds. does a person use in their regular every day conversation and one lady said 4 or 5 thousand and one of the men give her the laugh and said 700 was nearer the mark, and of course I didn't take no part in the argument as they

was all my elders but that didn't keep me from thinking over the question and maybe some of my readers would be interested in doing the same.

Well, in the first place you would naturally suppose that a woman's vocabulary was a lot bigger than a man's on acct. of them talking so much more, but on second thoughts that don't prove nothing as you will notice that the most women say the same thing over and over and a woman might say 10,000 wds. per day but only 10 different wds. like for inst.:

"I wished we had a fire. The house is cold," which she is libel to say a 1000 times makeing a total of 10,000 wds. that don't mean nothing.

As a matter of fact, a man though he don't talk nowheres near as much, don't repeat himself nowheres near as often, so wile a man may talk 100 wds. a day to a woman's 10,000, still they's libel to be 50 different wds. amongst his 100 and sometimes even more than that, though if a man does say 100 wds. the chances are that at least 50 of them is "Well."

Some men of course has more to say than others and they's been evenings in my career when I only said 2 wds. the whole evening namely "stay" and "pass" and a few afternoons spent outdoors when my conversation was just the numeral wds. "seven" and "eight."

When all is said and done, I suppose the number of wds. a person talks depends on what line of business they are in, like for example a doctor talks practically all the time where as a engineer on a R.R. or a fisherman don't hardly say nothing, and even some people talks more than others in the same business like for inst. a elevator man in a 22 story bldg. has twice as much to say as a elevator man in a 11 story bldg. and a train man on a subway local has to name maybe 30 or 35 stations while a train man on a express only names 4 or 5, but as far as that is concerned, for all the good they do, the both of them might as well keep their mouth shut.

A box office man in a N.Y. theatre only has to say 2 wds. all day, namely, "Seventeenth row."

A man that runs a garage can get along on even less, as all he has to do is say, "No," when people call up to ask is their car ready yet.

A traffic policeman's conversation varies according to what time of day it is. In the morning, he only has to say "What do you think you are trying to do?" which is 9 wds. all together and only 7 of them different, but along in the afternoon when he ain't feeling so genial he adds 2 wds. makeing it: "What do you think you are try-ing to do?"

The facts of the matter is that nobody likes nobody for their vocabulary and no man ever married a gal because she could say 5000 wds. besides yes or because she couldn't, and on the contrary one of my best friends is a man that don't hardly ever open his mouth only to take a fresh chew, but they say its nice for a person to know a whole lot of wds. even if they don't use them so when they are in church or rideing on a train or something they can amuse themselfs counting up the wds. they know.

As for a big vocabulary getting a person anywheres or doing them any good, they's a party liveing in our house that is 2 yrs. old and I don't suppose he has got a vocabulary of more than 200 wds. and even some of them sounds foreign, but this bird gets what-ever he wants and I don't know of nobody who I would rather trade jobs with.

Which is about all the wds. I can write about wds., only to recom-mend to the reader a kind of a game I tried out the other day which was a couple of days after the party and the game was to try and think every time before I spoke and count the number of wds. I used and count how many of them was necessary and how many could be left out and of course I forgot a couple times and said things without thinking or counting them, but you would be sur-prised at the few number of wds. it is necessary for a person to say in the course of a day, and personally I come to the conclusion that a dumb mute ain't so much to be pitied after all and the people around him less.

OUR FRIEND, THE DOG

Maurice Maeterlinck (Belgium)

Translated by Alexander Teixeira de Mattos

I

I have lost, within these last few days, a little bulldog. He had just completed the sixth month of his brief existence. He had no history. His intelligent eyes opened to look out upon the world, to love mankind, then closed again on the cruel secrets of death.

The friend who presented me with him had given him, perhaps

by antiphrasis,[1] the startling name of Pelléas.[2] Why rechristen him? For how can a poor dog, loving, devoted, faithful, disgrace the name of a man or an imaginary hero?

Pelléas had a great bulging, powerful forehead, like that of Socrates[3] or Verlaine;[4] and, under a little black nose, blunt as a churlish assent, a pair of large hanging and symmetrical chops, which made his head a sort of massive, obstinate, pensive and three-cornered menace. He was beautiful after the manner of a beautiful, natural monster that has complied strictly with the laws of its species. And what a smile of incorruptible innocence, of affectionate submission, of boundless gratitude and total self-abandonment lit up, at the least caress, that adorable mask of ugliness! Whence exactly did that smile come? From the melting eyes? From the ears pricked up to catch the words of man? From the forehead that unwrinkled to appreciate and love, or from the stump of a tail that wriggled at the other end to testify to the intimate and impassioned joy that filled his small being, happy once more to encounter the hand or the glance of the god to whom he surrendered himself?

Pelléas was born in Paris, and I had taken him to the country. His fat paws, shapeless and not yet stiffened, carried slackly through the unexplored pathways of his new existence his huge and serious head, flat-nosed and, as it were, rendered heavy with thought.

For this thankless and rather sad head, like that of an overworked child, was beginning the overwhelming work that oppresses every brain at the start of life. He had, in less than five or six weeks, to get into his mind, taking shape within it, a satisfactory conception of the universe. Man, aided by all the knowledge of his own elders and his brothers, takes thirty or forty years to outline that conception, but the humble dog has to unravel it for himself in a few days.

It was a question, then, of studying the ground, which can be scratched and dug up and which sometimes reveals surprising things; of casting at the sky, which is uninteresting, for there is nothing there to eat, one glance that does away with it for good and all; of discovering the grass, the admirable and green grass, the springy and cool grass, a field for races and sports, a friendly and boundless bed, in which lies hidden the good and wholesome couch-grass. It was a question, also, of making promiscuously a thousand

---

[1] *antiphrasis:* contradiction.
[2] *Pelléas:* hero of a romantic play of love in olden days written by Maeterlinck.
[3] *Socrates:* a Greek philosopher noted for his snubnosed ugliness.
[4] *Verlaine:* a French poet.

urgent and curious observations. It was necessary, for instance, with no other guide than pain, to learn to calculate the height of objects from the top of which you can jump into space ; to convince yourself that it is vain to pursue birds who fly away and that you are unable to clamber up trees after the cats who defy you there ; to distinguish between the sunny spots where it is delicious to sleep and the patches of shade in which you shiver ; to remark with stupefaction that the rain does not fall inside the houses, that water is cold, uninhabitable and dangerous, while fire is beneficent at a distance, but terrible when you come too near ; to observe that the meadows, the farm-yards and sometimes the roads are haunted by giant creatures with threatening horns, creatures good-natured, perhaps, and, at any rate, silent, creatures who allow you to sniff at them a little curiously without taking offense, but who keep their real thoughts to themselves. It was necessary to learn, as the result of painful and humiliating experiment, that you are not at liberty to obey all nature's laws without distinction in the dwelling of the gods ; to recognize that the kitchen is the privileged and most agreeable spot in that divine dwelling, although you are hardly allowed to abide in it because of the cook, who is a considerable, but jealous power ; to learn that doors are important and capricious volitions, which sometimes lead to felicity, but which most often, hermetically closed, mute and stern, haughty and heartless, remain deaf to all entreaties ; to admit, once and for all, that the essential good things of life, the indisputable blessings, generally imprisoned in pots and stew-pans, are almost always inaccessible ; to know how to look at them with laboriously acquired indifference and to practise taking no notice of them, saying to yourself that here are objects which are probably sacred, since merely to skim them with the tip of a respectful tongue is enough to let loose the unanimous anger of all the gods of the house.

And then, what is one to think of the table on which so many things happen that cannot be guessed ; of the derisive chairs on which one is forbidden to sleep ; of the plates and dishes that are empty by the time that one can get at them ; of the lamp that drives away the dark ? . . . How many orders, dangers, prohibitions, problems, enigmas has one not to classify in one's overburdened memory ! . . . And how to reconcile all this with other laws, other enigmas, wider and more imperious, which one bears within one's self, within one's instinct, which spring up and develop from one hour to the other, which come from the depths of time and the race, invade the blood, the muscles and the nerves and suddenly assert themselves more irresistibly and more powerfully than pain, the word of the master himself, or the fear of death?

Thus, for instance, to quote only one example, when the hour of sleep has struck for men, you have retired to your hole, surrounded by the darkness, the silence and the formidable solitude of the night. All is asleep in the master's house. You feel yourself very small and weak in the presence of the mystery. You know that the gloom is peopled with foes who hover and lie in wait. You suspect the trees, the passing wind and the moonbeams. You would like to hide, to suppress yourself by holding your breath. But still the watch must be kept; you must, at the least sound, issue from your retreat, face the invisible and bluntly disturb the imposing silence of the earth, at the risk of bringing down the whispering evil or crime upon yourself alone. Whoever the enemy be, even if he be man, that is to say, the very brother of the god whom it is your business to defend, you must attack him blindly, fly at his throat, fasten your perhaps sacrilegious teeth into human flesh, disregard the spell of a hand and voice similar to those of your master, never be silent, never attempt to escape, never allow yourself to be tempted or bribed and, lost in the night without help, prolong the heroic alarm to your last breath.

There is the great ancestral duty, the essential duty, stronger than death, which not even man's will and anger are able to check. All our humble history, linked with that of the dog in our first struggles against every breathing thing, tends to prevent his forgetting it. And when, in our safer dwelling-places of today, we happen to punish him for his untimely zeal, he throws us a glance of astonished reproach, as though to point out to us that we are in the wrong and that, if *we* lose sight of the main clause in the treaty of alliance which he made with us at the time when we lived in caves, forests and fens, *he* continues faithful to it in spite of us and remains nearer to the eternal truth of life, which is full of snares and hostile forces.

But how much care and study are needed to succeed in fulfilling this duty! And how complicated it has become since the days of the silent caverns and the great deserted lakes! It was all so simple, then, so easy and so clear. The lonely hollow opened upon the side of the hill, and all that approached, all that moved on the horizon of the plains or woods, was the unmistakable enemy. . . . But today you can no longer tell. Whom are you to suffer, whom to stop? . . . There is the road by which every one, even the poor, has the right to pass. Why? You do not know; it is a fact which you deplore, but which you are bound to accept. Fortunately, on the other hand, here is the fair path which none may tread. This path is faithful to the sound traditions; it is not to be lost sight of; for by it enter into your daily existence the difficult problems of life.

Would you have an example? You are sleeping peacefully in a ray of the sun that covers the threshold of the kitchen with pearls. The earthenware pots are amusing themselves by elbowing and nudging one another on the edge of the shelves trimmed with paper lace-work. The copper stew-pans play at scattering spots of light over the smooth white walls. The motherly stove hums a soft tune and dandles three saucepans blissfully dancing; and, from the little hole that lights up its inside, defies the good dog who cannot approach, by constantly putting out at him its fiery tongue. The clock, bored in its oak case, before striking the august hour of meal-time, swings its great gilt navel to and fro; and the cunning flies tease your ears. On the glittering table lie a chicken, a hare, three partridges, besides other things which are called fruits—peaches, melons, grapes—and which are all good for nothing. The cook guts a big silver fish and throws the entrails (instead of giving them to you!) into the dust-bin. Ah, the dust-bin! Inexhaustible treasury, receptacle of windfalls, the jewel of the house! You will have your share of it, an exquisite and surreptitious share; but it does not do to seem to know where it is. You are strictly forbidden to rummage in it. Therefore, let us close the watchful eye that has seen. Let us pretend to sleep and to dream of the moon. . . .

Hark! A gentle tapping at the blue window that looks out on the garden! What is it? Nothing; a bough of hawthorn that has come to see what we are doing in the cool kitchen. . . . But what is that? I hear steps! . . . Up, ears, open; nose on the alert! . . . It is the baker coming up to the rails, while the postman is opening a little gate in the hedge of lime-trees. They are friends; it is well; they bring something: you can greet them and wag your tail discreetly twice or thrice, with a patronizing smile. . . .

Another alarm! What is it now? A carriage pulls up in front of the steps. The problem is a complex one. Before all, it is of consequence to heap copious insults on the horses, great, proud beasts, who make no reply. Meantime, you examine out of the corner of your eye the persons alighting. They are well-clad and seem full of confidence. They are probably going to sit at the table of the gods. The proper thing is to bark without acrimony, with a shade of respect, so as to show that you are doing your duty, but that you are doing it with intelligence. Nevertheless, you cherish a lurking suspicion and, behind the guests' backs, stealthily, you sniff the air persistently and in a knowing way, in order to discern any hidden intentions.

But halting footsteps resound outside the kitchen. This time it is the poor man dragging his crutch, the unmistakable enemy, the hereditary enemy, the direct descendant of him who roamed outside the bone-crammed cave which you suddenly see again in your racial memory. Drunk with indignation, your bark broken, your teeth multiplied with hatred and rage, you are about to seize the irreconcilable adversary by the breeches, when the cook, armed with her broom, comes to protect the traitor, and you are obliged to go back to your hole, where, with eyes filled with impotent and slanting flames, you growl out frightful, but futile curses.

Is that all? Not yet; for the smallest life is made up of innumerable duties, and it is a long work to organize a happy existence upon the borderland of two such different worlds as the world of beasts and the world of men. How should we fare if we had to serve, while remaining within our own sphere, a divinity, not an imaginary one like to ourselves because the offspring of our own brain, but a god actually visible, ever present, ever active, and as foreign, as superior to our being as we are to the dog?

We now, to return to Pelléas, know pretty well what to do and how to behave on the master's premises. But the world does not end at the house-door, and, beyond the walls and beyond the hedge, there is a universe of which one has not the custody, where one is no longer at home, where relations are changed. How are we to stand in the street, in the fields, in the market-place, in the shops? In consequence of difficult and delicate observations, we understand that we must take no notice of passers-by; obey no calls but the master's; be polite, with indifference, to strangers who pet us. Next, we must conscientiously fulfil certain obligations of mysterious courtesy toward our brothers the other dogs, respect chickens and ducks; not appear to remark the cakes at the pastry-cooks, which spread themselves insolently within reach of the tongue; show to the cats, who, on the steps of the houses, provoke us by hideous grimaces, a silent contempt; and remember that it is lawful and even commendable to chase and strangle mice, rats, wild rabbits and, generally speaking, all animals that have not yet made their peace with mankind.

All this and so much more! . . . Was it surprising that Pelléas often appeared pensive in the face of those numberless problems, and that his humble and gentle look was often full of unreadable questions?

Alas, he did not have time to finish the long and heavy task. An ill of a mysterious character, which seems specially to punish the only animal that succeeds in leaving the circle in which it is born; an indefinite ill that carries off hundreds of intelligent little dogs, came to put an end to the destiny and the happy education of Pelléas. And now all those efforts to achieve a little more light; all that ardour in loving, that courage in understanding; all that affectionate gaiety and innocent fawning; all those kind and devoted looks, which turned to man to ask for his assistance against unjust death; all those flickering gleams which came from the profound abyss of a world that is no longer ours; all those nearly human little habits lie sadly in the cold ground, under a flowering elder-tree, in a corner of the garden.

II

We are alone, absolutely alone on this chance planet; and, amid all the forms of life that surround us, not one, excepting the dog, has made an alliance with us. A few creatures fear us, most are unaware of us, and not one loves us. In the world of plants, we have dumb and motionless slaves; but they serve us in spite of themselves. They simply endure our laws and our yoke; and, so soon as we lose sight of them, they hasten to betray us and return to their former wild and mischievous liberty. The rose and the corn, had they wings, would fly at our approach like the birds.

Among the animals, we number a few servants who have submitted only through indifference, cowardice or stupidity. They do not love us, do not know us, scarcely notice us. They are unaware of our life, our death, our departure, our return, our sadness, our joy, our smile. For thousands of years, they have been living at our side, as foreign to our thoughts, our affections, our habits as though the least fraternal of the stars had dropped them but yesterday on our globe. And, if, tomorrow, leaving their feelings toward us untouched, nature were to give them the intelligence and the weapons wherewith to conquer us, I confess that I should distrust the hasty vengeance of the horse, the obstinate reprisals of the ass, and the maddened meekness of the sheep. I should shun the cat as I should shun the tiger; and even the good cow, solemn and somnolent, would inspire me with but a wary confidence. As for the hen, with her round, quick eye, as when discovering a slug or a worm, I am sure that she would devour me without a thought.

III

Now, in this indifference and this total want of comprehension in which everything that surrounds us lives; in this incommunicable world, where there exist among the creatures no other relations than those of executioners and victims, eaters and eaten, where not the smallest sympathy has ever made a conscious leap from one species to another, one animal alone, among all that breathes upon the earth, has succeeded in breaking through the prophetic circle, in escaping from itself to come bounding toward us, definitely to cross the enormous zone of darkness, ice and silence that isolates each category of existence in nature's unintelligible plan. This animal, our good familiar dog, simple and unsurprising as may today appear to us what he has done, in thus perceptibly drawing nearer to a world in which he was not born and for which he was not destined, has nevertheless performed one of the most unusual and improbable acts that we can find in the general history of life. When was this recognition of man by beast, this extraordinary passage from darkness to light, effected? Did we seek out the poodle, the collie, or the mastiff from among the wolves and the jackals, or did he come spontaneously to us? We cannot tell. So far as our human annals stretch, he is at our side, as at present; but what are human annals in comparison with the times of which we have no witness? The fact remains that he is there in our houses, as ancient, as rightly placed, as perfectly adapted to our habits as though he had appeared on this earth, such as he now is, at the same time as ourselves. We have not to gain his confidence or his friendship: he is born our friend; while his eyes are still closed, already he believes in us: even before his birth, he has given himself to man. But the word "friend" does not exactly depict his affectionate worship. He is our intimate and impassioned slave, whom nothing discourages, whom nothing repels, whose ardent trust and love nothing can impair. He has solved, in an admirable and touching manner, the terrifying problem which human wisdom would have to solve if a divine race came to occupy our globe. He has loyally, religiously, irrevocably recognized man's superiority and has surrendered himself to him body and soul, without after-thought, without any intention to go back, reserving of his independence, his instinct and his character only the small part indispensable to the continuation of the life prescribed by nature. But he loves us not only in his consciousness and his intelligence: the very instinct of his race, the entire unconsciousness of his species, it appears, think only of us, dream only of being useful to us. To serve us better, to adapt himself better to our different needs, he has adopted every shape and been able infinitely to vary the faculties, the aptitudes which he places at our disposal. Is he to aid us in the pursuit of game in the plains? His legs lengthen inordinately, his muzzle tapers, his lungs widen, he becomes swifter than the deer. Does our prey hide under wood? The docile genius of the species, forestalling our desires, presents us with the basset, a sort of almost footless serpent, which steals into the closest thickets. Do we ask that he should drive our flocks? The same obliging genius grants him the requisite size, intelligence, energy and vigilance. Do we intend him to watch and defend our house? His head becomes round and monstrous, in order that his jaws may be more powerful, more formidable and more tenacious. Are we taking him to the south? His hair grows shorter and lighter, so that he may faithfully accompany us under the rays of a hotter sun. Are we going up to the north? His feet grow larger, the better to tread the snow; his fur thickens, in order that the cold may not compel him to abandon us. Is he intended only for us to play with, to amuse the leisure of our eyes, to adorn or enliven the home? He clothes himself in a sovereign grace and elegance, he makes himself smaller than a doll to sleep on our knees by the fireside, or even consents, should our fancy demand it, to appear a little ridiculous to please us.

You shall not find, in nature's immense crucible, a single living being that has shown a like suppleness, a similar abundance of forms, the same prodigious faculty of accommodation to our wishes. This is because, in the world which we know, among the different and primitive geniuses that preside over the evolution of the several species, there exists not one, excepting that of the dog, that ever gave a thought to the presence of man. Whether this impression be purely imaginary or correspond with a reality, it is sweet to establish that, at least in appearance, there is on the planet where, like unacknowledged kings, we live in solitary state, a being that loves us.

However the case may stand with these appearances, it is none the less certain that, among intelligent creatures that have rights, duties, a mission and a destiny, the dog is a really privileged animal. He is the only living being that has found and recognizes an indubitable, tangible, unexceptionable and definite god. He knows to what to devote the best part of himself. He knows to whom above him to give himself. He has not to seek for a perfect, superior and infinite power in the darkness, amid successive lies, hypotheses and dreams. That power is there, before him, and he moves in its light. He knows the supreme duties which we all do not know. He has a certain ideal.

IV

And it was thus that, the other day, before his illness, I saw my little Pelléas sitting at the foot of my writing-table, his tail carefully folded under his paws, his head a little on one side, the better to question me, at once attentive and tranquil, as a saint should be in the presence of God. He was happy with the happiness which we, perhaps, shall never know, since it sprang from the smile and the approval of a life incomparably higher than his own. He was there, studying, drinking in all my looks; and he replied to them gravely, as from equal to equal, to inform me, no doubt, that, at least through the eyes, he knew that he was saying to me all that love should say. And, when I saw him thus, young, ardent and believing, trusting and wonderstruck, as though he had been the first of his race and as though we were still in the first days of the world's existence, I envied the gladness of his certainty, compared it with the destiny of man, still plunging on every side into darkness, and said to myself that the dog who meets with a good master is the happier of the two.

OF THE INEQUALITY THAT IS AMONG US

Michel de Montaigne (France)

Plutarch [1] says somewhere that he does not find so great a difference between beast and beast as he does between man and man. He is speaking of qualities of soul and internal faculties. In truth, I find the distance so great between Epaminondas, [2] as I imagine him, and some that I know—I mean such as are endowed with common sense—that I am ready to go further than Plutarch and say that there is more difference between this and that man, than there is between this man and that beast: and that there are as many gradations of minds as there are cubits between this and heaven, and as innumerable.

But, as regards the estimate of men, it is remarkable that, ourselves excepted, nothing is judged save by its proper qualities. We commend a horse for his strength and swiftness, and not for his

---

[1] *Plutarch:* a great biographer of ancient times.
[2] *Epaminondas:* a Greek hero.

harness; a greyhound for his speed, not for his collar; a hawk for its wing, not for its jesses and bells. Why, in like manner, do we not value a man for what is properly his own? He has a great retinue, a beautiful palace, so much influence, so great an income: all these are about him, not in him. If you are bargaining for a horse, you remove his housing-cloths, you look at him naked and uncovered. Or if he is covered, as they anciently were offered to princes for sale, it is only for the less important parts, that you may not waste time over the beauty of his coat or the breadth of his crupper, but fix your attention chiefly on examining his legs, eyes, and feet, which are the most useful parts. Why, in making your estimate of a man, do you estimate him all wrapped and muffled up? He displays to us only such parts as are not in the least his own, and conceals those by which alone one may rightly judge of his value. It is the worth of the blade that you inquire into, not of the scabbard: you will not perhaps give a farthing for it if you have unsheathed it. You must judge him by himself, not by his accessories. And as one of the ancients very wittily says: "Do you know why you think him tall? You are counting in the height of his pattens." [3] The pedestal is no part of the statue. Measure him without his stilts; let him lay aside his wealth, and his titles, let him present himself in his shirt. Has he a body fitted for its functions, sound and vigorous? What sort of soul has he? Is it beautiful, capable, and happily provided with all its faculties? Is it rich with its own resources or with those of others? Has fortune no hand in the affair? Can it without blinking behold drawn swords? Is it calm, equable, and content? This is what we should regard, and by this judge of the vast differences that there are between us. Is he

> a sage, who keeps in check
> His baser self, who lives at his own beck,
> Whom neither poverty nor dungeon drear
> Nor death itself can ever put in fear,
> Who can reject life's goods, resist desire,
> Strong, firmly braced, and in himself entire,
> A hard smooth ball that gives you ne'er a grip,
> 'Gainst whom, when Fortune runs, she's sure to trip? [4]

Such a man is five hundred cubits above kingdoms and duchies; he is an empire to himself.

[3] *pattens:* heavy shoes.
[4] A quotation from one of the satires of Horace, a Roman poet.

FREEDOM OF CHOICE

DANTE ALIGHIERI (ITALY)

Translated by P. H. Wicksteed

The first principle of freedom is freedom of choice, which many
have on their lips but few in their understanding. For they get as
far as saying that free choice is free judgment in matters of will;
and herein they say the truth; but the import of the words is far
from them . . .

I say that a judgment is the link between apprehension [1] and
appetite. For first a thing is apprehended, then when apprehended
it is judged to be good or bad, and finally he who has so judged it
pursues or shares it. If then, the judgment altogether sets the appetite in motion, and is in no measure anticipated by it, it is free. But
if the judgment is moved by the appetite, which to some extent an-
ticipates it, it cannot be free, for it does not move of itself, but is
drawn captive by another. And hence it is that brutes cannot have
free judgment because their judgments are always anticipated by
appetite.

OF EXPENSE

FRANCIS BACON (ENGLAND)

Riches are for spending, and spending for honor and good actions.
Therefore extraordinary expense must be limited by the worth of
the occasion, for voluntary undoing may be as well for a man's country as for the kingdom of heaven. But ordinary expense ought to be
limited by a man's estate, and governed with such regard, as it be [2]
within his compass and not subject to deceit and abuse of servants,
and ordered to the best show, that the bills may be less than the esti-
mation abroad. Certainly, if a man will keep but of even hand, his
ordinary expenses ought to be but to the half of his receipts, and if
he think to wax rich, but to the third part.

It is no baseness for the greatest to descend and look into their
own estate. Some forbear it, not upon negligence alone, but doubting to bring themselves into melancholy, in respect they shall find it
broken. But wounds cannot be cured without searching. A man
had need, if he be plentiful in some kind of expense, to be as saving

[1] *apprehension:* seeing or perceiving.   [2] *as it be:* so that it shall be.

again in some other: as if he be plentiful in diet, to be saving in apparel; if he be plentiful in the hall, to be saving in the stable; and the like. For he that is plentiful in expenses of all kinds will hardly be preserved from decay.

In clearing of a man's estate, he may as well hurt himself in being too sudden, as in letting it run on too long, for hasty selling is commonly as disadvantageable as interest. Besides, he that clears at once will relapse, for, finding himself out of straits, he will revert to his customs; but he that cleareth by degrees induceth a habit of frugality, and gaineth as well upon his mind as upon his estate. Certainly, who hath a state to repair may not despise small things, and, commonly, it is less dishonorable to abridge petty charges than to stoop to petty gettings. A man ought warily to begin charges, which once begun will continue; but in matters that return not, he may be more magnificent.

MY CHÂTEAUX

George William Curtis (America)

In Xanadu did Kubla Khan
A stately pleasure-dome decree.
—*Coleridge.*

I am the owner of great estates. Many of them lie in the West; but the greater part are in Spain. You may see my western possessions any evening at sunset, when their spires and battlements flash against the horizon. But my finest castles are in Spain.

It is not easy for me to say how I know so much, as I certainly do, about my castles in Spain. The sun always shines upon them. They stand lofty and fair in a luminous, golden atmosphere, a little hazy and dreamy, perhaps, like the Indian summer, but in which no gales blow and there are no tempests. All the lofty mountains, and beautiful valleys, and soft landscapes, that I have not yet seen, are to be found in the grounds. They command a noble view of the Alps; so fine, indeed, that I should be quite content with the prospect of them from the highest tower of my castle, and not care to go to Switzerland.

The neighboring ruins, too, are as picturesque as those of Italy, and my desire of standing in the Coliseum,[1] and of seeing the shattered arches of the aqueducts stretching along the Campagna [2] and

Title: *Châteaux:* castles.　　　　[1] *Coliseum:* amphitheater at Rome.
[2] *Campagna:* plain surrounding Rome.

melting into the Alban Mount, is entirely quenched. The rich gloom of my orange groves is gilded by fruit as brilliant of complexion and exquisite of flavor as any that ever dark-eyed Sorrento [3] girls, looking over the high plastered walls of southern Italy, hand to the youthful travelers, climbing on donkeys up the narrow lane beneath.

The Nile flows through my grounds. The desert lies upon their edge, and Damascus stands in my garden. I am given to understand, also, that the Parthenon [4] has been removed to my Spanish possessions. The Golden Horn [5] is my fish preserve; my flocks of golden fleece are pastured on the plain of Marathon,[6] and the honey of Hymettus [7] is distilled from the flowers that grow in the vale of Enna [8]—all in my Spanish domains.

From the windows of those castles look the beautiful women whom I have never seen, whose portraits the poets have painted. The lights that never shone glance at evening in the vaulted halls upon banquets that were never spread. The bands I have never collected play all night long, and enchant the brilliant company that was never assembled, into silence.

In the long summer mornings the children that I never had, play in the gardens that I never planted. I hear their sweet voices sounding low and far away, calling, "Father! father!" I see a lost fairhaired girl, grown now into a woman, descending the stately stairs of my castle in Spain, stepping out upon the lawn, and playing with those children. They bound away together down the garden; but those voices linger, this time airily calling, "Mother! mother!"

But there is a stranger magic than this in my Spanish estates. The lawny slopes on which, when a child, I played, in my father's old country place, which was sold when he failed, are all there, and not a flower faded, nor a blade of grass sere. The green leaves have not fallen from the spring woods of half a century ago, and a gorgeous autumn has blazed undimmed for fifty years among the trees I remember.

Chestnuts are not especially sweet to my palate now, but those with which I used to prick my fingers when gathering them in New Hampshire woods are exquisite as ever to my taste, when I think of eating them in Spain. I never ride horseback now at home;

---

[3] *Sorrento:* town on the Bay of Naples.
[4] *Parthenon:* temple of Athena on the Acropolis of Athens.
[5] *Golden Horn:* the beautiful harbor of Constantinople.
[6] *Marathon:* site of a battle between Persians and Greeks.
[7] *Hymettus:* a mountain near Athens famed for its honey.
[8] *Enna:* a lovely valley in Sicily.

but in Spain, when I think of it, I bound over all the fences in the country, bare-backed, upon the wildest horses.

Plays are insufferable to me here—Prue and I never go. Prue, indeed, is not quite sure it is moral; but the theaters in my Spanish castles are of a prodigious splendor, and when I think of going there, Prue sits in a front box with me—a kind of royal box—the good woman, attired in such wise as I have never seen her here, while I wear my white waistcoat, which in Spain has no appearance of mending, but dazzles with immortal newness, and is a miraculous fit.

Yes, and in those castles in Spain, Prue is not the placid, breeches-patching helpmate, with whom you are acquainted, but her face has a bloom which we both remember, and her movement a grace which my Spanish swans emulate, and her voice a music sweeter than those that orchestras discourse. She is always there what she seemed to me when I fell in love with her, many and many years ago. The neighbors called her then a nice, capable girl; and certainly she did knit and darn with a zeal and success to which my feet and my legs have testified for nearly half a century. But she could spin a finer web than ever came from cotton, and in its subtle meshes my heart was entangled, and there has reposed softly and happily ever since.

So, when I meditate my Spanish castles, I see Prue in them as my heart saw her standing by her father's door. "Age cannot wither her." [9] There is a magic in the Spanish air that paralyzes Time. He glides by, unnoticed and unnoticing. I greatly admire the Alps, which I see so distinctly from my Spanish windows; I delight in the taste of the southern fruit that ripens upon my terraces; I enjoy the pensive shade of the Italian ruins in my gardens; I like to shoot crocodiles, and talk with the Sphinx upon the shores of the Nile, flowing through my domain; I am glad to drink sherbet in Damascus, and fleece my flocks on the plains of Marathon; but I would resign all these forever rather than part with that Spanish portrait of Prue for a day. Nay, have I not resigned them all forever, to live with that portrait's changing original?

I have often wondered how I should reach my castles. The desire of going comes over me very strongly sometimes, and I endeavor to see how I can arrange my affairs, so as to get away. To tell the truth, I am not quite sure of the route,—I mean, to that particular part of Spain in which my estates lie. I have inquired very particu-larly, but nobody seems to know precisely.

[9] *Age cannot wither her:* said of Cleopatra in Shakespeare's *Antony & Cleo-patra,* II, ii.

It occurred to me that Bourne, the millionaire, must have ascertained the safest and most expeditious route to Spain; so I stole a few minutes one afternoon and went into his office. He was sitting at his desk, writing rapidly, and surrounded by files of papers and patterns, specimens, boxes, everything that covers the tables of a great merchant. In the outer rooms clerks were writing. Upon high shelves over their heads were huge chests, covered with dust, dingy with age, many of them, and all marked with the name of the firm, in large black letters—"Bourne & Dye." They were all numbered also with the proper year; some of them with a single capital B and dates extending back into the last century, when old Bourne made the great fortune, before he went into partnership with Dye. Everything was indicative of immense and increasing prosperity.

There were several gentlemen waiting to converse with Bourne, and I waited until they went out. But others came in. There was no pause in the rush. All kinds of inquiries were made and answered. At length I stepped up.

"A moment, please, Mr. Bourne."

"What is it, sir?" he asked, blandly, but with wrinkled brow.

"Mr. Bourne, have you any castles in Spain?" said I, without preface.

He looked at me for a few moments without speaking, and without seeming to see me. His brow gradually smoothed, and his eyes, apparently looking into the street, were really, I have no doubt, feasting upon the Spanish landscape.

"Too many, too many," said he at length, musingly, shaking his head, and without addressing me.

"Will you tell me what you consider the shortest and safest route thither, Mr. Bourne? for, of course, a man who drives such an immense trade with all parts of the world will know all that I have come to inquire."

"My dear sir," answered he, wearily, "I have been trying all my life to discover it; but none of my ships have ever been there—none of my captains have any report to make. They bring me, as they brought my father, gold dust from Guinea; ivory, pearls, and precious stones, from every part of the earth; but not a fruit, not a solitary flower, from one of my castles in Spain. I have sent clerks, agents, and travellers of all kinds, philosophers, pleasure-hunters, and invalids, in all sorts of ships, to all sorts of places, but none of them ever saw or heard of my castles, except one young poet, and he died in a mad-house."

"Mr. Bourne, will you take five thousand at ninety-seven?"

hastily demanded a man, whom, as he entered, I recognized as a broker. "We'll make a splendid thing of it."

Bourne nodded assent, and the broker disappeared.

"Happy man!" muttered the merchant, as the broker went out; "he has no castles in Spain."

"I am sorry to have troubled you, Mr. Bourne," said I, retiring.

"I am glad you came," returned he; "but I assure you, had I known the route you hoped to ascertain from me, I should have sailed years and years ago. People sail for the North-west Passage,[10] which is nothing when you have found it. Why don't the English Admiralty fit out expeditions to discover all our castles in Spain?"

THE NOBLEST INSTRUMENT

CLARENCE DAY (AMERICA)

This diverting sketch comes from *Life With Father*—a volume which extracts ironic amusement from every detail of family life as seen from the point of view of a son at various ages. One of the most amusing chapters deals with that perennial bone of domestic contention, household accounts. The author's gift of humorous characterization and his "outrageous keenness of insight" place him in the front rank of American essayists.

❋   ❋   ❋

Father had been away, reorganizing some old upstate railroad. He returned in an executive mood and proceeded to shake up our home. We boys were summoned before him and informed that we must at once learn to play on something. We might not appreciate it now, he said, but we should later on. "You, Clarence, will learn the violin. George, you the piano. Julian—well, Julian is too young yet. But you older boys must have lessons."

I was appalled at this order. At the age of ten it seemed a disaster to lose any more of my freedom. The days were already too short for our games after school; and now here was a chunk to come out of playtime three days every week. A chunk every day, we found afterward, because we had to practice.

George sat at the piano in the parlor, and faithfully learned to pound out his exercises. He had all the luck. He was not an inspired player, but at least he had some ear for music. He also had the ad-

[10] *North-west Passage:* a long-sought passage by sea from the Atlantic to the Arctic region.

vantage of playing on a good robust instrument, which he didn't have to be careful not to drop, and was in no danger of breaking. Furthermore, he did not have to tune it. A piano had some good points.

But I had to go through a blacker and more gruesome experience. It was bad enough to have to come in from the street and the sunlight and go down into our dark little basement where I took my lessons. But that was only the opening chill of the struggle that followed.

The whole thing was uncanny. The violin itself was a queer, fragile, cigar-boxy thing, that had to be handled most gingerly. Nothing sturdy about it. Why, a fellow was likely to crack it putting it into its case. And then my teacher was queer too. He had a queer pickled smell.

I dare say he wasn't queer at all really, but he seemed so to me, because he was different from the people I generally met. He was probably worth a dozen of some of them, but I didn't know it. He was one of the violins in the Philharmonic, and an excellent player; a grave, middle-aged little man—who was obliged to give lessons. He wore a black, wrinkled frock coat, and a discolored gold watch-chain. He had small, black-rimmed glasses; not tortoise-shell, but with thin rims of metal. His violin was dark, rich, and polished, and would do anything for him. Mine was balky and awkward, brand new, and of a light, common color.

The violin is intended for persons with a passion for music. I wasn't that kind of person. I liked to hear a band play a tune that we could march up and down to, but try as I would, I could seldom whistle such a tune afterward. My teacher didn't know this. He greeted me as a possible genius.

He taught me how to hold the contraption, tucked under my chin. I learned how to move my fingers here and there on its handle or stem. I learned how to draw the bow across the strings, and thus produce sounds . . .

Does a mother recall the first cry of her baby, I wonder? I still remember the strange cry at birth of that new violin. My teacher, Herr M., looked as though he had suddenly taken a large glass of vinegar. He sucked in his breath. His lips were drawn back from his teeth, and his eyes tightly shut. Of course, he hadn't expected my notes to be sweet at the start; but still, there was something unearthly about that first cry. He snatched the violin from me, examined it, readjusted its pegs, and comforted it gently, by drawing his own bow across it.

He handed the instrument back to me with careful directions. I tucked it up under my chin again and grasped the end tight. I held my bow exactly as ordered. I looked up at him, waiting.

"Now," he said nervously.

I slowly raised the bow, drew it downward. . . . This time there were two dreadful cries in our little front basement. One came from my new violin and one from the heart of Herr M.

Herr M. presently came to, and smiled bravely at me, and said if I wanted to rest a moment he would permit it. He seemed to think I might wish to lie down awhile and recover. I didn't feel any need of lying down. All I wanted was to get through the lesson. But Herr M. was shaken. He was by no means ready to let me proceed. He looked around desperately, saw the music book, and said he would now show me that. We sat down side by side on the window-seat, with the book in his lap, while he pointed out the notes to me with his finger, and told me their names.

After a bit, when he felt better, he took up his own violin, and instructed me to watch him and note how he handled the strings. And then at last, he nerved himself to let me take my violin up again. "Softly, my child, softly," he begged me, and stood facing the wall. . . .

We got through the afternoon somehow, but it was a ghastly experience. Part of the time he was maddened by the mistakes I kept making, and part of the time he was plain wretched. He covered his eyes. He seemed ill. He looked often at his watch, even shook it as though it had stopped; but he stayed the full hour.

That was Wednesday. What struggles he had with himself before Friday, when my second lesson was due, I can only dimly imagine, and of course I never even gave them a thought at the time. During my third lesson, I saw the tears come to his eyes. He went to Father and said he was sorry but he honestly felt sure I'd never be able to play.

Father didn't like this at all. He said he felt sure I would. He dismissed Herr M. briefly—the poor man came stumbling back down in two minutes. In that short space of time, he had gallantly gone upstairs in a glow, resolved upon sacrificing his earnings for the sake of telling the truth. He returned with his earnings still running, but with the look of a lost soul about him, as though he felt that his nerves and his sanity were doomed to destruction. But he no longer struggled. He accepted this thing as his destiny. It was a grotesque, indeed a hellish experience, but he felt he must bear it.

He wasn't the only one—he was at least not alone in his sufferings. Mother, though expecting the worst, had tried to be hopeful about it, but at the end of a week or two I heard her and Margaret [1] talking it over. I was slaughtering a scale in the front basement, when Mother came down and stood outside the door in the kitchen hall and whispered, "Oh, Margaret!"

I watched them. Margaret was baking a cake. She screwed up her face, raised her arms, and brought them down with hands clenched.

"I don't know what we shall do, Margaret."

"The poor little feller," Margaret whispered. "He can't make the thing go."

This made me indignant. They were making me look like a lubber. I wished to feel always that I could make things go. . . .

I now began to feel a determination to master this thing. History shows us many examples of the misplaced determinations of men— they are one of the darkest aspects of human life, they spread so much needless pain: but I knew little history. And I viewed what little I did know romantically—I should have seen in such episodes their heroism, not their futility. Any rôle that seemed heroic attracted me, no matter how senseless.

Not that I saw any chance for heroism in our front basement, of course. You had to have a battlefield or something. I saw only that I was appearing ridiculous. But that stung my pride. I hadn't wanted to learn anything whatever about fiddles or music, but since I was in for it, I'd do it, and show them I could. A boy will often put in enormous amounts of his time trying to prove he isn't as ridiculous as he thinks people think him.

Meanwhile Herr M. and I had discovered that I was nearsighted. On account of the violin's being an instrument that sticks out in front of one, I couldn't stand close enough to the music book to see the notes clearly. He didn't at first realize that I often made mistakes from that cause. When he and I finally comprehended that I had this defect, he had a sudden new hope that this might have been the whole trouble, and that when it was corrected I might play like a human being at least.

Neither of us ventured to take up this matter with Father. We knew that it would have been hard to convince him that my eyes were not perfect, I being a son of his and presumably made in his image. So Herr M. instead lent me his glasses. These did fairly well. They turned the dim grayness of the notes into a queer bright

[1] *Margaret:* the cook.

distortion, but the main thing was they did make them brighter, so that I now saw more of them. How well I remember those little glasses. Poor, dingy old things. Herr M. was nervous about lending them to me; he feared that I'd drop them. It would have been safer if they had been spectacles: but no, they were pince-nez; and I had to learn to balance them across my nose as well as I could. I couldn't wear them up near my eyes because my nose was too thin there; I had to put them about half-way down where there was enough flesh to hold them. I also had to tilt my head back, for the music-stand was a little too tall for me. Herr M. sometimes mounted me on a stool, warning me not to step off. Then when I was all set, and when he without his glasses was blind, I would smash my way into the scales again.

All during the long winter months I worked away at this job. I gave no thought, of course, to the family. But they did to me. Our house was heated by a furnace, which had big warm air pipes; and sound travelled easily and ringingly through their roomy, tin passages. My violin could be heard in every part of the house. No one could settle down to anything while I was practicing. If visitors came they soon left. Mother couldn't even sing to the baby. She would wait, watching the clock, until my long hour of scale-work was over, and then come downstairs and shriek at me that my time was up.

It was a hard winter for Mother. She sometimes pleaded with Father; but no one could ever tell Father anything. He continued to stand like a rock against stopping my lessons.

Schopenhauer,[2] in his rules for debating, shows how to win a weak case by insidiously [3] transferring an argument from its right field, and discussing it instead from some irrelevant but impregnable angle. Father knew nothing of Schopenhauer, and was never insidious, but, nevertheless, he had certain natural gifts for debate. In the first place his voice was powerful and stormy, and he let it out at full strength, and kept on letting it out with a vigor that stunned his opponents. As a second gift, he was convinced at all times that his opponents were wrong. Hence, even if they did win a point or two, it did them no good, for he dragged the issue to some other ground then, where he and Truth could prevail. When Mother said it surely was plain enough that I had no ear, what was his reply? Why, he said that the violin was the noblest instrument invented by man. Having silenced her with this solid premise, he declared that it followed that any boy was lucky to be given the privilege of learn-

[2] *Schopenhauer:* see page 688.   [3] *insidiously:* imperceptibly.

ing to play it. No boy should expect to learn it immediately. It required persistence. Everything, he had found, required persistence. The motto was, Never give up.

All his life, he declared, he had persevered in spite of discouragements, and he meant to keep on persevering, and he meant me to, too. He said that none of us realized what he had had to go through. If he had been the kind that gave up at the very first obstacle, where would he have been now—where would any of the family have been? The answer was, apparently, that we'd either have been in a very bad way, poking round for crusts in the gutter, or else non-existent. We might have never even been born if Father had not persevered.

Placed beside this record of Father's vast trials overcome, the little difficulty of my learning to play the violin seemed a trifle. I faithfully spurred myself on again, to work at the puzzle.

Of course, I kept begging Herr M. to let me learn just one tune. Even though I seldom could whistle them, still I liked tunes; and I knew that, in my hours of practicing, a tune would be a comfort. That is, for myself. Here again I never gave a thought to the effect upon others.

Herr M., after many misgivings, to which I respectfully listened —though they were not spoken to me, they were muttered to himself, pessimistically—hunted through a worn old book of selections, and after much doubtful fumbling chose as simple a thing as he could find for me—for me and the neighbors.

It was spring now, and windows were open. That tune became famous. What would the musician who had tenderly composed this air, years before, have felt if he had foreseen what an end it would have, on Madison Avenue; and how, before death, it would be execrated by that once peaceful neighborhood. I engraved it on their hearts; not in its true form but in my own eerie versions. It was the only tune I knew. Consequently I played and replayed it.

Even horrors when repeated grow old and lose part of their sting. But those I produced were, unluckily, never the same. To be sure, this tune kept its general structure the same, even in my sweating hands. There was always the place where I climbed unsteadily up to its peak, and that difficult spot where it wavered, or staggered, and stuck; and then a sudden jerk of resumption—I came out strong on that. Every afternoon when I got to that difficult spot, the neighbors dropped whatever they were doing to wait for that jerk, shrinking from the moment, and yet feverishly impatient for it to come.

But what made the tune and their anguish so different each day?

I'll explain. The strings of a violin are wound at the end around pegs, and each peg must be screwed in and tightened till the string sounds just right. Herr M. left my violin properly tuned when he went. But suppose a string broke, or that somehow I jarred a peg loose. Its string then became slack and soundless. I had to re-tighten it. Not having an ear, I was highly uncertain about this. Our neighbors never knew at what degree of tautness I'd put such a string. I didn't myself. I just screwed her up tight enough to make a strong reliable sound. Neither they nor I could tell which string would thus appear in a new rôle each day, nor foresee the profound transformations this would produce in that tune.

All that spring this unhappy and ill-destined melody floated out through my window, and writhed in the air for one hour daily, in sunshine or storm. All that spring our neighbors and I daily toiled to its peak, and staggered over its hump, so to speak, and fell wailing through space.

Things now began to be said to Mother which drove her to act. She explained to Father that the end had come at last. Absolutely. "This awful nightmare cannot go on," she said.

Father pooh-poohed her.

She cried. She told him what it was doing to her. He said that she was excited, and that her descriptions of the sounds I made were exaggerated and hysterical—must be. She was always too vehement, he shouted. She must learn to be calm.

"But you're downtown, you don't have to hear it!"

Father remained wholly skeptical.

She endeavored to shame him. She told him what awful things the neighbors were saying about him, because of the noise I was making, for which he was responsible.

He couldn't be made to look at it that way. If there really were any unpleasantness then I was responsible. He had provided me with a good teacher and a good violin—so he reasoned. In short, he had done his best, and no father could have done more. If I made hideous sounds after all that, the fault must be mine. He said that Mother should be stricter with me, if necessary, and make me try harder.

This was the last straw. I couldn't try harder. When Mother told me his verdict I said nothing, but my body rebelled. Self-discipline had its limits—and I wanted to be out: it was spring. I skimped my hours of practice when I heard the fellows playing outside. I came home late for lessons—even forgot them. Little by little they stopped.

Father was outraged. His final argument, I remember, was that my violin had cost twenty-five dollars; if I didn't learn it the money would be wasted, and he couldn't afford it. But it was put to him that my younger brother, Julian, could learn it instead, later on. Then summer came, anyhow, and we went for three months to the seashore; and in the confusion of this Father was defeated and I was set free.

In the autumn little Julian was led away one afternoon, and imprisoned in the front basement in my place. I don't remember how long they kept him down there, but it was several years. He had an ear, however, and I believe he learned to play fairly well. This would have made a happy ending for Herr M. after all; but it was some other teacher, a younger man, who was engaged to teach Julian. Father said Herr M. was a failure.

ON LITERATURE

MAXIM GORKY (RUSSIA)

Translated by S. S. Koteliansky

Does one need to speak of the necessity of a serious study of literature, or at least of a wide acquaintance with it? Literature is the heart of the world, winged with all its joys and sorrows, with all the dreams and hopes of men, with their despair and wrath, with their reverence before the beauty of nature, their fears in face of her mysteries.

Literature may also be called the all-seeing eye of the world, whose glance penetrates into the deepest recesses of the human spirit. A book—so simple a thing and so familiar—is, essentially, one of the great and mysterious wonders of the world. Some one unknown to us, sometimes speaking an uncomprehensible language, hundreds of miles away, has drawn on paper various combinations of a score or so of signs, which we call letters, and when we look at them, we strangers, remote from the creator of the book, mysteriously perceive the meaning of all the words, the ideas, the feelings, the images; we admire the description of the scenes of nature, take delight in the beautiful rhythm of speech, the music of the words. Moved to tears, angry, dreaming, sometimes laughing over the motley [1] printed sheets, we grasp the life of the spirit, akin or foreign to ourselves. The book is, perhaps, the most complicated and

[1] *motley:* variegated.

mightiest of all the miracles created by man on his path to the happiness and power of the future.

There is no one universal literature, for there is yet no language common to all, but all literary creation, in prose and poetry, is saturated with the unity of feelings, thoughts, ideals shared by all men, with the unity of man's sacred aspiration toward the joy of the freedom of the spirit, with the unity of man's disgust at the miseries of life, the unity of his hopes of the possibility of higher forms of life, and with the universal thirst for something indefinable in word or thought, hardly to be grasped by feeling, that mysterious something to which we give the pale name of beauty, and which comes to an ever brighter and more joyous flower in the world, in our own hearts.

Whatever may be the inward differences of nations, races, individualities, however distinct may be the external forms of states, religious conceptions, and customs, however irreconcilable the conflict of classes—over all these differences, created by ourselves through centuries, hovers the dark and menacing specter of the universal consciousness of the tragic quality of life and the poignant sense of the loneliness of man in the world.

Rising from the mystery of birth, we plunge into the mystery of death. Together with our planet we have been thrown into incomprehensible space. We call it the Universe, but we have no precise conception of it, and our loneliness in it has such an ironical perfection that we have nothing with which to compare it. But the faint feeling of it is implanted in the instinct of nearly every man. This anguish that arises from the dim sense of the precariousness and tragedy of life is common to great and small, to every one who has the courage to look at life with open eyes.

The great virtue of literature is that it speaks to us as with a voice saying that Hen-Toy, the Chinaman, is as agonizingly unsatisfied with the love of woman as Don Juan, the Spaniard; that the Abyssinian sings the same songs of the sorrows and joys of love as the Frenchman; that there is an equal pathos in the love of a Japanese Geisha [2] and Manon Lescaut; [3] that man's longing to find in woman the other half of his soul has burned and burns with an equal flame men of all lands, all times.

A murderer in Asia is as loathsome as in Europe; the Russian miser Plushkin is as pitiable as the French Grandet; the Tartufes [4] of all countries are alike; misanthropes are equally miserable everywhere, and everywhere every one is equally charmed by the touch-

---

[2] *geisha:* professional entertainer in a tea house.
[3] *Manon Lescaut:* an unfortunate girl in a French story.
[4] *Tartufes:* a famous hypocrite in a play by Molière.

ing image of Don Quixote, the Knight of the Spirit. And after all, all men, in all languages, always speak of the same things, of themselves and their fate. Men of brute instincts are everywhere alike, the world of the intellect alone is infinitely varied.

With a clearness irresistibly convincing, fine literature gives us all these innumerable likenesses and infinite varieties—literature, the pulsing mirror of life, reflecting with quiet sadness or with anger, with the kindly laugh of a Dickens or the frightful grimace of Dostoevsky,[5] all the complications of our spiritual life, the whole world of our desires, the bottomless stagnant pools of banality [6] and folly, our heroism and cowardice in the face of destiny, the courage of love and the strength of hatred, all the nastiness of our hypocrisy and the shameful abundance of lies, the disgusting stagnation of our minds and our endless agonies, our thrilling hopes and sacred dreams—all by which the world lives, all that quivers in the hearts of men. Watching man with the eyes of a sensitive friend, or with the stern glance of a judge, sympathizing with him, laughing at him, admiring his courage, cursing his nullity [7]—literature rises above life, and, together with science, lights up for men the paths to the achievement of their goals, to the development of what is good in them.

It is obvious that literature cannot be completely free from what Turgeniev [8] called "the pressure of time." And it may be that the evil of the day poisons more often than it should the sacred spirit of beauty. But "the beautiful is the rare," and we most certainly often consider lacking in beauty insignificant habitual things—those habitual things which, as they recede into the past, acquire for our descendants all the marks and qualities of true, unfading beauty. Does not the austere life of ancient Greece appear to us beautiful? Does not the bloody, stormy, and creative epoch of the Renaissance with all its habitual cruelty enrapture us? It is more than probable that the great days of social catastrophe we are going through now will arouse the ecstasy, awe, and creativeness of the generations that will come after us.

Nor let us forget that though Balzac's [9] *Poor Relations*, Gogol's [8] *Dead Souls*, Dickens' *The Pickwick Papers*, are essentially books that describe conditions of actual life, there is hidden in them a great and imperishable lesson which the best university cannot provide, and which an average man will not have learned so exactly or so clearly after fifty years of hard-working life—the longing to raise

[5] *Dostoevsky:* a Russian novelist.
[6] *banality:* commonplaceness.
[7] *nullity:* nothingness.
[8] *Turgeniev, Gogol:* Russian novelists.
[9] *Balzac:* French novelist.

man above the external conditions of existence, to free him from the fetters of the degrading actuality, to show him to himself not as the slave, but as the lord of circumstance, the free creator of life. Literature believes that the ennobled will of men can and must destroy all errors, all that which, arresting the free development of the spirit, delivers man into the power of animal instincts.

When you look closely into the mighty stream of creative energy embodied in the word and image, you feel and believe that the great purpose of this stream is to wash away for ever all the differences between races, nations, classes, and, by freeing men from the hard burden of the struggle with each other, to direct all their forces to the struggle with the mysterious forces of nature.

Literature, the living and imaged history of the exploits and errors, of the excellences and failures of our ancestors, possessing the mighty power of influencing the organization of thought, of refining the crudity of the instincts, of educating the will, must finally fulfil her planetary *rôle*—the *rôle* of the power which most firmly and most intimately unites the peoples by the consciousness of their sufferings and longings, by the consciousness of the community of their desire for the happiness of a life that is beautiful and free.

The wider his knowledge, the more perfect is man; the keener and more eager man's interest in his fellow-men, the quicker we shall pass through our stations of the cross to the universal festival of mutual understanding, respect, and brotherhood—to our own glory.

After the bloody tempest [10] of malice and hatred, nothing could be more opportune than to present the wide picture of spiritual creation. Let men remember all that is truly human that the ages have taught us, that genius and talent have taught the world.

ON THINKING FOR ONE'S SELF

ARTHUR SCHOPENHAUER (GERMANY)

Translated by Belfort Bax

As the richest library unarranged is not so useful as a very moderate one well arranged, so the greatest amount of erudition,[1] if it has not been elaborated by one's own thought, is worth much less than a far smaller amount that has been well thought over. For it

[10] *tempest:* the World War.   [1] *erudition:* learning.

is through the combination on all sides of that which one knows, through the comparison of every truth with every other, that one assimilates one's own knowledge and gets it into one's power. One can only think out what one knows; hence one should learn something; but one only knows what one has thought.

One can apply one's self of set purpose only to reading and learning, but not to thinking proper. Thinking must, that is, be stimulated and maintained, like fire by a draught of air, by some interest in the subject itself, which may be either a purely objective [2] or a merely subjective [3] one. The latter is present only in the case of our personal interest, but the former only for thinking heads by nature, for which thought is as natural as breath, but which are very rare.

The distinction between the effect which thinking for one's self, and that which reading has upon the mind, is very great. Reading imposes thoughts upon the mind which are as foreign to the direction and mood which it has for the moment, as the seal is to the wax on which it impresses its stamp. The mind suffers thereby an entire compulsion from without, to think now this, now that, for which it has no desire, and no capacity. In thinking for itself, on the other hand, it follows its own natural impulse, as either external circumstance or some recollection has determined it for the moment. Perceptual surroundings, [4] namely, do not impress one definite thought upon the mind as reading does, but merely give it material and occasion to think that which is according to its nature and present disposition. Hence much reading deprives the mind of all elasticity, as a weight continually pressing upon it does a spring, and the most certain means of never having any original thoughts is to take a book in hand at once, at every spare moment.

Scholars are those who have read in books; but thinkers, geniuses, enlighteners of the world, and benefactors of the human race, are those who have directly read in the book of the world.

At bottom it is only our own fundamental conceptions which have truth and life, for it is they alone that one thoroughly and correctly understands. Alien thoughts that we read are the remnants of another's meal, the cast-off clothes of a strange guest. The alien thought arising within us is related to our own as the impression in stone of a plant of the early world is to the blooming plant of spring.

Reading is a mere substitute for original thought. In reading, one allows one's own thoughts to be guided by another in leading-

---

[2] *objective:* independent of personal advantage.
[3] *subjective:* purely personal.
[4] *perceptual surroundings:* the things we perceive around us.

strings. Besides, many books are only good for showing how many false paths there are, and how seriously one may miss one's way if one allows oneself to be guided by them ; but he whom genius guides, he, that is, who thinks for himself—he has the compass to find out the right way. One should only read when the source of original thoughts fails, which is often enough the case even with the best heads. But to scare away one's own original thoughts for the sake of taking a book in the hand is a sin against the Holy Ghost. In this case, one resembles a man who runs away from free nature in order to look at a herbarium,[5] or to contemplate a beautiful landscape in an engraving.

Even if sometimes one may find with ease in a book a truth or an insight already given, which one has worked out slowly, and with much trouble, by one's own thinking and combining; it is yet worth a hundred times more when one has attained it through one's original thought. Only then does it become an integral part, a living member of the whole system of our thoughts ; only then is it understood in all its grounds and consequences, and bears the color, the shade, the stamp of our whole mode of thought, and this because it has come at the precise time that the need for it was present, and therefore sits firmly, secure from dispossession. The self-thinker learns the authorities for his opinions afterwards, when they serve merely to confirm him in them and for his own strengthening. The book-philosopher, on the other hand, starts from them, in that he constructs a whole for himself out of the alien opinions he has read, which then resembles an automaton that has been put together out of foreign material, rather than a living man.

Truth that has only been learned cleaves to us like a limb that has been stuck on—a false tooth, a waxen nose. But that which has been acquired by original thought resembles the natural limb; it alone really belongs to us. On this rests the distinction between the thinker and the mere scholar.

Reading means thinking with an alien head, not one's own. But to original thought, from which a coherent whole, even if not a strictly rounded-off system, seeks to develop itself, nothing is more injurious than too great an influx of foreign thoughts through continual reading. For these, each sprung from another mind, belonging to another system, bearing another color, never of themselves flow together to form a whole of thought, of knowledge, of insight, and conviction, but rather set up a Babylonian [6] confusion of

---

[5] *herbarium:* collection of dried plants.
[6] *Babylonian:* see story of the Tower of Babel, Genesis 11.

tongues in the head, and rob the mind which has been filled with them of all clear insight, and thus almost disorganize it. This state is noticeable with many scholars, and the result is that they are behind many unlearned persons in healthy understanding, accurate judgment, and practical tact, the latter having always subordinated to and incorporated with their own thought what has come to them from without, through experience, conversation, and a little reading. The scientific *thinker* does this in a greater degree. Although he needs much knowledge, and therefore must read much, his mind is nevertheless strong enough to master all this, to assimilate it, to incorporate it into his system of thoughts, and so to subordinate it to the organically coherent whole of a magnificent insight, which is always growing. In this, his own thinking, like the ground bass of the organ, perpetually dominates all, and is never drowned by foreign tones, as is the case with merely polyhistorical [7] heads, in which, as it were, musical fragments from all keys run into one another, and the fundamental note is no more to be heard.

People who have occupied their life with reading, and who have derived their wisdom from books, resemble those who have acquired a correct knowledge of a country from many descriptions of travel. Such persons can give information about much, but at bottom they have no coherent, clear, fundamental knowledge of the structure of the country. Those, on the contrary, who have occupied their life with thought, resemble persons who have themselves been in that country. They alone know, properly speaking, what is in question, since they know the things there in their connection, and are truly at home in them.

ON TRANSLATING HOMER

Matthew Arnold (England)

As so much of the present volume is made up of translations, the problem of how far a translation can reproduce the content, spirit and style of the original is especially interesting. Every language has its own word order, its own idiomatic ways of expressing certain thoughts, and its own individual sound and rhythm. For instance, Greek is light, liquid and rapid; Latin dignified and sonorous. French is sharp pitched compared to guttural German. The sound and the syntax of each language represents the racial character and mode of thought; translating from one tongue to another destroys inevitably much of this

[7] *polyhistorical:* crammed with information.

racial quality. Poetry, of course, suffers most in translation since it loses its music. But by a skilful translator, the thought and feeling of the original can be to a great extent transferred. Matthew Arnold in the following extract points out some of the difficulties of translating the poetry of Homer into English.

❊   ❊   ❊

The study of classical literature is probably on the decline; but, whatever may be the fate of this study in general, it is certain that, as instruction spreads and the number of readers increases, attention will be more and more directed to the poetry of Homer, not indeed as part of a classical course, but as the most important poetical monument existing. Even within the last ten years two fresh translations of the *Iliad* have appeared in England. It may safely be asserted that neither of these works will take rank as the standard translation of Homer; that the task of rendering him will still be attempted by other translators. It may perhaps be possible to render to these some service, to save them some loss of labor, by pointing out rocks on which their predecessors have split, and the right objects on which a translator of Homer should fix his attention.

The translator of Homer should above all be penetrated by a sense of four qualities of his author: Homer is rapid in his movement, Homer is plain in his words and style, Homer is simple in his ideas, Homer is noble in his manner. Cowper renders him ill because he is slow in his movement, and elaborate in his style; Pope renders him ill because he is artificial both in his style and in his words; Chapman renders him ill because he is fantastic in his ideas; Mr. Newman renders him ill because he is odd in his words and ignoble in his manner.

*   *   *   *   *

Everyone knows the passage at the end of the eighth book of the *Iliad,* where the fires of the Trojan encampment are likened to the stars. The commencement of the passage is of great and celebrated beauty, and in translating this Pope has been singularly and notoriously fortunate. But the latter part of the passage, where Homer leaves the stars and comes to the Trojan fires, treats of the plainest, most matter-of-fact subject possible, and deals with this, as Homer always deals with every subject, in the plainest and most straightforward style. "So many in number, between the ships and the streams of Xanthus,[2] shone forth in front of Troy the fires kindled by the Trojans. There were kindled a thousand fires in the plain; and by each one there sat fifty men in the light of the blazing fire. And the horses, munching white barley and rye, and standing by the chariots, waited for the bright-throned Morning."

In Pope's translation, this plain story becomes the following:

> So many flames before proud Ilion [3] blaze,
> And brighten glimmering Xanthus with their rays;
> The long reflections of the distant fires
> Gleam on the walls, and tremble on the spires.
> A thousand piles the dusky horrors gild,
> And shoot a shady lustre o'er the field.
> Full fifty guards each flaming pile attend,
> Whose umbered [4] arms, by fits, thick flashes send;
> Loud neigh the coursers o'er their heaps of corn,
> And ardent warriors wait the rising morn.

It is for passages of this sort, which, after all, form the bulk of a narrative poem, that Pope's style is so bad. In elevated passages he is powerful, as Homer is powerful, though not in the same way; but in plain narrative, where Homer is still powerful and delightful, Pope, by the inherent fault of his style, is ineffective and out of taste.

Chapman's style is not artificial like Pope's nor his movement elaborate and self-retarding like the movement of Cowper. He is plain-spoken, fresh, vigorous, and, to a certain degree, rapid; and all these are Homeric qualities.

But I confess that I can never read twenty lines of Chapman's version without recurring to Bentley's cry, "This is not Homer!"

I have just been speaking of the plainness and directness of Homer's style; but the plainness and directness of the contents of his style, of his ideas themselves, is not less remarkable. But the Elizabethan literature in general, and Chapman in particular, is fanciful. Steeped in fantasticality up to its very lips, the Elizabethan age, newly arrived at the free use of the human faculties after their long term of bondage, [5] and delighting to exercise them freely, suffers from its own extravagance and can hardly bring itself to see an object quietly or to describe it temperately.

---

[2] *Xanthus:* a river near Troy.   [3] *Ilion:* Troy.   [4] *umbered:* shadowed.
[5] The Elizabethan age was the Renaissance, or period of enlightenment which followed the Dark Ages.

In Hector's famous speech at his parting from Andromache, Homer makes him say: "Nor does my own heart so bid me" (to keep safe behind the walls), "since I have learned to be staunch always, and to fight among the foremost of the Trojans, busy on behalf of my father's great glory, and my own." In Chapman's hands this becomes:

> The spirit I first did breathe
> Did never teach me that; much less, since the contempt of death
> Was settled in me, and my mind knew what a worthy was,
> Whose office is to lead in fight, and give no danger pass
> Without improvement. In this fire must Hector's trial shine:
> Here must his country, father, friends, be in him made divine.

You see how ingeniously Homer's plain thought is tormented, as the French would say, here. Homer goes on: "For well I know this in my mind and in my heart, the day will be, when sacred Troy shall perish—" Chapman makes this:

> And such a stormy day shall come, in mind and soul I know,
> When sacred Troy shall shed her towers, for tears of overthrow.

I might go on forever, but I could not give you a better illustration than this last, of what I mean by saying that the Elizabethan poet fails to render Homer because he cannot forbear to interpose a play of thought between his object and its expression.

And yet, in spite of this perfect plainness and directness of Homer's style, in spite of this perfect plainness and directness of his ideas, he is eminently noble; he works as entirely in the grand style, as Phidias, or Dante, or Michelangelo. This is what makes his translators despair. "To give relief," says Cowper, "to prosaic subjects" (such as dressing, eating, drinking, harnessing, travelling, going to bed), that is, to treat such subjects nobly, in the grand style, "without seeming unreasonably tumid,⁶ is extremely difficult." It is difficult, but Homer has done it. Homer is precisely the incomparable poet he is, because he has done it. His translator must not be tumid, must not be artificial, must not be literary; true. But then also he must not be commonplace, must not be ignoble. . . .

I think it will be found that the grand style arises in poetry, when a noble nature, poetically gifted, treats with simplicity or with severity a serious subject. . . .

Here is the great difficulty: the poets of the world have been

---

⁶ *tumid:* pompous.

many; there has been wanting neither abundance of poetical gift nor abundance of noble natures; but a poetical gift so happy, in a noble nature so circumstanced and trained, that the result is a continuous style, perfect in simplicity or perfect in severity, has been extremely rare. Some have caught this perfect strain now and then, in short pieces or single lines, but have not been able to maintain it through considerable works; others have composed all their productions in a style which, by comparison with the best, one must call secondary.

(Arnold next proceeds to show at a length too great for quotation why translators fail to reproduce Homer's nobility and how he thinks it might be done.)

Only, the poet who would reproduce this nobility must cultivate in himself a Greek virtue by no means common among the moderns in general, and the English in particular,—moderation. For Homer has not only the English vigor, he has the Greek grace. Homer's grandeur is not the mixed and turbid grandeur of the great poets of the north, of the authors of *Othello* and *Faust;* it is a lovely grandeur. Certainly his poetry has all the energy and power of the poetry of our ruder climates; but it has, besides, the pure lines of an Ionian [7] horizon, the liquid clearness of an Ionian sky. . . .

The one proper aim of the translator is to produce on the intelligent scholar, as nearly as possible, this general effect of Homer. Except as he reproduces this, he loses his labor.

SIGNIOR NICOLINI AND HIS LIONS

JOSEPH ADDISON (ENGLAND)

Joseph Addison and Richard Steele published in the eighteenth century a two-page periodical entitled *The Spectator* which contained the germs of both the modern newspaper and the modern magazine. In addition to a brief digest of the news, *The Spectator* contained an entertaining article humorously criticizing the manners, customs, and interests of the age.

❋   ❋   ❋

There is nothing that of late years has afforded matter of greater amusement to the town than Signior Nicolini's combat with a lion

---

[7] *Ionian:* Grecian. Greece is a semitropical country with a climate and scenery very different from that of north Europe.

in the Haymarket,[1] which has been very often exhibited to the general satisfaction of most of the nobility and gentry in the kingdom of Great Britain. Upon the first rumor of this intended combat, it was confidently affirmed, and is still believed by many in both galleries, that there would be a tame lion sent from the Tower every opera night, in order to be killed by Hydaspes.[2] Many likewise were the conjectures of the treatment which this lion was to meet with from the hands of Signior Nicolini; some supposed that he was to subdue him in recitativo, as Orpheus [3] used to serve the wild beasts in his time, and afterwards to knock him on the head; some fancied that the lion would not pretend to lay his paws upon the hero; several, who pretended to have seen the opera in Italy, had informed their friends that the lion was to roar twice or thrice to a thorough-base before he fell at the feet of Hydaspes. To clear up a matter that was so variously reported, I have made it my business to examine whether this pretended lion is really the savage he appears to be, or only a counterfeit.

But before I communicate my discoveries, I must acquaint the reader, that upon my walking behind the scenes last winter, as I was thinking on something else, I accidently jostled against a monstrous animal that extremely startled me, and upon my nearer survey of it, appeared to be a lion rampant.[4] The lion, seeing me very much surprised, told me, in a gentle voice, that I might come by him if I pleased: "for," (says he,) "I do not intend to hurt anybody." I thanked him very kindly, and passed by him. And in a little time after saw him leap upon the stage, and act his part with great applause. It has been observed by several that the lion has changed his manner of acting twice or thrice since his first appearance; which will not seem strange, when I acquaint my reader that the lion has been changed upon the audience three several times. The first lion was a candle-snuffer, who, being a fellow of a testy, choleric temper, overdid his part, and would not suffer himself to be killed so easily as he ought to have done; besides, it was observed of him that he grew more surly every time he came out of the lion, and having dropped some words in ordinary conversation, as if he had not fought his best, and that he suffered himself to be thrown upon his back in the scuffle, and that he would wrestle with Mr. Nicolini for what he pleased, out of his lion's skin, it was

---

[1] *Haymarket:* opera house in London.
[2] *Hydaspes:* character in the opera acted by Nicolini.
[3] *Orpheus:* Greek musician who charmed the beasts with his lyre.
[4] *rampant:* on its hind legs.

thought proper to discard him: and it is verily believed, to this day, that had he been brought upon the stage another time, he could certainly have done mischief. Besides, it was objected against the first lion, that he reared himself so high upon his hinder paws, and walked in so erect a posture, that he looked more like an old man than a lion.

The second lion was a tailor by trade, who belonged to the playhouse, and had the character of a mild and peaceable man in his profession. If the former was too furious, this was too sheepish, for his part; insomuch that after a short modest walk upon the stage, he would fall at the first touch of Hydaspes, without grappling with him, and giving him an opportunity of showing his variety of Italian trips: it is said, indeed, that he once gave him a rip in his flesh-color doublet; but this was only to make work for himself, in his private character of a tailor.

The acting lion at present is, as I am informed, a country gentleman, who does it for his diversion, but desires his name may be concealed. He says very handsomely in his own excuse that he does not act for gain, that he indulges an innocent pleasure in it; and that it is better to pass away an evening in this manner than in gaming and drinking: but at the same time says, with a very agreeable raillery upon himself, that if his name should be known, the ill-natured world might call him "The ass in the lion's skin." This gentleman's temper is made out of such a happy mixture of the mild and the choleric, that he outdoes both his predecessors, and has drawn together greater audiences than have been known in the memory of man.

I must not conclude my narrative, without taking notice of a groundless report that has been raised, to a gentleman's disadvantage of whom I must declare myself an admirer; namely, that Signior Nicolini and the lion have seen sitting peaceably by one another, and smoking a pipe together, behind the scenes; by which their common enemies would insinuate, that it is but a sham combat which they represent upon the stage: but upon inquiry I find that if any such correspondence has passed between them, it was not till the combat was over, when the lion was to be looked upon as dead, according to the received rules of the drama. Besides, this is what is practised every day in Westminster Hall, where nothing is more usual than to see a couple of lawyers, who have been tearing each other to pieces in the court, embracing one another as soon as they are out of it.

I would not be thought, in any part of this relation, to reflect upon Signior Nicolini, who in acting this part only complies with the wretched taste of his audience; he knows very well that the lion has many more admirers than himself; as they say of the famous equestrian statue on the Pont-Neuf at Paris, that more people go to see the horse than the king who sits upon it. On the contrary, it gives me a just indignation to see a person whose action gives new majesty to kings, resolution to heroes, and softness to lovers, thus sinking from the greatness of his behavior, and degraded into the character of the London Prentice. I have often wished that our tragedians would copy after this great master in action. Could they make the same use of their arms and legs, and inform their faces with as significant looks and passions, how glorious would an English tragedy appear with that action, which is capable of giving a dignity to the forced thoughts, cold conceits, and unnatural expressions of an Italian opera. In the meantime, I have related this combat of the lion to show what are at present the reigning entertainments of the politer part of Great Britain.

Audiences have often been reproached by writers for the coarseness of their tastes; but our present grievance does not seem to be the want of a good taste, but of common sense.

A DISSERTATION UPON ROAST PIG

Charles Lamb (England)

The following account of the history of cookery is purely fictitious. In it, Lamb is poking fun at people who indulge in extravagant enthusiasms. He selects his own fondness for roast pork as an example. First he writes a mock history of the art of roasting in the pompous style of a historical treatise. Then he falls to rhapsodizing over his favorite dish.

❋ ❋ ❋

Mankind, says a Chinese manuscript, which my friend M. was obliging enough to read and explain to me, for the first seventy thousand ages ate their meat raw, clawing or biting it from the living animal, just as they do in Abyssinia to this day. This period is not obscurely hinted at by their great Confucius [1] in the second chapter of his *Mundane Mutations*, where he designates a kind of golden age by the term Cho-fang, literally the Cook's holiday. The manuscript goes on to say that the art of roasting, or rather broiling

[1] *Confucius:* the great Chinese philosopher.

(which I take to be the elder brother), was accidentally discovered in the manner following. The swineherd, Ho-ti, having gone out into the woods one morning, as his manner was, to collect mast for his hogs, left his cottage in the care of his eldest son, Bo-bo, a great lubberly boy, who being fond of playing with fire, as younkers of his age commonly are, let some sparks escape into a bundle of straw, which kindling quickly, spread the conflagration over every part of their poor mansion, till it was reduced to ashes. Together with the cottage (a sorry antediluvian [2] makeshift of a building, you may think it), what was of much more importance, a fine litter of new-farrowed pigs, no less than nine in number, perished. China pigs have been esteemed a luxury all over the East from the remotest periods that we read of. Bo-bo was in utmost consternation, as you may think, not so much for the sake of the tenement, which his father and he could easily build up again with a few dry branches, and the labor of an hour or two, at any time, as for the loss of the pigs. While he was thinking what he should say to his father, and wringing his hands over the smoking remnants of one of those untimely sufferers, an odor assailed his nostrils, unlike any scent which he had before experienced. What could it proceed from?—not from the burnt cottage—he had smelt that smell before —indeed this was by no means the first accident of the kind which had occurred through the negligence of this unlucky young firebrand. Much less did it resemble that of any known herb, weed, or flower. A premonitory [3] moistening at the same time overflowed his nether [4] lip. He knew not what to think. He next stooped down to feel the pig, if there were any signs of life in it. He burnt his fingers, and to cool them he applied them in his booby fashion to his mouth. Some of the crumbs of the scorched skin had come away with his fingers, and for the first time in his life (in the world's life indeed, for before him no man had known it) he tasted— *crackling!* Again he felt and fumbled at the pig. It did not burn him so much now, still he licked his fingers from a sort of habit. The truth at length broke into his slow understanding, that it was the pig that smelt so, and the pig that tasted so delicious; and, surrendering himself up to the newborn pleasure, he fell to tearing up whole handfuls of the scorched skin with the flesh next it, and was cramming it down his throat in his beastly fashion, when his sire entered amid the smoking rafters, armed with retributory [5] cudgel, and finding how affairs stood, began to rain blows upon the

[2] *antediluvian:* before the Flood, ancient.   [3] *premonitory:* forewarning.
[4] *nether:* lower.   [5] *retributory:* punishing.

young rogue's shoulders, as thick as hailstones, which Bo-bo heeded not any more than if they had been flies. The tickling pleasure, which he experienced in his lower regions, had rendered him quite callous [6] to any inconveniences he might feel in those remote quarters. His father might lay on, but he could not beat him from his pig, till he had fairly made an end of it, when, becoming a little more sensible of his situation, something like the following dialogue ensued.

"You graceless whelp, what have you got there devouring? Is it not enough that you have burnt me down three houses with your dog's tricks, and be hanged to you, but you must be eating fire, and I know not what—what have you got there, I say?"

"O, father, the pig, the pig, do come and taste how nice the burnt pig eats."

The ears of Ho-ti tingled with horror. He cursed his son, and he cursed himself that ever he should beget a son that should eat burnt pig.

Bo-bo, whose scent was wonderfully sharpened since morning, soon raked out another pig, and fairly rending it asunder, thrust the lesser half by main force into the fists of Ho-ti, still shouting out, "Eat, eat, eat the burnt pig, father, only taste—O Lord,"— with such-like barbarous ejaculations, cramming all the while as if he would choke.

Ho-ti trembled in every joint while he grasped the abominable thing, wavering whether he should not put his son to death for an unnatural young monster, when the crackling scorching his fingers, as it had done his son's, and applying the same remedy to them, he in his turn tasted some of its flavor, which, make what sour mouths he would for a pretense, proved not altogether displeasing to him. In conclusion (for the manuscript here is a little tedious) both father and son fairly sat down to the mess, and never left till they had dispatched all that remained of the litter.

Bo-bo was strictly enjoined not to let the secret escape, for the neighbors would certainly have stoned them for a couple of abominable wretches, who could think of improving upon the good meat which God had sent them. Nevertheless strange stories got about. It was observed that Ho-ti's cottage was burnt down now more frequently than ever. Nothing but fires from this time forward. Some would break out in broad day, others in the nighttime. As often as the sow farrowed, so sure was the house of Ho-ti to be in a blaze; and Ho-ti himself, which was the more remarkable, instead of chastizing his son, seemed to grow more indulgent to him than ever. At length they were watched, the terrible mystery discovered,

[6] *callous:* hardened.

and father and son summoned to take their trial at Pekin, then an inconsiderable assize [7] town. Evidence was given, the obnoxious food itself produced in court, and verdict about to be pronounced, when the foreman of the jury begged that some of the burnt pig, of which the culprits stood accused, might be handed into the box. He handled it, and they all handled it, and burning their fingers, as Bo-bo and his father had done before them, and Nature prompting to each of them the same remedy, against the face of all the facts, and the clearest charge which judge had ever given,—to the surprise of the whole court, townsfolk, strangers, reporters, and all present—without leaving the box, or any manner of consultation whatever, they brought in a simultaneous verdict of Not Guilty.

The judge, who was a shrewd fellow, winked at the manifest iniquity [8] of the decision; and, when the court was dismissed, went privily, and bought up all the pigs that could be had for love or money. In a few days his Lordship's town house was observed to be on fire. The thing took wing, and now there was nothing to be seen but fires in every direction. Fuel and pigs grew enormously dear all over the district. The insurance offices one and all shut up shop. People built slighter and slighter every day, until it was feared that the very science of architecture would in no long time be lost to the world. Thus this custom of firing houses continued, till in process of time, says my manuscript, a sage arose, like our Locke, who made a discovery, that the flesh of swine, or indeed of any other animal, might be cooked (*burnt,* as they called it) without the necessity of consuming a whole house to dress it. Then first began the rude form of a gridiron. Roasting by the string, or spit, came in a century or two later, I forget in whose dynasty. By such slow degrees, concludes the manuscript, do the most useful, and seemingly the most obvious arts, make their way among mankind.—

Without placing too implicit faith in the account above given, it must be agreed that if a worthy pretext for so dangerous an experiment as setting houses on fire (especially in these days) could be assigned in favor of any culinary [9] object, that pretext and excuse might be found in ROAST PIG.

Of all the delicacies in the whole *mundus edibilis,* [10] I will maintain it to be the most delicate—*princeps obsoniorum.* [11]

I speak not of your grown porkers—things between pig and pork —those hobbydehoys—but a young and tender suckling—under a

---

[7] *assize:* court-session.　　　　　　[8] *iniquity:* injustice.
[9] *culinary:* connected with cooking.　　[10] *mundus edibilis:* world of edibles.
[11] *princeps obsoniorum:* prince of dainties.

moon old—guiltless as yet of the sty—with no original speck of the *amor immunditiæ,*[12] the hereditary failing of the first parent, yet manifest—his voice as yet not broken, but something between a childish treble, and a grumble—the mild forerunner or *præludium,* of a grunt.

He must be roasted. I am not ignorant that our ancestors ate them seethed, or boiled—but what a sacrifice of the exterior tegument![13]

There is no flavor comparable, I will contend, to that of the crisp, tawny, well-watched, not over-roasted, *crackling,* as it is well called —the very teeth are invited to their share of the pleasure at this banquet in overcoming the coy, brittle resistance—with the adhesive oleaginous [14]—O call it not fat—but an indefinable sweetness growing up to it—the tender blossoming of fat—fat cropped in the bud—taken in the shoot—in the first innocence—the cream and quintessence [15] of the child-pig's yet pure food—the lean, no lean, but a kind of animal manna—or, rather, fat and lean (if it must be so), so blended and running into each other, that both together make but one ambrosian [16] result, or common substance.

Behold him, while he is doing—it seemed rather a refreshing warmth, than a scorching heat, that he is so passive to. How equably he twirled round the string!—Now he is just done. To see the extreme sensibility of that tender age, he hath wept out his pretty eyes—radiant jellies—shooting stars—

See him in the dish, his second cradle, how meek he lieth!— wouldst thou have had this innocent grow up to the grossness and indocility which too often accompany maturer swinehood? Ten to one he would have proved a glutton, a sloven, an obstinate, disagreeable animal—wallowing in all manner of filthy conversation —from these sins he is happily snatched away—

> Ere sin could blight, or sorrow fade,
> Death came with timely care—

his memory is odoriferous—no clown curseth, while his stomach half rejecteth, the rank bacon—no coal-heaver bolteth him in reeking sausages—he hath a fair sepulchre in the grateful stomach of the judicious epicure [17]—and for such a tomb might be content to die.

---

[12] *amor immunditæ:* love of the world. [13] *tegument:* skin.
[14] *oleaginous:* fatty. [15] *quintessence:* finest extract.
[16] *ambrosian:* divine. Ambrosia was the food of the Greek gods.
[17] *epicure:* expert judge of fine foods.

He is the best of Sapors.[18] Pineapple is great. She is indeed almost too transcendent—a delight, if not sinful, yet so like to sinning, that really a tender-conscienced person would do well to pause—too ravishing for mortal taste, she woundeth and excoriateth [19] the lips that approach her—like lovers' kisses, she biteth—she is a pleasure bordering on pain from the fierceness and insanity of her relish—but she stoppeth at the palate—she meddleth not with the appetite—and the coarsest hunger might barter her consistently for a mutton chop.

Pig—let me speak his praise—is no less provocative of the appetite, than he is satisfactory to the criticalness of the censorious [20] palate. The strong man may batten on him, and the weakling refuseth not his mild juices.

I am one of those who freely and ungrudgingly impart a share of the good things of this life which fall to their lot (few as mine are in this kind) to a friend. I protest I take as great an interest in my friend's pleasures, his relishes, and proper satisfactions, as in mine own. "Presents," I often say, "endear Absents." Hares, pheasants, partridges, snipes, barndoor chickens (those "tame vilatic fowl"), capons, plovers, brawn, barrels of oysters, I dispense as freely as I receive them. I love to taste them, as it were, upon the tongue of my friend. But a stop must be put somewhere. One would not, like Lear, "give everything." I make stand upon pig. Methinks it is an ingratitude to the Giver of all good flavors, to extra-domiciliate, or send out of the house, lightly (under pretext of friendship, of I know not what), a blessing so particularly adapted, predestined, I may say, to my individual palate—it argues an insensibility.

I remember a touch of conscience in this kind at school. My good old aunt, who never parted from me at the end of a holiday without stuffing a sweetmeat, or some nice thing, into my pocket, had dismissed me one evening with a smoking plum-cake, fresh from the oven. On my way to school (it was over London Bridge) a gray-headed old beggar saluted me (I have no doubt at this time of day that he was a counterfeit). I had no pence to console him with, and in the vanity of self-denial, and the very coxcombry of charity, schoolboy like, I made him a present of—the whole cake. I walked on a little, buoyed up, as one is on such occasions, with a sweet soothing of self-satisfaction; but before I had got to the end of the bridge, my better feelings returned, and I burst into tears, thinking how ungrateful I had been to my good aunt, to go and give her

---

[18] *Sapors:* flavors. [19] *excoriateth:* burns. [20] *censorious:* critical.

good gift away to a stranger, that I had never seen before, and who might be a bad man for aught I knew; and then I thought of the pleasure my aunt would be taking in thinking that I—I myself, and not another—would eat her nice cake—and what should I say to her the next time I saw her—how naughty I was to part with her pretty present—and the odor of that spicy cake came back upon my recollection, and the pleasure and the curiosity I had taken in seeing her make it, and her joy when she sent it to the oven, and how disappointed she would feel that I had never had a bit of it in my mouth at last—and I blamed my impertinent spirit of alms-giving, and out-of-place hypocrisy of goodness, and above all I wished never to see the face again of that insidious, good-for-nothing, old gray imposter.

Our ancestors were nice in their method of sacrificing these tender victims. We read of pigs whipped to death with something of a shock, as we hear of any other obsolete [21] custom. It would be curious to inquire (in a philosophical light merely) what effect this process might have toward intenerating and dulcifying a substance, naturally so mild and dulcet [22] as the flesh of young pigs. It looks like refining a violet. Yet we should be cautious, while we condemn the inhumanity, how we censure the wisdom of the practice. It might impart a gusto—

His sauce should be considered. Decidedly, a few bread crumbs, done up with his liver and brains, and a dash of mild sage. But banish, dear Mrs. Cook, I beseech you, the whole onion tribe. Barbecue your whole hogs to your palate, steep them in shalots, stuff them out with plantations of the rank and guilty garlic; you cannot poison them, or make them stronger than they are—but consider, he is a weakling—a flower.

ADVICE TO A YOUNG FRENCHMAN
STARTING FOR ENGLAND

André Maurois (France)

Translated by J. W. Jeaffreson

You are going to dwell in a far country, remote not in miles (it is a shorter journey than from Paris to Lyons) but in ideas and customs. You are going to dwell in a difficult, mysterious land. During

---

[21] *obsolete:* discontinued.   [22] *dulcet:* sweet.

the first days you will think: "The attempt is hopeless; I shall never know them; they will never understand me; the gulf is too wide to be bridged." Rest easy. It can be bridged. Tell yourself that, once they have adopted you, they will be your staunchest friends. Read Lawrence's book *Revolt in the Desert,* and you will see how that Englishman went back alone into a dangerous desert to hunt for a nameless Arab left behind by the caravan. Such is the friendship of the best among them. I put it to the test during the War. It is worthy of being won, even at the cost of some effort. Think also that in spite of this apparent difficulty you need but observe a few rules in order not to affright them.

CLOTHES

Just two principles. Dress as they do; dress simply. As they do—because they are conformists. If you go golfing in riding-breeches, or if you turn up to dine at a regimental mess in knicker-bockers, you will shock and sadden them. But you will shock them far more if you have the bad taste to be overdressed. Here, let no clothes be too perfect, no boots too new. Miss Harrison, in her *Reminiscences of a Student's Life,* tells of the pleasure she experienced on seeing the Duke of Devonshire come to receive the degree of doctor *honoris causa* [1] at Cambridge in boots so "holy" that his socks showed through. "By those socks," she says, "I knew him for truly ducal."

CONVERSATION

So long as you have not found your depth, speak little. Nobody will take your silence amiss. When you have held your tongue for three years, they will think: "This is a nice quiet young fellow." Be modest. An Englishman will tell you: "I've got a little place in the country"; when he invites you down, you will discover the little place to be a mansion with three hundred rooms. If you are world's champion at tennis, say: "Yes, I play a pretty fair game." If you have crossed the Atlantic all by yourself, say: "Yes, I do a little sailing." If you have written books, say nothing. They will themselves find out your qualities in time, and will say to you laughingly: "I have heard things about you"; they will be pleased with you. If you are treated unjustly (this will happen; unjust they occasionally are), go straight to them and explain wherein you think them in the wrong. The chances are they will admit it.

[1] *honoris causa:* given as an honor.

They are keen on playing the game. If France is attacked in your presence, counter-attack brutally; you will go up one.

A golden rule: never ask questions. I lived six months in the same tent as an Englishman and shared his tub; he never inquired whether I was married, what I did in peace time, or what books I was reading. If you must tell your secrets, you will be listened to with polite indifference. Beware of confidences regarding others. Tittle-tattle exists here as elsewhere, but it is both uncommoner and more serious. There is no mean between silence and scandal. Prefer silence.

Do not imagine your intellectual worth will bring you any prestige (except in a very small set in London and at the Universities). One thing only matters: your character. I do not think you can so much as conceive the contempt in which Englishmen of a certain type hold literary culture. You are going to a country where a man will frankly say to an author: "Books? I have never read a single one. When I try, I at once realize that nothing I read sticks. . . . So, what's the use?" However, they leave you free to read and chaff you gently if you do, much as one might chaff a collector of rhinoceros-horns. But they find the rhinoceros-taste more intelligible. . . .

Side by side with the "athletic" you must get to know the "aesthetic" [2] type. In the small intellectual set to which I have referred, you will long feel at a disadvantage. Cultivated Englishmen are rare, but their culture is exquisite; their epigrams are swift and subtle, their taste fastidious and sound. They are contemptuous and delightful, a dangerous blend for your vanity. You will yearn to please them but will find it difficult to strike the right note. Seek for it in a mixture of nonchalance and preciosity.[3] Write an essay on cocktails, another on the Chinese poets.

When you want to convince them, do not argue too well. Being a Frenchman, you will imagine you have scored completely, having demonstrated that you are right. It leaves them cold whether logic shows them to be right or wrong. On the contrary, they mistrust too perfect reasoning. At Geneva, when our delegates handed them the protocol of disarmament, they rejected it because it was clear. "It will never work," they said. What they like is a policy which has stood the test of time, ancient maxims, and rooted habits. To induce them to do something new, show them that they have been doing it all along. Put your logic out to grass during your whole stay.

[2] *aesthetic:* artistic.   [3] *preciosity:* interest in rarities.

ACTIVITY

Do not work too much. Above all do not be what they call "fussy." Wait till you are asked to do things. Do not with intemperate eagerness rush to meet your task. "Are they idlers?" you ask. Yes, somewhat; but their main idea is that the desire to do too much smacks of pride. See how they walk; rather slowly, with strides too long. Thus it is that they go ahead in life. They are not fond of hustling fate. In the army they always told me never to refuse a mission, but never to ask for one. They are ambitious like all men, but they are not bad at concealing it.

JUSTICE

Do no murder in England. You would be hanged for it. With a French jury, provided you have a little imagination, a romantic face, and clever counsel, you can save your neck without much trouble. The twelve English jurors will listen with wrathful astonishment to the story of your sentimental pains and will cause you to be hanged by the neck until you be dead. Be prudent. Avoid their courts of law. Their judges are terrible and will hold you guilty before you have oped your mouth. Their barristers cross-examine with such diabolical skill that, in order to escape the hail of questions, you will confess to having taken Nelson's column.[4] Bear in mind that respect for the law is greater here than elsewhere. In English, "Keep off the grass" does not mean *Marchez sur ce gazon.*[5]

FOOD

Before setting out you will have been told that food in England is bad. True, cooks and chefs are not up to the French mark. But if you know how to lay out your hunger wisely, you will manage to feed to perfection. Here there are two meals that are first-class: breakfast and tea; one that is middling: lunch; one that is bad: dinner. Reserve your appetite for the two former. Learn to experience new pleasures: porridge, haddock, marmalade. At lunch feed on the great red joint of beef or admirable rosy ham. Manfully thrust the pudding far from you, saying firmly, "I don't care for sweets." In England every second shop is a "sweet" shop and yet Englishmen despise sweets. Leave them to children and women. . . .

[4] *Nelson's column:* a great public monument.
[5] *Marchez sur ce gazon:* walk on the turf.

Above all, rejoice in the beholding of things. You will love the landscapes which look as if they had been painted by Constable or Gainsborough.[6] You will love the gardens, which are a trifle wild, and the thick close-cropped lawns. You will love London which, amid its grey-gold haze, with the red smudges of its motor-buses and the dark smudges of its policemen, is like a huge Turner.[6] You will love its theaters with their comfortable stalls, pretty attendants, and short intervals. You will love its book-shops, appetizing and multicolored as its shops full of exotic fruits, and especially will you love the books . . . only say it not.

THE COLOR OF JAPAN

Gonnoské Komai (Japan)

The poetry in the following interpretation of Japan (condensed and rearranged from the original) is mostly by the same author, who also is his own translator.

❈　❈　❈

How brilliant and translucent is the water all around our Islands. The very pebbles on the shore, as under the waves, appear like precious gems. On lifting our eyes, the richly tinted sky seems to be a priceless brocade woven in sun-shot mist.

As we approach the Land of the Rising Sun, we are welcomed by the marvellous Mount Fuji, dominating land and sea—soft and beautiful if seen from afar but sternly gigantic the closer we approach it.

Rejoicing Hermits climb upon this mighty peak above the clouds,
The sacred Dragons older grow in this deep pool beyond the sky:
The everlasting snow is white as the white silks of her I love;
Smoke drifts along the mountain-side as 'twere her wafted veil,
While peerless Fuji's form recalls her white unfolded fan
Reversed to the rejected Earth from the Far Eastern Sky.

There is much color of a kind that appeals strongly to us Japanese in the celebrated poem of Ikkyuh on a happy New Year's Day:

Bold Pine and graceful Bamboo join
To grace my Gate this New Year's Day,
And mark a mile upon the Road
To that dim Land where journeys end!
Shall we, dear friends, rejoice or wail?

[6] *Constable, Gainsborough, Turner:* English painters.

Taken together, this somber green of the pine and the gay pale blue-green of the bamboo may be regarded as the distinctive national color of Japan, and form the common background of every transient outburst of brighter hues.

Essential as air and water are the pine and bamboo to our everyday life in Japan. Whether growing in forests and thickets, delighting us with dappled shades and the changeful music of their waving branches, or cut down in the service of man, we Japanese cannot live without them. Fortunately, like air and water, the pine-tree and bamboo abound throughout the country. They constitute the invariable materials for building purposes as well as for the manufacture of hundreds of useful objects in our houses. The pine, the king of our forests, furnishes us with timber and fuel, while the young bamboo gives us the finest and most durable material for covering our wooden clogs and sandals in their bright, glistening yellow rinds, which turn to a pale yellow when dried. Furthermore, we use the sheaths of the larger bamboo for waterproof paper. In the spring-time the bamboo provides us in its tender yellow roots with a delicious vegetable eaten either alone or with fish or rice. From the common chopsticks we use at our tables down to our clogs and sandals, we owe a constant debt of gratitude to our modest but graceful bamboo.

Were you to visit the Isles of Matsusima you would see hundreds of islets picturesquely covered with thousands of well-shaped pine-trees, reflected in the calm, blue waters beneath. Or go to Maiko-no-Hama, where majestic old pines, with their great weather-beaten roots emerging from the soil, seem to us to be dancing in their joy at the sunshine and the beauty in the midst of which they live. They face the lovely Awajisima Island and its surrounding waters, charmingly decorated with fishing boats and white seagulls. No less delightful is Miyajima, with its thousands of soft-grey stone lanterns reflected in the still, blue waters of the Inland Sea of Japan.

As the plum-blossom, the emblem of Purity and Elegance, which leads the dance of all the flowers in Old Japan, begins to smile, we rejoice at the advent of Spring. We admire the plum-tree as she nobly gleams in white and crimson. To enable you to realize the rich magnificence of our noble plum-tree in full bloom I should have to take you with me to Tsukigase or Hakkei-Yen, where you could bathe your eyes in the lavish beauties of hundreds of them, forming an ocean of vivid color, rendered still more intoxicating by their all-pervading fragrance! Of one such scene an ancient poet writes:

For two score miles along the banks
Of winding Tsukigase,
The plum-tree petals' snowy white
Out-glows the lovely vale.
The famous Chinese orchard with
Three hundred trees at Seiko
Is but a faint reminder
Of this ocean of rich bloom!
Days after my departure thence
My flowing sleeves are bathed still
In its delicious odor.

Strange to say, in our country we often give the name of Plum-tree to our women . . . Madame or Miss Umé-ko. By the sweet Law of Association the mere mention of the Plum-tree recalls to our Japanese mind the sweet nightingale—"Uguisu." One of our poets pictures for us a lovely girl, hiding herself behind her paper-screen and listening to the passionate notes of the bird as it shoots through the branches of the plum-tree:

I fain would draw my shohji
To see the Nightingale:
But fearing to alarm her,
I crouch behind the screen,
Flooded in the ecstacy
Of that o'erflowing passion!

It is the happy lot of our beloved and distant Sun-rise Yamato-Land, which like England "never did nor never shall lie at the proud foot of a conquerer," to be enveloped with the sweetest of blossoms, the embodiment of our national spirit—Yamato-Damasii—once every year. Go where you will, to the Park of Uyéno or to the Banks of the Sumida, and you will be enchanted by a lavish display of cherry blossoms in full bloom. The loveliest view of the spring in all Japan is on the Arasiyama Hill in Kyoto. As we stand on the Togekkyoh-Bridge, with fallen petals of cherry blossom floating like butterflies through the perfumed air, we see beneath us rafts swinging down the rapid waters of the blue Katsura, while around us brightly clad village girls from Yasé and Ohara poise above their laughing eyes light loads of the daintiest flowers.

Everywhere color! even music being imagined as voicing its beauty. Color—with movement—is also the dominant charm of

"BUT FEARING TO ALARM HER
I CROUCH BEHIND THE SCREEN"

those inevitable companions of Japanese flowers . . . the capricious tribe of Butterflies who ring all the possible changes of tint, and often outvie all the jewels of the mine with their flashing wings.

> Oh, glorious Spring!
> Each living thing
> Breathes Beauty past compare:
> Flowers fly, and butterflies,
> Like flowers, scent the air:
> But which is flower or butterfly,
> I vow I can't declare.

Just before the rice-planting throughout the length and breadth of our country, where every nook and corner is tilled with the invaluable help of our most obedient, industrious, and willing women, the fields are covered by the golden flowers of the rape fascinatingly contrasted with the red flowerets of our *Gengé-soh,* spreading a prodigious carpet woven by the skilful hands of Nature over the whole land. Green grasses and red *Gengé* give place to the rich brown of the soil when those plants are dug in as natural fertilizers for the all-important rice.

If by romantic chance you went astray in our countryside, you might well hope to have the following delightful experience recounted by one of our poets:

> I had lost my way in the open field,
> Where a lovely girl was gathering
> Violets under the smiling sun:
> And I asked her to guide me home.
> She nodded and pointed the way with her flowers
> Towards a spot where two gay butterflies
> Leisurely fluttered off in the azure!

When caught by the rain in the fields one is often reminded of an old poem which gives a glimpse of the amiable and nature-loving philosophy of the Japanese:

> Check your haste and save your skin,
> Strange sojourner at our inn;
> The hedge beckons you in vain
> Rushing wildly through the rain.
> Had you snuggled near the birds,
> Listening to their merry words,
> Soon the shower had passed away
> With promise of a sunny day.

Then comes Wistaria—the dainty *Fuji-no-Hana*:

> Slender lady,
> Softly smiling, white and purple,
> Exquisite in grace, yet modest,
> What a lesson can she teach us:
> Like a lovely lady, lovelier,
> In delicious clinging languor,
> As she leans on a strong arm,
> So Wistaria, when she clings
> To a bamboo-stem or pine-tree.

It may interest my readers to learn that the word representing color is also one of the words expressing love in the Japanese language and that we regard love as the color of our human life. Perhaps this will excuse the introduction of a little characteristic Japanese poem in which both love and color play their parts with just a touch of jealousy:

> My bride at dawn a rosebud plucked
> That breathed the morning air,
> Then looking in her glass, she placed
> That rival in her hair;
> And asked me, pouting saucily,
> "Which is the lovelier, say?"
> But, piqued, I answered jestingly
> "Of course, the Flower of May"
> My lovely bride in anger cried
> And crushed the flower's ch
> "Hereafter take, instead
> Such rosebuds in your a

Here is another:

> Darling, tell m
> I am not jea
> But I only wish
> If you really wa
> Throug the rain
> With
> Ho
> Is

Azalea in w
by Iris of var
of thousands of t

(slip overlaying page)

Yama thrown upon Lake Chusenji. Speaking of the Lakes of Japan one must not forget to mention the celebrated eight views near Lake Biwa, in the neighborhood of Kyoto, which cover an area of over 187 miles.

1. Sunset from Seta Bridge.
2. The evening Snow on Mount Hira.
3. The home-bound Sailing Boats at Yabasi.
4. The quiet evening Rain upon the huge Single Pine-tree of Kara-saki.
5. The Autumnal Moon at the Isiyama Temple.
6. The returning Wild Geese at Awazu, and
7. The serene breeze of Awazu, and
8. The Mii Temple with

in America, however, the same philosophy of life which to dominate the entire world. Only in America pushed further and its results are more plainly results which make Ferrero object to the philosoph

* * *

One day, in New York, I was praising an architecture to an American architect of gr

1 *Hokku*: a brief poem in the stanza form show

he answered with a touch of satire, "my fellow countrymen would willingly spend a hundred million dollars to build a church as beautiful as St. Mark's in Venice, but they would command me, as a condition of my undertaking the work, to finish it within eighteen months."

That is a significant phrase. How is it possible to beautify a world which is incessantly in transformation, wherein nothing is stable, and which wishes to multiply everything it possesses—buildings, as it would furniture? To create beautiful palaces, to construct beautiful furniture, to attain the distant ideal of perfection, time is essential—time and wise deliberation, reasonable limitation of the multiplicity of human demands, and a certain stability in taste. No one could have built St. Mark's or Notre Dame [1] in eighteen months, and France could not have created her famous decorative styles of the eighteenth century if public taste had been so fickle as ours, and if everybody at that time had wished every ten years to change his furniture.

The crises in the decorative arts are, however, still relatively slight in comparison with the general intellectual and moral confusion into which the doctrine of Quantity has plunged men's minds, by substituting a standard of Quantity in place of the traditional standard of Quality.

It is this continual confusion between quantitative and qualitative standards which prevents the modern world from steering a true course amid the gravest moral questions. Take, for example, the question of progress. Is there an idea more popular today, or a word more often repeated, than "progress"? And yet if to every person who pronounces this word we were to put the question, "What do you mean by progress?" few indeed would be able to answer with precision. There is a thing still stranger. In this century of progress, the whole world deplores ten times a day the decadence [2] of all things. How can such a contradiction be explained? The answer is simply that the same act may be judged as a phenomenon of progress or of decadence, according as it is viewed from the standpoint of Quality or of Quantity. Set an architect and a locomotive builder to disputing about the modern world. The former will maintain that the world is reverting to barbarism because it multiplies cities and hastily and hideously constructed villages without being able to create a single one of those marvellous monuments which are the glory of the Middle Ages. The latter will reply that the world moves forward, because the population, number, and

[1] *Notre Dame:* a beautiful cathedral in Paris.   [2] *decadence:* decline.

size of the cities, the amount of cultivated land, the extension of railroads, increase without cessation. The interlocutors will never come to understand each other, just as two men who look at the world through spectacles of different colors can never agree on the color of their environment. The riddle of America, which for some time past has bothered Europe so much, is merely another example of this permanent confusion of standards which characterizes the age in which we live.

America is the country where the principles of Quantity, which have become so powerful during the last one hundred and fifty years, have achieved their most extraordinary triumph. An active, energetic, vigorous nation has found itself master of an enormous territory, portions of which were very fertile and other portions very rich in mines and forests, at the very moment when our civilization finally invented the machine which makes possible the exploitation of vast countries and the swift creation of wealth: the steam-engine.

Less cumbered by old traditions than the elder nations, and with a vast continent in front of her, America has marched along the new roads of history with a rapidity and an energy for which there is no precedent. Ten, fifteen, thirty times in a single century has she multiplied her population, her cities, and all the wealth coveted by many. She has created, in careless and prodigal profusion, a society which has subordinated all former ideas of perfection to a new ideal; ever building on a grander scale and ever building more swiftly. It is not true that America is indifferent to the higher activities of mind, but the effort which she spends upon the arts and sciences is, and will long remain, subordinate to the great historic task of the United States, the intensive cultivation of a huge continent. Intellectual things will remain subordinate, although very many Americans of the upper classes would wish that it were otherwise.

It is indisputable that the modern world demands two contradictory things, speed and perfection. We wish to conquer the earth and its treasures with all possible haste. To this end, we have created tremendous machinery and have uncovered new forces in nature. It is a huge task, no doubt, but to accomplish it we must renounce almost all the artistic and moral perfections which used to be at once the torment and joy and pride of our forefathers. It is a painful necessity indeed, against which our age revolts, and from which it seeks in vain every possible channel of escape.

Let us strip off the last shred of illusion. Deterioration must ever continue amongst the ideals of perfection which our ancestors worshipped, so long as population multiplies and the demands and aspirations of all classes, as well as all expenses, public and private, continue to increase on the scale and with the momentum with which they are increasing at this moment. Even if this formidable revolution should slacken a trifle, the ideal of Quantity will spread its empire over the earth, and morality and beauty must of necessity be subordinated to the prime necessities of constructing machines ever increasing in speed and power, of expanding cultivated land, and of working new mines. Art like industry, agriculture like literature, will be compelled to increase their production to the continuous deterioration of their quality, and our secret discontent will grow in proportion as our triumphs increase. Unable ourselves to decide between Quality and Quantity, we shall never know whether the great drama of the world at which we are looking is a marvelous epoch of progress or a melancholy tragedy of decadence.

From this singular situation, there is only one possible way of escape; a method which has no precedent in the world's history. It is that very method, however, which men will not hear spoken of. It would be absolutely essential to create a movement of public opinion through religious, political, or moral means, which should impose upon the world a reasonable limit to its desires. To the age in which we live, it seems impossible to express an idea seemingly more absurd than this. The material situation of every one of us is today bound up with this formidable movement, which drives men ceaselessly to increase the making and spending of wealth. Think what an economic crisis there would be if this movement were to slow down. All the moral systems which governed the world down to the French Revolution forced upon men the belief that they would grow more perfect as they grew simpler. When religion and custom were not sufficient to teach men to set limits to their needs and desires, then these old moral systems had recourse to sumptuary laws. In direct contrast to this, the nineteenth century affirms that man grows more perfect in proportion as he produces and consumes. So confusing are the definitions of legitimate desires and vices, of reasonable expenses and inordinate luxury, that in this century it is almost impossible to differentiate between the one and the other.

A vast revolution has been brought into being, the greatest, perhaps, which history can show; but if the new principles which our century has borne to the front should be developed until they insured the ultimate and supreme triumph of Quantity, would it be possible to escape what would amount to the demolition of the whole fabric of the glorious civilization bequeathed to us by the centuries; of religious doctrines and the principles upon which morality is based, as well as all the traditions of the arts?

History knows better than do we the dusky roads of the future, and it is idle for us to wish to see the way along them; but in spite of our ignorance of the future, we have duties toward the past and toward ourselves, and is it not one of these duties to call the attention of our generation to the possibility of this catastrophe, even if our generation likes to turn its face away from it? Very often during my travels in America, I used to ask myself whether men of various intellectual interests might not find in this duty something to strengthen their conscience for the part which they must play in the world.

If we except medicine, which aims to cure our bodily ills, those sciences which are concerned with discoveries useful to industry, and those arts which entertain the public, all other branches of intellectual activity are today in dire confusion. Is there a pious clergyman who has not asked himself in moments of discouragement what good it is to preach the virtues of the Christian faith in a century whose dynamic power springs from an exaltation of pride and an emancipation of passion which amount almost to delirium? What intelligent historian is there who does not now and then ask himself why he persists in telling over again the events of the past to a generation which no longer looks ahead, and which rushes violently on the future, head down like a bull? What philosopher is there who does not feel himself sometimes hopelessly adrift, like a being fallen upon the earth, from another planet, in an age which no longer is passionately interested in anything except economic reality? What artist is there who seeks not merely to make money, but to reach the perfection of his ideal, who has not cursed a thousand times this frenzied hurly-burly in the midst of which we live?

How many times as he travelled across the territory of the two Americas, watching all day fields of wheat and rye, or plantations of maize or coffee, extending to the very edge of the solitary horizon, how many times has the historian [3] of antiquity brooded over those fragments of marble wrought by the Greeks in such perfection, which we admire in our museums, and pondered upon the fragments of the great Roman system of jurisprudence [4] preserved in the *"Corpus juris."* Did not the Greeks and Romans succeed in reaching this

[3] *historian:* the author himself.   [4] *jurisprudence:* law.

marvellous perfection in the arts and laws because there came a time when they were willing to cease extending the limits of their empire over the earth and all the treasures it contains? Have we not conquered vast deserts with our railroads just because we have been able to renounce almost all the artistic and moral perfections which were the glory of the ancients?

In the light of this idea, the historian felt that he had come to understand all the better ancient civilization and our own, and that his eyes were able to pierce more deeply into the shadowy depths of human destiny. A civilization which pursues its desire for perfection beyond a certain limit ends by exhausting its energy in the pursuit of an object at once too narrow and impossible of attainment. On the other hand, a civilization which allows itself to be intoxicated by the madness of mere size, by speed, by quantity, is destined to end in a new type of crass and violent barbarism. But the point where these two opposing forces of life find their most perfect equilibrium [5] changes continually from age to age; and any epoch approaches more or less near this point according to the degree of activity of the two forces struggling within it. The artist, the priest, the historian, the philosopher, in moments of discouragement, when they feel themselves assailed by the temptation to think only of a career or of money, may well find new strength in the idea that each of them is working in his different way to preserve an ideal of perfection in men's souls—it may be a perfection of art or of morality, of the intellect or of the spirit. Let them remember that this ideal, limited as it may seem, serves as a dike to prevent our civilization from being engulfed in an overwhelming flood of riches and from sinking in an orgy of brutality. This task is so great and so noble that those who strive for it ought surely to feel that they do not live in vain.

THE ROOK

ANTON CHEKHOV (RUSSIA)

The rooks [1] had arrived and swarmed in great circles around the Russian cornfields. I singled out the most important-looking I could find, and began to talk to him. Unfortunately I hit upon a rook who was a moralist and a great reasoner; consequently our conversation was a dull one.

---

[5] *equilibrium*: balance.　　　　　　　　　[1] *rook*: an old world crow.

This is what we talked about:

I. "It's said that you rooks live to a great age. The naturalists cite you and the pike as the chief examples of longevity. How old are you?"

The Rook. "I am three hundred and seventy-six years old."

I. "Well, I never! You've lived precious long! In your place, old bird, the devil only knows how many articles I could have written for the *Russian Antiquarian* and the *Historical Journal*. If I had lived three hundred and seventy-six years, I can't imagine how many novels, stories, plays, scenes and other trifles I should have written. What numbers of fees I should have pocketed! Now, what have you, old rook, done during all these years?"

The Rook. "Nothing, Mr. Man. I have only eaten, drunk, slept and multiplied."

I. "Shame! I really feel shame for you, silly old bird. You have lived in the world three hundred and seventy-six years, and you are as stupid today as you were three hundred years ago. Not a ha'p'orth of progress."

The Rook. "Wisdom, Mr. Man, comes not from age, but from education and learning. Look at China—she has existed much longer than I have, and she is still as great a simpleton today as she was a thousand years ago."

I (with astonishment). "Three hundred and seventy-six years! What do you call that? An eternity! During that time I should have been able to attend lectures in every faculty; I could have been married twenty times; tried every profession and employment; attained the devil only knows what high rank, and, no doubt, have died a Rothschild. Just think of it, you fool, one rouble placed in a bank at five per cent compound interest becomes in two hundred and eighty-three years a million. Just calculate. That means, if you placed one rouble on interest two hundred and eighty-three years ago, you would have had a million roubles today. Ah, you fool, you fool! Are you not ashamed, don't you feel a fool to be so stupid?"

The Rook. "Not at all. We are stupid; but we can comfort ourselves with the thought that during the four hundred years of our life we do fewer foolish things than man does during his forty years. Yes, Mr. Man, I have lived three hundred and seventy-six years, and I have never once seen rooks make war on one another, or kill one another, and you can't remember a single year without war. We do not rob one another, or open savings banks or schools for modern languages; we do not bear false witness or blackmail; we do not write bad novels and bad verse, or edit blasphemous newspapers. . . . I have lived three hundred and seventy-six years, and I have never seen that our mates have been unfaithful to or have injured their husbands . . . and with you, Mr. Man, how is it? We have no flunkeys, no back-biters, no sycophants,[2] no swindlers, no panderers, no hypocrites. . . ."

At that moment this talker was called by his companions, and he flew away over the fields before he had time to finish his sentence.

WHAT THE AMERICAN RHODES SCHOLAR GETS FROM OXFORD

Frank Aydelotte (America)

Cecil Rhodes, an Englishman who made a great fortune in South Africa, left it to found scholarships at Oxford University, England, for boys from the British colonies, from Germany, and from the United States. Mr. Aydelotte, long chairman of the committee which awards these scholarships in America, contrasts in the following essay the academic system, the sports, the talk, the vacations, and the international point of view in English and American educational institutions.

❊　❊　❊

I

The most obvious thing which the Rhodes Scholar gets from Oxford is a degree, and such is the objectiveness of Oxford's academic requirements and such the sincerity of her standards that it is a degree to which a definite meaning can be attached.

The requirements for any Oxford degree look on paper rather less extensive and ambitious than do those for the same degree in an American university. What the English academic discipline lacks in extent as compared with ours is made up in thoroughness. The requirements mean all, or more than all, they say. The method of examination is such as to make cramming of little avail, and a man must depend for his showing on what he really knows. The difference between English and American standards for undergraduate work may be understood by looking for a moment at the type of men who get the highest academic distinctions in the two countries. In the United States, these distinctions may be won by a man of

[2] *sycophant:* a servile flatterer.

first-class ability, provided he is moderately faithful to his work throughout his four years; or they may be won by a man of average ability who works early and late, makes every minute count, and fulfils every requirement to the letter. It may be questioned whether we have in the United States any academic honors the standard for which is so high as to demand the latter type of work from the former type of man. The English idea of first-class honors is precisely this: that they should be obtainable only by a man of first-class ability who has done the hardest and best work of which he was capable.

The American student at Oxford misses almost all the academic machinery that he has been used to in his native university. At Oxford there are no "courses" in the American sense of the term. There are no record cards in the Registrar's office, no "signing up" for the lectures he expects to attend, no required number of hours per week, no daily assignments, no mid-term tests or hour exams. The Rhodes Scholar is a little puzzled on his first Monday morning, and on a great many mornings thereafter, to know just what he is expected to do at a given hour and moment. Shall he read this volume, or master such and such a table of dates, or attend such and such a lecture, or perchance wander down High Street in search of tobacco, or shall he spend a few hours in the shop of one of the delightful Oxford booksellers adding to the riches of his shelves in exchange for the inferior riches of his purse? The world of work and of play, and of a thousand delightul pursuits which lie midway between the two, is all before him where to choose. His only hard-and-fast academic engagement is to call on his tutor once a week at a specified hour to read an essay which he has written on a specified topic. There is a list of lectures which he may, or may not, find it to his interest to attend. The lecturer keeps no roll of the members of his class, and it is the common practice of undergraduates to sample various courses at the beginning of the term and to continue only in those which seem to them worth while. This is the practice which one's tutor usually recommends. The result is that lecture courses at Oxord begin commonly with good-sized audiences which taper off to a small and faithful few by the end of the term.

The academic system at Oxford, if one may call it such, is wonderfully simple. The method is to prescribe not what the undergraduate is supposed to "take," but what he is supposed to know, to allow him a certain length of time in which to acquire that knowledge, and then to examine him in order to see whether or not he has acquired it. Even the word "acquire" is a little false to what Oxford expects of a man. Her theory of liberal knowledge is rather the development of power of thought, of grasp of a certain limited field of knowledge, than the acquisition of a store of facts, though the latter is, of course, necessary to the former. Whereas the American undergraduate takes courses, the Oxford man studies a subject.

The tutorial method of instruction is a natural outgrowth of the form of Oxford's academic requirements, and hence it is that American attempts to graft the tutorial method onto our ordinary system of instruction by courses have failed to produce the same results as come from the English system. The heart of that is the conceiving of undergraduate work in terms of what a man should know, instead of conceiving it in terms of the processes by which that knowledge is to be acquired. At Oxford a man's work is outlined (in the book which corresponds most nearly to the catalog of an American university, namely, the *Examination Statutes*) entirely in terms of the examinations which he must pass for his degree. He prepares himself for these examinations by his own efforts under the direction of his tutor. The tutor acts as guide, philosopher, and friend; he will help his charge by every kind of advice and criticism to make the most of his own abilities and of the instructional facilities provided by the university and the colleges; but he considers it no part of his duty to do the undergraduate's work for him. Success depends, more than anything else, on a man's own industry and initiative. It is fatally easy to waste a great deal of precious time getting down to work. On the other hand, a man who is able to plan for himself, and who has the energy and the initiative to work without constant supervision, can go as far and as fast as he likes. Perhaps capacity for independent work is the most important academic result of the Oxford system of education.

The American Rhodes Scholar gets from Oxford not merely a new attitude toward his work, but also a new respect for examinations. In the United States examinations are not, as a rule, viewed with much favor; and it is the fashion at present to consider them as a very untrustworthy means of measuring intellectual ability. There are not wanting those persons in England who believe that in their own country too much attention is paid to examinations and too great weight attached to their results. However this may be, the English have developed the fine art of examining to a very high degree of acuracy. This is proved by the fact that the results of the examinations at Oxford and Cambridge offer a good basis for prediction of success in after-life; there is not in the United States the discrepancy between success in college studies and success in after-life which our humorous writers would sometimes lead us to believe; but the correspondence is not so marked, especially in political life, in this country as it is in England. Oxford examinations are more severe but less pedantic than ours. It is a principle in England that a man shall not be examined by those persons who have the responsibility of teaching him. English examinations come at the end of a year or of two years of work rather than term by term, or week by week. They are usually of the essay type, and their attempt is to discover power of dealing with the subject rather than merely to test the memory for specific details. In the ordinary Honor School a man will have from seven to twelve three-hour papers following each other at the rate of two a day for the better part of a week. Cramming for such a series of tests is impossible. The advice usually given by one's tutor is to get away from Oxford, forget about books, and play tennis or golf for a few days before the examinations begin. In the examination-room a student confronted by a paper of ten or twelve questions will spend the first two hours on the two questions which he knows most about, answering each as exhaustively and thoughtfully as possible. In his third hour he will answer two or three more briefly but as well as he can.

In the English system a man is marked qualitatively on the basis of what he writes rather than quantitatively on the basis of what he leaves out. After the papers are all read he appears before his examiners for an oral, in which they have ample opportunity to test him on any topics which he did not mention in his answers. His effort must be to show at some points in his papers first-class work, which means in England answers which not merely contain information but are also well thought out and well written.

It is easy to see from what has been said that one of the most important things which a Rhodes Scholar gets from Oxford is a powerful impulse to re-examine all his conceptions of educational theory and practice—a process of the highest value whatever may be the result.

II

But life at Oxford is not all work. Indeed, the hardest part of an Oxford man's work is done in the vacations, and term-time (which altogether is a little less than twenty-six weeks in the year) is very largely given to living the Oxford life. From this life the American Rhodes Scholar gets a great deal that he could never get from books. For him, even more than for Englishmen, it is well worth while. In the first place, it is a very beautiful life, though the surface of it is, like the face of a glacier, overstrewn with a miscellaneous drift of academic stupidity and youthful folly which, at the first glance, more or less conceal the beauty that lies beneath. But at its heart Oxford life is worthy of its setting. It is not strange that this beauty should come home to the undergraduate but slowly. Only in after years, on one of those visits which Americans show such a decided tendency to make back to the home of their English foster-mother, will he be able to see in true perspective the significance of these eager undergraduate days—days of intense effort, of struggle with great tasks, of listening to half-heeded words of great teachers, of light-hearted, high-spirited converse with men too many of the best of whom will visit Oxford quadrangles no more. Then some night as he walks back to his lodgings after dinner at High Table—that stateliest of all the rites of academic hospitality—the moonlight on sleeping walls and towers will thrill him with the sense of the tangled, interwoven beauty of this life that once was his.

If I were to single out from all the beauty and intensity and good-fellowship of this life the two things which are likely to mean most to the American, I should say they are talk and sport. Perhaps these are two things which occupy most of the waking hours of the average English undergraduate. If he spends four or five hours a day at his books and lectures, he is considered reasonably indus-trious, and may with good conscience spend ten or twelve on social affairs with his fellows, in numberless breakfasts, lunches, teas, coffees, and club meetings, or in keen athletic competition with them on the river or the courts or the broad playing fields with which the university and the colleges are so generously supplied.

Most Rhodes Scholars would say that Oxford talk is the best talk in the world. I do not believe that this is due so much to any pecu-liar virtue of the men who compose the university as to the fact that the life is so arranged as to provide the leisure and the stimulus for it. As to its educational value, most Rhodes Scholars would say that the testimony of such diverse characters as Cardinal Newman and Robert Louis Stevenson, which sounds rather extravagant to American ears, was no whit too strong. In the almost unique inti-macy and good-fellowship of Oxford life, where for the moment men from every nation and every class are living together and sur-veying the nations of the earth in human and humorous companion-ship, the Rhodes Scholar, if he has in him the capacity for wisdom, learns the difference between an abstract formula and a living point of view. But he feeds intellectually on a rich diet which not every man can digest. The Rhodes Scholar will need all his charac-teristically scanty store of general information and more than all of the scanty American tolerance of ideas not current in the United States. If he have the capacity for assimilation, if he can become a part of what he meets, he may return from Oxford to the United States a citizen of the world.

Rhodes Scholars are usually athletes, but they have much to learn from Oxford sports, and they take eager pleasure in learning it. The difference between sport at Oxford and sport in the United States is almost the difference between work and play. In the United States athletics are managed by members of the faculty who have the rare gifts needed for such important work. Teams are coached and trained by experts. The costumes and implements are designed by other experts, all to the end of producing the maximum skill and efficiency of which the human frame and the human mind are capable. The result is greater public interest in athletic contests and probably a higher degree of athletic skill than is the rule in England, though this is difficult to measure, since neither country plays exactly the games which attract the greatest interest in the other.

At Oxford athletics are entirely in the hands of the undergradu-ates. There are no paid coaches ; and if in a given college at a given moment no old player is available to coach the team or the boat, it is not uncommon to apply to the captain of a rival team for some useful suggestions and criticisms, which are sure to be given with the utmost candor and liberality. The management of athletics at Oxford is distinctly amateurish and could undoubtedly be improved in efficiency by American methods. Training is earnest but not scientific. The choosing of the members of crews and teams is left to the captain and such advisers as he may select. There are so many forms of athletics and participation is so nearly universal that there are almost no spectators at college matches, and fewer than in the United States at the major inter-university contests.

This sport for sport's sake at Oxford is one of the finest experi-ences among the many fine opportunities opened by a Rhodes Schol-arship. Freed from the curse of spectators, there is no finer moral and social training in the world than sport. Without the spectators, compulsion to win, which makes football such a nerve-racking occu-pation in the United States, no longer exists. Under the conditions obtaining at Oxford and Cambridge, the idea that it would be a thousand times better to lose a game than to commit the slightest unfair action does not need to be argued. It is taken for granted just as it is taken for granted in every sport in the United States which has not become a spectacle for the crowd. The absence of spectators takes nothing from the keenness of the contest, but it makes that keenness a healthy, normal, human desire to win or to do one's best, rather than a frenzied feeling that the only two courses before the player are victory or suicide. The absence of spectators implies that the Oxford athlete must buy his own togs and pay his own expenses, which men do cheerfully. Playing fields are, of course, owned by the college, and the barge on the river and the expensive shells in which the crews row are paid for by the college boat-club. For the rest men buy their own equipment, and it is no uncommon thing for the members of a team of an Oxford college going to play a college in Cambridge to be assessed so much per head to pay the travelling expenses. All this simplification of sport gives a better opportunity for the emergence of its true moral and social values. These values exist just as truly in American college sports, and it is no small credit to the inherent sportsmanship of American players and coaches that they do persist, in the face of the terrific and often unscrupulous pressure of spectators and supporters who are interested not in the true values of sport but only in victory.

III

The Rhodes Scholar spends one-half of his year at Oxford; he has a six weeks' holiday at Christmas, another five or six weeks at Easter-time, and four months in the summer. It is perhaps fair to say that something like half of what he gets from his experience comes from these vacations, when he has the opportunity to travel in England and on the Continent, and to study European life and languages. Not that the vacations are all play. Under the Oxford system, term-time is the season for mapping out work, covering the ground hastily, getting together books, and listening to lectures; the hard grinding, filling in the chinks and reading round the subject in the way necessary for a creditable showing in the honor examinations must all be done in the vacation. Every vacation a man must make a careful balance between the demands of his Oxford work and the interest of foreign lands. The typical Rhodes Scholar way of doing this is to avoid too much travel, to settle in some English or Continental town, spend five or six hours a day on Oxford studies, and the rest of the day in seeing the sights and in learning the manners, and perhaps the language, of the people. The three years of a Rhodes scholarship wisely spent will give a man a command of at least one European language, and perhaps a working knowledge of one or two more, together with that kind of understanding of English and Continental life which comes from living with the people, and which does not come from merely travelling through the countries.

Some men confine their vacations to England and the near-by countries of the Continent; some journey farther afield into Russia, the Balkan States, the Near East, and the Holy Land; an occasional Rhodes Scholar finishes off his Oxford career by returning home around the world.

The result of these vacations is that the Rhodes Scholar comes back with some idea not merely of the English way of looking at life, but also of that of two or three European nations. He is an internationalist of a human rather than merely theoretical sort. This can hardly be said to simplify international problems for him. Perhaps it tends instead to give him an idea of their complexity. Living in a country where, because of the extent of that League of Nations called the British Empire, international problems are discussed more constantly and more intelligently than anywhere else on earth, he learns, or begins to learn, the lesson of the interdependence of nations; he learns to realize the necessity of understanding and serving the interests of others in order best to serve our own. And he comes back with the longing to have his country, which responds so quickly and so generously to the call of the plague-stricken and the starving, respond also to that less piercing but more important call of the best men of all nations for the help of the strongest in meeting the problems of the day, which, however met, threaten to tax the strength of civilization.

The Rhodes Scholar also gets out of his Oxford experience a new conception of the kinship of the English-speaking nations of the world. He wakes up to the discovery, rarely made on this side of the Atlantic, that our common speech and common law are only significant of a common way of looking at life—a common belief in freedom, in individual effort, and in sportsmanship, which are the real heritage of the Anglo-Saxon race. And he comes to see, as Rhodes saw, that this code of life which preserves the peace among single men of wide individual differences, which stimulates individual initiative and yet makes possible common action, which places justice and integrity above cleverness, which loves institutions and distrusts logic, which (usually) makes reforms slowly, anxious always to unite the best of the old with the best of the new, trying to repair the building of the state rather than to tear it down and rebuild it again—that this point of view distinguishes the whole English-speaking race. He is likely to come furthermore to the belief that this point of view, if it could be applied to international problems as it has been so successfully to disputes between man and man, would work out slowly but surely the riddle of these perplexing times. Perhaps this is the truest and most valuable of all the ideas which the American Rhodes Scholar gets from Oxford.

READING PROBLEMS ON THE ESSAY

1. *With the Photographer:* How far are the events in this sketch true to life? Point out examples of exaggeration. What is the purpose of this exaggeration? Put the idea of the essay in a single sentence.

2. *Love's Minor Frictions:* Outline this essay by major points discussed. Note in your outline illustrations of these points given in the essay. Check the sentences in which the authors pass from point to point and indicate why these transitions are skillful. Can you name other points of friction, or give fresh illustrations from your own experience of difficulties discussed in this essay? If these are minor points of friction, mention some you would describe as major and show why they are so.

3. *The Searchings of Jonathan:* What picture does this essay give you of the relation between the husband and wife, their common tastes and interests? Do they ever quarrel over their difficulties? Why doesn't Jonathan find what he hunts? Have you known any Jonathans? Are you one? Give examples from your own experience in hunting for things fruitlessly. How does this essay illustrate the point of the preceding?

4. *Dinner Table Talk:* What is the secret of a successful dinner? What criticism does Warner offer of conversation at a very large dinner? What is Warner's definition of good conversation? Write a one-paragraph summary of the essay.

5. *A Small Vocabulary May Have a Big Kick:* What does the ignorant language of the imaginary writer add to either the entertainment value or the point of this essay? Number around the class and turn into correct English the paragraph that falls to your share. What is Ring Lardner's idea as to the value of a large vocabulary? How large a vocabulary does the imaginary writer have? Is Lardner correct in his estimate of the average size of our vocabularies?

6. *Our Friend, the Dog:* What does Maeterlinck consider the greatest problem of the growing puppy? Are the various actions of Pelléas true to dog life? What difference does Maeterlinck see between the relation to man of the dog and of other domestic animals? Is he fair to the other animals? Why does Maeterlinck consider the dog happier than man?

7. *Of the Inequality That Is Among Us:* How does Montaigne think the natural inequalities of men are disguised? How does he propose to detect gradations of mind? Compare the tests he proposes with the intelligence tests you have taken in school.

8. *Freedom of Choice:* Give examples to explain what Dante means by choosing freely according to judgment as contrasted with being captive

to appetite. How largely are most people's lives governed by rational choice? How free are you in this sense? How can education make you freer?

9. *Of Expense:* Point out examples of Bacon's condensing much thought in a few words. Do you agree with Bacon as to the proportion of expenditure to income that he suggests? How did he hit upon those special figures? Would Bacon approve of spending according to a budget? What would he think of buying on the installment plan? Has this essay any special meaning for our generation?

10. *My Châteaux:* This essay explains the meaning of a proverbial saying —castles in Spain. Where are the author's Spanish estates really located? Prove. Picture the author's tastes and interests from the things he places on his "estates." Why does he introduce Mr. Bourne, the millionaire, into the discussion? Several routes to one's "Spanish estates" are discussed in ensuing essays. What are they? Compare this essay with Lamb's *Dream Children* and Hilton's *Lost Horizon*. What is the difference? This essay and *The Noblest Instrument* both have delightful styles. What is the difference between them?

11. *The Noblest Instrument:* Point out what ideas in this essay represent the author's feelings as a boy and what are his mature reflections as he looks back on the experience. Is the essay true to boy nature? Outline the character of the father; the mother. Does the son at any stage of his development fail to respect his father? Point out incidents which show the funny side of the boy's study of music; the pathetic side. From what does the humor arise? How is this essay an incomplete but still unified treatment of its subject?

12. *On Literature:* What knowledge springs from a wide acquaintance with the literatures of the world? Give further examples from your own reading of similar ideas and feelings expressed by writers of different race or time. What message does great literature bring to the thoughtful reader?

13. *Thinking for One's Self:* Compare Schopenhauer's description of reading with that given in the introductory chapter and in the analysis of the essay (page 639). Is reading necessarily a "substitute for thought"? How can one read and think at the same time? Do large numbers of people read as slavishly as Schopenhauer thinks? Is it really possible, as he says, to spend too much time with books? Why?

14. *On Translating Homer:* What difficulties of the translator—not only of Homer but of any foreign tongue—are outlined in this essay? Point out in what way translators of Homer have failed, and prove these points as far as you can by analyzing passages quoted in the essay. List three or four qualities of some work of literature in English or in a foreign tongue which the translator must reproduce to be faithful to his original.

15. *Signior Nicolini and His Lions:* Who were the lions? What is amusing in Addison's description of them? What criticisms of the opera and of the audience are offered by Addison? Can you apply the last two paragraphs to the audience and actors of any modern motion picture?

16. *The Rook:* In what way does the bird think that rooks excel men? Why does the man think that the rook has wasted its chances? Are the man's ideas in any sense a proof of the bird's criticisms? Write a one-paragraph summary of the essay contrasting the ideas of rook and man.

17. *A Dissertation on Roast Pig:* By what devices does Lamb make his story sound plausible at the start? How by choice of words and incidents does he give the whole an extravagant turn which reveals to us shortly that it is a hoax? Find humorous anachronisms in the narrative. List the points of excellence in roast pig mentioned by Lamb in the second half of the essay and summarize them in a simply worded paragraph. Compare this with the essay as Lamb wrote it and see what point is entirely lost by the change of style. Go through the second half of the essay pointing out why Lamb uses so many large words. What is the effect of his numerous comparisons? Which seems to you the most effective of all his exaggerations?

18. *Advice to a Young Frenchman:* List what you think after reading this essay are the prominent traits of the French and the English. Which of these are points of strength and which of weakness? Should you give a visitor to America similar advice? If not, what points should you stress as a help to popularity in America?

19. *The Color of Japan:* In what respect does Japanese life seem different from ours? What is the dark background behind the beauty of Japan? Is Japan any more colorful than America? How? Is there a difference in the way the beauty of the two countries has been produced? Why is this? Are Americans as appreciative of natural beauty? What do the poems add to our understanding of Japan and the Japanese attitude?

20. *The Riddle of America:* Give definite illustrations of what Ferrero means by the standards of quality and quantity. Compare this discussion with Galsworthy's narrative essay entitled *Quality.* Why does Ferrero think America has set up quantity as a standard? Do you agree with his criticism of American cities and villages? Why is the quantity standard slower in conquering Europe? Do you agree that to pursue quantity we must sacrifice the life of the spirit—art—morality—civilization itself? How does Ferrero think civilization can be saved?

21. *What the American Rhodes Scholar Gets Out of Oxford:* Point out several major differences between the English and American systems of doing academic work. Which system will promote the steadiest, hardest work, and the most lasting knowledge? What two things take the place at Oxford of the American class discussion? Why is Oxford talk "the best in the world"? Contrast sports at Oxford and in American schools. Which system of athletics will reach the larger number of students and train them to include outdoor exercise in their later lives? Contrast the American and English college vacations. How should a Rhodes Scholarship broaden the American student's international viewpoint? Could any features of the English system be profitably used in our high schools?

FURTHER READINGS IN THE ESSAY

Essie Chamberlain (editor): *A Mirror for Americans*

Essie Chamberlain (editor): *Essays Old and New*, revised edition, especially such selections as Agnes Repplier: *A Kitten*, Helen Keller: *Three Days to See*, Christopher Morley: *On Doors*, William Allen White: *Mary White*, Lincoln Steffens: *I Get a Colt to Break In*, Elbert Hubbard: *A Message to Garcia*

William Cunningham (editor): *Understanding America*

Roberts and Rand (editors): *Let's Read*

Harold Tinker (editor): *Essays Yesterday and Today*

Leonard and Pooley (editors): *Introducing Essays*, especially such selections as A Worker: *On the Industrial Scrapheap* and Ralph Bergengren: *The Plumber Appreciated*

Charles Lamb: *Poor Relations*

Walter Prichard Eaton: *The Professor Goes to Lunch* (*Atlantic Monthly*)

Katherine Fullerton Gerould: *Ringside Seats* (in Rankin, Nevins, Solve and Wells: *Further Adventures in Essay Reading*)

John Galsworthy: *Quality* (in Sharon Brown: *Essays of Our Time*)

Robert Louis Stevenson: *Travels with a Donkey*
   An Apology for Idlers

David Grayson: *On Being Where You Belong* (in Hanes-McCoy: *Readings in Contemporary Literature*)

Theodore Roosevelt: *A Boy's Book Rambles* (in Hanes-McCoy: *Readings in Contemporary Literature*)

Dallas Lore Sharp: *Turtle Eggs for Agassiz* (*Atlantic Monthly*)
   A Bed in a Laboratory (*Atlantic Monthly*)

Clarence Day: *Father Tries to Make Mother Like Figures*

Selected essays in current magazines

SUGGESTIONS FOR ORIGINAL ESSAYS

1. In the Dentist's Office. 2. Getting on with My Chum. 3. Who Has No Pencil? 4. Talk in the Locker Room. 5. A High School Student's Vocabulary. 6. Training a Pet. 7. Intelligence Tests and What They Do Not Show. 8. Learning to Choose. 9. The Perils of Installment Buying. 10. My Personal Castle in Spain. 11. Dancing School. 12. How Some Favorite Book Illustrates Gorky's Ideas about Literature. 13. Don't Believe Everything You See in Print. 14. On Translating Some Foreign Author You Have Read in the Original. 15. On Slapstick Movie Comics. 16. What the Day Lily Might Say to the Man. 17. Select some fad or weakness of your own or of others and burlesque it either by a fictitious history or an extravagant rhapsody; as for instance, A Dissertation on Candy Bars. 18. Advice to a Foreigner Visiting America. 19. A Travel Sketch from My Own Journeys. 20. Our Skyscraper Architecture. 21. Examinations I Have Taken. 22. The Conversation of High School Students.

XI

Lyric Poetry

WHAT the personal essay does in prose, the lyric poem does with greater intensity in verse. It catches the moment as it flies, and records the emotion, the mood, or the reflection of the poet in that instant. We live, as some one has said, in three worlds: the world of nature, the world of men, and the world within our own hearts and minds—the world of fancy and reflection. Experiences in each of these worlds stir the poet's sensitive nature. "His heart," quotes Poe, "is like a suspended lute: at every touch, it resounds." The experiences of the poet are the same as those we meet ourselves in the great outdoors; in friendship, family life, love, or loyalty to land and leaders; and in the inner world of dream, vision and religious faith. But few of us have the power to express these experiences. The gifted poet puts our responses to life—and his own—into the compact form of verse, which concentrates a world of thought and feeling into a few lines, and re-enforces the mood or idea by the accompaniment of appropriate rhythm—just as in the motion picture, music is used to heighten the effect of emotional scenes. To seek for our own experiences thus cut, polished, and reset like flashing jewels in the golden ring of poetry, is one of the great charms of reading verse.

The word lyric was used by the Greeks to describe this type of personal poetry, because such a poem was often sung by its author to the music of the lyre, or Grecian harp. Lyric verse now assumes many forms. First, there are songs, either actually written to music or written in singable language. There are lyrics which, while musical and rhythmic, are not songlike in structure. There are sonnets, with their fixed subject treatment, length, rhythm, and rhyme scheme. There are odes, or long formal songs, usually suitable only for solemn rendition by a great chorus. And there are elegies, or lyrics of grief addressed to the departed.

All of these lyrics show two qualities of style: word music and rhythm; and imagery often heightened by figures of speech.

THE RHYTHMS OF VERSE

Three great arts—poetry, music and the dance—were simultaneously born, and like human triplets, they bear an interesting resemblance to each other. Before the dawn of history, as a band of successful hunters or triumphant warriors approached the tribal village, they began to shout out joyfully the success of their expedition. As they came into the village stockade, their first thought was to dance in thanksgiving about the totem pole or image of the tribal god, erected in the open space in the center of the village— just as we so often see the savages do in motion pictures laid in Africa. As they circled around and around, their tumultuous cries naturally fell into time with the rhythm of their march or dance. To keep the crowd moving in unison, some inspired genius invented the tomtom—first musical instrument of the human race. Thus the marching and dancing rhythms of our primitive ancestors stamped themselves upon music and poetry, which still preserve as their dominant rhythms the one step, waltz time, march time, and two step swings. Rowers, reapers, threshers, and men and maidens treading the grapes in the wine presses likewise sang at their work, and their songs, too, took on the rhythms of their toil, which often resembled those of the march and dance.

This is obvious to anyone who has a feeling for the swing of music, but some of you may not be so expert in picking up the rhythm of poetry. Can you tell which of the following lines of poetry is in one step rhythm, which in waltz time, which in march time, and which in two step rhythm?

1. Once upon a midnight dreary, while I pondered weak and weary;
   While I nodded nearly napping, suddenly there came a tapping
   As of someone gently rapping, rapping at my chamber door.
2. Bird of the wilderness,
   Blithesome and cumberless,
   Oh, to be one in the desert with thee!
3. The stag at eve had drunk his fill
   Where danced the moon on Monan's rill.
4. 'Twas the night before Christmas and all through the house
   Not a creature was stirring not even a mouse.

As you say these lines over, you will notice that their rhythm or swing is due to the fact that the accented syllables recur at regular intervals. In other words, just as in the pattern of a scalloped border or lace edging, a single design is repeated over and over thus :

being the design whose repetition gives a pattern or rhythm to the border ; so in a line of poetry, there is repeated a certain arrangement of accented and unaccented syllables. The lines quoted above are printed below with the accents marked so you can pick out this repeated accent pattern. ′ marks an accented syllable and ˘ an unaccented syllable.

1. Ónce ŭp | ón ă | mídnĭght | dréarў— ′ ˘ is repeated.

2. Bírd ŏf thĕ | wíldĕrnĕss | blíthesŏme ănd | cúmbĕrlĕss— ′ ˘ ˘ is repeated.

3. Thĕ stág | ăt éve | hăd drúnk | hĭs fíll— ˘ ˘ ′ is repeated.

4. Twăs thĕ níght | bĕfŏre Chríst | măs ănd áll | thrŏugh thĕ hoúse— ˘ ˘ ′ is repeated.

You can see that if we could tune in on a radio broadcast by a reader speaking these poems, we could dance to them just as well as to music because 1 is in one step rhythm ; 2 is in waltz time, 3 is in march time ; and 4 is in two step rhythm. These rhythms are usually called for convenience by the names given them by the Greeks. One step rhythm is called trochaic ; waltz rhythm is dactyllic ; marching rhythm is iambic ; and two step rhythm is anapestic.

The swing of the poem is affected by the number of times the accent pattern is repeated in a line, a long line giving a slower movement to a poem than a short one. A repeated accent pattern is called a poetic foot, as it is the unit by which rhythm is measured. The following names are given to poetry with the indicated number of feet in each line.

One foot: monometer—| Bĕhóld |

Two feet: dimeter—| Táke hĕr ŭp | téndĕrlў |

Three feet: trimeter:—| Ăs hĕ síngs | ĭn hĭs bóat | ŏn thĕ báy |

Four feet: tetrameter—| Téll mĕ | nót ĭn | móurnfŭl | númbĕrs |

Five feet: pentameter—| Thĕ cúr | fĕw tólls | thĕ knéll | ŏf párt | ĭng
dáy |

Six feet: hexameter—| Ăs óne | fŏr kníght | lў joústs | ănd fíerce |
ĕncoúnt | ĕrs fít |

Seven feet: septameter:—| Thĕre's nót | ă jóy | thĕ wórld | căn gíve |
lĭke thát | ĭt tákes | ăwáy |

Eight feet: Octometer—| Ónce ŭp | ón ă | mídnĭght | dréarў | whíle
Ī | póndĕred | wéak ănd | wéarў |

Sometimes, as in a measure of music, a rest or pause takes the
place of one or more syllables, as in the lines:

(1) Bléssĭngs | ón thĕe | líttlĕ | mán ˘ |
(2) Líft hĕr wĭth | cáre ˘ ˘ |

Some of you may want to look through the poetry units in this
volume to see whether you can pick up the rhythms of different
poems, just as you pick up the rhythms of a dance orchestra at a
party. But remember that just as you would never start dancing
till the orchestra had finished the opening notes of the piece and
fallen into the swing of the dance tune, so you cannot always tell
by the first line of a poem, either, what it is going to be; you must
read on a line or two to catch the swing. The first beats of both a
musical tune and a word tune are likely to be irregular!

In order to avoid the monotony of an invariable rhythm, poets
often combine two rhythms in one poem. This can be done with
one step and waltz rhythm as the heavy beat comes at the first
of the foot in both, and the change from ´ ˘ to ´ ˘ ˘ does not break
the swing.

Óvĕr | mánў ă | quaínt ănd | cúrĭoŭs | vólume | óf fŏr | góttĕn | lóre ˘ |

It can also be done with march and two step rhythm as in both
of these the accent is at the end of the foot.

Cŏme ín | tŏ thĕ gárd | ĕn Maúd, |
Ī ăm hére | ăt thĕ gáte | ălóne |

Monotony is also avoided by breaking the lines with pauses or
by using words which one holds like whole notes in music and
which may take the place of several syllables in the rhythm.

It's the white road westwards is the road that I must tread
To the green grass, the cool grass, and rest for heart and head,
To the violets and the brown brooks and the thrushes' song
In the fine land, the west land, the land where I belong.

The music of verse is produced not only by rhythm but by the melody of the words themselves. Rhyme, or ending lines in the same stanza with words of similar sound; alliteration, or beginning several words in the same or adjacent line with the same letter; employing words which are in themselves musical; and onomatopoeia, or using words which imitate the sounds being described, all add to the music of verse. And whatever adds to its music adds to its expressive power.

It is not expected that students laboriously endeavor to recognize all these rhythms and musical devices with unfailing accuracy or spoil the enjoyment of lyrics by painfully scanning the lines. It is hoped, however, that a general knowledge of the subject of poetic rhythm will help many of you to feel more keenly and readily the manifold music of verse. Choral reading by the whole class of poems with marked rhythm will help you catch the basic beat.

IMAGERY AND FIGURES OF SPEECH

The statement has already been made in the introductory chapter that the poet gives an idea to us in the form of a concrete picture or image and that this image in our mind warms with emotion what might otherwise be a cold abstraction. These images are called up either by descriptive words or by comparisons. Writers have a number of different ways of making comparisons, which are called figures of speech. However, the student should remember that it is perceiving the comparison that is important. The names of the various figures of speech and the differences between them are not the essential things to dwell upon.

When a poet says one thing is *like* another, we call his comparison a *simile* since he uses the word which expresses the similarity, as in, "My love is like a red, red rose." The word *as* is sometimes used in a simile instead of *like;* for example, "She is as cheerful as a sunbeam." Sometimes two things seem so nearly alike to a writer that he literally calls them identical; as in, "Sarcasm is a dangerous weapon." Such a comparison is called a metaphor (a word which means in Greek putting one for the other). A writer may think of an inanimate object as alive and personify it, as in "the thirsty blade drank blood." Or he may give life to some abstract idea as in,

"Oh death, where is thy sting,
O grave, thy victory?"

Closely related to personification is *apostrophe*—a figure in which one addresses the dead as living or the absent as present as in:

"Mother, come back from that echoless shore."

The writer may use something associated with an idea as a symbol for it; as in "The pen is mightier than the sword," where *pen* stands for literature and the *sword* for military force. This figure is called *metonomy*. Sometimes a writer will use a part of an object to represent the whole—a figure called *synecdoche*, and illustrated in the expression, "She gave him her hand in marriage." The husband's hope is naturally to obtain more than her hand! Sometimes, on the other hand, a writer gives us a striking contrast, or *antithesis,* as in "God made the country; man made the town." Antithesis gives a sharper sting to satire; as in,

> "Stain her honor or her new brocade;
> Forget her prayers or miss a masquerade,
> Or lose her heart or necklace at a ball."

Other forms of contrast are sarcasm and that more subtle veiled sarcasm entitled irony, the contrast being that you mean the exact opposite of what you say.

In humorous description or in making a point strongly, an author sometimes exaggerates greatly. For instance Irving describes Ichabod Crane's feet as shovels and says his hands dangled a mile out of his sleeves. This is called *hyperbole*. On the other hand, it is sometimes more effective to understate a point, as did the wit who remarked that "nothing was so annoying as to be obscurely hanged," or as did Mark Twain when he said that the reports of his death had been "greatly exaggerated."

A final figure often used by poets and other writers has no element of comparison. It is epigram—or putting a great deal of thought in a compact, pithy, quotable saying, like "Fools rush in where angels fear to tread," "Hope springs eternal in the human breast," "Men get and forget; women give and forgive," and "A little learning is a dangerous thing."

As we remarked earlier of poetic rhythms, your authors hope your enjoyment of the poetry in this volume will not be obscured by having tediously to search out figures of speech. None the less, the more things you can easily notice about a poem as you read it, the more you will enjoy it. The important thing, however, is to lose yourself in the thought or feeling of the selection, for the meaning of a poem is more important than the technical devices by which it is conveyed.

One parting word of help is offered the beginner at reading poetry. Poets often invert their sentences in order to make the rhythm run smoothly. To compress much thought into small space, they also often describe and explain their nouns by the use of long elaborate explanatory modifiers and appositives. If you will accustom yourself to these two constructions, the most complex verse will present you only that difficulty with which all noble thought confronts our minds—the necessity of rising to the level of the subject, which, be assured, will not stoop to us!

A COIN

SARA TEASDALE (AMERICA)

Into my heart's treasury
    I slipped a coin
That time cannot take
    Nor a thief purloin.—
Oh better than the minting   5
    Of a gold crowned king
Is the safe kept memory
    Of a lovely thing.

SPRING SONG

ANTIPATER OF SIDON (GREECE)

Translated by F. A. Wright

Now swallows build beneath the eaves,
    And shape anew their rounded home;
Now meadows smile with tender leaves,
    And know that spring has come.

Now is the hour for ships to go,   5
    And lightly o'er the billows leap;
While winter winds no longer blow
    Or vex the ocean deep.

Come then, ye shipmen, hoist the sail,
  And from its nest the anchor haul;   10
Coil the wet ropes and take the gale;
  Lo I, Priapus, call.

SPRING AND AUTUMN

OHOGIMI (JAPAN)

Translated by Basil H. Chamberlain

When Winter turns to Spring,
Birds that were songless make their songs resound,
Flowers that were flowerless cover all the ground;
  Yet 'tis no perfect thing.
I cannot walk, so tangled is each hill;   5
So thick the herbs, I cannot pluck my fill.
  But in the autumn-tide
I cull the scarlet leaves and love them dear,
And let the green leaves stay, with many a tear,
  All on the fair hill-side.   10
No time so sweet as that. Away! away!
Autumn's the time I fain would keep alway.

VAGABOND SONG

BLISS CARMAN (CANADA)

There is something in the autumn that is native to my blood—
Touch of manner, hint of mood;
And my heart is like a rhyme,
With the yellow and the purple and the crimson keeping time.

The scarlet of the maples can shake me like a cry   5
Of bugles going by.
And my lonely spirit thrills
To see the frosty asters like a smoke upon the hills.

There is something in October sets the gipsy blood astir;
We must rise and follow her,   10
When from every hill of flame
She calls and calls each vagabond by name.

12. *Priapus:* a god of the out of doors.

FROST TONIGHT

EDITH M. THOMAS (AMERICA)

Apple-green west and an orange bar,
And the crystal eye of a lone, one star . . .
And "Child, take the shears and cut what you will.
Frost tonight—so clear and dead-still."

Then I sally forth, half sad, half proud,   5
And I come to the velvet, imperial crowd,
The wine-red, the gold, the crimson, the pied,—
The dahlias that reign by the garden-side.

The dahlias I might not touch till tonight!
A gleam of the shears in the fading light,   10
And I gathered them all,—the splendid throng,
And in one great sheaf I bore them along.

In my garden of Life with its all-late flowers,
I heed a Voice in the shrinking hours:
"Frost tonight—so clear and dead-still". . .   15
Half sad, half proud, my arms I fill.

VELVET SHOES

ELINOR WYLIE (AMERICA)

Let us walk in the white snow
    In a soundless space;
With footsteps quiet and slow,
    At a tranquil pace.

I shall go shod in silk,   5
    And you in wool,
White as a cow's white milk,
    More beautiful
Than the breast of a gull.

We shall walk through the still town   10
    In a windless peace;
We shall step upon white down,
    Upon silver fleece,
    Upon softer than these.

We shall walk in velvet shoes:
   Wherever we go
Silence will fall like dews
   On white silence below.
   We shall walk in the snow.   15

SKATING AT NIGHT

WILLIAM WORDSWORTH (ENGLAND)

This is an extract from *The Prelude,* an autobiography written in verse by Wordsworth. He lived as a child in an English region of lakes and mountains somewhat like the American Adirondacks.

❊   ❊   ❊

In the frosty season, when the sun
Was set, and visible for many a mile
The cottage windows blazed through twilight gloom,
I heeded not their summons: happy time
It was indeed for all of us—for me   5
It was a time of rapture! Clear and loud
The village clock tolled six,—I wheeled about,
Proud and exulting like an untired horse
That cares not for his home. All shod with steel,
We hissed along the polished ice in games   10
Confederate, imitative of the chase
And woodland pleasures,—the resounding horn,
The pack loud chiming, and the hunted hare.
So through the darkness and the cold we flew,
And not a voice was idle; with the din   15
Smitten, the precipices rang aloud;
The leafless trees and every icy crag
Tinkled like iron; while far distant hills
Into the tumult sent an alien sound
Of melancholy not unnoticed, while the stars   20
Eastward were sparkling clear, and in the west
The orange sky of evening died away.
Not seldom from the uproar I retired
Into a silent bay, or sportively
Glanced sideway, leaving the tumultuous throng,   25
To cut across the reflex of a star
That fled, and, flying still before me, gleamed
Upon the glassy plain; and oftentimes,

When we had given our bodies to the wind,
And all the shadowy banks on either side   30
Came sweeping through the darkness spinning still
The rapid line of motion, then at once
Have I, reclining back upon my heels,
Stopped short; yet still the solitary cliffs
Wheeled by me—even as if the earth had rolled   35
With visible motion her diurnal round!
Behind me did they stretch in solemn train,
Feebler and feebler, and I stood and watched
Till all was tranquil as a dreamless sleep.

MORNING

Mohammed Ben Osman Ben Ali Nakkash (Turkey)

Translated in Dublin University Magazine

Another night is fled,
        Another morning rises red;
The silver stars that twinkle
Through saffron curtains here and there
        Gleam like the pearls that sprinkle   5
        A virgin's golden hair.
New beams and brighter smile
Along the skies, and while
        Aurora's colors clamber
The mountains of the dawn,   10
        The sun, a globe of amber,
In silentness has drawn
Within his own warm sphere, as morn by morn he draws
Each glistening straw that strews the Way of Straws.

HEAVEN'S BLUE

Victor Rydberg (Sweden)

Translated by Ernest W. Nelson

Wonderful
Unfathomed clearness,
O Heavenly azure,
        That, smiling,

9. *Aurora:* goddess of the dawn.

Descends to me,　　　　　　　　5
Lifting my soul
　　To cool spaces
　　And holy serenity!
Enchanting Nirvana,
Where, bathed in purity,　　　　10
I exhale myself
In the infinite,
　　And reborn
In the next breath,
Baptized in longing,　　　　　15
　　Sink back
To the dust of Earth.

THE CLOUD

PERCY BYSSHE SHELLEY (ENGLAND)

I bring fresh showers for the thirsting flowers
　　From the seas and the streams;
I bear light shade for the leaves when laid
　　In their noonday dreams;
From my wings are shaken the dews that waken　5
　　The sweet buds every one,
When rocked to rest on their mother's breast,
　　As she dances about the sun.
I wield the flail of the lashing hail,
　　And whiten the green plains under;　　　10
And then again I dissolve it in rain,
　　And laugh as I pass in thunder.

I sift the snow on the mountains below,
　　And their great pines groan aghast;
And all the night 'tis my pillow white,　　　15
　　While I sleep in the arms of the blast.
Sublime on the towers of my skyey bowers,
　　Lightning, my pilot, sits;
In a cavern under is fettered the thunder—
　　It struggles and howls by fits;　　　　20
Over earth and ocean, with gentle motion,
　　This pilot is guiding me,

9. *Nirvana:* the heaven of the Hindu religion, which teaches that after death each soul is reabsorbed in the divine spirit from which it separated at birth.

Lured by the love of the genii that move
 In the depths of the purple sea;
Over the rills, and the crags, and the hills,   25
 Over the lakes, and the plains,
Wherever he dream, under mountain or stream,
 The spirit he loves remains;
And I, all the while, bask in heaven's blue smile,
 Whilst he is dissolving in rains.   30

The sanguine sunrise, with his meteor eyes,
 And his burning plumes outspread,
Leaps on the back of my sailing rack,
 When the morning-star shines dead,
As on the jag of a mountain-crag,   35
 Which an earthquake rocks and swings,
An eagle, alit, one moment may sit,
 In the light of its golden wings.
And when sunset may breathe, from the lit sea
  beneath,
 Its ardors of rest and love,
And the crimson pall of eve may fall   40
 From the depth of heaven above,
With wings folded I rest, on mine airy nest,
 As still as a brooding dove.

That orbèd Maiden, with white fire laden,   45
 Whom mortals call the Moon,
Glides glimmering o'er my fleece-like floor,
 By the midnight breezes strewn;
And wherever the beat of her unseen feet,
 Which only the angels hear,
May have broken the woof of my tent's thin roof,   50
 The stars peep behind her, and peer!
And I laugh to see them whirl and flee,
 Like a swarm of golden bees;
When I widen the rent in my wind-built tent,   55
 Till the calm rivers, lakes, and seas,
Like strips of the sky fallen through me on high,
 Are each paved with the moon and these.

33. *rack:* loose flying clouds left after a storm.

I bind the sun's throne with a burning zone,
    And the moon's with a girdle of pearl;   60
The volcanoes are dim, and the stars reel and swim,
    When the whirlwinds my banner unfurl.
From cape to cape, with a bridge-like shape,
    Over a torrent of sea,
Sunbeam proof, I hang like a roof,   65
    The mountains its columns be.
The triumphal arch through which I march
    With hurricane, fire, and snow,
When the powers of the air are chained to my chair,
    Is the million-colored bow;   70
The sphere-fire above its soft colors wove,
    While the moist earth was laughing below.

I am the daughter of earth and water
    And the nursling of the sky;
I pass through the pores of the ocean and shores;   75
    I change, but I cannot die.
For after the rain, when, with never a stain,
    The pavilion of heaven is bare,
And the winds and sunbeams, with their convex gleams,
    Build up the blue dome of air,   80
I silently laugh at my own cenotaph,
    And out of the caverns of rain,
Like a sprite from the gloom, like a ghost from the tomb,
    I rise and unbuild it again.

SMILE, O EARTH

Walt Whitman (America)

Smile, O voluptuous, cool-breath'd earth!
Earth of the slumbering and liquid trees!
Earth of the departed sunset—earth of the mountains, misty-
    topt!
Earth of the vitreous pour of the full moon, just tinged with blue!
Earth of shine and dark, mottling the tide of the river!   5
Earth of the limpid gray of clouds, brighter and clearer for my
    sake!
Far-swooping, elbow'd earth—rich, apple-blossom'd earth!
Smile, for your lover comes!

59. *zone:* girdle.   81. *cenotaph:* empty tomb.   4. *vitreous:* like glass.

WINDY NIGHTS

Robert Louis Stevenson (Scotland)

Whenever the moon and stars are set,
  Whenever the wind is high,
All night long in the dark and wet,
  A man goes riding by.
Late in the night when the fires are out,   5
Why does he gallop and gallop about?

Whenever the trees are crying aloud,
  And ships are tossed at sea,
By, on the highway, low and loud,
  By at the gallop goes he.   10
By at the gallop he goes, and then
By he comes back at the gallop again.

THE TREE

Björnsterne Björnson (Norway)

The Tree's early leaf buds were bursting their brown;
"Shall I take them away?" said the Frost, sweeping down.
    "No, leave them alone
    Till the blossoms have grown,"
Prayed the Tree, while he trembled from rootlet to crown.   5

The Tree bore his blossoms, and all the birds sung:
"Shall I take them away?" said the Wind, as he swung.
    "No, leave them alone
    Till the blossoms have grown,"
Said the Tree, while his leaflets quivering hung.   10

The Tree bore his fruit in the midsummer glow:
Said the child, "May I gather thy berries now?"
    "Yes, all thou canst see:
    Take them; all are for thee,"
Said the Tree, while he bent down his laden boughs low.   15

ON THE DEATH OF LESBIA'S SPARROW

CAIUS VALERIUS CATULLUS (ROME)

Translated by Sir Theodore Martin

To a Roman lady whom he called by the fictitious name of Lesbia and for whom he entertained a hopeless passion, Catullus addressed many graceful poems such as the following.

❊   ❊   ❊

Loves and Graces, mourn with me,
Mourn, fair youths, wher'er ye be!
Dead my Lesbia's sparrow is,
Sparrow, that was all her bliss,
Than her very eyes more dear;   5
For he made her dainty cheer,
Knew her well, as any maid
Knows her mother, never strayed
From her bosom, but would go
Hopping round her, to and fro,   10
And to her, and her alone,
Chirrup'd with such pretty tone.
Now he treads that gloomy track,
Whence none ever may come back.
Out upon you, and your power,   15
Which all fairest things devour,
Orcus' gloomy shades, that e'er
Ye took the bird that was so fair!
Ah, the pity of it! Thou
Poor Bird, thy doing 'tis, that now   20
My loved one's eyes are swollen and red
With weeping for her darling dead.

A BIRD

EMILY DICKINSON (AMERICA)

A bird came down the walk:
He did not know I saw;
He bit an angle worm in halves
And ate the fellow raw.

17. *Orcus:* the land of the dead.

And then he drank a dew   5
From a convenient grass,
And then hopped sidewise to the wall
To let a beetle pass.

He glanced with rapid eyes
That hurried all abroad—   10
They looked like frightened beads. I thought
He stirred his velvet head

Like one in danger; cautious,
I offered him a crumb,
And he unrolled his feathers   15
And rowed him softer home

Than oars divide the ocean,
Too silver for a seam,
Or butterflies, off banks of noon,
Leap, plashless, as they swim.   20

TO THE CUCKOO

WILLIAM WORDSWORTH (ENGLAND)

O Blithe New-comer! I have heard
I hear thee and rejoice.
O Cuckoo! shall I call thee Bird,
Or but a wandering Voice?

While I am lying on the grass   5
Thy twofold shout I hear;
From hill to hill it seems to pass
At once far off, and near.

Though babbling only to the Vale,
Of sunshine and of flowers,   10
Thou bringest unto me a tale
Of visionary hours.

Thrice welcome, darling of the Spring!
Even yet thou art to me
No bird, but an invisible thing,   15
A voice, a mystery;

The same whom in my schoolboy days
    I listened to; that cry
Which made me look a thousand ways
    In bush, and tree, and sky.   20

To seek thee did I often rove
    Through woods and on the green;
And thou wert still a hope, a love;
    Still longed for, never seen.

And I can listen to thee yet;   25
    Can lie upon the plain
And listen, till I do beget
    That golden time again.

O blessèd Bird! the earth we pace
    Again appears to be   30
An unsubstantial, faery place;
    That is fit home for thee!

THE EAGLE

ALFRED TENNYSON (ENGLAND)

He clasps the crag with crooked hands,
Close to the sun in lonely lands,
Ringed with the azure world, he stands.

The wrinkled sea beneath him crawls;
He watches from his mountain walls,
And like a thunderbolt he falls.   5

A SYMPHONY IN GRAY

RUBEN DARIO (NICARAGUA)

Translated by G. D. Craig

The ocean like some mirror-surface vast
Reflects the zinc-hued sky that dims the day;
By distant flocks of birds a blot is cast
Upon the burnished background, pallid gray.

The sun with face of glass, opaque and round, 5
Paces the zenith like a man outworn;
The sea wind seeks the shade and rest profound,
Making a pillow of his sable horn.

The waves that writhe their leaden forms here seem
To groan beneath the pier among its piles. 10
Upon a cable seated, in a dream
A sailor smoking thinks of far-off isles
Where vague and misty all the landscape smiles.

An old sea wolf, the hot Brazilian sun
Has bronzed his face with rays of darting fire; 15
In Chinese seas the bellowing typhoon
Has seen him drink his gin despite its ire.

The sea foam charged with niter and iodine
Long years has known his shining ruddy nose,
His crispy locks, his muscles big and fine, 20
His woolen cap, the blouse of drill he shows.

Amid the clouds of pipe-smoke upward rolled
The old man sees that distant, misty shore,
Whither one sultry eve 'neath skies of gold
His bark with all sails set put forth of yore. 25

The tropic afternoon the sea wolf sleeps,
All things are merged in changing hues of gray;
A soft yet mighty brush appears to sweep
The curved horizon's boundary away.

The locust through the tropic afternoon 30
Teases his ancient hoarse guitar to sing;
And the cricket starts his one monotonous tune
On his violin with but a single string.

IN THE WHITE LAND

KONSTANTIN BALMONT (RUSSIA)

Translated by Babette Deutsch and Avrahm Yarmolinsky

The candid psalm of Silence rises whitely burning,
The icy wastes are lit with sunset's radiant yearning.
The drowsy elements in yawning vistas freeze,
And voiceless are the argent Polar liturgies.

4. *argent:* silver. *liturgies:* ceremonial prayers.

Above the sea of whiteness, crimson curtains falling;   5
No fields or forests here, clear crystal shines appalling.
White altars stretch beneath the changeless icy skies,
A prayer, not suppliant, a psalm, not voiced,—arise.

A NIGHTMARE

W. S. GILBERT (ENGLAND)

This witty piece is one of the lyrics in a light opera by Gilbert and
Sullivan called *Iolanthe*. Other comic operas by this famous pair are
The Mikado, H.M.S. Pinafore, Trial by Jury, and *The Pirates of
Penzance*—all of which are as lively and timely today as when these
gay satires on life, character, and institutions were first written.

❋   ❋   ❋

When you're lying awake with a dismal headache, and repose is
     tabooed by anxiety,
I conceive you may use any language you choose to indulge in,
     without impropriety;
For your brain is on fire—the bedclothes conspire of usual slumber
     to plunder you:
First your counterpane goes and uncovers your toes, and your
     sheet slips demurely from under you;
Then the blanketing tickles—you feel like mixed pickles, so ter-
     ribly sharp is the pricking,   5
And you're hot, and you're cross, and you tumble and toss till
     there's nothing 'twixt you and the ticking.
Then the bedclothes all creep to the ground in a heap, and you pick
     'em all up in a tangle;
Next your pillow resigns and politely declines to remain at its usual
     angle!
Well, you get some repose in the form of a doze, with hot eye-balls
     and head ever aching,
But your slumbering teems with such horrible dreams that you'd
     very much better be waking.   10
For you dream you are crossing the Channel, and tossing about in
     a steamer from Harwich,
Which is something between a large bathing machine and a very
     small second-class carriage,
And you're giving a treat (penny ice and cold meat) to a party of
     friends and relations—
They're a ravenous horde—and they all came on board at Sloane
     Square and South Kensington Stations.

11. *Harwich:* pronounced to rhyme with "carriage" in the next line.

And bound on that journey you find your attorney (who started
  that morning from Devon);   15
He's a bit undersized, and you don't feel surprised when he tells
  you he's only eleven.
Well, you're driving like mad with this singular lad (by-the-bye,
  the ship's now a four-wheeler),
And you're playing round games, and he calls you bad names when
  you tell him that "ties pay the dealer";
But this you can't stand, so you throw up your hand, and you
  find you're as cold as an icicle,
In your shirt and your socks (the black silk with gold clocks),
  crossing Salisbury Plain on a bicycle: 20
And he and the crew are on bicycles too—which they've somehow
  or other invested in—
And he's telling the tars all the particu*lars* of a company he's interested in—
It's a scheme of devices, to get at low prices, all goods from cough
  mixtures to cables
(Which tickled the sailors) by treating retailers, as though they
  were all vege*tables*—
You get a good spadesman to plant a small tradesman (first take
  off his boots with a boot-tree),   25
And his legs will take root, and his fingers will shoot, and they'll
  blossom and bud like a fruit tree—
From the greengrocer tree you get grapes and green pea, cauli-
  flower, pineapple, and cranberries,
While the pastry-cook plant, cherry brandy will grant, apple puffs,
  and three-corners, and banberries—
The shares are a penny, and ever so many are taken by Rothschild
  and Baring,
And just as a few are allotted to you, you awake with a shudder
  despairing—   30
You're a regular wreck, with a crick in your neck, and no wonder
  you snore, for your head's on the floor, and you've needles and
  pins from your soles to your shins, and your flesh is a-creep,
  for your left leg's asleep, and you've cramp in your toes, and a
  fly on your rose, and some fluff in your lung, and a feverish
  tongue, and a thirst that's intense, and a general sense that you
  haven't been sleeping in clover;
But the darkness has passed, and it's daylight at last, and the night
  has been long—ditto, ditto my song—and thank goodness
  they're both of them over!

THE COACH OF LIFE

ALEXANDER PUSHKIN (RUSSIA)

Translated by Babette Deutsch and Avrahm Yarmolinsky

Though often somewhat heavy-freighted,
The coach rolls at an easy pace;
And Time, the coachman, grizzly-pated,
But smart, alert,—is in his place.

We board it lightly in the morning   5
And on our way at once proceed.
Repose and slothful comfort scorning,
We shout: "Hey, there! Get on! Full speed!"

Noon finds us done with reckless daring,
And shaken up. Now care's the rule.   10
Down hills, through gulleys roughly faring,
We sulk, and cry: "Hey, easy, fool!"

The coach rolls on, no pitfalls dodging.
Toward evening, more accustomed grown,
We drowse, while to the night's dark lodging   15
Old coachman Time drives on, drives on.

SELECTIONS FROM THE RUBÁIYÁT

OMAR KHAYYÁM (PERSIA)

Translated by Edward Fitzgerald

The following are scattered stanzas from a long poem by a famous
Persian poet, astronomer and mathematician—Omar Khayyám—
expressing his speculations as to the mystery of life and his theory as
to how to make the most of it.

❋   ❋   ❋

I

Wake! For the Sun who scatter'd into flight
The Stars before him from the Field of Night,
    Drives Night along with them from Heav'n, and strikes
The Sultan's Turret with a Shaft of Light.

LOOK TO THE BLOWING ROSE ABOUT US—"LO,
LAUGHING," SHE SAYS, "INTO THE WORLD I BLOW,
AT ONCE THE SILKEN TASSEL OF MY PURSE
TEAR, AND ITS TREASURE ON THE GARDEN THROW."

V

Iram indeed is gone with all his Rose,
And Jamshyd's Sev'n-ring'd Cup where no one knows;   10
    But still a Ruby gushes from the Vine,
And many a Garden by the Water blows.

XIV

Look to the blowing Rose about us—"Lo,   5
Laughing," she says, "into the world I blow,
    At once the silken tassel of my Purse
Tear, and its Treasure on the Garden throw."

XVIII

They say the Lion and the Lizard keep
The Courts where Jamshyd gloried and drank deep:
    And Bahram, that great Hunter—the Wild Ass   15
Stamps o'er his Head, but cannot break his Sleep.

XIX

I sometimes think that never blows so red
The Rose as where some buried Caesar bled;
    That every Hyacinth the Garden wears
Dropt in her Lap from some once lovely Head.   20

XX

And this reviving Herb whose tender Green
Fledges the River-Lip on which we lean—
    Ah, lean upon it lightly! for who knows
From what once lovely Lip it springs unseen!

XXII

For some we loved, the loveliest and the best   25
That from his Vintage rolling Time has prest,
    Have drunk their Cup a Round or two before,
And one by one crept silently to rest.

XXIII

And we, that now make merry in the Room
They left, and Summer dresses in new bloom,   30
    Ourselves must we beneath the Couch of Earth
Descend—ourselves to make a Couch—for whom?

9-10-15. *Iram, Jamshyd, Bahram:* Persian heroes of old.

XXXI

Up from Earth's Center through the Seventh Gate
I rose, and on the Throne of Saturn sate,
    And many a Knot unravell'd by the Road;
But not the Master-knot of Human Fate.   35

XXXII

There was the Door to which I found no Key;
There was the Veil through which I could not see:
    Some little talk awhile of Me and Thee
There was—and then no more of Thee and Me.   40

XXXIII

Earth could not answer; nor the Seas that mourn
In flowing Purple, of their Lord forlorn;
    Nor rolling Heaven, with all his Signs reveal'd
And hidden by the sleeve of Night and Morn.

XLIV

Why, if the Soul can fling the Dust aside,   45
And naked on the Air of Heaven ride,
    Wer't not a Shame—wer't not a Shame for him
In this clay carcase crippled to abide?

XLV

'Tis but a Tent where takes his one-day's rest
A Sultan to the realm of Death addrest;   50
    The Sultan rises, and the dark Ferrásh
Strikes, and prepares it for another Guest.

XLVI

And fear not lest Existence closing your
Account, and mine, should know the like no more;
    The Eternal Sáki from that Bowl has pour'd   55
Millions of Bubbles like us, and will pour.

XLVII

When You and I behind the Veil are past,
Oh but the long long while the World shall last,
    Which of our Coming and Departure heeds
As the Sev'n Seas should heed a pebble-cast.   60

55. *Sáki:* lord.

XLVIII

A Moment's Halt—a momentary taste
Of Being from the Well amid the Waste—
   And Lo!—the phantom Caravan has reach'd
The Nothing it set out from—Oh, make haste!

LXIV

Strange, is it not? that of the myriads who   65
Before us pass'd the door of Darkness through
   Not one returns to tell us of the Road,
Which to discover we must travel too.

XL

As then the Tulip for her morning sup
Of Heav'nly Vintage from the soil looks up,   70
   Do you devoutly do the like, till Heav'n
To Earth invert you like an empty Cup.

ON LOVE AND CHANGE

HEINRICH HEINE (GERMANY)

Translated by Ruth Mary Weeks

SHADOW LOVE

Shadow love and shadow kisses,
Shadow life we all pursue.
Deem you there is aught that misses
Death and change, forever true?

All we hold the best and surest   5
Melts like idle dreams away.
Hearts forget whose love is purest
As eyelids close at close of day.

FIRST LOVE

First love though luckless, makes a god.
Second luckless love, a fool.   10
Such a loving fool am I.
Sun and moon and stars on high
Laugh, while I laugh back—and die!

MEMORY

FOOZOOLI (TURKEY)

Translated in Dublin University Magazine

The characters the slight reed traces
    Remain indelible through ages;
Strange, then, that Time so soon effaces
    What Feeling writes on Memory's pages!

THE ROAD NOT TAKEN

ROBERT FROST (AMERICA)

Two roads diverged in a yellow wood,
And sorry I could not travel both
And be one traveler, long I stood
And looked down one as far as I could
To where it bent in the undergrowth;   5

Then took the other, as just as fair,
And having perhaps the better claim
Because it was grassy and wanted wear;
Though as for that, the passing there
Had worn them really about the same,   10

And both that morning equally lay
In leaves no step had trodden black.
Oh, I marked the first for another day!
Yet, knowing how way leads on to way,
I doubted if I should ever come back.   15

I shall be telling this with a sigh
Somewhere ages and ages hence:
Two roads diverged in a wood, and I,
I took the one less traveled by,
And that has made all the difference.   20

THE LAST WORD

Matthew Arnold (England)

Creep into thy narrow bed,
Creep, and let no more be said!
Vain thy onset! all stands fast.
Thou thyself must break at last.

Let the long contention cease!   5
Geese are swans, and swans are geese.
Let them have it how they will!
Thou art tired; best be still.

They out-talked thee, hissed thee, tore thee?
Better men fared thus before thee;   10
Fired their ringing shot and passed,
Hotly charged—and sank at last.

Charge once more, then, and be dumb?
Let the victors, when they come,
When the forts of folly fall,   15
Find thy body by the wall!

ON THE BIRTH OF HIS SON

Su Tung-p'o (China)

Translated by Arthur Whaley

Families, when a child is born
Want it to be intelligent.
I, through intelligence,
Having wrecked my whole life,
Only hope the baby will prove   5
Ignorant and stupid.
Then he will crown a tranquil life
By becoming a Cabinet Minister.

ALL FOR LOVE

George Gordon, Lord Byron (England)

O talk to me not of a name great in story;
The days of our youth are the days of our glory:
And the myrtle and ivy of sweet two and twenty
Are worth all your laurels, though ever so plenty.

Oh Fame! if I e'er took delight in thy praises,   5
'Twas less for the sake of thy high sounding phrases,
Than to see the bright eyes of my dear one discover
She thought that I was not unworthy to love her.

There chiefly I sought thee, there only I found thee;
Her glance was the best of the rays that surround thee;   10
When it sparkled o'er aught that was bright in my story,
I knew it was love, and I felt it was glory.

LAUGH AND BE MERRY

John Masefield (England)

I

Laugh and be merry, remember, better the world with a song,
Better the world with a blow in the teeth of the wrong.
Laugh, for the time is brief, a thread the length of a span,
Laugh and be proud to belong to the old proud pageant of man.

II

Laugh and be merry: remember in olden time,   5
God made Heaven and Earth for joy He took in a rhyme,
Made them, and filled them full with the strong red wine of His
    mirth,
The splendid joy of the stars: the joy of the earth.

III

So we must laugh and drink from the deep blue of the sky,
Join the jubilant song of the great stars sweeping by,   10
Laugh, and battle, and work, and drink of the wine outpoured
In the dear green Earth, the sign of the joy of the Lord.

3. *myrtle and ivy:* The poet means garlands of these leaves and flowers, such
as happy young people wore in olden times.

IV

Laugh, and be merry together, like brothers akin,
Guesting awhile in the rooms of a beautiful inn,
Glad till the dancing stops, and lilt of the music ends.   15
Laugh till the game is played; and be you merry, my friends.

AT PEACE

AMADO NERVO (MEXICO)

Translated by G. D. Craig

I bless thee, Life, my sun now all but set,
For false hope never hast thou given me yet;
Nor toils nor pain unmerited I've met;
For now the rough road's past, I can detect
'Twas I that was my own fate's architect;   5
That if from things I sweet or bitter drew,
Their gall or honey to myself was due;
From rosebush planted always roses grew.

Winter, indeed, will end my proud endeavor;
Thou never said'st that May should last forever!   10
Long, doubtless, have I found the nights of pain,
That nights should all be good thou ne'er didst feign;
Through others still in saintly calm I've lain.
I've loved, been loved, the sun has kissed my face,
Nought dost thou owe me, Life! We are at peace!   15

ECSTASY

VICTOR HUGO (FRANCE)

Translated by Ruth Mary Weeks

Alone by the sea on a starry night,
Not a cloud in the sky, not a sail in sight,
My eyes pierce through terrestrial bars,
Till the whole earth seems to voice one cry,
Till hills and woods seem to question "Why"   5
    Of the waves of the sea, of the blaze of the stars.

And the golden stars in their galaxies
In deep, sweet, blended harmonies
Sing as their fiery crowns they nod;
And the surging sea that knows no rest   10
Speaks with the voice of its foaming crest:
"It is our Lord, Almighty God."

THE IDEAL

Giosuè Carducci (Italy)

Translated by G. L. Bickersteth

Bright star, thou with thy radiant fires
On days and years alike dost shine
From Heaven; as, in some Gothic shrine
High over all the climbing spires

Of marble black and white, upon   5
The topmost pinnacle doth stand
Jesse's sweet daughter, calm and grand
And glistening like a golden sun.

On champaign seamed with silver streaks
Of winding river she looks down,   10
On waving corn and distant town
And gleaming snow on Alpine peaks.

Though drifting clouds enwrap her, yet
Her shining face smiles through the mist
When dawning May the earth hath kissed   15
And sad November suns are set.

THE SWORD

Soloman Bloomgarten (Lithuania)

Formulated by Marie Syrkin

In the blossom-land Japan
Somewhere thus an old song ran.
Said a warrior to a smith
"Hammer me a sword forthwith.

3. *Gothic:* a style of architecture in which the mediaeval cathedrals were built.
7. *Jesse's daughter:* The Virgin Mary. The reference is to a statue of the Madonna on the cathedral spire. 11. *champaign:* a plain.

Make the blade 5
Light as wind on water laid.
Make it long
As the wheat at harvest song.
Supple, swift
As a snake, without rift, 10
Full of lightnings, thousand-eyed!
Smooth as silken cloth and thin
As the web that spiders spin.
And merciless as pain, and cold."

"On the hilt what shall be told?" 15

"On the sword's hilt, my good man,"
Said the warrior of Japan,
"Trace for me
A running lake, a flock of sheep,
And one who sings her child to sleep." 20

DEIRDRE

JAMES STEPHENS (IRELAND)

Deirdre's fatal beauty, like that of Helen of Troy, brought war upon
Ireland, of which she was the innocent cause and the tragic victim.

Do not let any woman read this verse!
It is for men, and after them their sons,
And their sons' sons.

The time comes when our hearts sink utterly;
When we remember Deirdre and her tale, 5
And that her lips are dust.

Once she did tread the earth: men took her hand;
They looked into her eyes and said their say.
And she replied to them.

More than two thousand years it is since she 10
Was beautiful: she trod the waving grass;
She saw the clouds.

Two thousand years! The grass is still the same;
The clouds as lovely as they were that time
When Deirdre was alive.   15

But there has been again no woman born
Who was so beautiful; not one so beautiful
Of all the women born.

Let all men go apart and mourn together!
No man can ever love her! Not a man   20
Can dream to be her lover!

No man can bend before her! No man say—
What could one say to her? There are no words
That one could say to her!

Now she is but a story that is told
Beside the fire! No man can ever be   25
The friend of that poor queen.

TO HELEN

EDGAR ALLAN POE (AMERICA)

This poem is a tribute to the influence of an older woman who be-
friended Poe in his youth.

❋   ❋   ❋

Helen, thy beauty is to me
    Like those Nicean barks of yore
That gently, o'er a perfumed sea,
    The weary way-worn wanderer bore
    To his own native shore.   5

On desperate seas long wont to roam,
    Thy hyacinth hair, thy classic face,
Thy Naiad airs, have brought me home
    To the glory that was Greece
    And the grandeur that was Rome.   10

Lo! in yon brilliant window-niche
  How statue-like I see thee stand,
The agate lamp within thy hand!
  Ah, Psyche, from the regions which
  Are Holy Land!   15

THERE BE NONE OF BEAUTY'S DAUGHTERS

GEORGE GORDON, LORD BYRON (ENGLAND)

There be none of Beauty's daughters
  With a magic like thee;
And like music on the waters
  Is thy sweet voice to me;
When, as if its sounds were causing   5
  The charmed ocean's pausing,
The waves lies still and gleaming
  And the lulled winds seem dreaming!

And the midnight moon is weaving
  Her bright chain o'er the deep,   10
Whose breast is gently heaving
  As an infant's asleep.
So the spirit bows before thee
  To listen and adore thee,
With a full but soft emotion,   15
  Like the swell of summer's ocean.

SIMPLEX MUNDITIIS

BEN JONSON (ENGLAND)

Still to be neat, still to be dressed,
As you were going to a feast;
Still to be powdered, still perfumed:
Lady, it is to be presumed,

---

4. *wanderer*: probably Ulysses, who wandered storm tossed so long after the Trojan War before he could reach his native land. Poe compares himself and his stormy life to the struggles of Ulysses for home and peace. 8. *Naiad*: a nymph. 14. *Psyche*: the Greek goddess of the soul. Poe's kind, cultivated friend seems to him to represent all that is finest in the life of the spirit.

Title. *Simplex Munditiis*: sophisticated simplicity—a phrase by which the Latin poet Horace describes a Roman girl.

Though art's hid causes are not found,   5
All is not sweet, all is not sound.
Give me a look, give me a face
That makes simplicity a grace;
Robes loosely flowing, hair as free:
Such sweet neglect more taketh me   10
Than all the adulteries of art.
They strike mine eyes, but not my heart.

ONE GIRL

SAPPHO (GREECE)

Translated by Dante Gabriel Rossetti

I

Like the sweet apple which reddens upon the topmost bough,
A-top on the topmost twig,—which the pluckers forgot, somehow—
Forget it not, nay, but got it not, for none could get it till now.

2

Like the wild hyacinth flower which on the hills is found,
Which the passing feet of the shepherds for ever tear and wound, 5
Until the purple blossom is trodden in the ground.

TO ROUGE THE LIPS

LADY LI CHING-CHAO (CHINA)

Translated by Wan Ying Hsieh

She comes down from the swing;
Weary, she wipes her little hands.
Like heavy dew on lightsome flowers
The tiny beads of sweat
Have dampened her thin dress.   5

She spies some one who comes;—
Her slippers fall; her gold pin slips;
Shyly she runs away,
Yet leaning on the door she turns
And smiling smells   10
The blue spring flowers she holds.

ANGELINA

PAUL LAURENCE DUNBAR (AMERICA)

When de fiddle gits to singin' out a ol' Vahginny reel;
An' you 'mence to feel a ticklin' in yo' toe an' in yo' heel;
Ef you t'ink you got 'uligion an' you wants to keep it, too,
You jes' bettah tek a hint an' git yo'self clean out o' view.
Case de time is mighty temptin' when de chune is in de swing,   5
Fu' a darky, saint or sinner man, to cut de pigeon-wing.
An' you couldn't help f'om dancin' ef yo' feet was boun' wif twine,
When Angelina Johnson comes a-swingin' down de line.
Don't you know Miss Angelina? She's de da'lin' of de place.
W'y, dey ain't no high-toned lady wif sich mannahs an' sich
          grace.   10
She kin move across the cabin, wif its planks all rough an' wo';
Jes' de sam's ef she was dancin' on ol' mistus' ballroom flo'.
Fact is, you do' see no cabin—evaht'ing you see look grand,
An' dat one ol' squeaky fiddle soun' to you jes' lak a ban';
Cotton britches look lak broadclof an' a linsey dress look fine,   15
When Angelina Johnson comes a-swingin' down de line.
Some folks say dat dancin's sinful, an' de blessed Lawd, dey say,
Gwine to punish us fu' steppin' w'en we hyeah de music play.
But I tell you I don' b'lieve it, fu' de Lawd is wise and good,
And he made de banjo's metal an' he made de fiddle wood,   20
An' he made de music in dem, so I don' quite t'ink he'll keer
Ef our feet keeps time a little to de melodies we hyeah.
W'y, dey's somep'n' downright holy in de way our faces shine,
When Angelina Johnson comes a-swingin' down de line.
Angelina steps so gentle, Angelina bows so low,   25
An' she lif' huh sku't so dainty dat huh shoetop skacely show;
An' dem teef o' huh'n a-shinin', ez she tek you by de han'—
Go 'way, people, d'ain't anothah sich lady in de lan'!
When she's movin' thoo de figgers er a-dancin' by huhse'f,
Folks jes' stan' stock-still a-sta'in', an' dey mos' nigh hol's dey
          bref;   30
An' de young mens, dey's a-sayin', "I's gwine mek dat damsel
          mine,"
When Angelina Johnson comes a-swingin' down de line.

SPANISH DANCER

Rainer Maria Rilke (Germany)

Translated by Babette Deutsch and Avrahm Yarmolinsky

As in one's hand a sulphur-match burns white
before it flames, and giddily unfurls
its thrusting tongues:—thus circling in the sight
of crowding watchers, hurried, hot and bright,
her round dance spreads in white and widening whirls.   5

And suddenly it is sheer flame and flare.

Then with her glance she kindles her tossed hair
and with more daring artistry, leaps higher
and wheels her vesture in this passion of fire,
whence her bare arms, each like a startled snake,   10
stretch sinuously rattling and awake.
And then: as though the fire were strangling stuff,
she gathers it together,—flings it off
with one imperious gesture, her proud eyes
watching: where raging on the ground it lies,   15
and keeps on flaming, nor submits, a-spin.—
Yet certain and triumphant, with a sweet
and gracious smile, she lifts her perfect chin
and stamps it out with little furious feet.

THE OLD WOMAN

Joseph Campbell (Ireland)

As a white candle
In a holy place,
So is the beauty
Of an aged face.

As the spent radiance   5
Of the winter sun,
So is a woman
With her travail done,

Her brood gone from her,
  And her thoughts as still
As the waters
  Under a ruined mill.   10

SING ME A SONG

ROBERT LOUIS STEVENSON (SCOTLAND)

Sing me a song of a lad that is gone,
  Say, could that lad be I?
Merry of soul he sailed on a day
  Over the sea to Skye.

Mull was astern, Rum on the port,   5
  Egg on the starboard bow;
Glory of youth glowed in his soul;
  Where is that glory now?

Sing me a song of a lad that is gone,
  Say, could that lad be I?   10
Merry of soul he sailed on a day
  Over the sea to Skye.

Give me again all that was there,
  Give me the sun that shone!
Give me the eyes, give me the soul,   15
  Give me the lad that's gone!

Sing me a song of a lad that is gone,
  Say, could that lad be I?
Merry of soul he sailed on a day
  Over the sea to Skye.   20

Billow and breeze, islands and seas,
  Mountains of rain and sun,
All that was good, all that was fair,
  All that was me is gone.

ANDREA DEL SARTO

ROBERT BROWNING (ENGLAND)

Andrea del Sarto was called the "faultless painter" because of his almost perfect technique. In spite of this technique, however, he was surpassed as an artist by painters who were less skilful with the pencil and brush. This was because his pictures lack inspiration or spiritual meaning. Browning in this poem shows us Andrea talking half to himself and half to his selfish, frivolous wife, who is obviously not listening to his words but scheming how she can make use of her infatuated husband for her own ends. Andrea is trying to think out the reason for his failure to achieve true greatness. The story he tells was taken by Browning from the chapter on del Sarto in Vasari's *Lives of the Most Excellent Italian Painters, Sculptors and Architects*. Vasari, himself an artist as well as a biographer, was a pupil of del Sarto. In lines 145–218, Andrea refers to the fact that when he had gone to France to paint for the art-loving king, Francis I, his wife, angry that she could not get money from him for her family, summoned him home to Florence. Andrea came, bringing a sum of money entrusted to him by Francis for the purchase of Italian art treasures. With this money, Andrea built himself a house in Florence, and never returned to France. All other details in the relationship of husband and wife are made clear in the poem.

❄   ❄   ❄

But do not let us quarrel any more,
No, my Lucrezia; bear with me for once.
Sit down and all shall happen as you wish.
You turn your face, but does it bring your heart?
I'll work then for your friend's friend, never fear,   5
Treat his own subject after his own way,
Fix his own time, accept, too, his own price,
And shut the money into this small hand
When next it takes mine. Will it? tenderly?
Oh, I'll content him—but tomorrow, Love!   10
I often am much wearier than you think,
This evening more than usual, and it seems
As if—forgive now—should you let me sit
Here by the window with your hand in mine
And look a half hour forth on Fiesole,   15
Both of one mind, as married people use,

15. *Fiesole:* a hill town near Florence.

Quietly, quietly, the evening through,
I might get up tomorrow to my work
Cheerful and fresh as ever. Let us try.
Tomorrow, how you shall be glad for this!   20
Your soft hand is a woman of itself,
And mine the man's bared breast she curls inside.
Don't count the time lost, neither; you must serve
For each of the five pictures we require—
It saves a model. So! keep looking so—   25
My serpentining beauty, rounds on rounds!
—How could you ever prick those perfect ears,
Even to put the pearl there! oh, so sweet—
My face, my moon, my everybody's moon,
Which everybody looks on and calls his,   30
And, I suppose, is looked on by in turn,
While she looks—no one's; very dear, no less!
You smile? why, there's my picture ready made.
There's what we painters call our harmony!
A common grayness silvers everything—   35
All in a twilight, you and I alike
—You, at the point of your first pride in me
(That's gone you know), but I, at every point;
My youth, my hope, my art, being all toned down
To yonder sober pleasant Fiesole.   40
There's the bell clinking from the chapel-top;
That length of convent-wall across the way
Holds the trees safer, huddled more inside;
The last monk leaves the garden; days decrease
And autumn grows, autumn in everything.   45
Eh? the whole seems to fall into a shape
As if I saw alike my work and self
And all that I was born to be and do,
A twilight-piece. Love, we are in God's hand.
How strange now looks the life he makes us lead;   50
So free we seem, so fettered fast we are!
I feel he laid the fetter; let it lie!
This chamber, for example—turn your head—
All that's behind us! You don't understand
Nor care to understand about my art,   55
But you can hear at least when people speak;
And that cartoon, the second from the door

57. *cartoon:* an outline drawing for a picture.

—It is the thing, Love! so such things should be—
Behold Madonna! I am bold to say.
I can do with my pencil what I know,   60
What I see, what at bottom of my heart
I wish for, if I ever wish so deep—
Do easily, too—when I say, perfectly,
I do not boast, perhaps. Yourself are judge
Who listened to the Legate's talk last week,   65
And just as much they used to say in France.
At any rate 'tis easy, all of it!
No sketches first, no studies, that's long past—
I do what many dream of all their lives—
Dream? strive to do, and agonize to do,   70
And fail in doing. I could county twenty such
On twice your fingers, and not leave this town,
Who strive—you don't know how the others strive
To paint a little thing like that you smeared
Carelessly passing with your robes afloat,   75
Yet do much less, so much less, someone says,
(I know his name, no matter) so much less!
Well, less is more, Lucrezia! I am judged.
There burns a truer light of God in them,
In their vexed, beating, stuffed, and stopped-up brain,   80
Heart, or whate'er else, than goes to prompt
This low-pulsed forthright craftsman's hand of mine.
Their works drop groundward, but themselves, I know,
Reach many a time a heaven that's shut to me,
Enter and take their place there sure enough,   85
Though they come back and cannot tell the world.
My works are nearer heaven, but I sit here.
The sudden blood of these men! at a word—
Praise them, it boils, or blames them, it boils, too.
I, painting from myself and to myself,   90
Know what I do, am unmoved by men's blame
Or their praise either. Somebody remarks
Morello's outline there is wrongly traced,
His hue mistaken—what of that? or else,
Rightly traced and well ordered—what of that?   95
Speak as they please, what does the mountain care?
Ah, but a man's reach should exceed his grasp,
Or what's a heaven for? all is silver-gray,

93. *Morello:* a ridge of the Apennines.

Placid and perfect with my art—the worse!
I know both what I want and what might gain— 100
And yet how profitless to know, to sigh
"Had I been two, another and myself,
Our head would have o'erlooked the world!" No doubt.
Yonder's a work, now, of that famous youth,
The Urbinate who died five years ago. 105
('Tis copied, George Vasari sent it me.)
Well, I can fancy how he did it all,
Pouring his soul, with kings and popes to see,
Reaching, that Heaven might so replenish him,
Above and through his art—for it gives way; 110
That arm is wrongly put—and there again—
A fault to pardon in the drawing's lines,
Its body, so to speak! its soul is right,
He means right—that a child may understand.
Still, what an arm! and I could alter it. 115
But all the play, the insight, and the stretch—
Out of me! out of me! And wherefore out?
Had you enjoined them on me, given me soul,
We might have risen to Rafael, I and you.
Nay, Love, you did give all I asked, I think— 120
More than I merit, yes, by many times.
But had you—oh, with the same perfect brow,
And perfect eyes, and more than perfect mouth,
And the low voice my soul hears, as a bird
The fowler's pipe, and follows to the snare— 125
Had you, with these the same, but brought a mind!
Some women do so. Had the mouth there urged
"God and the glory! never care for gain.
The present by the future, what is that?
Live for fame, side by side with Agnolo! 130
Rafael is waiting. Up to God all three!"
I might have done it for you. So it seems—
Perhaps not. All is as God overrules.
Besides, incentives come from the soul's self;
The rest avail not. Why do I need you? 135
What wife had Rafael, or has Agnolo?
In this world, who can do a thing, will not—

---

105. *Urbinate:* Raphael (1483–1520), greatest of all Italian painters. 106.
George Vasari: author of the lives of the painters in which del Sarto's biography
occurs. 130. *Agnolo:* Michael Angelo (1475–1564), a great sculptor, painter, and
architect of the Renaissance period in Italy.

And who would do it, cannot, I perceive.
Yet the will's somewhat—somewhat, too, the power—
And thus we half-men struggle. At the end,   140
God, I conclude, compensates, punishes.
'Tis safer for me, if the award be strict,
That I am something underrated here,
Poor this long while, despised, to speak the truth.
I dared not, do you know, leave home all day,   145
For fear of chancing on the Paris lords.
The best is when they pass and look aside;
But they speak sometimes; I must bear it all.
Well may they speak! That Francis, that first time,
And that long festal year at Fontainebleau!   150
I surely then could sometimes leave the ground,
Put on the glory, Rafael's daily wear,
In that humane great monarch's golden look—
One finger in his beard or twisted curl
Over his mouth's good mark that made the smile,   155
One arm about my shoulder, round my neck,
The jingle of his gold chain in my ear,
I painting proudly with his breath on me,
All his court round him, seeing with his eyes,
Such frank French eyes, and such a fire of souls   160
Profuse, my hand kept plying by those hearts—
And, best of all, this, this, this face beyond,
This in the background, waiting on my work,
To crown the issue with a last reward!
A good time, was it not, my kingly days?   165
And had you not grown restless—but I know—
'Tis done and past; 'twas right, my instinct said;
Too live the life grew, golden and not gray—
And I'm the weak-eyed bat no sun should tempt
Out of the grange whose four walls make his world.   170
How could it end in any other way?
You called me, and I came home to your heart.
The triumph was—to reach and stay there; since
I reached it ere the triumph, what is lost?
Let my hand frame your face in your hair's gold,   175
You beautiful Lucrezia that are mine!
"Rafael did this, Andrea painted that—

150. *Fontainebleau:* the royal palace in France where Andrea worked for
Francis in 1518. 170. *grange:* farmhouse.

The Roman's is the better when you pray,
But still the other's Virgin was his wife—"
Men will excuse me. I am glad to judge   180
Both pictures in your presence; clearer grows
My better fortune, I resolve to think.
For, do you know, Lucrezia, as God lives,
Said one day Agnolo, his very self,
To Rafael . . . I have known it all these years . . .   185
(When the young man was flaming out his thoughts
Upon a palace-wall for Rome to see,
Too lifted up in heart because of it)
"Friend, there's a certain sorry little scrub
Goes up and down our Florence, none cares how,   190
Who, were he set to plan and execute
As you are pricked on by your popes and kings,
Would bring the sweat into that brow of yours!"
To Rafael's!—And indeed the arm is wrong.
I hardly dare—yet, only you to see,   195
Give the chalk here—quick, thus the line should go!
Ay, but the soul! he's Rafael! rub it out!
Still, all I care for, if he spoke the truth,
(What he? why, who but Michel Agnolo?
Do you forget already words like those?)   200
If really there was such a chance, so lost,
Is, whether you're—not grateful—but more pleased.
Well, let me think so. And you smile indeed!
This hour has been an hour! Another smile?
If you would sit thus by me every night,   205
I should work better, do you comprehend?
I mean that I should earn more, give you more.
See, it is settled dusk now; there's a star;
Morello's gone, the watch-lights show the wall,
The cue-owls speak the name we call them by.   210
Come from the window, Love—come in, at last,
Inside the melancholy little house
We built to be so gay with. God is just.
King Francis may forgive me. Oft at nights
When I look up from paintings, eyes tired out,   215
The walls become illumined, brick from brick
Distinct, instead of mortar, fierce bright gold,
That gold of his I did cement them with!

178. *The Roman's:* because so much of Raphael's work was done in Rome.

Let us but love each other. Must you go?
That Cousin here again? he waits outside?　　　　　220
Must see you—you, and not with me? Those loans!
More gaming debts to pay? you smiled for that?
Well, let smiles buy me! have you more to spend?
While hand and eye and something of a heart
Are left me, work's my ware, and what's it worth?　　225
I'll pay my fancy. Only let me sit
The gray remainder of the evening out,
Idle, you call it, and muse perfectly
How I could paint were I but back in France,
One picture, just one more—the Virgin's face,　　　230
Not yours this time! I want you at my side
To hear them—that is, Michel Agnolo—
Judge all I do and tell you of its worth.
Will you? Tomorrow, satisfy your friend.
I take the subjects for his corridor,　　　　　235
Finish the portrait out of hand—there, there,
And throw him in another thing or two
If he demurs: the whole should prove enough
To pay for this same cousin's freak. Beside,
What's better and what's all I care about,　　　240
Get you the thirteen scudi for the ruff!
Love, does that please you? Ah but what does he,
The Cousin? what does he to please you more?

I am grown peaceful as old age tonight.
I regret little. I would change still less.　　　245
Since there my past life lies, why alter it?
The very wrong to Francis!—it is true
I took his coin, was tempted and complied,
And built this house and sinned and all is said.
My father and my mother died of want.　　　250
Well, had I riches of my own? You see
How one gets rich! Let each one bear his lot.
They were born poor, lived poor, and poor they died;
And I have labored somewhat in my time
And not been paid profusely. Some good son　　255
Paint my two hundred pictures—let him try!
No doubt, there's something strikes a balance. Yes,
You loved me quite enough it seems tonight.
This must suffice me here. What would one have?

In heaven, perhaps, new chances, one more chance— 260
Four great walls in the New Jerusalem,
Meted on each side by the angel's reed,
For Leonard, Rafael, Agnolo and me
To cover—the three first without a wife,
While I have mine! So—still they overcome 265
Because there's still Lucrezia,—as I choose.
Again the Cousin's whistle! Go, my Love.

EPILOGUE TO ASOLANDO

ROBERT BROWNING (ENGLAND)

This *self* portrait by Robert Browning was the last work to come
from his pen. It sums up the philosophy of his whole life and work.

❊ ❊ ❊

At the midnight in the silence of the sleep-time,
    When you set your fancies free,
Will they pass to where—by death, fools think, imprisoned—
Low he lies who once so loved you, whom you loved so,
    —Pity me? 5

Oh, to love so, be so loved, yet so mistaken!
    What had I on earth to do
With the slothful, with the mawkish, the unmanly?
Like the aimless, helpless, hopeless, did I drivel!
    —Being—who? 10

One who never turned his back but marched breast forward,
    Never doubted clouds would break,
Never dreamed, though right were worsted, wrong would
    triumph,
Held we fall to rise, are baffled to fight better,
    Sleep to wake. 15

No, at noonday in the bustle of man's work-time
    Greet the unseen with a cheer!
Bid him forward, breast and back as either should be,
"Strive and thrive!" cry "Speed—fight on, fare ever
    There as here!"

CHANT PAGAN

Rudyard Kipling (England)

This poem pictures a soldier who has come back to England after the Boer War and finds it hard to fit into the old commonplace routine after the stirring experiences he has been through in the great open spaces of South Africa.

❅   ❅   ❅

Me that 'ave been what I've been—
Me that 'ave gone where I've gone—
Me that 'ave seen what I've seen—
    'Ow can I ever take on
With awful old England again,   5
An' 'ouses both sides of the street,
And 'edges two sides of the lane,
And the parson an' gentry between,
An' touchin' my 'at when we meet—
    Me that 'ave been what I've been?   10

Me that 'ave watched 'arf a world
'Eave up all shiny with dew,
Kopje on kop to the sun,
An' as soon as the mist let 'em through
Our 'elios winkin' like fun—   15
Three sides of a ninety-mile square,
Over valleys as big as a shire—
Are ye there? Are ye there? Are ye there?
An' then the blind drum of our fire . . .
An' I'm rollin' 'is lawns for the Squire,   20
                    Me!

Me that 'ave rode through the dark
Forty mile, often, on end,
Along the Ma'ollisberg Range,
With only the stars for my mark   25
An' only the night for my friend,
An' things runnin' off as you pass,
An' things jumpin' up in the grass,

13. *Kopje:* hill.

An' the silence, the shine an' the size
Of the 'igh, unexpressible skies—   30
I am takin' some letters almost
As much as a mile to the post,
An' "mind you come back with the change!"

                           Me!

Me that saw Barberton took   35
When we dropped through the clouds on their 'ead,
    An' they 'ove the guns over and fled—
    Me that was through Di'mond 'Ill,
    An' Pieters an' Springs an' Belfast—
From Dundee to Vereeniging all—   40
    Me that stuck out to the last
    (An' five bloomin' bars on my chest)—
I am doin' my Sunday-school best,
By the 'elp of the Squire an' 'is wife
(Not to mention the 'ousemaid an' cook),   45
To come in an' 'ands up an' be still,
    An' honestly work for my bread,
    My livin' in that state of life
    To which it shall please God to call

                           Me!   50

Me that 'ave followed my trade
In the place where the Lightnin's are made,
    'Twixt the Rains and the Sun and the Moon—
    Me that lay down an' got up
    Three years with the sky for my roof—   55
That 'ave ridden my 'unger an' thirst
    Six thousand raw mile on the hoof
    With the Vaal and the Orange for cup,
    An' the Brandwater Basin for dish,—
Oh! it's 'ard to be'ave as they wish   60
(Too 'ard, an' a little too soon),
I'll 'ave to think over it first—

                           Me!

I will arise an' get 'ence;—
I will trek South and make sure   65
If it's only my fancy or not
That the sunshine of England is pale,
And the breezes of England are stale,

58–59. Sections of South Africa.

An' there's somethin' gone small with the lot;
For *I* know of a sun an' a wind,
An' some plains and a mountain be'ind,   70
An' some graves by a barb-wire fence;
An' a Dutchman I've fought 'oo might give
Me a job were I ever inclined,
To look in an' offsaddle an' live   75
Where there's neither a road nor a tree—
But only my Maker an' me.
And I think it will kill me or cure,
So I think I will go there an' see.

                                        Me!

CHICAGO

CARL SANDBURG (AMERICA)

Hog-Butcher for the World,
Tool-maker, Stacker of Wheat,
Player with Railroads and the Nation's Freight-handler;
Stormy, husky, brawling,
City of the Big Shoulders: 5
They tell me you are wicked and I believe them, for I
    have seen your painted women under the gas lamps
    luring the farm boys.
And they tell me you are crooked, and I answer, Yes, it
    is true I have seen the gunman kill and go free to kill
    again.
And they tell me you are brutal and my reply is, On the
    faces of women and children I have seen the marks
    of wanton hunger.
And having answered so I turn once more to those who
    sneer at this my city, and I give them back the sneer
    and say to them:
Come and show me another city with lifted head singing
    so proud to be alive and coarse and strong and
    cunning.   10
Flinging magnetic curses amid the toil of piling job on
    job, here is a tall bold slugger set vivid against the
    little soft cities;

Fierce as a dog with tongue lapping for action, cunning
 as a savage pitted against the wilderness,
 Bareheaded,
 Shoveling,
 Wrecking,
 Planning,
 Building, breaking, rebuilding,
Under the smoke, dust all over his mouth, laughing with
 white teeth,
Under the terrible burden of destiny laughing as a young
 man laughs,
Laughing even as an ignorant fighter laughs who has
 never lost a battle,
Bragging and laughing that under his wrist is the pulse,
 and under his ribs the heart of the people,
 Laughing!
Laughing the stormy, husky, brawling laughter of
 youth; half-naked, sweating, proud to be Hog-
 butcher, Tool-maker, Stacker of Wheat, Player with
 Railroads, and Freight-handler to the Nation.

15

20

THE ANGUISH OF LOVE

Hafiz (Persia)

Translated by John Hindley

I have borne the anguish of love, which ask me not to
 describe:
I have tasted the poison of absence, which ask me not to
 relate.

Far through the world have I roved, and at length I have
 chosen
A sweet creature (a ravisher of hearts), whose name ask
 me not to disclose.

The flowing of my tears bedews her footsteps
In such a manner as ask me not to utter.

5

On yesternight from her own mouth with my own ears
    I heard
Such words as pray ask me not to repeat.

Why dost thou bite thy lip at me? What dost thou not
    hint that I may have told?
I have devoured a lip like a ruby: but whose, ask me not
    to mention.   10

Absent from thee, and the sole tenant of my cottage,
I have endured such tortures, as ask me not to enumerate.

Thus am I, HAFIZ, arrived at extremity in the ways of
    Love.
Which, alas! ask me not to explain.

CUPID A RUNAWAY

Meleager (Greece)

Translated by Walter Leaf

Lost a boy! A runaway!
    Raise the hue and cry O!
From his bed at break of day
    Naughty Love did fly O!
Fleet he is, a quiver bears,   5
    Wings upon his shoulder;
Saucy laugh and dainty tears;
    None can chatter bolder.
What his country none can tell,
    Nor his sire before him;   10
Land and sea and heaven and hell
    Swear they never bore him.
All disown him, all detest;
    Hurry! While you're staying
Sure the rascal in some breast   15
    Other snares is laying.
Ho, you rogue! I spy your lair!
    Now you cannot fly, sir,
Lurking with your arrows there
    In my Zeno's eye, sir!   20

Title. *Cupid:* the mischievous boy god of love.

LESBIA RAILING

CAIUS VALERIUS CATULLUS (ROME)

Translated by Jonathan Swift

Lesbia forever on me rails.
To talk of me she never fails.
Now, hang me, but for all her art,
I find that I have gained her heart.
My proof is this: I plainly see   5
The case is just the same with me;
I curse her every hour sincerely,
Yet, hang me, but I love her dearly.

THE WOMEN

ARISTOPHANES (GREECE)

FROM *Thesmophorizusae*
Translated by Collins

They're always abusing the women,
    As a terrible plague to men:
They say we're the root of all evil,
    And repeat it again and again;
Of war, and quarrels, and bloodshed,   5
    All mischief, be what it may!
And pray, then, why do you marry us,
    If we're all the plagues you say?
And why do you take such care of us,
    And keep us so safe at home,   10
And are never easy a moment
    If ever we chance to roam?
When you ought to be thanking heaven
    That your Plague is out of the way,
You all keep fussing and fretting—   15
    "Where is *my* Plague today?"
If a Plague peeps out of the window,
    Up go the eyes of men;
If she hides, they all keep staring
    Until she looks out again.   20

1. *rails:* scolds.

DISDAIN

LEOPOLDO LUGONES (ARGENTINE)

Translated by G. Dundas Craig

If but one single kindly look
From your eyes I might obtain,
Not life itself a price would seem
Too great such prize to gain.

If rancor on your part should strike   5
With fatal poniard blow,
Were't yours the hand that brought the pain,
Content to death I'd go.

But what assuredly will give
A painful death I could not brook   10
Is that for me you neither have
The poniard stroke nor kindly look.

COME NOT NEAR MY SONGS

ANONYMOUS (SHOSHONE INDIAN)

Translated by Mary Austin

Come not near my songs,
You who are not my lover,
Lest from out that ambush
Leaps my heart upon you!

When my songs are glowing   5
As an almond thicket
With the bloom upon it,
Lies my heart in ambush
All amid my singing.
Come not near my songs,   10
You who are not my lover!

Do not hear my songs,
You who are not my lover!
Over-sweet the heart is,
Where my love has bruised it,   15
Breathe you not that fragrance,
You who are not my lover.
Do not stoop above my song,
With its languor on you,
Lest from out my singing,   20
Leaps my heart upon you!

TO THE NOT IMPOSSIBLE HIM

EDNA ST. VINCENT MILLAY (AMERICA)

How shall I know, unless I go
  To Cairo and Cathay,
Whether or not this blessed spot
  Is blest in every way?

Now it may be, the flower for me   5
  Is this beneath my nose;
How shall I tell, unless I smell
  The Carthaginian rose?

The fabric of my faithful love
  No power shall dim or ravel   10
Whilst I say here,—but oh, my dear,
  If I should ever travel!

THE RIVER MERCHANT'S WIFE: A LETTER

LI T'AI-PO (CHINA)

Translated by Ezra Pound

While my hair was still cut straight across my forehead
I played about the front gate, pulling flowers.
You came by on bamboo stilts, playing horse,
You walked about my seat, playing with blue plums.
And we went on living in the village of Chokan: 5
Two small people, without dislike or suspicion.

2. *Cathay*: China.

At fourteen I married My Lord you.
I never laughed, being bashful.
Lowering my head, I looked at the wall.
Called to, a thousand times, I never looked back.   10
At fifteen I stopped scowling,
I desired my dust to be mingled with yours
Forever and forever and forever.
Why should I climb the lookout?

At sixteen you departed,   15
You went into far Ku-to-yen, by the river of swirling eddies,
And you have been gone five months.
The monkeys make sorrowful noise overhead.
You dragged your feet when you went out.
By the gate now, the moss is grown, the different mosses, 20
Too deep to clear them away!
The leaves fall early this autumn, in wind.
The paired butterflies are already yellow with August
Over the grass in the West garden;
They hurt me. I grow older.   25
If you are coming down through the narrows of the river Kiang,
Please let me know beforehand,
And I will come out to meet you
                    As far as Cho-fu-Sa.

THE MORNING GLORY

FROM THE BOOK OF ODES
CONFUCIUS (CHINA)

Translated by Helen Waddell

The morning glory climbs above my head,
Pale flowers of white and purple, blue and red.
    I am disquieted.

Down in the withered grasses something stirred;
I thought it was his footfall that I heard.   5
    Then a grasshopper chirred.

I climbed the hill just as the new moon showed,
I saw him coming on the southern road.
    My heart lays down its load.

SPRING SONG

FROM THE SONG OF SONGS (HEBREW)

This book in the Old Testament section of *The Bible* tells the story of a happy marriage. The speaker is the young bride. In the following episode, her husband has returned after an absence.

❉ ❉ ❉

The voice of my beloved! behold, he cometh leaping
    upon the mountains, skipping upon the hills.
My beloved is like a roe or a young hart: behold, he
    standeth behind our wall, he looketh forth at the
    windows, shewing himself through the lattice.   5
My beloved spake, and said unto me, Rise up my love,
    my fair one, and come away.
For lo, the winter is past, the rain is over and gone;
The flowers appear on the earth; the time of the singing
    of birds is come, and the voice of the turtle is heard   10
    in our land;
The fig tree putteth forth her green figs, and the vines
    with the tender grape give a good smell. Arise, my
    love, my fair one, and come away.
O my dove, that art in the clefts of the rock, in the secret   20
    places of the stairs, let me see thy countenance, let
    me hear thy voice; for sweet is thy voice, and thy
    countenance is comely.
My beloved is mine, and I am his: he feedeth among the
    lilies.   25
Until the day break, and the shadows flee away, turn my
    beloved, and be thou like a roe or a young hart upon
    the mountains of Bether.

ADVICE TO A GIRL

THOMAS CAMPION (ENGLAND)

Never love unless you can
Bear with all the faults of man!
Men sometimes will jealous be
Though but little cause they see,
And hang the head of discontent,   5
And speak what straight they will repent.

10. *turtle:* turtle dove.

Men, that but one Saint adore,
Make a show of love to more;
Beauty must be scorn'd in none,
Though but truly served in one: 10
For what is courtship but disguise?
True hearts may have dissembling eyes.

Men, when their affairs require,
Must awhile themselves retire;
Sometimes hunt, and sometimes hawk,   15
And not ever sit and talk:—
If these and such-like you can bear,
Then like, and love, and never fear!

MEETING AT NIGHT: PARTING AT MORNING

ROBERT BROWNING (ENGLAND)

I

The gray sea and the long black land;
And the yellow half-moon large and low;
And the startled little waves that leap
In fiery ringlets from their sleep,
As I gain the cove with pushing prow,   5
And quench its speed i' the slushy sand.

Then a mile of warm sea-scented beach;
Three fields to cross till a farm appears;
A tap at the pane, the quick sharp scratch
And blue spurt of a lighted match,   10
And a voice less loud, through its joys and fears,
Than the two hearts beating each to each!

II

Round the cape of a sudden came the sea,
And the sun looked over the mountain's rim:
And straight was a path of gold for him,
And the need of a world of men for me.   15

READING PROBLEMS ON THE LYRIC

1. *The Coin:* Put in your own words the thought of this poem. What is the "coin?" Than what is it better?

2. *Spring Song:* Contrast the effect of spring on bird and poet.

3. *Spring and Autumn:* How does the poet think autumn is superior to spring? Is that really the reason we love autumn?

4. *Vagabond Song:* To how many different things does Carman compare the sights of autumn? Find here and elsewhere poems giving different impressions of autumn.

5. *Frost Tonight:* For what do the frost and the flowers stand as symbols in the Garden of Life?

6. *Velvet Shoes:* In how many comparisons does the author give us the sense of the softness of snow and the silence it brings?

7. *Skating at Night:* How does Wordsworth make us feel the cold, the landscape, the wintry sky? How does he give us the thrill of the skater in motion?

8. *Morning:* In how many words has the poet suggested the colors of sunrise?

9. *Heaven's Blue:* What effect on the mind of gazing on the boundless sky is here described? What other natural scenes give one the same feeling?

10. *The Cloud:* Why does Shelley use such a rapidly moving rhythm for this poem? Through how many changes does the cloud pass in this poem? What law of physics and chemistry does Shelley illustrate concretely in this beautiful series of pictures? Select lines that are beautiful in wording and show why the words are well chosen either for description or melody.

11. *Smile, O Earth:* Go over each image in this poem and decide from the things described and the mere sound of the words, what season it is. Compare the images and rhythm in this poem and *Skating at Night.*

12. *Windy Nights:* How does the rhythm of this poem carry out the comparison Stevenson uses to describe the wind?

13. *The Tree:* What is the purpose of nature as indicated in this poem? Is this true?

14. *On the Death of Lesbia's Sparrow:* What impression do you form of Lesbia from this poem? Find a passage in this poem almost identical with a line in *The Rubáiyát.* Is Catullus interested in the bird?

15. *A Bird:* What extraordinary contrasts does the author note in the bird's habits and behavior? Find touches of accurate observation. How has the author conveyed the essential mystery of all strange forms of life?

16. *To the Cuckoo:* What does the bird call back to the poet's mind? Why called a "golden time"? (Explain this by the last stanza.) What does the bird represent to Wordsworth both as boy and man?

17. *The Eagle:* How do the music of the verse and the setting Tennyson gives the bird express the power of the eagle?

18. *Symphony in Gray:* Should you have found a brilliant or stormy day

as good a setting for the old sailor's reverie? Why does the poet open and close with description of the setting? Which is better—the seaward or the landward views?

19. *In the White Land:* What is the voice of the Arctic? What quality in the scene does the author emphasize?

20. *A Nightmare:* How many sentences does this poem contain? Why is it written thus? What is particularly dreamlike about the experiences in the dreams? What is humorously lifelike about the end?

21. *The Coach of Life:* Prove the accuracy of Pushkin's description of man's attitude toward life at various ages.

22. *The Rubáiyát:* What seems the outstanding fact about life according to Omar? Which is his best statement of the brevity of life and why? How important does the individual seem to Omar? To what questions can Omar find no answers? What does Omar think is the best thing life has to offer us?

23. *Love and Change:* Why does Heine regard love and life as shadows? Why does the universe laugh at luckless love?

24. *Memory:* What is the only thing that can partly defeat time?

25. *The Road Not Taken:* What is the theme of this poem? Why has he chosen the road he took? Does Frost mean he has made a mistake in his choice?

26. *The Last Word:* What message does this poem carry to reformers who seem to fail?

27. *On the Birth of a Son:* What does Su Tung-p'o think is the secret of popular success? How can intelligence wreck a life? How is worldly success satirized?

28. *All for Love:* What is the greatest value of fame to Byron?

29. *Laugh and Be Merry:* Contrast the attitude toward life of Masefield and Omar. To which does life seem more important? Are the facts stated in their poems different? How explain the difference in attitude? How does the rhythm of this poem reenforce the idea?

30. *At Peace:* Whom does the poet blame for his failure? Why? Why does he bless life?

31. *Ecstasy:* Explain the question earth asks. What answer do sea and stars give?

32. *The Ideal:* How is an ideal like the Madonna's statue? Does the Virgin herself represent an ideal?

33. *The Sword:* Why does the poet contrast the sword and the hilt? Why does the warrior want the lake, sheep, mother, and child carved on the sword?

34. *Deirdre:* Why is this poem addressed to men only? Does it express a masculine attitude toward this legendary beauty? What could one say to her? Will some one of you write a poem *to* her—not just *about* her? Look up her story in *English Literature,* page 6.

35. *To Helen:* What is the character of Helen and what the nature of her influence? Show the latter by analysis of some of the things to which

she is compared. Why does Poe use glory for Greece and grandeur for Rome?

36. *There Be None of Beauty's Daughters:* Compare the effect on Poe of Helen with the effect on Byron of this lady as revealed in the comparisons he uses. Read the poem aloud and account for its melody.

37. *Simplex Munditiis:* Put the thought of this poem into a balanced epigram, like: God made the country; man made the town.

38. *One Girl:* Picture the girl. Do stanzas 1 and 2 give you the same impression?

39. *To Rouge the Lips:* What is the age of this girl? What is her charm?

40. *Angelina:* Why does Dunbar show us Angelina dancing? In how many ways does he convey to us the native refinement and sweetness of her character? Is beauty of face and figure the charm Dunbar emphasizes?

41. *Spanish Dancer:* How does the poet give the effect of artistic control in the midst of the whirlwind of changing passions expressed by the dance? Do you like all the comparisons? Contrast the dancing of Angelina and the Spanish dancer.

42. *The Old Woman:* Which image seems to you most appropriate to express the beauty of age—the candles or the winter sunset? Why are her thoughts "still"?

43. *Sing Me a Song:* Who is the "lad that is gone" and in what ways *is* he gone? Explain the last two lines.

44. *Andrea del Sarto:* What has happened before the poem opens? Do you think the method of work to which Andrea agrees will produce great art? Why does Andrea consider himself a failure? Whom does he blame at first? finally? What does he mean by "a man's reach should exceed his grasp"? In this connection, explain why he says it is "the worse" that his pictures are "faultless." Estimate Lucrezia's character.

45. *Epilogue to Asolando:* What great quality does Browning claim for himself? Compare the character painted in this poem with those shown in *The Last Word* (page 763).

46. *Chant Pagan:* What contrast does the speaker feel between his African experiences and his life in England? What does he mean by "Me!"?

47. *Chicago:* How does the free verse rhythm help to depict the rush and power of the great city? List the ugly things and the splendid things about Chicago on which Sandburg comments. Why is he proud of his city?

48. *Anguish of Love:* In spite of his lack of detail, does the lover convey to us an impression of passionate emotion? How? Do you admire his reticence?

49. *Cupid a Runaway:* Is this poem about Cupid or Zeno? Prove.

50. *Lesbia Railing:* What does the lover's scolding really prove?

51. *The Women:* How do the women prove they can't be such plagues after all?

52. *Disdain:* Why does the lover wish for hatred rather than indifference?

53. *Come Not Near My Songs:* Is the speaker in love? Why does she not wish the non-lover to hear her song?

54. *To the Not Impossible Him:* Is the advice in this poem good or do you prefer a love based on ignorance of other possibilities?

55. *The River Merchant's Wife:* What is the strength of a love which has developed like that of the couple described in this poem?

56. *The Morning Glory:* Why this title instead of *The Return*?

57. *Spring Song:* This poem and the two preceding form a sequence. What part of the experience is expressed in this poem? Why does the poet dwell on the season and its influence on nature?

58. *Advice to a Girl:* What three points must a woman understand in masculine conduct in order to marry happily?

59. *Meeting at Night: Parting at Morning:* Which point mentioned by Campion is developed more fully in these stanzas? Explain the last line. Select phrases that picture vividly in a word or two.

FURTHER READINGS IN LYRIC POETRY

Francis T. Palgrave: *Golden Treasury*
Louis Untermeyer: *Yesterday and Today*
   This Singing World
   Modern British and American Poetry
Jessie Rittenhouse: *Little Book of Modern Verse*
   Second Book of Modern Verse
   Little Book of Modern British Verse
G. S. Carhart and P. A. McGhee: *Magic Casements*
Marguerite Wilkinson: *Contemporary Poetry*
Hanes and McCoy: *Readings in Contemporary Literature*
St. John W. Lucas: *Oxford Book of French Verse*
Arthur Quiller-Couch: *Oxford Book of English Verse*
Carl Van Doren and G. M. Sapolla: *The World's Best Poetry*
Babette Deutsch and Avram Yarmolinsky: *Modern Russian Poetry*
F. A. Wright: *Poets of the Green Anthology*
George Dundas Craig: *The Modernist Trend in Spanish American Poetry*
Margarete Münsterberg: *A Harvest of German Verse*
   Hispanic Anthology

SUGGESTIONS FOR ORIGINAL VERSE

1. Frame comparisons to describe some such familiar objects as clouds, snow, rain, moving traffic, etc. Agree as a class upon some stanza form and meter and see if each of you can set your comparison to this rhythm. Combine the best lines and stanzas into a class poem.

2. Let groups who are specially interested try the same method with emotions or other inner experiences.

3. Write portraits in verse similar in stanza form and rhythm to *The Old Woman.*

XII

The Song

"LET me write the songs of a nation, and I care not who makes its laws." So spoke a literary critic. He believed that the emotional appeal of songs habitually sung, fixes in the popular mind certain conceptions of love, duty, and patriotism more strongly than all the moral precepts of the schools and all the laws on the statutes.

A great song is simple in thought and style; it deals with the common experiences of mankind; it makes an emotional appeal. It does not philosophize or argue; it touches the heart.

The differences in racial temperament are nowhere more obvious than in the songs of different nations. These differences will show in the attitude toward the subject of the song, the mood, the rhythm, and the imagery employed. Yet the fundamental kinship of all human hearts in their basic experience is likewise nowhere more strikingly revealed.

ANNIE LAURIE

WILLIAM DOUGLAS (SCOTLAND)

Maxwelton's braes are bonnie
    Where early fa's the dew,
And it's there that Annie Laurie
    Gied me her promise true—
Gied me her promise true,   5
    Which ne'er forgot will be;
And for bonnie Annie Laurie
    I'd lay me doun and dee.

Her brow is like the snaw-drift;
    Her throat is like the swan;   10
Her face it is the fairest
    That e'er the sun shone on—

1. *braes:* meadows. 8. *dee:* die.

797

That e'er the sun shone on—
　　And dark blue is her ee;
And for bonnie Annie Laurie
　　I'd lay me doun and dee.　　　　　　　　　15

Like dew on the gowan lying
　　Is the fa' o' her fairy feet;
And like winds in summer sighing,
　　Her voice is low and sweet—　　　　　　20
Her voice is low and sweet—
　　And she's a' the world to me;
And for bonnie Annie Laurie
　　I'd lay me doun and dee.

THE INDIAN SERENADE

Percy Bysshe Shelley (England)

I arise from dreams of thee
　　In the first sweet sleep of night,
When the winds are breathing low,
　　And the stars are shining bright.
I arise from dreams of thee,　　　　　　　5
　　And a spirit in my feet
Hath led me—who knows how?
　　To thy chamber window, Sweet!

The wandering airs they faint
　　On the dark, the silent stream—　　　　10
The champak's odors fail
　　Like sweet thoughts in a dream;
The nightingale's complaint,
　　It dies upon her heart,
As I must die on thine,　　　　　　　　　15
　　O belovèd as thou art!

O lift me from the grass!
　　I die! I faint! I fail!
Let thy love in kisses rain
　　On my lips and eyelids pale.　　　　　　20
My cheek is cold and white, alas!
　　My heart beats loud and fast:
O press it to thine own again,
　　Where it will break at last!

14. ee: eye.　11. champak: magnolia.

ON WINGS OF SONG

Heinrich Heine (Germany)

Translated by Margarete Münsterberg

On wings of song so lightly
   I bear thee far away:
A nook is beckoning brightly
   Where Ganges' waters play.

A blossoming garden is lying   5
   In moonlight calm and clear,
The lotus flowers are sighing
   For thee, their sister dear.

The violets banter and slyly
   They peep at the star-rays pale,   10
The roses are whispering shyly
   Some fragrant fairy-tale.

The gentle gazelles come leaping,
   And hearken what we say;
The sacred river is sweeping   15
   And murmuring far away.

To rest shall we be sinking
   Under the shady palm,
The blissful quiet drinking
   And dreaming dreams of balm.   20

ACROSS THE WATER

Alexander Petöfi (Hungary)

Translated by Alice Stone Blackwell

The river has o'er flowed its banks;
   Beyond it stands thy cot.
The countryside is flooded wide—
   My rose, expect me not!

20. *balm:* healing peace.

THE SONG

The causeway and the bridge are gone,   5
　They vanished like a dream;
Now the last fragments of the bridge
　Are floating down the stream.

Upon a hill I stand and gaze
　Far to the other side.   10
A dove is flying on swift wings
　Across the waters wide.
I know not if that flitting thing
　A living dove may be,
Or if perchance it is a sigh   15
　Breathed from my heart toward thee!

THE FAR AWAY PRINCESS

EDMOND ROSTAND (FRANCE)

Translated by Ruth Mary Weeks

For a maid of the hue
He can readily view
Will the common man sue
As sweetheart.

But since blonde or brunette
One may easily get,   5
My heart shall be set
Far apart.

Untested is he
Whose attainable She   10
He may constantly see
And caress.

Press her quick-yielded hand!
My love—understand—
Of a far away land   15
Is princess.

Supremely to burn
Is to love sans return
And forever; to learn
The sharp smart   20

Of a love without gain,
More noble since vain;
Thus hopelessly fain
Is my heart.

For divine is the gleam   25
Of love's fancies that stream
Through an uncertain dream.
Ah yes!

Let me dream on, I pray,
Die, or dream on for aye   30
Of a far, far away
Princess.

FANCY

WILLIAM SHAKESPEARE (ENGLAND)

Tell me, where is fancy bred,
Or in the heart or in the head?
How begot, how nourishèd?
        Reply, reply.

It is engendered in the eyes,   5
With gazing fed: and fancy dies
In the cradle where it lies.
        Let us all ring fancy's knell;
        I'll begin it. Ding, Dong, bell.

THE NIGHT HAS A THOUSAND EYES

FRANCIS WILLIAM BOURDILLON (ENGLAND)

The night has a thousand eyes,
    And the day but one;
Yet the light of the bright world dies
    With the dying sun.

18. *sans:* without.

The mind has a thousand eyes,
  And the heart but one;
Yet the light of a whole life dies
  When love is done.   5

MAID OF ATHENS

George Gordon, Lord Byron (England)

Maid of Athens, ere we part,
Give, oh, give me back my heart!
Or, since that has left my breast,
Keep it now, and take the rest!
Hear my vow before I go,   5
Ζώη μοῦ, σᾶς ἀγαπῶ.

By those tresses unconfined,
Wooed by each Aegean wind;
By those lids whose jetty fringe
Kiss thy soft cheeks' blooming tinge;   10
By those wild eyes like the roe,
Ζώη μοῦ, σᾶς ἀγαπῶ.

By that lip I long to taste;
By that zone-encircled waist;
By all the token-flowers that tell   15
What words can never speak so well;
By love's alternate joy and woe,
Ζώη μοῦ, σᾶς ἀγαπῶ.

Maid of Athens! I am gone;
Think of me, sweet! when alone.   20
Though I fly to Istambol,
Athens holds my heart and soul;
Can I cease to love thee? No!
Ζώη μοῦ, σᾶς ἀγαπῶ.

6. These Greek words mean: My life, I love you. 8. *Aegean:* sea bordering
Greece. 12. *Istamboul:* Constantinople.

CHERRY RIPE

KASHMIRI SONG

LAURENCE HOPE (ENGLAND)

Pale hands I loved beside the Shalimar,
    Where are you now? Who lies beneath your spell?
Whom do you lead on Rapture's roadway, far,
    Before you agonize them in farewell?

Oh, pale dispensers of my joys and pains,   5
    Holding the doors of Heaven and of Hell,
How the hot blood rushed wildly through the veins
    Beneath your touch, until you waved farewell.

Pale hands, pink tipped, like lotus buds that float
    On those cool waters where we used to dwell,   10
I would have rather felt you round my throat,
    Crushing out life, than waving me farewell!

CHERRY RIPE

ANONYMOUS (ENGLAND)

There is a garden in her face
    Where roses and white lilies blow;
A heavenly paradise is that place,
    Wherein all pleasant fruits do grow;
There cherries grow that none may buy,   5
Till Cherry-Ripe themselves do cry.

Those cherries fairly do enclose
    Of orient pearl, a double row,
Which when her lovely laughter shows,
    They look like rose-buds fill'd with snow: 10
Yet them no peer nor prince may buy,
Till Cherry-Ripe themselves do cry.

Her eyes like angels watch them still;
    Her brows like bended bows do stand,
Threat'ning with piercing frowns to kill   15
    All that approach with eye or hand
These sacred cherries to come nigh,
Till Cherry-Ripe themselves do cry!

1. *Shalimar:* the summer palace of the Persian king in Cashmere, surrounded by lovely gardens and a lake.

THE SONG

SILVIA

WILLIAM SHAKESPEARE (ENGLAND)

Who is Silvia? What is she,
   That all our swains commend her?
Holy, fair, and wise is she;
   The heavens such grace did lend her,
That she might admirèd be.   5

Is she kind as she is fair?
   For beauty lives with kindness.
Love does to her eyes repair,
   To help him of his blindness,
And, being help'd, inhabits there.   10

Then to Silvia let us sing,
   That Silvia is excelling;
She excels each mortal thing
   Upon the dull earth dwelling:
To her let us garlands bring.   15

GREEN GROW THE RASHES

ROBERT BURNS (SCOTLAND)

CHORUS.—Green grow the rashes, O;
     Green grow the rashes, O;
       The sweetest hours that e'er I spend
       Are spent amang the lasses, O.

There's nought but care on ev'ry han',
   In every hour that passes, O: 5
What signifies the life o' man,
   And 'twere na for the lasses, O?

The war'ly race may riches chase,
   An' riches still may fly them, O;
An' tho' at last they catch them fast,   10
   Their hearts can ne'er enjoy them, O.

2. *rashes:* rushes.

But gie me a cannie hour at e'en,
   My arms about my dearie, O;
An' war'ly cares, an' war'ly men,   15
   May a' gae tapsalteerie, O.

For you sae douce, ye sneer at this;
   Ye're nought but senseless asses, O:
The wisest man the warl' e'er saw,
   He dearly loved the lasses, O.   20

Auld Nature swears the lovely dears
   Her noblest work she classes, O:
Her prentice han' she tried on man,
   An' then she made the lasses, O.

SOLDIER, REST

SIR WALTER SCOTT (SCOTLAND)

Soldier, rest! thy warfare o'er,
   Sleep the sleep that knows not breaking,
Dream of battled fields no more,
   Days of danger, nights of waking.
In our isle's enchanted hall   5
   Hands unseen thy couch are strewing;
Fairy strains of music fall,
   Every sense in slumber dewing.
Soldier, rest! thy warfare o'er,
Dream of fighting fields no more;   10
Sleep the sleep that knows not breaking,
Morn of toil, nor night of waking.

No rude sound shall reach thine ear,
   Armor's clang, or war-steed champing;
Trump nor pibroch summon here   15
Mustering clan, or squadron tramping.
Yet the lark's shrill fife may come
   At the daybreak from the fallow,
And the bittern sound his drum,
   Booming from the sedgy shallow.   20

16. *tapsalteerie:* topsy-turvy. 17. *douce:* solemn.

15. *Trump:* trumpet. *Pibroch:* a tune on the bagpipe calling the clan into action.

Ruder sounds shall none be near,
Guards nor warders challenge here;
Here's no war-steed's neigh and champing,
Shouting clans or squadrons stamping.

Huntsman, rest! thy chase is done;   25
     While our slumbrous spells assail ye
Dream not, with the rising sun,
     Bugles here shall sound reveille.
Sleep! the deer is in his den;
     Sleep! thy hounds are by thee lying;   30
Sleep! nor dream in yonder glen
     How thy gallant steed lay dying.
Huntsman, rest! thy chase is done;
Think not of the rising sun,
For, at dawning to assail ye,   35
Here no bugles sound reveille.

SWEET AND LOW

ALFRED TENNYSON (ENGLAND)

Sweet and low, sweet and low,
     Wind of the western sea,
Low, low, breathe and blow,
     Wind of the western sea!
Over the rolling waters go,   5
Come from the dying moon, and blow,
     Blow him again to me:
While my little one, while my pretty one, sleeps.

Sleep and rest, sleep and rest,
     Father will come to thee soon;   10
Rest, rest, on mother's breast,
     Father will come to thee soon;
Father will come to his babe in the nest,
Silver sails all out of the west
     Under the silver moon;   15
Sleep, my little one, sleep, my pretty one, sleep.

STUDENT SONG

ROBERT LOUIS STEVENSON (SCOTLAND)

They say that at the core of it
    This life is all regret;
But we've scarce learned the lore of it,
    We're only youngsters yet.
We only ask some more of it, some more of it,   5
    We only ask some more of it
    —The less we're like to get!

Though ill may be the close of it,
    It's fair enough at morn;
And the manner to dispose of it   10
Is just to pluck the rose of it
    When first the rose is born.
Is first to pluck the rose of it, the rose of it, the
        rose of it,
    Is just to pluck the rose of it,
    The de'il may take the thorn!   15

The opinions of the old of it
    Depict a doleful land;
For the guide-books that are sold of it,
The ill that we are told of it,
    Would make Columbus stand.   20
But come let's take a hold of it, a hold of it,
    a hold of it,
    But come let's take a hold of it
    With Alexander's hand.

When sages call the roll of it
    How sad their looks appear!   25
But there's fire in every coal of it
And hope is in the soul of it
    And never a word of fear.
So love we then the whole of it, the whole of it,
    the whole of it,
    So love we then the whole of it   30
    For as long as we are here.

WHEN ALL THE WORLD IS YOUNG, LAD

CHARLES KINGSLEY (ENGLAND)

When all the world is young, lad,
And all the trees are green;
And every goose a swan, lad,
And every lass a queen;
Then hey for boot and horse, lad,   5
And round the world away;
Young blood must have its course, lad,
And every dog his day.

When all the world is old, lad,
And all the trees are brown;   10
And all the sport is stale, lad,
And all the wheels run down;
Creep home, and take your place there,
The spent and maimed among:
God grant you find one face there,   15
You loved when all was young.

A WET SHEET AND A FLOWING SEA

ALLAN CUNNINGHAM (SCOTLAND)

A wet sheet and a flowing sea,
A wind that follows fast
And fills the white and rustling sail
And bends the gallant mast;
And bends the gallant mast, my boys,   5
While like the eagle free
Away the good ship flies, and leaves
Old England on the lee.

O for a soft and gentle wind!
I heard a fair one cry;   10
But give to me the snoring breeze
And white waves heaving high;
And white waves heaving high, my lads,
The good ship tight and free—
The world of waters is our home,   15
And merry men are we.

1. *sheet:* sail.

There's tempest in yon hornèd moon,
    And lightning in yon cloud;
But hark the music, mariners!
    The wind is piping loud;   20
The wind is piping loud, my boys,
    The lightning flashes free—
While the hollow oak our palace is,
    Our heritage the sea.

THE LIGHT OF OTHER DAYS

Thomas Moore (Ireland)

Oft in the stilly night
    Ere slumber's chain has bound me,
Fond Memory brings the light
    Of other days around me:
        The smiles, the tears   5
        Of boyhood's years,
The words of love then spoken;
        The eyes that shone,
        Now dimm'd and gone,
The cheerful hearts now broken!   10
Thus in the stilly night
    Ere slumber's chain has bound me,
Sad Memory brings the light
    Of other days around me.

When I remember all   15
    The friends so link'd together
I've seen around me fall
    Like leaves in wintry weather,
        I feel like one
        Who treads alone   20
Some banquet-hall deserted,
        Whose lights are fled
        Whose garlands dead,
And all but he departed!
Thus in the stilly night   25
    Ere slumber's chain has bound me,
Sad Memory brings the light
    Of other days around me.

THE LOST CHORD

Adelaide Procter (England)

Seated one day at the organ,
I was weary and ill at ease,
And my fingers wandered idly
Over the noisy keys;
I know not what I was playing,   5
Or what I was dreaming then,
But I struck one chord of music
Like the sound of a great Amen.

It flooded the crimson twilight
Like the close of an angel's Psalm,   10
And it lay on my fevered spirit
With a touch of infinite calm;
It quieted pain and sorrow
Like love overcoming strife,
It seemed the harmonious echo   15
From our discordant life.

It linked all perplexed meanings
Into one perfect peace,
And trembled away into silence
As if it were loth to cease.   20
I have sought, but I seek it vainly,
That one lost chord divine,
Which came from the soul of the organ
And entered into mine.

It may be that Death's bright angel   25
Will speak in that chord again;
It may be, that only in Heaven
I shall hear that grand Amen.

LITTLE BOY BLUE

Eugene Field (America)

The little toy dog is covered with dust
But sturdy and staunch he stands;
The little toy soldier is red with rust,
And his musket molds in his hands.

Time was when the little toy dog was new,   5
   And the soldier was passing fair;
And that was the time when our Little Boy Blue
   Kissed them and put them there.

"Now don't you go till I come," he said,
   "And don't you make any noise!"   10
So, toddling off to his trundle bed,
   He dreamt of the pretty toys;
And, as he was dreaming, an angel song
   Awakened our Little Boy Blue—
Oh! the years are many, the years are long,   15
   But the little toy friends are true!

Ay, faithful to Little Boy Blue they stand,
   Each in the same old place,
Awaiting the touch of a little hand,
   The smile of a little face;   20
And they wonder, as waiting the long years through
   In the dust of that little chair,
What has become of our Little Boy Blue
   Since he kissed them and put them there.

THE SONG OF SPRING

GIL VICENTE (PORTUGAL)

I'll away to the garden,
   For winter is over;
The rose is awake
   To the song of her lover!
I will go and discover   5
The passionate Nightingale singing above her.

From the boughs green and golden
   That slope to the river,
A nymph gathers lemons
   To give to her lover:
I will go and discover   10
The shy little Nightingale singing above her.

Near the vineyard, where often
I've spied out a rover,
Sits a damsel who sings   15
To be heard by her lover:
I will go and discover
The bold little Nightingale singing above her.

COME, LASSES AND LADS

Anonymous (England)

Come, lasses and lads, get leave of your dads,
And away to the maypole hie,
For ev'ry he has got a she,
And fiddler's standing by;
For Willie shall dance with Jane,   5
And Johnny has got his Joan,
To trip it, trip it, trip it, trip it, trip it up and down,
To trip it, trip it, trip it, trip it, trip it up and down.

"You're out," says Dick, "Not I," says Nick,
" 'Twas the fiddler played it wrong";   10
" 'Tis true," says Hugh, and so says Sue,
And so says ev'ry one.
The fiddler then began
To play the tune again,
And ev'ry girl did trip it, trip it, trip it to the men,   15
And ev'ry girl did trip it, trip it, trip it to the men.

Then after an hour they went to a bow'r,
And play'd for ale and cakes,
The kisses too, till they were due,
The lasses held the stakes.   20
The girls did then begin
To quarrel with the men,
And bade them take their kisses back, and give them their own
    again,
And bade them take their kisses back, and give them their own
    again.

And there they sat until it was late,   25
   And tired the fiddler quite
With singing and playing, without any paying
   From morning until night.
They told the fiddler then
   They'd pay him for his play,   30
And each gave twopence, twopence, twopence, twopence and went
     away,
And each gave twopence, twopence, twopence, twopence and went
     away.

"Good night," says Harry, "Good night," says Mary,
   "Good night," says Dolly to John,
"Good night," says Sue, "Good night," says Hugh,   35
   "Good night," says ev'ry one.
Some walked and some did run,
   Some loiter'd on the way,
And bound themselves by kisses twelve to meet next holiday,
And bound themselves by kisses twelve to meet next holiday.   40

WHEN ICICLES HANG BY THE WALL

WILLIAM SHAKESPEARE (ENGLAND)

When icicles hang by the wall,
   And Dick the shepherd blows his nail,
And Tom bears logs into the hall,
   And milk comes frozen home in pail,
When blood is nipped and ways be foul,   5
Then nightly sings the staring owl,
   "Tu-whit, tu-who!" a merry note,
While greasy Joan doth keel the pot.

When all aloud the wind doth blow,
   And coughing drowns the parson's saw,   10
And birds sit brooding in the snow,
   And Marian's nose looks red and raw,
When roasted crabs hiss in the bowl,
Then nightly sings the staring owl,
   "Tu-whit, tu-who!" a merry note,   15
While greasy Joan doth keel the pot.

2. *blows his nail:* blows on his fingernails. 8. *keel the pot:* cool the contents by
ladling it. 10. *saw:* sermon.

CAVALIER TUNES

ROBERT BROWNING (ENGLAND)

I

Kentish Sir Byng stood for his King,
Bidding the crop-headed Parliament swing;
And, pressing a troop unable to stoop
And see the rogues flourish and honest folk droop,
Marched them along, fifty-score strong,   5
Great-hearted gentlemen, singing this song:
God for King Charles! Pym and such carles
To the Devil that prompts 'em their treasonous parles!
Cavaliers, up! Lips from the cup,
Hands from the pasty, nor bite take nor sup   10
Till you're—

    Marching along, fifty-score strong,
    Great-hearted gentlemen, singing this song!

Hampden to hell, and his obsequies' knell.
Serve Hazelrig, Fiennes, and young Harry as well!
England, good cheer! Rupert is near!   15
Kentish and loyalists, keep.we not here,

    Marching along, fifty-score strong,
    Great-hearted gentlemen, singing this song!

Then God for King Charles! Pym and his snarls
To the Devil that pricks on such pestilent carles!
Hold by the right, you double your might;   20
So, onward to Nottingham, fresh for the fight.

    Marching along, fifty-score strong,
    Great-hearted gentlemen, singing this song!

II

Boot, saddle, to horse and away!
Rescue my castle before the hot day
Brightens to blue from its silvery gray.
    Boot, saddle, to horse, and away!

1. *King:* King Charles the First, who was later deposed by the Puritan Revolution. 2. *crop-headed Parliament:* the Puritan Parliament. 13–14. *Hampden, etc.:* supporters of the Revolution.

Ride past the suburbs, asleep as you'd say;
Many's the friend there, will listen and pray
"God's luck to gallants that strike up the lay—
    Boot, saddle, to horse, and away!"   5

Forty miles off, like a roebuck at bay,
Flouts Castle Brancepeth the Roundhead's array.   10
Who laughs, "Good fellows ere this, by my fay,
    Boot, saddle, to horse, and away!"

Who? My wife Gertrude; that, honest and gay,
Laughs when you talk of surrendering. "Nay!
I've better counsellors; what counsel they?   15
    Boot, saddle, to horse, and away!"

THE PRINCE'S SONG

HOLGER DRACHMANN (DENMARK)

Translated by Charles Harvey Genung

Princess, I come from out a land that lieth—
    I know not in what arctic latitude:
Though high in the bleak north, it never sigheth
    For sunny smiles; they wait not to be wooed.
Our privilege we know: the bright half-year   5
    Illumines sea and shore with sunlit glory.
In twilight then our fertile fields we ear,
    And round our brows we twine a wreath of story.

When winter decks with frost the bearded oak,
    In songs and sagas we our youth recover;   10
Around the hearthstone crowd the listening folk,
    While on the wall mysterious shadows hover.
The summer night, suffused with loving glow,
    The future, dawning in a golden chalice,
Enkindles hope in hearts of high and low,   15
    From peasant's cottage to the royal palace.

The snow of winter spreads o'er hill and valley
    Its soft and silken blue-white veil of sleep;
The springtime bids the green-clad earth to rally,
    When through the budding leaves the sunbeams peep.   20

7. *ear:* cultivate.

The autumn brings fresh breezes from the ocean
　　And paints the lad's fair cheeks a rosy red;
The maiden's heart is stirred with new emotion,
　　When summer's fragrance o'er the world is spread.

To roam in our fair land is like a dream, 25
　　Through these still woods, renowned in ancient story,
Along the shores, deep-mirrored in the gleam
　　Of fjords that shine beneath the sky's blue glory.
Upon the meadows where the flowers bloom
　　The elfin maidens hide themselves in slumbers, 30
But soon along the lakes where shadows gloom
　　In every bosky nook they'll dance their numbers.

There are no frowning crags on our green mountains,
　　No dark, forbidding cliffs where gorges yawn;
The streams flow featly seaward from their fountains, 35
　　As through the silent valley steals the dawn.
Here nature smooths the rugged, tames the savage.
　　And men born here in victory are kind,
Forbearing still the foeman's land to ravage,
　　And in defeat they bear a steadfast mind.

I'm proud of land, of kindred, and of nation;
　　I'm proud my home is where the waters flow;
Afar I see in golden radiation
　　My native land like sun through amber glow.
Its warmth revives my heart, however lonely: 45
　　Forgive me, Princess, if my soul's aflame,—
But rather be at home, a beggar only,
　　Than, exiled thence, have universal fame.

CORRYMEELA

Moira O'Neill (Ireland)

Over here in England I'm helpin' wi' the hay,
And I wisht I was in Ireland the livelong day;
Weary on the English hay, an' sorra take the wheat!
Och! Corrymeela, an' the blue sky over it.

35. *featly:* easily, smoothly.

There's a deep dumb river flowin' by beyont the heavy trees, 5
This livin' air is moithered wi' the hummin' o' the bees;
I wisht I'd hear the Claddagh burn go runnin' through the heat,
Past Corrymeela, wi' the blue sky over it.

The people that's in England is richer nor the Jews,
There's not the smallest young gossoon but thravels in his shoes! 10
I'd give the pipe between me teeth to see a barefut child,
Och! Corrymeela, an' the low south wind.

Here's hands so full o' money an' hearts so full o' care,
By the luck o' love! I'd still go light for all I did go bare.
"God save ye, colleen dhas," I said; the girl she thought me wild! 15
Fair Corrymeela, an' the low south wind.

D'ye mind me now, the song at night is mortal hard to raise,
The girls are heavy goin' here, the boys are ill to plase;
When ones't I'm out this workin' hive, 'tis I'll be back again—
Aye, Corrymeela, in the same soft rain. 20

The puff o' smoke from one ould roof before an English town!
For a *shaugh* wid Andy Feelan here I'd give a silver crown,
For a curl o' hair like Mollie's ye'll ask the like in vain,
Sweet Corrymeela, an' the same soft rain.

MY OLD KENTUCKY HOME

Stephen Foster (America)

The sun shines bright in the old Kentucky home;
    'T is summer, the darkies are gay;
The corn-top's ripe, and the meadow's in the bloom,
    While the birds make music all the day.

The young folks roll on the little cabin floor, 5
    All merry, all happy and bright;
By-'n'-by hard times comes a-knocking at the door:—
    Then my old Kentucky home, good night!

    Weep no more, my lady,
    O, weep no more today!
We will sing one song for the old Kentucky home, 10
    For the old Kentucky home, far away.

They hunt no more for the possum and the coon,
   On the meadow, the hill, and the shore;
They sing no more by the glimmer of the moon,   15
   On the bench by the old cabin door.
The day goes by like a shadow o'er the heart,
   With sorrow, where all was delight;
The time has come when the darkies have to part:—
   Then my old Kentucky home, good night!   20

The head must bow, and the back will have to bend,
   Wherever the darky may go;
A few more days, and the trouble all will end,
   In the fields where the sugar canes grow.
A few more days for to tote the weary load,   25
   No matter, 't will never be light;
A few more days till we totter on the road:—
   Then my old Kentucky home, good night!

    Weep no more, my lady,
    O, weep no more today!   30
We will sing one song for the old Kentucky home,
   For the old Kentucky home, far away.

A HOME ON THE RANGE

Traditional (America)

Among the cowboys and frontiersmen of the western plains grew up
a store of songs and ballads anonymously created and improved at each
retelling, just as were the ballads of olden days. The following is such
a song.

❋   ❋   ❋

Oh, give me a home where the buffalo roam,
Where the deer and the antelope play,
Where seldom is heard a discouraging word
And the skies are not cloudy all day.

    Home, home on the range,   5
    Where the deer and the antelope play;
    Where seldom is heard a discouraging word
    And the skies are not cloudy all day.

Where the air is so pure, the zephyrs so free,
The breezes so balmy and light,   10
That I would not exchange my home on the range
For all of the cities so bright.

The red man was pressed from this part of the West,
He's likely no more to return
To the banks of Red River where seldom if ever   15
Their flickering camp-fires burn.

How often at night when the heavens are bright
With the light from the glittering stars,
Have I stood here amazed and asked as I gazed
If their glory exceeds that of ours.   20

Oh, I love these wild flowers in this dear land of ours,
The curlew I love to hear scream,
And I love the white rocks and the antelope flocks
That graze on the mountain-tops green.

Home, home on the range,   25
Where the deer and the antelope play;
Where seldom is heard a discouraging word
And the skies are not cloudy all day.

SONG OF THE HOUSE

NAVAHO INDIANS (AMERICA)

Translated by A. M. Stephen

Sung by the shaman or medicine man at a Navaho house-warming.

❋   ❋   ❋

Rising Sun! When you shall shine,
Make this house happy.
Beautify it with your beams;
Make this house happy.

God of Dawn ! Your white blessings spread ;
Make this house happy.
Guard the doorway from all evil ;
Make this house happy.

White Corn ! Abide herein ;
Make this house happy.   10

Soft Wealth may this hut cover much ;
Make this house happy.

Male Rain ! Your virtues send ;
Make this house happy.

Corn Pollen ! Bestow content ;   15
Make this house happy.

May peace around this family dwell ;
Make this house happy.

9. *White Corn:* the spirit of. 11. *Soft Wealth:* skins, blankets, etc. 14. *Male:* heavy.

READING PROBLEMS ON THE SONG

1. *Annie Laurie:* How does this, the world's most famous love song, illustrate the qualities of a song described in the introduction?

2. *The Indian Serenade:* To what does this song owe its beauty: setting, melody, theme?

3. *On Wings of Song:* Why do you suppose the lover wishes to bear his sweetheart away, if only in imagination?

4. *Across the Water:* How does the poet convey to us his feelings without discussing them?

5. *The Far Away Princess:* In how many ways is the Princess far away? Why does the poet consider his love "more noble since vain"?

6. *Fancy:* State the difference between fancy and true love hinted in this poem.

7. *The Night Has a Thousand Eyes:* Explain lines 5 and 6.

8. *Maid of Athens:* How does the simplicity of this poem heighten its effect?

9. *Kashmiri Song:* Is the woman described in this poem? How are her beauty and charm suggested? To the lover, of what does she seem a part?

10. *Cherry Ripe* and *Silvia:* What charms do these girls have above and beyond their beauty? Are these the qualities that still make girls popular?

11. *Green Grow the Rashes:* What is Burns' opinion of women? Explain lines 23–24.

12. *Soldier Rest:* How do the images and rhythm in this song add to its lulling quality?

13. *Sweet and Low:* Analyze the words to see why the poem is so melodious. What does the repetition of words add?

14. *Student Song:* Explain lines 16–20. What is meant by Alexander's hand? What is youth's attitude toward life as seen by Stevenson?

15. *When All the World Is Young, Lad:* What does the parallelism of the stanzas add to the idea of the poem? Explain the indicated contrasts.

16. *A Wet Sheet and a Flowing Sea:* In how many ways does this song convey the adventurous spirit of the young sailor and the lure of the sea?

17. *The Light of Other Days:* Explain the word *light.* How do the comparisons used in this poem give the reader the emotion of the poet as he thinks of the past?

18. *The Lost Chord:* What does the lost chord symbolize? Why can the poet not recapture it?

19. *Little Boy Blue:* Is the point of this song the story it tells, or does the story express someone's feeling? If so, what feeling and whose?

20. *The Song of Spring:* What is the dominant note in the song of spring? Why does the poet vary the adjective applied to the nightingale?

21. *Come Lasses and Lads:* With what does the stanza form and rhythm of this song coincide?

22. *When Icicles Hang by the Wall:* How does Shakespeare indicate the cold and discomfort of the winter season?

23. *Cavalier Tunes:* Look up the cavaliers in English history and then show how in his rhythm, language, anecdotes, and small details Browning has caught their spirit and character. What is admirable in them?

24. *The Prince's Song, Corrymeela, My Old Kentucky Home,* and *Home on the Range:* Compare the devices by which the different poets make us feel their love for their native lands. Can you see racial differences in character and temperament in the Danish, Irish, and American poets? Although Stephen Foster is not a Negro, has he caught the tone of Negro sentiment in *My Old Kentucky Home?* Compare the description of a big new country in *Home on the Range* and in *Chant Pagan* (page 782). Which is the most skillful? Why?

25. *Song of the House:* What seven blessings does the poet pray for this house? Are these the foundations of a happy home?

FURTHER READINGS IN THE SONG

Most of the following collections contain both words and music.

Charles Vincent: *Fifty Shakespeare Songs*
Juliet Raphail: *Madrigal and Minstrelsy*
Cecil Sharp: *One Hundred English Folk Songs*
Farnsworth and Sharp: *Folk Songs and Art Songs*

THE SONG

Granville Bantock: *One Hundred Folk Songs of All Nations*
Walter Scott: *Minstrelsy of the Scottish Border*
Albert E. Wier: *Songs the Whole World Sings*
Ansco Music Sales Co.: *Everybody's Favorite Songs*
  Arrangements by Paul Hall.
Negro Spirituals: *Hear Dem Bells*
    Golden Slippers
    Nobody Knows the Trouble I've Seen
    Swing Low, Sweet Chariot
    Deep River
    Old Man River

SUGGESTIONS FOR ORIGINAL SONGS

Set to some familiar tune: 1. A School Song Expressing the Ideals of Our School. 2. A Football Song. 3. A Class Day Song. 4. Farewell to the Seniors. 5. A Song for Our City. 6. Spring Song for Our State. 7. A Camp-fire Song. 8. A Club Song. 9. A Personal Song of Your Own Choosing.

XIII

The Sonnet

THE reflective quality improper to a song reaches full expression in the sonnet. The sonnet is a literary type invented by the Italian poet Petrarch to embody the reactions of mind or heart to a single moment of experience. The sonnet consists of fourteen lines. The first eight lines, or octet, describe the incident, scene, place, person, thing, or circumstance which has caught the poet's attention. The last six lines, or sestet, give the poet's reaction to this topic—whether it be a purely philosophic reflection or an emotional outburst. Even the emotion in a sonnet, however, is intellectualized and philosophized. Indeed, the sonnet might be called the lyric of the mind, as the song is the lyric of the heart.

The sonnet has several fixed rhyme patterns into one of which the poet must fit his thought. The necessity to adapt to this set pattern stimulates the poet to ponder, to condense, to polish, until the great sonnet becomes the most perfect example of literary workmanship, and the most heavily freighted with meaning and implication of any poetic form. It is the ambition of every great actor to play *Hamlet ;* it is the ambition of every poet to write successful sonnets. Each is the supreme test of perfect mastery within its art.

RHYME SCHEME OF THE SONNET

The Italian form :

> octet : a b b a a b b a
> sestet : c d e c d e

The English forms :

> (1) octet : a b a b a b a b
> sestet : c d c d e e
> (2) octet : a b b a a b b a
> sestet : c d d c e e

SCORN NOT THE SONNET

William Wordsworth (England)

Scorn not the sonnet; Critic, you have frowned,
Mindless of its just honors. With this key
Shakespeare unlocked his heart; the melody
Of this small lute gave ease to Petrarch's wound;
A thousand times this pipe did Tasso sound;   5
With it Camoëns soothed an exile's grief;
The sonnet glittered a gay myrtle leaf
Amid the cypress with which Dante crowned
His visionary brow; a glow-worm lamp,
It cheered mild Spenser, called from Faery-land   10
To struggle through dark ways; and when a damp
Fell round the path of Milton, in his hand
The Thing became a trumpet; whence he blew
Soul-animating strains—alas too few.

TO LAURA

Petrarch (Italy)

Translated by Chapel Lofft

Down my cheeks bitter tears incessant rain,
And my heart struggles with convulsive sighs,
When, Laura, upon you I turn my eyes,
For whom the world's allurements I disdain.
But when I see that gentle smile again,   5
That modest, sweet, and tender smile, arise,
It pours on every sense a blest surprise;
Lost in delight is all my torturing pain.
Too soon this heavenly transport sinks and dies.
When all thy soothing charms my fate removes   10
At thy departure from my ravish'd view,
To that sole refuge its firm faith approves,
My spirit from my ravish'd bosom flies,
And wing'd with fond remembrance follows you.

4–5–8. *Petrarch, Tasso, Dante* are Italian poets. 6. *Camoëns:* a Portuguese poet.
3–10–12. *Shakespeare, Spenser, Milton* are English poets.

OF BEATRICE D'PORTINARI, ON ALL SAINTS DAY

DANTE ALIGHIERI (ITALY)

Translated by Dante Gabriel Rossetti

Dante fell in love with the fourteen-year-old Beatrice on the occasion described below. Though each married another, Dante worshipped Beatrice from afar until her early death, and dedicated to her his *Vita Nuova*, a sonnet series describing the "new life" he owed to her influence. In his *Divine Comedy*, Beatrice guides Dante through Paradise during the poet's dream-journey through the after world.

❊   ❊   ❊

Last All Saints' holy-day, even now gone by,
    I met a gathering of damozels:
    She that came first, as one doth who excels,
Had Love with her, bearing her company:
A flame burned forward through her steadfast eye,   5
    As when in living fire spirit dwells:
    So, gazing with the boldness which prevails
O'er doubt, I knew an angel visibly.
As she passed on, she bowed her mild approof
    And salutation to all men of worth   10
Lifting the soul to solemn thoughts aloof.
    In Heaven itself that lady had her birth,
I think, and is with us for our behoof:
    Blessed are they who meet her on the earth.

THE MODEL AND THE STATUE

MICHAEL ANGELO BUONARROTI (ITALY)

Translated by John Addington Symonds

It is interesting to know that Michael Angelo—the great painter, sculptor, architect, and military engineer of Florence, Italy—could also on occasion write a beautiful sonnet.

❊   ❊   ❊

When divine Art conceives a form and face,
    She bids the craftsman for his first essay
    To shape a simple model in mere clay:
This is the earliest birth of Art's embrace.

From the live marble in the second place
   His mallet brings into the light of day
   A thing so beautiful that who can say
   When time shall conquer that immortal grace?
Thus my own model I was born to be—
   The model of that nobler self, whereto   10
   Schooled by your pity, lady, I shall grow.
Each overplus and each deficiency
   You will make good. What penance then is due
   For my fierce heat, chastened and taught by you?

TO HELEN

PIERRE RONSARD (FRANCE)

Translated by Ruth Mary Weeks

When you are old and gray, at night, by candlelight,
Seated beside the fire to wind the flax and spin,
Say then, chanting my lines and inly wondering:
"Ronsard praised my beauty once when it was bright."

Then shall no serving maid who hears you thus rehearse   5
This tale, drowsing at her task and half asleep,
Fail straightway at my name full wide awake to leap,
Blessing your name for my immortal verse.

Deep in the earth my body shall be laid;
I shall take my repose in the myrtles' clustering shade.   10
By your hearth you shall nod—a bent and aged wife—
Regretting my eager love and your proud disdain.
Live—ye who hear me—nor wait for tomorrow's gain.
Gather today the blossoming roses of life.

BRIGHT STAR

JOHN KEATS (ENGLAND)

The young poet, John Keats, who knew he was dying of tuberculosis and could never marry, found no peace in his passionate love for

Fanny Brawne. To her is addressed the following—the last sonnet to come from his pen.

* * *

Bright star! would I were steadfast as thou art—
Not in lone splendor hung aloft the night,
And watching, with eternal lids apart,
Like Nature's patient sleepless Eremite,
The moving waters at their priestlike task   5
Of pure ablution round earth's human shores,
Or gazing on the new soft fallen mask
Of snow upon the mountains and the moors—
No—yet still steadfast, still unchangeable,
Pillow'd upon my fair love's ripening breast,   10
To feel for ever its soft fall and swell,
Awake for ever in a sweet unrest,
Still, still to hear her tender-taken breath,
And so live ever—or else swoon to death.

HOW DO I LOVE THEE?

ELIZABETH BARRETT BROWNING (ENGLAND)

The talented poetess, Elizabeth Barrett, was an invalid confined to her sofa by a jealous and tyrannical father when she met the young poet, Robert Browning. Under Browning's influence, she regained her health and escaped her father's tyranny. During their courtship, Miss Barrett wrote a series of sonnets to Robert Browning, which she showed him for the first time after their marriage. The following is an especially beautiful one.

* * *

How do I love thee? Let me count the ways.
I love thee to the depth and breadth and height
My soul can reach, when feeling out of sight
For the ends of being, and ideal grace.
I love thee to the level of every day's   5
Most quiet need, by sun and candlelight.
I love thee freely, as men strive for right;
I love thee purely, as they turn from praise.
I love thee with the passion put to use
In my old griefs, and with my childhood's faith.   10

4. *Eremite:* hermit priest.

I love thee with a love I seemed to lose
With my lost saints—I love thee with the breath,
Smiles, tears, of all my life!—and, if God choose,
I shall but love thee better after death.

FIRST LOVES

AUGUSTE ANGELLIER (FRANCE)

Translated by Ruth Mary Weeks

First loves are but love's clumsy first essay,
Faint flickering fires, a transitory lure
For hearts confused and souls still immature
Where dimly gleams the dawn of fuller day.

To know a deathless love, supreme, mature,   5
Needs hearts that have arisen from defeat,
Whose long exertions and whose secret heat
Have shaped by grievous strokes the soul's contour.

Real love is only by such souls conceived
Whom fate has sculptured into finished line,   10
Who find each other by love's certain sign,
And know each other in stature full achieved,

Exchanging gravely a tenderness secure
And powers of love by gradual growth made sure.

NO LONGER MOURN

WILLIAM SHAKESPEARE (ENGLAND)

No longer mourn for me when I am dead
Than you shall hear the surly, sullen bell
Give warning to the world that I am fled
From this vile world, with vilest worms to dwell.
Nay, if you read this line, remember not   5
The hand that writ it; for I love you so
That I in your sweet thoughts would be forgot
If thinking on me then should make you woe.

1. *essay:* trial, experiment.

Oh, if, I say, you look upon this verse
When I perhaps compounded am with clay,   10
Do not so much as my poor name rehearse,
But let your love even with my life decay,
    Lest the wise world should look into your moan
    And mock you with me after I am gone.

REMEMBER

CHRISTINA ROSSETTI (ENGLAND)

Remember me when I am gone away,
Gone far away into the silent land;
When you can no more hold me by the hand,
Nor I half turn to go, yet turning stay.
Remember me when no more, day by day,   5
You tell me of the future that you planned;
Only remember me; you understand
It will be late to counsel then or pray.
Yet if you should forget me for a while
And afterwards remember, do not grieve;   10
For if the darkness and corruption leave
A vestige of the thoughts that once I had,
Better by far you should forget and smile
Than that you should remember and be sad.

ON THE DEATH OF A PIOUS LADY

OLOF WEXIONIUS (SWEDEN)

Translated by Sir Edmund Gosse

The earthly roses at God's call have made
    Way, lady, for a dress of heavenly white,
    In which thou walk'st with other figures bright,
Once loved on earth, who now, like thee arrayed,
Feast on two-fold ambrosia, wine and bread;   5
    They lead thee up by sinuous paths of light
    Through lilied fields that sparkle in God's sight,
And crown thee with delights that never fade.
O thou thrice-sainted mother, in that bliss,
Forget not thy two daughters, whom a kiss   10

At parting left as sad as thou art glad;
In thy deep joy think how for thee they weep,
Or conjure through the shifting glass of sleep
The saint heaven hath, the mother once they had.

THE TRICKS OF PLEASING

ADAM MICKIEWICZ (POLAND)

Translated by Charles Harvey Genung

The tricks of pleasing thou hast aye disdained;
  Thy words are plain, and simple all thy ways;
  Yet throngs, admiring, tremble 'neath thy gaze,
And in thy queenly presence stand enchained.
Amid the social babble unconstrained,
  I heard men speak of women words of praise,
  And with a smile each turned some honeyed phrase.
Thou cam'st,—and lo! a sacred silence reigned.
Thus when the dancers with each other vie,
  And through the merry mazes whirling go,
Abruptly all is hushed: they wonder why,
  And no one can the subtle reason show.
The poet speaks: "There glides an angel by!"
  The guests all dimly feel, but few do know.

A SECRET

ALEXIS FELIX ARVERS (FRANCE)

Translated by Ruth Mary Weeks

My heart has its secret; my life its mystery:
A passion immortal in an instant deep sown,
Which, bitterly hopeless, unspoken must be
And by her who inspired it can never be known.

Alas, that so near her I ever shall fare—
Forever beside her, fore'er unperceived;
That away all my days upon earth shall thus wear
With nothing demanded and nothing received.

For she whom God made thus so tenderly sweet,
She follows her path, unobserving, discreet,   10
And hears not the murmur of love neath her feet.

To a duty austere keeping faith piously,
If this poem so full of herself she shall see,
She will say, "Who then is it," nor know it is she.

TO A FRIEND
WILLIAM SHAKESPEARE (ENGLAND)

When to the sessions of sweet silent thought
I summon up remembrance of things past,
I sigh the lack of many a thing I sought,
And with old woes new wail my dear time's waste:
Then can I drown an eye, unused to flow,   5
For precious friends hid in death's dateless night,
And weep afresh love's long since cancelled woe,
And moan the expense of many a vanished sight:
Then can I grieve at grievances foregone,
And heavily from woe to woe tell o'er   10
The sad account of fore-bemoanèd moan,
Which I new pay as if not paid before:
    But if the while I think on thee, dear friend,
    All losses are restored and sorrows end.

TOMORROW
LOPE DE VEGA (SPAIN)
Translated by H. W. Longfellow

Lord, what am I, that with unceasing care
  Thou did'st seek after me, that Thou did'st wait
  Wet with unhealthy dews before my gate,
And pass the gloomy nights of winter there?

Oh, strange delusion, that I did not greet   5
  Thy blest approach, and oh, to heaven how lost
  If my ingratitude's unkindly frost
Has chilled the bleeding wounds upon Thy feet.

4. *old woes—waste:* weep again for old troubles. 8. *expense:* loss. 11. *fore-bemoaned moan:* old griefs.

How oft my guardian angel gently cried,
    "Soul, from thy casement look, and thou shalt see
How He persists to knock and wait for thee!"   10
      And oh, how often to that Voice of sorrow,
"Tomorrow we will open," I replied,
    And when the morrow came I answered still "Tomorrow."

THE CORAL REEF

José-Maria de Heredia (Cuba)

Translation by Henry Johnson

The sunlight 'neath the sea like some strange dawn
Enfolds the coral-trees of the abyss,
Whose deep, warm basins show commingled there
The animal a flower, the flower alive.
And all that salt or iodine has tinged,   5
Moss, hairy weed, urchins, anemones,
Spread the dull purple of their sumptuous forms
O'er coral-bottoms pale, with myriad pores.
With scales more splendid than the enamel's blaze,
A great fish swims across the branches, slow,   10
And indolent, through the transparent shades;
But suddenly he moves his fin of fire
And flashes through the dull, unmoving blue
A quivering gold and pearl and emerald.

BEECH TREES

Sister M. Madeleva (America)

I passed a wood of beech trees yesterday
And I am shaken with its beauty yet.
Why should my breath catch and my eyes be wet
Because a hundred trees some yards away
Know simply how to dress in simple gray,   5
Are poised beyond the need of epithet
And beautiful past power to forget?
I dare not think how they will look in May.

6 *urchins, anemones:* flower-like animal forms of the sea deeps.   2. *abyss:* depths.

6. *epithet:* descriptive word.

They wore illustrious yellow in the fall.
Their beauty is no thing at which they guess. 10
And when they put on green, and when they carry
Fans open in the sun or folded small,
I'll look through tears at ultimate loveliness:
Beeches in May, beeches in February.

THE SOWERS

GABRIELE D'ANNUNZIO (ITALY)

Translated by Rudolph Altrocchi

The sturdy peasants plod across the field
Leading the oxen, slow and placid-faced;
Behind them smokes the furrow, iron-traced,
And open for the coming season's yield.
Then with a widespread gesture of the hand 5
The sower casts the grains; the agèd seem
To lift to heaven all their prayers and dream
Of copious harvests—if the Lord command.
Almost a pious human gratitude
Honors the earth today. In the faint light 10
Of dusk the temples of the hills, snow-white,
Arise at vespers, while men lift a crude
Plain chant on high, and there is in their mien
A sacerdotal majesty serene.

O, WORLD

GEORGE SANTAYANA (AMERICA)

O world, thou choosest not the better part!
It is not wisdom to be only wise,
And on the inward vision close the eyes,
But it is wisdom to believe the heart.
Columbus found a world and had no chart, 5
Save one that faith deciphered in the skies;
To trust the soul's invincible surmise
Was all his science and his only art.

14. *sacerdotal:* priest-like.

Our knowledge is a torch of smoky pine
That lights the pathway but one step ahead   10
Across a void of mystery and dread.
Bid, then, the tender light of faith to shine
By which alone the mortal heart is led
Unto the thinking of the thought divine.

THE PIONEER

EDNA ST. VINCENT MILLAY (AMERICA)

Written as a tribute to Susan B. Anthony, Elizabeth Cady Stanton,
and Lucretia Mott—the three American pioneers of the woman's
rights movement.

❋   ❋   ❋

Upon this marble bust that is not I
Lay the round formal wreath that is not fame;
But in the forum of my silenced cry
Root ye the living tree whose sap is flame.
I that was proud and valiant am no more;—   5
Save as a dream that wanders wide and late,
Save as a wind that rattles the stout door,
Troubling the ashes in the sheltered grate.
The stone will perish; I shall be twice dust.
Only my standard on a taken hill   10
Can cheat the mildew and the red brown rust
And make immortal my adventurous will.
Even now the silk is tugging at the staff:
Take up the song; forget the epitaph.

TEARS

LIZETTE WOODWORTH REESE (AMERICA)

When I consider Life and its few years—
A wisp of fog betwixt us and the sun;
A call to battle, and the battle done
Ere the last echo dies within our ears;
A rose choked in the grass; an hour of fears;   5
The gusts that past a darkening shore do beat;
The burst of music down an unlistening street,—
I wonder at the idleness of tears.

3. *forum:* place for public discussion. 14. *epitaph:* sentiments carved on a
tombstone.

Ye old, old dead, and ye of yesternight,
Chieftains, and bards, and keepers of the sheep, 10
By every cup of sorrow that you had,
Loose me from tears, and make me see aright
How each hath back what once he stayed to weep:
Homer his sight, David his little lad!

14. Homer was blind. King David lost his son.

READING PROBLEMS ON THE SONNET

1. *Scorn Not the Sonnet:* For what does Wordsworth think great writers have used the sonnet form? Read sonnets by the mentioned authors in this and other anthologies to test the fitness of the words he uses for the sonnets of each (key, melody, lute, etc.).

2. *To Laura, Of Beatrice d' Portinari, The Model and the Statue:* What influence do the ladies celebrated in these sonnets exert upon their lovers? Which poet has most strikingly stated this point?

3. *To Helen:* Reread the lyrics on the brevity of life (pages 756-762). Show how the definite personal application of this idea in Ronsard's sonnet gives it a deeper significance.

4. *Bright Star:* Is Keats wishing the unattainable in longing for a love as calm as the contemplation of earth by the stars? How do the phases of nature indicated as the objects of the star's contemplation heighten the effect of calm serenity?

5. *How Do I Love Thee:* Explain fully in your own words the six major tests of true love set forth in this poem.

6. *First Loves:* What two facts convince Angellier that first loves are not so genuinely satisfying as those formed in maturity?

7. *No Longer Mourn* and *Remember:* Which poet is really willing to be forgotten for the sake of the beloved's happiness?

8. *On the Death of a Pious Lady:* Show from this sonnet how devout religious faith softens the cruelty of death.

9. *The Tricks of Pleasing* and *A Secret:* These sonnets describe somewhat similar women. What quality of the lady is especially stressed in each sonnet? Which sonnet contains the most impressive comparison?

10. *To a Friend:* From this sonnet define the value of friendship.

11. *Tomorrow:* In what ways does God seek and wait for us? In what ways do our guardian angels cry, "Look?"

12. *The Coral Reef:* Select words from this sonnet that give the special qualities of light and color peculiar to the submarine world.

13. *Beech Trees:* Is the poet describing the trees or their influence upon her? Answer the question asked in lines 3–7.

14. *The Sowers:* What gives the season of plowing and sowing its solemn atmosphere? Has Millet expressed the same idea in his picture of *The Sower?*

15. *O World:* What does Santayana mean by "only wise"? Make a list of the "invincible surmises" that great pioneers have followed in spite of misunderstanding and opposition.

16. *The Pioneer:* What does the author think the pioneers in any cause would consider the most genuine tribute to their memory? What does she mean by the last line? What is the true immortality of the reformer? Which image best expresses the disturbing influence of a progressive idea? Select quotable lines and phrases from this sonnet.

17. *Tears:* Which comparison best expresses the brevity of life? Why does this very brevity convince the author of the "idleness of tears?" Explain the last two lines.

FURTHER READINGS IN THE SONNET

S. Wassington: *Sonnets of Europe*
Denys Bray: *The Original Order of Shakespeare's Sonnets*
William Robertson: *The Golden Book of English Sonnets*
Sir Arthur P. Quiller-Couch: *English Sonnets*
Houston Peterson: *The Book of Sonnet Sequences*
  See anthologies listed under the lyric for further individual sonnets.

SUGGESTIONS FOR ORIGINAL SONNETS

1. To a Stream-Line Train. 2. To an Airlane or Aviator. 3. To a Great City at Night. 4. To a Skyscraper. 5. To a Transcontinental Highway. 6. To a Violinist. 7. To a Tap Dancer. 8. To a Fine Photo-play Actor. 9. To a Genuine Teacher. 10. To a Real Comrade. 11. To a Library. 12. To a Laboratory. 13. To a School Desk.

XIV

The Ode

AN ODE, a lyric of more elaborate character than a song, is suited for dignified rendition by a chorus in commemoration of some public event, great person, cause, or idea. The father of the ode was the Greek poet Pindar, whose most beautiful and famous odes were tributes to the winners of the great Pan-Hellenic athletic games at Olympia, after which our modern Olympics are named. These athletic triumphs gave rise to great rejoicing in the home district of the winner; a poet was engaged to write an ode of praise; and choruses were trained to sing this ode at the ovation extended to the returning hero. In Pindar's odes, the success of the individual athlete is lifted to a higher plane than that of physical prowess; and admiration for the beautiful and good in physique, sportsmanship, and character is merged with patriotism, morality, and reverence for the gods. Since the days of Pindar, the ode has preserved this exalted character, and to whatever the subject treated, the ode has ever given a wider, more civic, and more philosophic significance than the purely personal subject of a song.

As the ode was originally designed for choral rendition, it was written in the form of an anthem with stanzas called the strophe, the antistrophe, and the epode. The strophe was sung by one half of the chorus; the antistrophe by the other half; and the epode by the whole group. The stanzas are written so that the antistrophe will be an answer to the strophe, and the epode will then summarize or complete the idea. In a long ode, this triple arrangement may be repeated several times. Modern odes, while not usually following this stanza arrangement, preserve the formality, elevation, and choral tone of the older odes.

TO ALCIMEDON AND TIMOSTHENES

PINDAR (GREECE)

Translated by Abraham Moore

Alcimedon and Timosthenes were victors among the youths in wrestling, the former at the Olympic, the latter at the Nemean Games. Olympia was a shrine to Zeus, king of the gods, and the games were opened by religious sacrifice.

❊   ❊   ❊

STROPHE

Olympia, mother of the games
Where worth his golden chaplet claims;
Mistress of truth, whose fate-exploring priest
From the slain victim learns, if highest Jove
Whose hand the dazzling thunder throws,   5
Views with regard the dauntless breast,
That, fired with virtue's noblest love,
Pants but for fame and victory's sweet repose—

ANTISTROPHE

Such tribute gracious Heaven allows
To athletes' pure and pious vows—   10
Do thou, Olympian grove, whose branches wave
O'er Alpheus' stream, accept the wreaths I bear—
Triumphal strains. A deathless name
Thy glorious guerdon gives the brave.
Not all the same distinctions share:
Various the paths divine that lead to fame.

EPODE

You valiant youths, kind destiny consign'd
To Jove your natal genius: he thy name,
Timosthenes, proclaimed in Nemea's game,
While Olympic wreaths Alcimedon entwined.   20

4. *Jove:* Zeus. 14. *guerdon:* prize or award.

Of beauty's manliest mold was he;
Nor fail'd his act the warrant of his face;
Crown'd with the wrestler's victory,
Aegina's isle he named his native place,
Where all to justice bow, that sits above, 25
Saviour at once and judge, by ordinance of Jove.

* * * * * *

ANTISTROPHE

And what of he who trained the two?
He was a glorious athlete, too;
And though perhaps not all with this agree,
Yet if his youthful conquests should my string 30
Sound for Milesias, then I pray
Fling not envy's stone at me,
For I his Nemean feats will sing
And later triumphs in Pancration fray.

EPODE

With ease from practice's lips instruction flows. 35
Who does the thing himself with excellence
Can better teach than inexperience.
Perfect beyond his peers Milesias knows
The athletic discipline and plan,
That when the game shall rouse him to the fray, 40
Harden and frame the practised man
To bear th' adored and dangerous prize away.
Today his boast Alcimedon must be,
The thirtieth youth his art hath train'd for victory.

STROPHE

He with the smiles of fortune bright, 45
Nor wanting valor's manliest might,
Hath to four luckless brave opponents doom'd
The sad return, the path obscure, the tale
Of shame; and in his grandsire's heart
Youth's long-extinguish'd lamp relumed. 50
When glory's cheering beams prevail,
Old age revives and death forgets his dart.

31. *Milesias:* the coach of the two boys, who had also triumphed himself at
Nemea and in other contests.

ANTISTROPHE

Now let the loud-recording lay
Awaken memory to display
What other triumphs in the wrestler's war   55
Their family achieved. Gain'd from the games
On their proud busts six chaplets bloom.
Their kinsman's rite the dead shall share;
Its praise departed virtue claims;
The trump of glory echoes in the tomb.   60

EPODE

Iphion, uncle of Alcimedon,
Heard ere he died, and shall delighted tell
The athlete's father of the crown that fell
By Jove's good gift to his distinguish'd son.
Still may the god his blessings shower   65
On their fair deeds, and chase disease away;
Nor Nemesis with vengeful power
Thwart the promise of their prosperous day.
Grant them long life, to fortune's ills unknown,
Their country's weal enhance, and crown it with their own.   70

THE GOLDEN MEAN

HORATIUS FLACCUS (ROME)

Translated by Sir William Watson

Lucinius, wouldst thou wisely steer
The barque which is thy soul,
Not always trust her without fear
Where deep-sea billows roll;
Nor, to the sheltered beach too near,   5
Risk shipwreck on the shoal.

Who sees in fortune's golden mean
All his desires comprised,
Midway the cot and court between
Hath well his life devised;   10
For riches hath not envied been,
Nor for their lack despised.

61–62. His uncle, who died after Alcimedon's triumph, will carry the news to the victor's father in the land of the dead. 67. *Nemesis:* fate.
1. *Lucinius:* a wealthy friend and patron of the poet, Horace.

Most rocks the pine that soars afar,
    When leaves are tempest-whirled.
Direst the crash when turrets are   15
    In dusty ruin hurled.
The thunder loveth best to scar
    The white brows of the world.

The steadfast mind, that to the end
    Is fortune's victor still,   20
Hath yet a fear, though Fate befriend,
    A hope, though all seem ill.
Jove can at will the winter send,
    Or call the spring at will.

Full oft the darkest day may be   25
    Of morrows bright the sire.
His bow not everlastingly
    Apollo bends in ire.
At times the silent muses he
    Wakes with his dulcet lyre.   30

When stormy narrows round thee roar,
    Be bold; naught else avails.
But when thy canvas swells before
    Too proudly prospering gales,
For once be wise with coward's lore,   35
    And timely reef thy sails.

ON SHAKESPEARE

JOHN MILTON (ENGLAND)

What needs my Shakespeare for his honored bones
The labor of an age in pilèd stones?
Or that his hallowed reliques should be hid
Under a star y-pointing pyramid?

28. *Apollo:* god of the sun and of the arts.   29. *Muses:* patron deities of the
different arts, as poetry, music, the dance, etc.
3. *reliques:* bodily remains.

Dear son of memory, great heir of fame,   5
What need'st thou such weak witness of thy name?
Thou in our wonder and astonishment
Hast built thyself a livelong monument.

For whilst, to the shame of slow-endeavoring art,
Thy easy numbers flow, and that each heart   10
Hath from the leaves of thy unvalued book
Those Delphic lines with deep impression took,
Then thou, our fancy of itself bereaving,
Dost make *us* marble with too much conceiving,
And so sepùlchred in such pomp dost lie   15
That kings for such a tomb would wish to die.

THE MAID OF ORLEANS

FRIEDRICH VON SCHILLER (GERMANY)

Translated by James Clarence Mangan

The *Maid of Orleans* is Joan of Arc, who, having liberated France
from conquest by the English, was burned as a heretic.

❋   ❋   ❋

At thee *the Mocker* sneers in cold derision,
    Through thee he seeks to desecrate and dim
Glory for which he hath no soul or vision,
    For "God" and "Angel" are but sounds with him.
He makes the jewels of the heart his booty,   5
And scoffs at Man's Belief and Woman's Beauty.

Yet thou—a lowly shepherdess!—descended
    Not from a kingly but a godly race,
Are crowned by Poësy! Amid the splendid
    Of Heaven's high stars she builds thy dwelling place,   10
Garlands thy temples with a wreath of glory,
And swathes thy memory in eternal Story.

12. *Delphic:* at Delphi in Greece was situated the famous oracle of Apollo.
Delphic thus means divine or prophetic, as the words of the oracle were supposed
to be inspired by the god. 14. *conceiving:* imagining, meditating.

The Base of this weak world exult at seeing
 The Fair defaced, the Lofty in the dust;
Yet grieve not! There are godlike hearts in being   15
 Which worship still the Beautiful and Just.
Let Momus and his mummers please the crowd,
Of nobleness alone a noble mind is proud.

THE POETS

ARTHUR O'SHAUGHNESSY (IRELAND)

We are the music-makers,
 And we are the dreamers of dreams,
Wandering by lone sea-breakers,
 And sitting by desolate streams;
World-losers and world-forsakers,   5
 On whom the pale moon gleams:
Yet we are the movers and shakers
 Of the world for ever, it seems.
With wonderful deathless ditties
We build up the world's great cities,   10
 And out of a fabulous story
 We fashion an empire's glory.
One man with a dream, at pleasure,
 Shall go forth and conquer a crown;
And three with a new song's measure   15
 Can trample an empire down.

We, in the ages lying
 In the buried past of the earth,
Built Nineveh with our sighing,
 And Babel itself with our mirth;   20
And o'erthrew them with prophesying
 To the old of the new world's worth;
For each age is a dream that is dying,
 Or one that is coming to birth.

17. *Momus:* god of mockery and fault finding.
9. *ditties:* songs. 19. *Nineveh and Babel* (Babylon): capital cities of ancient empires.

HOW SLEEP THE BRAVE

William Collins (England)

This poem was written to express England's tribute to the soldiers and sailors who had died in the struggle with France for possession of her colonies.

❈　❈　❈

How sleep the brave who sink to rest
By all their country's wishes blest!
When Spring, with dewy fingers cold,
Returns to deck their hallow'd mold,
She there shall dress a sweeter sod   5
Than Fancy's feet have ever trod.

By fairy hands their knell is rung,
By forms unseen their dirge is sung;
There Honour comes, a pilgrim grey,
To bless the turf that wraps their clay;   10
And Freedom shall awhile repair,
To dwell a weeping hermit there!

MESSAGE TO SIBERIA

Alexander Pushkin (Russia)

Translated by Max Eastman

The Tsars of old Russia exiled to penal colonies in Siberia those who rebelled against their tyranny and sought to change the form of the Russian government.

❈　❈　❈

Deep in the Siberian mine,
Keep your patience proud;
The bitter toil shall not be lost,
The rebel thought unbowed.

The sister of misfortune, Hope,   5
In the under-darkness dumb
Speaks joyful courage to your heart:
The day desired will come.

And love and friendship pour to you
Across the darkened doors, 10
Even as round your galley-beds
My free music pours.

The heavy-hanging chains will fall,
The walls will crumble at a word;
And Freedom greet you in the light, 15
And brothers give you back the sword.

ODE TO FANCY

John Keats (England)

Ever let the Fancy roam;
Pleasure never is at home:
At a touch sweet Pleasure melteth,
Like to bubbles when rain pelteth;
Then let wingèd Fancy wander 5
Through the thought still spread beyond her:
Open wide the mind's cage-door,
She'll dart forth, and cloudward soar.
O sweet Fancy! let her loose;
Summer's joys are spoilt by use, 10
And the enjoying of the Spring
Fades as does its blossoming;
Autumn's red-lipp'd fruitage too,
Blushing through the mist and dew,
Cloys with tasting. What do then? 15
Sit thee by the ingle, when
The sear faggot blazes bright,
Spirit of a winter's night;
When the soundless earth is muffled,
And the cakèd snow is shuffled 20
From the ploughboy's heavy shoon;
When the Night doth meet the Noon
In a dark conspiracy
To banish Even from her sky.
Sit thee there, and send abroad, 25
With a mind self-overaw'd,
Fancy, high-commission'd:—send her!
She has vassals to attend her.

She will bring, in spite of frost,
Beauties that the earth hath lost.
She will bring thee, all together,
All delights of summer weather;
All the buds and bells of May,
From dewy sward or thorny spray;
All the heapèd Autumn's wealth,
With a still, mysterious stealth.
She will mix these pleasures up
Like three fit wines in a cup,
And thou shalt quaff it :—thou shalt hear
Distant harvest-carols clear;
Rustle of the reapèd corn;
Sweet birds antheming the morn;
And, in the same moment—hark!
'Tis the early April lark,
Or the rooks, with busy caw,
Foraging for sticks and straw.
Thou shalt, at one glance, behold
The daisy and the marigold;
White-plumed lilies, and the first
Hedge-grown primrose that hath burst;
Shaded hyacinth, alway
Sapphire queen of the mid-May;
And every leaf, and every flower
Pearlèd with the self-same shower.
Thou shalt see the field-mouse peep
Meagre from its cellèd sleep;
And the snake all winter-thin
Cast on sunny bank its skin;
Freckled nest-eggs thou shalt see
Hatching in the hawthorn-tree,
When the hen-bird's wing doth rest
Quiet on her mossy nest;
Then the hurry and alarm
When the bee-hive casts its swarm;
Acorns ripe down-pattering,
While the autumn breezes sing.

Oh, sweet Fancy! let her loose;
Everything is spoilt by use:
Where's the cheek that doth not fade,
Too much gazed at? Where's the maid

30

35

40

45

50

55

60

65

70

Whose lip mature is ever new?
Where's the eye, however blue,
Doth not weary? Where's the face
One would meet in every place?
Where's the voice, however soft,   75
One would hear so very oft?
At a touch sweet Pleasure melteth
Like to bubbles when rain pelteth.
Let then wingèd Fancy find
Thee a mistress to thy mind: 80
Dulcet-eyed as Ceres' daughter,
Ere the God of Torment taught her
How to frown and how to chide;
With a waist and with a side
White as Hebe's, when her zone   85
Slipt its golden clasp, and down
Fell her kirtle to her feet,
While she held the goblet sweet,
And Jove grew languid.—Break the mesh
Of the Fancy's silken leash;   90
Quickly break her prison-string,
And such joys as these she'll bring.
—Let the wingèd Fancy roam,
Pleasure never is at home.

TO AUTUMN

JOHN KEATS (ENGLAND)

Season of mists and mellow fruitfulness,
    Close bosom-friend of the maturing sun;
Conspiring with him how to load and bless
    With fruit the vines that round the thatch-eaves run;
To bend with apples the mossed cottage-trees,   5
    And fill all fruit with ripeness to the core;
    To swell the gourd, and plump the hazel shells
With a sweet kernel; to set budding more,
    And still more, later flowers for the bees,
    Until they think warm days will never cease,   10
    For Summer has o'er-brimmed their clammy cells.

Who hath not seen thee oft amid thy store?
  Sometimes whoever seeks abroad may find
Thee sitting careless on a granary floor,
  Thy hair soft-lifted by the winnowing wind;   15
Or on a half-reaped furrow sound asleep,
  Drowsed with the fume of poppies, while thy hook
    Spares the next swath and all its twinèd flowers:
And sometimes like a gleaner thou dost keep
  Steady thy laden head across a brook;   20
Or by a cider-press, with patient look,
    Thou watchest the last oozings hours by hours.

Where are the songs of Spring? Ay, where are they?
  Think not of them, thou hast thy music too,—
While barrèd clouds bloom the soft-dying day,   25
  And touch the stubble-plains with rosy hue;
Then in a wailful choir the small gnats mourn
  Among the river sallows, borne aloft
    Or sinking as the light wind lives or dies;
And full-grown lambs loud bleat from hilly bourn;   30
  Hedge-crickets sing; and now with treble soft
  The red-breast whistles from a garden-croft;
    And gathering swallows twitter in the skies.

ON HIS DAUGHTER'S MARRIAGE

Giosuè Carducci (Italy)

Translated by Lois Saunders

Tuscan mountains, and you, O peaceful woodlands of olive,
Under whose shade I have stood, silent in love's happy visions;
Golden harvest, and vines with your bursting grapes grown purple
In the warm sunlight, amid gay peals of joyous laughter;

Sun of my youthful years, smile on the innocent maiden,   5
Torn from my arms by love, a bride 'neath the Tuscan heavens.
Smile thou upon her, and all that fate has ever denied me
Grant to her, giving her peace in her heart's deep affections.

32. *croft:* enclosed piece of ground.

Hush! breathe it not, O ye hills, and whisper it not, O ye olives!
Tell it not, kindly sun, though thou all seeing, well knowest   10
That on the far side of yon hill, lie, perchance awaiting her coming,
My dear ones, who lived in sadness, and perished in sorrow.

Earnestly upward she gazes, she feels in her bosom
Thrill the throbbing of life, while a subtle air breathes in her tresses,
While the breath of the hills, as the sun is setting around her,   15
Stirs on her girlish head the snow-white veil that enfolds her.

READING PROBLEMS ON THE ODE

1. *To Alcimedon and Timosthenes:* Is the Greek attitude toward athletics different from ours in any way? From whom was athletic skill supposed to come? What type of athlete would the Greek gods permit to win? Do you agree with Pindar's definition of a good coach?

2. *The Golden Mean:* What principles for the conduct of a successful life does Horace lay down? Horace proposed as one test of literary style "Multum in parvo"—which means much in little. What image in this poem best illustrates this principle?

3. *On Shakespeare:* What is the livelong monument Shakespeare has built himself? How does he "make us marble?"

4. *The Maid of Orleans:* Why does the base man sneer at goodness and greatness, and exult at their downfall? What does Schiller think is likely to be the only reward of greatness during one's own lifetime?

5. *The Poets:* What contribution does O'Shaughnessy think poets make to progress? Is this an important one? At what cost to themselves do poets make this contribution? (See lines 5–8.)

6. *How Sleep the Brave:* What reward does the soldier reap for his patriotic devotion? Why does the poet personify Honor and Freedom as mourners at his grave?

7. *Message to Siberia:* What does Pushkin offer to martyrs to a cause as their great reward? Does he necessarily mean by the last stanza that the particular prisoners he addresses will be freed?

8. *Ode to Fancy:* In what way can the mind triumph over time and circumstance? Select word pictures from this poem that prove Keats' keen observation. Do you agree that Fancy "never is at home"?

9. *To Autumn:* Select from this poem lines which give clear pictures; which give the autumn feeling; which are especially musical. Find mentioned details of color, scent, taste, sound. To whom is stanza 2 addressed?

10. *On His Daughter's Marriage:* Where is the wedding ceremony held? Why does the poet address the sun, the mountains, the olive groves? How is this poem typical of the feeling of loving age toward youth?

FURTHER READINGS IN THE ODE

Block: *Russia*
Coleridge: *Ode to France*
Dryden: *Ode for Saint Cecelia's Day*
Heine: *Gold*
Horace: *Book One:* Odes 14, 22, 37
       Book Two: Ode 11
       Book Three: Odes 1, 13, 29
Housman: *On an Athlete Dying Young*
Lowell: *Commemoration Ode*
Shelley: *To the West Wind*
Tennyson: *On the Death of the Duke of Wellington*
Van Dyke: *God of the Open Air*
Wordsworth: *Ode to Duty*

SUGGESTIONS FOR ORIGINAL ODES

1. To Our Alumnæ. 2. To the Graduating Class. 3. To Our Football Team. 4. To a Modern Athlete. 5. To a Public Benefactor. 6. To a Violin. 7. To My Weekly Allowance.

XV

The Elegy

AN ELEGY expresses grief for the death of someone dear either to the poet himself or to the general public. The most beautiful of all elegies were written by the ancient Greeks, and strangely enough, their brevity and reticence impress the reader more than the lengthy brilliance of many a great modern. The Greek elegiac poet lets his subject speak for itself. It is, indeed, a subject for which words are inadequate. Music comes nearer to embodying the grief, the hope, the faith which alternate in our hearts as the shadow of bereavement falls upon us; and the greatest of all elegies are musical. But some of the noblest poems in every tongue also deal with this subject. They are noble not only in the profundity of the grief expressed but in their triumph through faith, hope, duty, or endurance over the spiritual prostration and despair which follows loss.

First among the selections quoted below are five poems from the *Greek Anthology*,[1] a collection made in Grecian days of the best short works of Greek lyric poets. Many of these poems are epitaphs written with the restraint and simplicity characteristic of Greek art.

ON THE SPARTANS WHO FELL AT THERMOPYLAE

SIMONIDES (GREECE)

> Tell at Sparta, passerby,
> Here at her command we lie.

[1] *Anthology:* this word in Greek meant a garland. A collection of fine poems was beautifully named a garland of verse.

Title. *Thermopylae:* this was a mountain pass in northern Greece where a Greek rear guard of 300 Spartans held at bay an invading army of Persians. Only when 299 of these Spartans lay dead in the pass could the Persians advance. But meanwhile Greece had had time to gather an army for defense.

PARMENIO (GREECE)

Translated by J. W. Mackail

Him, who over changed paths of earth and
sea sailed on the mainland and went afoot
upon the deep, Spartan valor held back on
three hundred spears; be ashamed, O mountains and seas.

ON A SINGING GIRL

ANONYMOUS (GREECE)

Translated by J. W. Mackail

Blue-eyed Musa, the sweet-voiced nightingale, suddenly this little grave holds voiceless, and she lies like a stone who was so
accomplished and so famous. Fair Musa, be
this dust light over thee.

THOU LIEST DEAD

SAPPHO (GREECE)

Translated by Sir Edwin Arnold

Thou liest dead, and there will be no memory left behind
Of thee or thine in all the earth, for never didst thou bind
The roses of Pierian streams upon thy brow; thy doom
Is writ to flit with unknown ghosts in cold and nameless gloom.

TO HELIODORA

MELEAGER (GREECE)

Translated by F. A. Wright

My Heliodora, in the earth beneath
 Tears still to thee I send;
Poor relics of my heart, a gift to Death,
 From love that knows no end.

3. *Pierian streams:* a river whose source was the fountain from which the Muses
drank. The meaning is that the dead friend is not a poet whose fame might have
survived him.

With tender offerings to thy grave I come;
  My tears libations make;
My longing eyes gaze fondly on thy tomb
  For our dear love's dear sake.

Useless my gifts, my anguish and my pain;
  In death thou dost abide.
Thy Meleager cries, and cries in vain
  By that dark river side.

Ah me, ah me! where's now the cherished flower,
  That His fierce fingers crushed?
The blossom scarce had reached perfection's hour;
  He cast it in the dust.

Kind earth, all mother, on my knees I pray,
  Guard her whom still I weep;
Her gentle body on thy bosom lay,
  And let her softly sleep.

ON THE POET'S WIFE

NIBI (JAPAN)

Translated by Basil H. Chamberlain

Like to the stream that finds
The downward path it never may retrace,
Like to the shapeless winds,
Poor mortals pass away without a trace.
So she I love has left her place,
And, in a corner of my widowed couch,
Wrapp'd in the robe she wove me, I must crouch
Far from her fond embrace.

LADIES OF YESTER-YEAR

FRANÇOIS VILLON (FRANCE)

Translated by Dante Gabriel Rossetti

François Villon—friend of king and beggar—was a vagabond poet
of the fifteenth century, whose adventures and hairbreadth escapes
have been dramatized in a play called *If I Were King* and in an

6. *libation:* an offering of wine poured out for the gods.

operetta, *The Vagabond King,* the first successful musical motion picture.

The identity of the lovely ladies of yester-year listed by Villon is a matter of little importance. Except for two figures from classical mythology (Flora and Echo) and two real Greek women (Hipparchia and Thaïs—the latter the beloved of Alexander the Great), they are all drawn from medieval France. Though Bertha was the mother of Charlemagne and Blanche the mother of Saint Louis, only two of these once famous ladies have left any real mark on history or legend —Héloïse and Joan of Arc. But the recital of their names carries with it the mystery and romance of vanished yesterdays—days when they were young and fair, loving and beloved.

The form of the poem is that of the French ballade, with its three stanzas and an envoy at the end, its intricate rhyme scheme, and its recurrent refrain—all of which the poet-translator has accurately reproduced.

❊ ❊ ❊

Tell me now in what hidden way is
    Lady Flora the lovely Roman?
Where Hipparchia, and where is Thaïs,
    Neither of them the fairer woman?
    Where is Echo, beheld of no man,   5
Only heard on river and mere,—
    She whose beauty was more than human?
But where are the snows of yester-year?

Where's Héloïse, the learned nun,
    For whose sake Abeillard, I ween,   10
Lost manhood and put priesthood on?
    (From love he won such dule and teen!)
    And, where I pray you is the Queen
Who willed that Buridan should steer
    Sewed in a sack's mouth down the Seine? . . .   15
But where are the snows of yester-year?

White Queen Blanche, like a queen of lilies,
    With a voice like any mermaiden,—
Bertha Broadfoot, Beatrice, Alice,
    And Ermengarde the lady of Maine,—   20
    And that good Joan whom Englishmen
At Rouen doomed and burned her there,
    Mother of God, where are they then? . . .
But where are the snows of yester-year?

6. *mere:* lake. 12. *dule and teen:* grief and trouble.

Nay, never ask this week, fair lord,   25
 Where they are gone, nor yet this year,
Except with this for an overword,—
 But where are the snows of yester-year?

HIGHLAND MARY

Robert Burns (Scotland)

Ye banks, and braes, and streams around
 The castle o' Montgomery,
Green be your woods, and fair your flowers,
 Your waters never drumlie!
There Summer first unfald her robes,   5
 And there the langest tarry;
For there I took the last fareweell
 O' my sweet Highland Mary.

How sweetly bloomed the gay green birk
 How rich the hawthorn's blossom,   10
As underneath their fragrant shade
 I clasped her to my bosom!
The golden hours on angel wings
 Flew o'er me and my dearie;
For dear to me as light and life   15
 Was my sweet Highland Mary.

Wi' monie a vow, and locked embrace,
 Our parting was fu' tender;
And, pledging aft to meet again,
 We tore oursels asunder;   20
But O, fell death's untimely frost,
 That nipped my flower sae early!
Now green's the sod, and cauld's the clay,
 That wraps my Highland Mary!

O pale, pale now, those rosy lips,   25
 I aft hae kissed sae fondly!
And closed for aye the sparkling glance
 That dwelt on me sae kindly!

4. *drumlie:* muddy. 5. *unfald:* unfold. 9. *birk:* birch.

And mould'ring now in silent dust
  That heart that lo'ed me dearly!
But still within my bosom's core
  Shall live my Highland Mary.

ENSHRINED WITHIN THIS HEART

Antonín Sova (Czechoslovakia)

Translated by Libuse Breuer Scholten

Your home is all enshrined within this heart of mine . . .
I see a hill, as on this sprig of dwarfèd pine
I gaze,—a path, and wooded gorge; I hear again
The echoes there—and all this nearness brings me pain.
These bellflowers, withered now, were wont to peal   5
As evening from the silence of the stars did steal.
I kiss the humble daisy from the fallow land
Where home gleamed through the dusk, while we walked hand
    in hand.
Upon the arbor wall this yellow-gray moss grew,
Where in the fragrance of the rose I rested oft with you.   10
And from the weeping willow tree I plucked this leaf,
Where o'er your sun-flecked grave it stands so mute with grief.

FOR HER BROTHER

Tumadir Al-Khansa (Arabia)

Translated by E. Powys Mathers

Weep, weep, weep!
These tears are for my brother.
Henceforth that veil which lies between us,
That recent earth,
Shall not be lifted again.
You have gone down to the bitter water   5
Which all must taste,
And you went pure, saying:
"Life is a buzz of hornets about a lance point."

But my heart remembers, O son of my father and mother,   10
I wither like summer grass,
I shut myself in the tent of consternation.

He is dead, who was the buckler of our tribe
And the foundation of our house,
He has departed in calamity.   15

He is dead, who was the lighthouse of courageous men,
Who was for the brave
As fires lighted upon the mountains.

He is dead, who rode costly horses,
Shining in his garments.   20
The hero of the long shoulder belt is dead.
The young man of valiance and beauty breathes no more;
The right hand of generosity is withered,
And the beardless king of our tribe shall breathe no more.

He shall be cold beneath his rock.   25

Say to his mare Alwa
That she must weep
As she runs riderless for ever. . . .

When the red millstone ground the flowers of youth,
You shattered a thousand horses against the squadrons;   30
High on the groaning flanks of Alwa
You lifted the bright skirts of your silver mail.

How effortless were your rhymes of combat
Chanted in tumult, O my brother!
They pierced like lances,   35
They live among our hearts for ever.

Let the stars go out,
Let the sun withdraw his rays;
He was our star and sun.

Who now will gather in the strangers at dusk   40
When the sad North whistles with her winds?
You have laid down and left in the dust, O wanderers,
Him who nourished you with his flocks
And bared his sword for your salvation.
He lies among the tombs of our fathers,   45
Where the days and the years shall pass over him.

While you have tears, O daughters of the Solomides,
Weep! Weep! Weep!

LAMENT OF A FATHER FOR HIS SON

PAIUTE INDIAN (AMERICA)

Son, my son!
I will go up to the mountain
And there I will light a fire
To the feet of my son's spirit,
And there will I lament him;   5
Saying,
O my son,
What is my life to me, now you are departed?
Son, my son,
In the deep earth   10
We softly laid thee
In a chief's robe,
In a warrior's gear.
Surely there,
In the spirit land   15
Thy deeds attend thee!
Surely,
The corn comes to the ear again!
But I, here,
I am the stalk that the seed-gatherers   20
Descrying empty, afar, left standing.
Son, my son!
What is my life to me, now you are departed?

IN MEMORIAM

ALFRED TENNYSON (ENGLAND)

Tennyson's most intimate college friend—a young man of great promise whom many expected to become the leading statesman of England—died just after graduation during a European tour. Tennyson wrote a long poem expressing his grief, doubts, and questions after his death. From this poem, *In Memoriam,* come the following stanzas expressing his faith that death is not the end of life.

❊ ❊ ❊

Thy voice is on the rolling air;
   I hear thee where the waters run;
   Thou standest in the rising sun,
And in the setting thou art fair.

What art thou then? I cannot guess;   5
   But tho' I seem in star and flower
   To feel thee some diffusive power,
I do not therefore love thee less.

My love involves the love before;
   My love is vaster passion now;   10
   Tho' mix'd with God and Nature thou,
I seem to love thee more and more.

Far off thou art, but ever nigh;
   I have thee still, and I rejoice;
   I prosper, circled with thy voice;   15
I shall not lose thee tho' I die.

THE MASTER

EDWIN ARLINGTON ROBINSON (AMERICA)

The following poem is a tribute to and analysis of the character of a great leader—Abraham Lincoln.

❊ ❊ ❊

A flying word from here and there
Had sown the name at which we sneered,
But soon the name was everywhere,
To be reviled and then revered:

A presence to be loved and feared,
We cannot hide it, or deny
That we, the gentlemen who jeered,
May be forgotten by and by.   5

He came when days were perilous
And hearts of men were sore beguiled;
And having made his note of us,   10
He pondered and was reconciled.
Was ever master yet so mild
As he, and so untamable?
We doubted, even when he smiled,   15
Not knowing what he knew so well.

He knew that undeceiving fate
Would shame us whom he served unsought;
He knew that he must wince and wait—
The jest of those for whom he fought;   20
He knew devoutly what he thought
Of us and of our ridicule;
He knew that we must all be taught
Like little children in a school.

We gave a glamor to the task   25
That he encountered and saw through,
But little of us did he ask,
And little did we ever do.
And what appears if we review
The season when we railed and chaffed?   30
It is the face of one who knew
That we were learning while we laughed.

The face that in our vision feels
Again the venom that we flung,
Transfigured to the world reveals   35
The vigilance to which we clung.
Shrewd, hallowed, harassed, and among
The mysteries that are untold,
The face we see was never young,
Nor could it wholly have been old.   40

For he, to whom we had applied
Our shopman's test of age and worth,
Was elemental when he died,
As he was ancient at his birth:
The saddest among kings of earth,   45
Bowed with a galling crown, this man
Met rancor with a cryptic mirth,
Laconic—and Olympian.

The love, the grandeur, and the fame
Are bounded by the world alone;   50
The calm, the smoldering, and the flame
Of awful patience were his own:
With him they are forever flown
Past all our fond self-shadowings,
Wherewith we cumber the Unknown   55
As with inept, Icarian wings.

For we were not as other men:
'Twas ours to soar and his to see.
But we are coming down again,
And we shall come down pleasantly;   60
Nor shall we longer disagree
On what it is to be sublime,
But flourish in our perigee
And have one Titan at a time.

THE KNIGHT'S TOMB

Samuel Taylor Coleridge (England)

Where is the grave of Sir Arthur O'Kellyn?
Where may the grave of that good man be?—
By the side of a spring, on the breast of Helvellyn,
Under the twigs of a young birch tree!

47. *cryptic:* concealing its meaning. 48. *Laconic:* saying little. 56. *Icarian:* Icarus tried to fly on wings of wax and feathers. He flew too near the sun, which melted his wings, and he fell into the sea and was drowned. 63. *perigee:* the point in the orbit of a planet when it is nearest to the earth. 64. *Titan:* giant.

3. *Helvellyn:* a mountain peak among the English lakes.

The oak that in summer was sweet to hear,   5
And rustled its leaves in the fall of the year,
And whistled and roared in the winter alone,
Is gone—and the birch in its stead is grown—
The Knights' bones are dust,
And his good sword rust—   10
His soul is with the saints, I trust.

FROM AN AFTERNOON CALLER

Sister M. Madeleva (America)

I called at your
New house today
To hear the words
You do not say;

To watch the eyes   5
I cannot see,
The hands you do not
Give to me.

I waited there
A quiet while   10
In the lost wonder
Of your smile,

And found a home
Austere and new
That has enshrined   15
And hallowed you.

I love this house
Where you are dead.
Your new grave leaves me
Comforted.   20

GEORGE GRAY

Edgar Lee Masters (America)

The Spoon River Anthology is a volume of epitaphs supposedly composed for themselves after death by the dead who sleep in the cemetery on the hill in the town of Spoon River.[1] One of the epitaphs is quoted below.

❊   ❊   ❊

I have studied many times
The marble which was chiseled for me—
A boat with a furled sail at rest in a harbor.
In truth it pictures not my destination
But my life.   5
For love was offered me and I shrank from its disillusionment;
Sorrow knocked at my door but I was afraid;
Ambition called to me but I dreaded the chances.
Yet all the while I hungered for meaning in my life.
And now I know that we must lift the sail   10
And catch the winds of destiny
Wherever they drive the boat.
To put meaning in one's life may end in madness,
But life without meaning is the torture
Of restlessness and vague desire—   15
It is a boat longing for the sea and yet afraid.

THE LAST INVOCATION

Walt Whitman (America)

At the last, tenderly,
From the walls of the powerful, fortressed house,
From the clasp of the knitted locks—from the keep of the well-
    closed doors,
Let me be wafted.

[1] *Spoon River:* a thinly veiled reference to Lewiston, Illinois, where the poet lived for many years. The names in the poem—if not the characters—are fictitious.

Let me glide noiselessly forth;
With the key of softness unlock the locks—with a whisper
Set ope the doors, O Soul!

Tenderly! be not impatient!
(Strong is your hold, O mortal flesh!
Strong is your hold, O love.)   10

READING PROBLEMS ON THE ELEGY

1. *On the Spartans Who Fell at Thermopylæ:* Which epitaph do you prefer and why?

2. *On a Singing Girl* and *Thou Liest Dead:* What idea we associate with death seldom appears in a Greep epitaph? Upon what idea is each epitaph centered?

3. *To Heliodora:* How does this poem differ from the preceding epitaphs? Select from this poem the finest lines and tell why you select them.

4. *On the Poet's Wife:* Do lines 5–8 or lines 1–4 give you the deeper sense of grief? Would either passage be as effective alone? Why?

5. *Ladies of Yester-Year:* How does the structure and verse form of this poem contribute to its dreamy charm? What in particular is the effect of the repeated refrain? Why is the thought of the refrain so well embodied in its image?

6. *Highland Mary* and *Enshrined Within This Heart:* To what have the bereaved lovers partly transferred their affection? Why? Why does the scene of their last meetings seem a fitting shrine for their memories?

7. *For Her Brother:* Upon what idea is the mourner centered in this poem? Does she think merely of her own feelings? In how many ways is the greatness of her brother's loss brought out?

8. *Lament of a Father for His Son:* Explain lines 12–17. What do lines 18–20 add to the idea of lines 7 and 22?

9. *In Memoriam:* Where does Tennyson still feel the presence of his friend? Is this what immortality means to you?

10. *The Master:* This poem packs a great deal of meaning into each line. Go over it sentence by sentence, putting each statement in your own words or giving illustrations for each point made. Summarize in single sentences what the attitude toward Lincoln of his contemporaries was; what his attitude toward them was; and what Robinson's general idea of Lincoln now is. Compare this poem and French's statue of Lincoln in the Washington Memorial. (Look at both sides of the face.)

11. *The Knight's Tomb:* In what ways does Coleridge give us the sense of romantic antiquity in this poem?

Title. *Invocation:* calling or summoning.

12. *From an Afternoon Caller:* What comfort does her visit to the grave bring to the author? Explain why she uses this seemingly light and casual title.

13. *George Gray:* Sum up in one word the flaw in George Gray's character. How can we give our lives meaning? This poem is in so-called "free verse." How does its rhythm differ from that of ordinary poetry? See also *The Last Invocation* for this point.

14. *The Last Invocation:* What are the house, the locks, the doors, the key? What forces hold the soul to earth, according to Whitman? In what mood does Whitman face death? Compare with *The Death of Socrates* (pages 917–920.)

FURTHER READINGS IN THE ELEGY

Allen: *Rock Me to Sleep*
Antipater: *To Anacreon*
Arnold: *Requiescat*
R. Browning: *Evelyn Hope*
E. B. Browning: *To Flush, My Dog*
Catullus: *Through Many a Region Borne*
Finch: *The Blue and the Gray*
Gray: *Elegy Written in a Country Churchyard*
Goldsmith: *Elegy on a Mad Dog*
Millay: *Elegy*
Milton: *Lycidas*
Shelley: *Adonais*
Shakespeare: *Fear No More the Heat of the Sun*
Wolf: *Burial of Sir John Moore*

SUGGESTIONS FOR ORIGINAL ELEGIES

1. To a Lost Pet. 2. To a Deceased Teacher. 3. To Workmen Who Have Died in Building Our Skyscrapers. 4. To the Victims of Speed. 5. To All Those Lost in Some Great Catastrophe (like a flood). 6. To Law Enforcement Officers Who Die in Pursuit of Duty.

XVI

The Letter

ALL of us have written that half narrative type of essay called a letter, in which we tell the news and air our views. And all of us have rejoiced at receiving diverting and stimulating letters from others. In a letter, the writer is very plainly and definitely talking to his correspondent; the writing is merely a means of carrying his voice. Therefore the charm of a letter is the charm of all good conversation, though in a letter the talk is more deliberate and considered than in a face-to-face exchange of ideas.

The secret of successful letter writing is to give one's correspondent a feeling of actually being present with the letter writer in the scenes and events described and of actually hearing his voice utter the thoughts and feelings expressed. Thus the first principle is a natural, intimate style, and the second a gift of quick picturization. The good letter writer selects from his own experience the details that will most truly portray his life and most keenly interest his correspondent; and he does not just give this news, but comments on it, letting his mind play over the facts presented and touch them with hilarity, pathos, satire, reflection, or argument, as the case may be. "Do you find," asks Lowell of one of his friends, "do you find the real inside of him in his letters? This is a pretty sure test." Yet we expect, too, a certain considerate and well-bred reserve which passes lightly over the disagreeable, painful, and annoying, and takes refuge from them in the charming surface of life.

Though we have records of earlier epistolary communications, the history of letter writing as a literary art begins with the seventeenth and eighteenth centuries when the appetite for news was awakening yet there were no newspapers to satisfy it, and when Madame de Sévigné, the Earl of Chesterfield, and Sir Horace Walpole described in letters the dazzling spectacle of that age of elegance. Of Walpole's letters, Thackeray writes: "Fiddles sigh all through them; wax lights, fine dress, fine jokes, fine plate, fine coaches, glitter and sparkle there." No less interesting were the letters in which the revolutionary spirits of the early nineteenth century like Byron and Shelley poured forth their criticisms of society and their dreams of reform. Even the business letters of men like Sherman and Lincoln bring to us a more intimate view of their greatness. And entertaining beyond all others are the later letters of Sydney Smith, the droll bishop; Edward Lear, who invented nonsense verse; Thackeray who satirized shams and pretences with such inimitable irony: or Edward Fitzgerald, country gentleman, yachtsman, and translator of the Persian *Rubáiyát*, who conveyed into letters the flavor of his rarely sensitive and imaginative views of nature, people, and books. It is from the fun of catching these unusual people off guard and simply themselves that the delight in reading their letters arises. For they are delightful people, and it is delightful people who write delightful letters.

THE ERUPTION OF VESUVIUS

Pliny the Younger (Rome)

Pliny the Elder, a Roman traveller and scientist, lost his life in studying at close hand the eruption of Vesuvius which buried beneath ashes and lava Pompeii and Herculaneum—two cities which have recently been excavated and which form a complete museum of ancient Roman life. Pliny's nephew here gives his own view of the same eruption to the famous Roman historian, Cornelius Tacitus.

❋ ❋ ❋

The letter which, in compliance with your request, I wrote to you concerning the death of my uncle has raised, it seems, your curiosity to know what terrors and dangers attended me while I continued at Misenum; for there, I think, my account broke off.

"Though my shock'd soul recoils, my tongue shall tell." My uncle having left us, I spent such time as was left on my studies (it was on their account indeed, that I had stopped behind), till it was time for my bath. After which I went to supper, and then fell into a short and uneasy sleep. There had been noticed for many days before a trembling of the earth, which did not alarm us much, as this is quite an ordinary occurrence in Campania; but it was so particularly violent that night that it not only shook but actually overturned, as it would seem, everything about us.

My mother rushed into my chamber, where she found me rising, in order to awaken her. We sat down in the open court of the house, which occupied a small space between the buildings and the sea. As I was at that time but eighteen years of age, I know not whether I should call my behavior, in this dangerous juncture, courage or folly; but I took up Livy, and amused myself with turning over that author, and even making extracts from him, as if I had been perfectly at my leisure. Just then, a friend of my uncle's, who had lately come to him from Spain, joined us, and observing me sitting by my mother with a book in my hand, reproved her for her calmness, and me at the same time for my careless security: nevertheless I went on with my author.

Though it was now morning, the light was exceedingly faint and doubtful; the buildings all around us tottered, and though we stood upon open ground, yet as the place was narrow and confined, there was no remaining without imminent danger; we therefore resolved to quit the town. A panic-stricken crowd followed us, and pressed on us in dense array to drive us forward as we came out. Being at a convenient distance from the houses, we stood still, in the midst of a most dangerous and dreadful scene.

The chariots, which we had ordered to be drawn out, were so agitated backwards and forwards though upon the most level ground, that we could not keep them steady, even by supporting them with large stones. The sea seemed to roll back upon itself, and to be driven from its banks by the convulsive motion of the earth; the shore was considerably enlarged, and several sea animals were left upon it. On the other side, a black and dreadful cloud, broken with rapid, zigzag flashes, revealed behind it variously shaped masses of flame: these last were like sheet-lightning, but much larger.

Upon this our Spanish friend, whom I mentioned above, addressed himself to my mother and me with great energy and urgency: "If your brother, if your uncle be safe, he certainly wishes you may be so too; but if he perished, it was his desire, no doubt, that you might both survive him: why therefore do you delay your escape a moment?" "We could never think of our own safety," we said, "while uncertain of his." Upon this our friend left us, and withdrew from the danger with the utmost precipitation.

Soon afterwards, the cloud began to descend, and cover the sea. It had already surrounded and concealed the island of Capreæ and the promontory of Misenum. My mother now besought, urged, even commanded me to make my escape, at any rate, which, as I was young, I might easily do; as for herself, she said, her age rendered all attempts of that sort impossible; however, she would willingly meet death if she could have the satisfaction of seeing that she was not the occasion of mine. But I absolutely refused to leave her, and, taking her by the hand, compelled her to go with me. She complied with great reluctance, and not without reproaches to herself for retarding my flight.

The ashes now began to fall upon us, though in no great quantity. I looked back; a dense dark mist seemed to be following us, spreading itself over the country like a cloud. "Let us turn out of the highroad," I said, "while we can still see, for fear that, should we fall in the road, we should be pressed to death in the dark, by the crowds that are following us." We had scarcely sat down when night came upon us, not such as we have when the sky is cloudy, or when there is no moon, but that of a room when it is shut up, and all the lights put out. You might hear the shrieks of women, the screams of children, and the shouts of men; some calling for their children, others for their parents, others for their husbands, and seeking to recognize each other by the voices that replied; one lamenting his own fate, another that of his family; some wishing to die, from the very fear of dying; some lifting their hands to the gods; but the greater part convinced that there were now no gods at all, and that the final endless night of which we have heard had come upon the world.

It now grew lighter, which we imagined to be rather the forerunner of an approaching burst of flames (as in truth it was) than the return of day: however, the fire fell at a distance from us: then again we were immersed in thick darkness, and a heavy shower of ashes rained upon us, which we were obliged every now and then to stand up to shake off, otherwise we should have been crushed and buried in the heap.

I might boast that, during all this scene of horror, not a sigh, or expression of fear, escaped me, had not my support been grounded in that miserable, though mighty, consolation, that all mankind were involved in the same calamity, and that I was perishing with the world itself. At last this dreadful darkness was dissipated by degrees, like a cloud of smoke; the real day returned, and even the sun shone out, though with a lurid light, as when an eclipse is coming on. Every object that presented itself to our eyes (which were extremely weakened) seemed changed, being covered deep with ashes as if with snow. We returned to Misenum, where we refreshed ourselves as well as we could, and passed an anxious night between hope and fear; though, indeed, with a much larger share of the latter: for the earthquake still continued, while many frenzied persons ran up and down heightening their own and their friends' calamities by terrible predictions. However, my mother and I, notwithstanding the danger we had passed, and that still threatened us, had no thoughts of leaving the place, till we could receive some news of my uncle.

And now, you will read this narrative without any view of inserting it in your history, of which it is not in the least worthy; and indeed you must put it down to your own request if it should appear not worth even the trouble of a letter. Farewell.

IN THE COUNTRY

MADAME DE SÉVIGNÉ (FRANCE)

It is interesting to see this clever, wealthy, titled lady—friend of kings and wits—withdrawing herself twice a year from the splendors of Paris in the days of the Grand Monarch, Louis XIV, to improve her country estate and enjoy the beauties of nature. Like all the best letters of this indefatigable correspondent, the following are addressed to her daughter, whose marriage had taken her to Provence.

❊   ❊   ❊

LES ROCHERS.[1] September 29—October 2, 1675

I found my woods perfectly beautiful and full of leafy gloom; the trees which were so little when you saw them last are all grown very large, beautiful and flourishing; they have been trimmed, and now form a delightful shade; they are between forty and fifty feet high: do not you see something of a mother's fondness in this minute detail? Consider I planted them myself, and have tended them *when they were no higher than this,* as M. de Monbason says of his children. It is a retreat formed expressly for meditation. I am persuaded you would make the most of it, were you here: I think of you at every step, I regret your absence, I languish for your company. . . . These walks have a beauty, a tranquillity, a repose, a silence, to which I cannot yet accustom myself.

November 10-13

We have a little summer in autumn, cold but pleasant. I live abroad like a wild creature. . . . I take long walks. As I am

[1] *Les Rochers:* The Rocks, Madame de Sévigné's country estate in Brittany.

unacquainted with the use of an arm chair, I repose *mea corporea falma* [3] in my shady avenues, where I pass the day attended by a footman, and do not return till the night is well shut in, and the fire and tapers make the room cheerful. I cannot bear this time of year, when the evenings are neither long nor short, unless I have someone to talk to; and I am better pleased with being alone in the woods than alone in a room.

May 27, 1680

I was yesterday at Buron, and returned from thence this evening. I have been ready to weep at the desolation of this estate; [4] there were the finest trees in the world upon it, and my son, in his last journey, gave them the finishing stroke. He would have even sold a little copse, which was the finishing ornament of the place. Is this not lamentable? He scraped together in this way four hundred pistoles—of which he had not a single penny left a month after. . . . The afflicted dryads, [5] the venerable sylvan [6] deities, driven from their ancient abodes, and not knowing where to hide their heads; the old crows, who had inhabited the summits of our lofty oaks for upward of two centuries; and the melancholy owls, who dwelt beneath the impenetrable shades of their branches, from whence, with their shrill cries, they denounced approaching misfortune—all, methought, crowded around me with their complaints; and who knows but several of our old oaks might have spoken, like that in which Clarinda [7] was enclosed? This place was once a *luogo d'incanto* ("a place of enchantment"), if there ever was one. In short, my imagination was so forcibly struck with the scene of desolation that presented itself that I returned home in sorrow; nor was the supper which the first president gave me able to rouse my spirits.

November 30, 1689

I would not be anywhere but where I am. *Passing the winter at Les Rochers* sounds terrific. It is the most agreeable thing in the world. I sometimes laugh and say, "This, then, is what is called passing a winter in the woods." Madame Coulanges said to me the other day, "Leave your damp Rochers!" Damp! When the sun

---

[3] *mea corporea falma:* my burdensome body.
[4] *desolation of this estate:* her spendthrift son had sold the timber on it to pay for a trip.
[5] *dryads:* tree nymphs.   [6] *sylvan:* woodland.
[7] *Clarinda:* a character in a then popular romance.

shines, it penetrates on every side into these woods; it is a dry soil, exposed to the direct rays of the meridian sun, so that the most delicate constitution could not take cold; and the setting sun has a fine effect from the end of a long grove. When it rains, we have a good room, a good fire, and two card tables: This is now the case, as we have a good deal of company, who do not interrupt me, for I do as I please. When we have none, we are still better off, as reading affords a pleasure superior to every other.

ON VIENNA

Lady Mary Wortley Montagu (England)

Vienna, September 8, 1716

I am now, my dear sister, safely arrived at Vienna. We traveled by water from Ratisbon, a journey perfectly agreeable, down the Danube, in one of those little vessels that they very properly call wooden houses, having in them all the conveniences of a palace— stoves in the chambers, kitchens, etc. They are rowed by twelve men each, and move with such an incredible swiftness that in the same day you have the pleasure of a vast variety of prospects, and within the space of a few hours you have the pleasure of seeing a populous city, adorned with magnificent palaces, and the most ro- mantic solitudes, which appear distant from the commerce of man- kind, the banks of the Danube being charmingly diversified with woods, rocks, mountains covered with vines, fields of corn, large cities, and ruins of ancient castles.

This town, which has the honor of being the Emperor's residence, did not at all answer my expectation nor ideas of it, being much less than I expected to find it; the streets are very close, and so narrow one cannot observe the fine fronts of the palaces, though many of them are all built of fine white stone, and are excessive high; for as the town is too little for the number of people that desire to live in it, the builders seem to have projected to repair that misfortune by clapping one town on the top of another, most of the houses being of five, and some of them of six, stories. You may easily imagine that, the streets being so narrow, the rooms are ex- tremely dark, and, what is an inconvenience much more intolerable in my opinion, there is no house that has so few as five or six families in it. The apartments of the greatest ladies, and even of the minis- ters of state, are divided but by a partition from that of a tailor or shoemaker, and I know nobody that has above two floors in any house—one for their own use, and one higher for their servants. Those that have houses of their own let out the rest of them to whoever will take them, and thus the great stairs—which are all of stone—are as common and as dirty as the street.

It is true, when you have once traveled through them, nothing can be more surprisingly magnificent than the apartments. They are commonly a suite of eight or ten large rooms, all inlaid, the doors and windows richly carved and gilt, and the furniture such as is seldom seen in the palaces of sovran princes in other countries. Their apartments are adorned with hangings of the finest tapestry of Brussels, prodigious large looking-glasses in silver frames, fine Japan tables, beds, chairs, canopies, and window-curtains of the richest Genoa damask or velvet, almost covered with gold lace or embroidery. All this is made gay by pictures and vast jars of Japan china, and large lusters [1] of rock crystal.

I have already had the honor of being invited to dinner by several of the first people of quality, and I must do them the justice to say, the good taste and magnificence of their tables very well answer to that of their furniture. I have been more than once entertained with fifty dishes of meat, all served in silver, and well dressed; the dessert proportionable, served in the finest china. But the variety and richness of their wines is what appears the most surprising; the constant way is to lay a list of their names upon the plates of the guests along with the napkins, and I have counted several times to the number of eighteen different sorts, all exquisite in their kinds.

I was yesterday at Count Schoonbourn the Vice-Chancellor's garden, where I was invited to dinner. I must own I never saw a place so perfectly delightful as the Faubourg [2] of Vienna. It is very large, and almost wholly composed of delicious palaces. If the emperor found it proper to permit the gates of the town to be laid open, that the Faubourgs might be joined to it, he would have one of the largest and best-built cities in Europe. Count Schoonbourn's villa is one of the most magnificent; the furniture all rich brocades, so well fancied and fitted up nothing can look more gay and splendid; not to speak of a gallery full of rarities of coral, mother-of-pearl, and throughout the whole house a profusion of gilding, carving, fine painting, the most beautiful porcelain, statues of alabaster and ivory, and vast orange- and lemon-trees, in gilt pots. The dinner was perfectly fine and well ordered, and made still more agreeable by the good humor of the count. I have not yet been at court,

---

[1] *lusters:* chandeliers.   [2] *Faubourg:* suburb.

being forced to stay for my gown, without which there is no waiting on the Empress; though I am not without great impatience to see a beauty that has been the admiration of so many different nations. When I have had the honor, I will not fail to let you know my real thoughts, always taking a particular pleasure in communicating them to my dear sister.

A CHANNEL CROSSING

SYDNEY SMITH (ENGLAND)

The following diverting travel letter gives an intimate view of England's wittiest nineteenth-century clergyman.

❀　❀　❀

ROUEN, October 6, 1835

My dearest Child,

——fell ill in London, and detained us a day or two. At Canterbury, the wheel would not turn round; we slept there, and lost our passage the next day at Dover: this was Wednesday—a day of mist, fog, and despair. It blew a hurricane all that night, and we were kept awake by thinking of the different fish by which we should be devoured on the following day. I thought I should fall to the lot of some female porpoise, who, mistaking me for a porpoise, but finding me only a parson, would make a dinner of me. We were all up and at the quay by five in the morning.

The captain hesitated very much whether he would embark, and your mother solicited me in pencil notes not to do so; however, we embarked,—the French Ambassador, ourselves, twenty Calais shopkeepers, and a variety of all nations. The passage was tremendous: Hibbert had crossed four times, and the courier [1] twenty; I had crossed three times more, and we none of us ever remember such a passage. I lay along the deck, wrapped in a cloak, shut my eyes, and, as to danger, reflected that it was much more apparent than real; and that, as I had so little life to lose it was of little consequence whether I was drowned, or died, like a resident clergyman, from indigestion. Your mother was taken out more dead than alive.

We were delighted with the Hotel Dessein at Calais; eggs, butter, bread, coffee—everything better than in England—the hotel itself magnificent. We all recovered, and stayed there the day; and pro-

[1] *courier:* guide.

ceeded to sleep at Montreuil, forty miles, where we were still more improved by a good dinner. The next day, twenty miles farther, to Abbeville; from thence, sixty miles the next day to this place, where we found a superb hotel, and are quite delighted with Rouen; the churches far exceed anything in England in richness of architectural ornament. The old buildings of Rouen are most interesting. All that I refuse to see is, where particular things were done to particular persons;—the square where Joan of Arc was burnt,—the house where Corneille was born. The events I admit to be important; but, from long experience, I have found that the square where Joan of Arc was burnt, and the room where Corneille was born, have such a wonderful resemblance to other rooms and squares, that I have ceased to interest myself about them.

Tomorrow we start for Mantes, and the next day we shall be at Paris. Travelling is extremely slow—five miles an hour. I find the people now as I did before, most delightful; compared to them we are perfect barbarians. Happy the man whose daughter were half as well-bred as the chambermaid at Dessein's, or whose sons were as polished as the waiter! God bless you, dear child! Give my love to Froggy and Doggy. Your affectionate father,

SYDNEY SMITH

ITALY AND ART GALLERIES

THOMAS HUXLEY (ENGLAND)

Written to his daughter, Mrs. Roller, by one of England's most distinguished scientists.

❋ ❋ ❋

HOTEL DE MILANO, FLORENCE, March 7, 1885

We have been here more than a week and have discovered two things, first that the wonderful "art treasures," of which all the world has heard, are a sore burden to the conscience if you don't go to see them, and an awful trial to the back and legs if you do; and thirdly, that the climate is productive of a peculiar kind of relaxed throat. M.'s [1] throat discovered it, but on inquiry, it proved to be a law of nature, at least, so the oldest inhabitants say. We called on them today.

[1] *M.'s:* Mrs. Huxley's.

But it is a lovely place for all that, far better than Rome as a place to live in, and full of interesting things. We had a morning at the Uffizi [2] the other day, and came back with minds enlarged and backs broken. Tomorrow we contemplate attacking the Pitti,[2] and doubt not the result will be similar. By the end of the week our minds will probably be so large, and the small of the back so small that we should probably break if we stayed any longer, so think it prudent to be off to Venice. . . . And mind we have letters waiting for us there, or your affectionate Pater will emulate the historical "cocky."

I got much better at Siena, probably the result of the medicinal nature of the city, the name of which, as a well-instructed girl like you knows, is derived from senna, which grows wild there, and gives the soil its peculiar pigmentary character.

But unfortunately, I forgot to bring any with me, and the effect went off during the first few days of our residence here, when I was, as the Italians say, *"molto basso nel bocca."* [3] However I am picking up again now, and if people wouldn't call upon us, I feel there might be a chance for me.

Doctor M—— [4] has just been called in to a case of sore throat in the person of a young lady here and is quite happy. The young lady probably will not be, when she finds herself converted into a sort of inverted mustard-pot, with the mustard outside! She is one of a very nice family of girls, who (by contrast) remind us of our own.

Ever your loving (to all) father,

PATER

ON MODESTY

CHARLES LOUIS DE SECONDAT MONTESQUIEU (FRANCE)

Translated by Mr. Ozell

The *Persian Letters* of Montesquieu, from which this selection has been made, are a satire on French society in the eighteenth century. This method of attack, by means of letters said to have been written by a foreigner curious to understand the ways of the French, has been utilized by many writers who came after Montesquieu, both French

---

[2] *Uffizi and Pitti:* old Florentine palaces which have been converted into art galleries. They contain more famous pictures per square foot of wall space than any other galleries in the world.

[3] *"molto basso nel bocca":* down in the mouth.

[4] *Doctor M—:* Mrs. Huxley.

and English. A notable example of this method in English is *The Citizen of the World* by Oliver Goldsmith.

❋   ❋   ❋

PARIS, the 20th of the Moon Rhamazan, 1713

Rica to . . .

I have known some people whose virtue was so natural to them that they were hardly sensible of it: they adhered to their duty without any force upon themselves, and followed it as it were by instinct: far from exalting their rare qualities in their discourse, they seemed not to have yet reached their own knowledge. These are the men I love; not those virtuous folks that seem to be amazed at their being so, and look upon a good action as a prodigy, which must fill everybody with wonder that hears of it.

I meet everywhere with people that are eternally talking of themselves: their conversation is a looking-glass that always presents you with their impertinent figure: they will hold you a discourse about the least accidents that ever befell them, and think their being concerned in them must make them considerable to you: there is nothing but what they have done, seen, said, or thought: they are the universal model; an inexhaustible subject of comparisons; a spring of examples never to be dried up. How wretchedly insipid is praise, when it bounds back to the place it comes from!

Some days ago a man of this character plagued us for two hours together with his merit and his great talents: but as there is no perpetual motion in the world, he at last was silent. A little of the talk then fell to our share, and we took hold of the opportunity.

One that seemed to be a little troubled with the spleen, began to complain of the many tiresome disturbers of conversation: "What, nothing but fools that are eternally giving you their own characters, and bringing everything home to themselves!"

"Your observation is just," cried our talker abruptly: "ah! if men would but act like me! I never praise myself: I have wealth and birth; I spend handsomely; my friends tell me I do not want wit: but you never hear me talk of these things: if I have any good qualities, that which I value myself most upon is my modesty."

I could not but wonder at this impertinent creature; and while he was running on, I said to myself: happy the man who has vanity enough not to speak well of himself; who stands in awe of his hearers, and will not venture to set up his merit against the pride and self-love of other people.

ON THE CHOICE OF FRIENDS

Philip Dormer Stanhope, Earl of Chesterfield (England)
to his son, Philip Stanhope

October 9, 1747

. . . People will, in a great degree, and not without reason, form their opinion of you upon that which they have of your friends; and there is a Spanish proverb which says very justly, "Tell me whom you live with, and I will tell you who you are." One may fairly suppose that a man who makes a knave or a fool his friend has something very bad to do or to conceal. But, at the same time that you carefully decline the friendship of knaves and fools, if it can be called friendship, there is no occasion to make either of them your enemies, wantonly and unprovoked; for they are numerous bodies, and I would rather choose a secure neutrality, than alliance or war, with either of them. You may be a declared enemy to their vices and follies, without being marked out by them as a personal one. Their enmity is the next dangerous thing to their friendship. Have a real reserve with almost everybody, and have a seeming reserve with almost nobody; for it is very disagreeable to seem reserved, and very dangerous not to be so. Few people find the true medium; many are ridiculously mysterious and reserved upon trifles, and many imprudently communicative of all they know.

The next thing to the choice of your friends is the choice of your company. Endeavor, as much as you can, to keep company with people above you. Do not mistake, when I say company above you, and think that I mean with regard to their birth; that is the least consideration; but I mean with regard to their merit, and the light in which the world considers them.

There are two sorts of good company: one, which is called the *beau monde,* and consists of those people who have the lead in courts and in the gay part of life; the other consists of those who are distinguished by some peculiar merit, or who excel in some particular and valuable art or science. For my own part, I used to think myself in company as much above me, when I was with Mr. Addison and Mr. Pope,[1] as if I had been with all the princes in Europe.

You may possibly ask me whether a man has it always in his power to get into the best company? and how? I say, Yes, he has, by deserving it; provided he is but in circumstances which enable

---

[1] *Addison and Pope:* great English writers.

him to appear upon the footing of a gentleman. Merit and good breeding will make their way everywhere. Knowledge will introduce him, and good breeding will endear him, to the best companies; for, as I have often told you, politeness and good breeding are absolutely necessary to adorn any or all other good qualities or talents. Without them no knowledge, no perfection whatsoever, is seen in its best light. The scholar, without good breeding, is a pedant; the philosopher a cynic; the soldier a brute; and every man disagreeable.

BEING SOLICITED FOR A DONATION

Horace Walpole (England)

Hannah More, a pioneer agitator for woman's rights, who was also an authoress and an active charity worker, asked Horace Walpole for a gift to a favorite charity. This witty society man, art collector, author, and politician replied as follows.

❊ ❊ ❊

Berkeley Square, February 20, 1790

It is very provoking that people must always be hanging or drowning themselves, or going mad, that you, Mistress, may have the diversion of exercising your pity and good nature, and charity, and intercession, and all that beadroll of virtues that make you so troublesome and amiable, when you might be ten times more agreeable by writing things [1] that would not cost one above half a crown at a time. You are an absolute walking hospital, and travel about into lone and by-places, with your doors open to house stray casualties! I wish at least that you would have some children yourself, that you might not be plaguing one for all the pretty brats that are starving and friendless. . . . Well, as your newly-adopted pensioners have two babes, I insist on your accepting two guineas [2] for them instead of one. If you cannot circumscribe your own charities, you shall not stint mine, Madam, who can afford it much better, and who must be dunned for alms, and do not scramble over hedges and ditches in searching for opportunities of flinging away my money on good works. I employ mine better at auctions, and in buying pictures and baubles, and hoarding curiosities, that in truth I cannot keep long, but that will last forever in my cata-

[1] *things:* her books.
[2] *guineas:* a guinea was a gold piece worth a little more than a pound.

logue and make me immortal! Alas! Will they cover a multitude
of sins? Adieu! I cannot jest after *that* sentence.

Yours most sincerely,

HORACE WALPOLE

FROM A SICK BED

CHARLES LAMB (ENGLAND)

July 27, 1805

Dear Archimedes,[1]—Things have gone on badly with thy un-
geometrical friend; but they are on the turn. My old housekeeper
has shown signs of convalescence, and will shortly resume the power
of the keys, so I shan't be cheated of my tea and liquors. Wind in
the West, which promotes tranquillity. Have leisure now to anticipate seeing thee again. Have been taking leave of tobacco in a
rhyming address. Had thought that vein had long since closed up.
Find I can rhyme and reason, too. Think of studying mathematics,
to restrain the fire of my genius, which G. D. recommends. Have
frequent bleedings at the nose, which shows plethoric. Maybe
shall try the sea myself, that great scene of wonders. Got incredibly
sober and regular; shave oftener, and hum a tune, to signify cheer-
fulness and gallantry.

Suddenly disposed to sleep, having taken a quart of pease with
bacon and stout. Will not refuse Nature, who has done such
things for me!

Nurse! don't call me unless Mr. Manning comes.

—What! the gentleman in spectacles?—Yes.

C. L.

ON SPELLING A NAME

LEWIS CARROLL (ENGLAND)

The author of *Alice in Wonderland* first told these stories to some
children of whom he was very fond. He also wrote them letters like
the following.

❈　❈　❈

CHRIST CHURCH, OXFORD, March 8, 1880

My Dear Ada,—(Isn't that your short name? "Adelaide" is all
very well, but you see when one is dreadfully busy one hasn't time

---

[1] *Archimedes:* a Greek mathematician and scientist. Lamb nicknames a mathe-
matical friend, Archimedes.

to write such long words—particularly when it takes one half an hour to remember how to spell it—and even then one has to go and get a dictionary to see if one has spelt it right, and of course the dictionary is in another room, at the top of a high bookcase—where it has been for months and months, and has got all covered with dust—so one has to get a duster first of all, and nearly choke oneself in dusting it—and when one has made out at last which is dictionary and which is dust, even then there's the job of remembering which end of the alphabet "A" comes—for one feels pretty certain it isn't in the middle—then one has to go and wash one's hands before turning over the leaves—for they've got so thick with dust one hardly knows them by sight—and, as likely as not, the soap is lost and the jug is empty, and there's no towel, and one has to spend hours and hours in finding things—and perhaps after all one has to go off to the shop to buy a new cake of soap—so, with all this bother, I hope you won't mind my writing it short and saying, "My dear Ada"). You said in your last letter you would like a likeness of me: so here it is, and I hope you will like it—I won't forget to call the next time but one I'm in Wallington.

Your very affectionate friend,
Lewis Carroll

GAINING A FOOTHOLD

Sidney Lanier (America)

The poet-musician, Sidney Lanier, almost an invalid, and desperately poor, in a letter of September 24, 1873, addressed to his wife, expressed the hope that he might secure employment in a Baltimore orchestra. "It is, therefore, a *possibility* . . . that I may be first flute in the Peabody Orchestra, on a salary of $120 a month, which, with five flute scholars, would grow to $200 a month, and so . . . we might dwell in the beautiful city, among the great libraries, and midst the music, the religion, and the art that we love—and I could write my books, and be the man I wish to be."

The realization of this dream is described in the letter below.

❊ ❊ ❊

33 Denmead St., Baltimore, Md., January 6, 1878

The painters, the whitewashers, the plumbers, the locksmiths, the carpenters, the gas-fitters, the stove-put-upers, the carmen, the piano-movers, the carpet-layers,—all these have I seen, bar-

candidate for President by the Chicago Republican convention, or any other convention, for reasons personal to myself. I claim that the Civil War, in which I simply did a man's fair share of work, so perfectly accomplished peace, that military men have an absolute right to rest, and to demand that the men who have been schooled in the arts and practice of peace shall now do their work equally well. Any senator can step from his chair at the Capitol into the White House, and fulfill the office of President with more skill and success than a Grant, Sherman, or Sheridan, who were soldiers by education and nature, who filled well their office when the country was in danger, but were not schooled in the practices by which civil communities are, and should be, governed. I claim that our experience since 1865 demonstrates the truth of this my proposition. Therefore I say that "patriotism" does not demand of me what I construe as a sacrifice of judgment, of inclination, and of self-interest. I have my personal affairs in a state of absolute safety and comfort. I owe no man a cent, have no expensive habits or tastes, no complications or indirect liabilities, envy no man his wealth or power, and would account myself a fool, a madman, an ass, to embark anew, at sixty-five years of age, in a career that may, at any moment, become tempest-tossed by the perfidy, the defalcation, the dishonesty, or neglect of any one of a hundred thousand subordinates utterly unknown to the President of the United States, not to say the eternal worriment by a vast host of impecunious friends and old military subordinates. Even as it is, I am tortured by the charitable appeals of poor distressed pensioners, but as President, these would be multiplied beyond human endurance. I remember well the experiences of Generals Jackson, Harrison, Tyler, Grant, Hayes, and Garfield, all elected because of their military services, and am warned, not encouraged, by their sad experience. No,—count me out. The civilians of the U. S. should, and must, buffet with this thankless office, and leave us old soldiers to enjoy the peace we fought for, and think we earned.

> With profound respect,
> Your friend,
> W. T. SHERMAN

OFFERING CRITICISM

ABRAHAM LINCOLN (AMERICA)

President Lincoln appointed General Joseph Hooker to the command of the Federal Army of the Potomac, which had been decisively

gained with, reproached for bad jobs, and finally paid off. I have also coaxed my landlord into all manner of outlays for damp walls, cold bathrooms, and other like matters. I have furthermore bought at least three hundred and twenty-seven household utensils which suddenly came to be absolutely necessary to our existence. I have moreover hired a colored gentlewoman who is willing to wear out my carpets, burn out my ranges, freeze out my water-pipes, and be generally useful. I have also moved my family into our new home, have had a Xmas tree for the youngsters, have looked up a cheap school for Harry and Sidney, have discharged my daily duties as first flute of the Peabody Orchestra, have written a couple of poems and part of an essay on Beethoven and Bismarck, have accomplished at least a hundred thousand miscellaneous nothings, and have *not,* in consequence of the aforesaid, sent to you and my dear Maria the loving greetings whereof my heart has been full during the whole season. We are in a state of supreme content with our new home; it really seems to me as incredible that myriads of people have been living in their own homes heretofore as to the young couple with a first baby it seems impossible that a great many other couples have had similar prodigies. It is simply too delightful. Good heavens, how I wish that the whole world had a Home!

I confess I am a little nervous about the gas-bills, which must come in, in the course of time; and there are the water-rates and several sorts of imposts and taxes; but the dignity of being liable for such things (!) is a very supporting consideration. No man is a Bohemian [1] who has to pay water-rates and a street-tax. Every day when I sit down in my dining-room—*my* dining-room !—I find the wish growing stronger that each poor soul in Baltimore, whether saint or sinner, could come and dine with me. How I would carve out the merry thoughts for the old hags ! How I would stuff the big wall-eyed rascals till their rags ripped again ! There was a knight of old times who built the dining-hall of his castle across the highway, so that every wayfarer must perforce pass through : there the traveller, rich or poor, found always a trencher and wherewithal to fill it. Three times a day, in my own chair at my own table, do I envy that knight and wish that I might do as he did.

---

[1] *Bohemian:* a term applied to footloose poor artists and writers without a home of their own. It originally meant gipsy.

to write such long words—particularly when it takes one half an hour to remember how to spell it—and even then one has to go and get a dictionary to see if one has spelt it right, and of course the dictionary is in another room, at the top of a high bookcase—where it has been for months and months, and has got all covered with dust—so one has to get a duster first of all, and nearly choke oneself in dusting it—and when one has made out at last which is dictionary and which is dust, even then there's the job of remembering which end of the alphabet "A" comes—for one feels pretty certain it isn't in the middle—then one has to go and wash one's hands before turning over the leaves—for they've got so thick with dust one hardly knows them by sight—and, as likely as not, the soap is lost and the jug is empty, and there's no towel, and one has to spend hours and hours in finding things—and perhaps after all one has to go off to the shop to buy a new cake of soap—so, with all this bother, I hope you won't mind my writing it short and saying, "My dear Ada"). You said in your last letter you would like a likeness of me: so here it is, and I hope you will like it—I won't forget to call the next time but one I'm in Wallington.

Your very affectionate friend,

LEWIS CARROLL

GAINING A FOOTHOLD

SIDNEY LANIER (AMERICA)

The poet-musician, Sidney Lanier, almost an invalid, and desperately poor, in a letter of September 24, 1873, addressed to his wife, expressed the hope that he might secure employment in a Baltimore orchestra. "It is, therefore, a *possibility* . . . that I may be first flute in the Peabody Orchestra, on a salary of $120 a month, which, with five flute scholars, would grow to $200 a month, and so . . . we might dwell in the beautiful city, among the great libraries, and midst the music, the religion, and the art that we love—and I could write my books, and be the man I wish to be."

The realization of this dream is described in the letter below.

❊ ❊ ❊

33 Denmead St., BALTIMORE, MD., January 6, 1878

The painters, the whitewashers, the plumbers, the locksmiths, the carpenters, the gas-fitters, the stove-put-upers, the carmen, the piano-movers, the carpet-layers,—all these have I seen, bar-

DECLINING A NOMINATION

WILLIAM TECUMSEH SHERMAN (AMERICA)

In 1884 Mr. Blaine (speaker of the House of Representatives) wrote a letter to General Sherman informing him that his name was to be presented as a candidate for the Presidency in the approaching convention in Chicago.

❋ ❋ ❋

ST. LOUIS, MISSOURI, May 28, 1884

Hon. J. G. Blaine:

My dear Friend: I have received your letter of the 25th; shall construe it as absolutely confidential, not intimating even to any member of my family that I have heard from you; and though you may not expect an answer, I hope you will not construe one as unwarranted. I have had a great many letters from all points of the compass to a similar effect, one or two of which I have answered frankly; but the great mass are unanswered. I ought not to subject myself to the cheap ridicule of declining what is not offered, but it is only fair to the many really able men who rightfully aspire to the high honor of being President of the United States to let them know that I am not and must not be construed as a rival.

In every man's life there occurs an epoch when he must choose his own career, and when he may not throw the responsibility, or tamely place his destiny in the hands of friends. Mine occurred in Louisiana when, in 1861, alone in the midst of a people blinded by supposed wrongs, I resolved to stand by the Union as long as a fragment of it survived to which to cling. Since then, through faction, tempest, war, and peace, my career has been all my family and friends could ask. We are now in a good home of our choice, with reasonable provision for old age, surrounded by kind and admiring friends, in a community where Catholicism is held in respect and veneration, and where my children will naturally grow up in contact with an industrious and frugal people. You have known and appreciated Mrs. Sherman from childhood, have also known each and all the members of my family, and can understand, without an explanation from me, how their thoughts and feelings should and ought to influence my action; but I will not even throw off on them the responsibility.

I will not, in any event, entertain or accept a nomination as a candidate for President by the Chicago Republican convention, or any other convention, for reasons personal to myself. I claim that the Civil War, in which I simply did a man's fair share of work, so perfectly accomplished peace, that military men have an absolute right to rest, and to demand that the men who have been schooled in the arts and practice of peace shall now do their work equally well. Any senator can step from his chair at the Capitol into the White House, and fulfill the office of President with more skill and success than a Grant, Sherman, or Sheridan, who were soldiers by education and nature, who filled well their office when the country was in danger, but were not schooled in the practices by which civil communities are, and should be, governed. I claim that our experience since 1865 demonstrates the truth of this my proposition. Therefore I say that "patriotism" does not demand of me what I construe as a sacrifice of judgment, of inclination, and of self-interest. I have my personal affairs in a state of absolute safety and comfort. I owe no man a cent, have no expensive habits or tastes, no complications or indirect liabilities, envy no man his wealth or power, and would account myself a fool, a madman, an ass, to embark anew, at sixty-five years of age, in a career that may, at any moment, become tempest-tossed by the perfidy, the defalcation, the dishonesty, or neglect of any one of a hundred thousand subordinates utterly unknown to the President of the United States, not to say the eternal worriment by a vast host of impecunious friends and old military subordinates. Even as it is, I am tortured by the charitable appeals of poor distressed pensioners, but as President, these would be multiplied beyond human endurance. I remember well the experiences of Generals Jackson, Harrison, Tyler, Grant, Hayes, and Garfield, all elected because of their military services, and am warned, not encouraged, by their sad experience. No,—count me out. The civilians of the U. S. should, and must, buffet with this thankless office, and leave us old soldiers to enjoy the peace we fought for, and think we earned.

With profound respect,

Your friend,
W. T. Sherman

OFFERING CRITICISM

Abraham Lincoln (America)

President Lincoln appointed General Joseph Hooker to the command of the Federal Army of the Potomac, which had been decisively